A
Calendar of Documents
and
Related Historical Materials
(1961–1970)

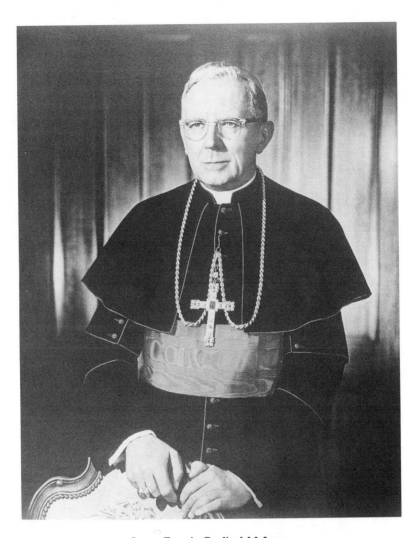

James Francis Cardinal McIntyre

Calendar of Documents
and
Related Historical Materials

in the
Archival Center
Archdiocese of Los Angeles
for
His Eminence
JAMES FRANCIS CARDINAL McINTYRE

VOLUME TWO
1961–1970

Prepared by
Sister Mary Rose Cunningham
C.S.C.

With a Preface and Historical Introduction by
MSGR. FRANCIS J. WEBER

Saint Francis Historical Society
Mission Hills, California
1994

[The Archival Center gratefully acknowledges the dedicated interest of Daniel Donohue and the generous support of the Dan Murphy Foundation in the publication of this book.]

The compiler wishes to thank Gladys Posakony for her assistance in correcting the galleys.

Designed and printed by BookMasters, Inc.
Ashland, Ohio
in a press run of 300 copies

The Library of Congress Catalogue
Number for this book is CD3119.S35G6

Table of Contents

Listing for the Year
1961

Mc3341. A-1961
Mother M. Anselm to J. Francis Cardinal
 McIntyre
January 12, 1961. Cornwell Heights, Pennsyl-
vania

Before a definitive life of Mother Katherine
Drexel can be written, some personal impressions, quotations, and testimonies of her virtue
and character are needed. If you have any remembrances, the committee would appreciate
having them. (English 1 pg.)

Mc3342. A-1961
J. Francis Cardinal McIntyre to Mother M.
 Anselm
January 18, 1961. Los Angeles, California

Although Mother Katherine Drexel was not
known by me personally, the work that she
and her Sisters did was well known during my
twenty-five years working in New York. (English 1 pg.)

Mc3343. A-1961
Arbp. Egidio Vagnozzi to J. Francis Cardinal
 McIntyre
February 23, 1961. Washington, D.C.

The proposal for an International Water Year
by Mr. Olindo R. Angelillo needs some investigation. (English 1 pg.) On February 27, 1961,
the Cardinal asks Rev. Thomas McElhatton to
inquire about Mr. Angelillo. (English 1 pg.)

Mc3344. A-1961
J. Francis Cardinal McIntyre to Arbp. Karl
 Alter
March 5, 1961. Los Angeles, California

Formal resignation from the Administration
Board of NCWC after the recent statement was
issued that the Bishops want a long term loan at
low interest as Federal Aid to Education. (English 1 pg.)

Mc3345. A-1961
Msgr. William McDonald to J. Francis Cardi-
 nal McIntyre
March 13, 1961. Washington, D.C.

Since Dr. Konrad Adenauer is visiting in the
United States, it seems an appropriate time to
give an honorary degree if the members of the
Board approve. (English 1 pg.) On March 16,
1961, Bishop Bell states that he is certain that
the Cardinal would approve. (English 1 pg.)

Mc3346. A-1961
Rev. Thomas McElhatton OP to J. Francis
 Cardinal McIntyre
March 16, 1961. Los Angeles, California

Mr. Olindo Angelillo does not claim to be a
practicing Catholic. He has a plan to provide
water to all arid regions of the world. Recognition by the Holy See is very important to him.
(English 2 pgs.)

Mc3347. A-1961
Mrs. Patricia Alneti to J. Francis Cardinal
 McIntyre
March 17, 1961. Riverside, California

A request for an autographed gift that can be
raffled at the bazaar to raise funds to finish the
school. (English 1 pg.) On April 13, 1961, the
Cardinal sends medals of Our Lady of the Angels. (English 1 pg.)

Mc3348. A-1961
Rabbi Maurice Abramson to J. Francis Cardi-
 nal McIntyre
April 30, 1961. Santa Monica, California

The Rabbi agrees with the statement issued
by the Cardinal that all authority comes from
God. He states that this concept should be
taught. (English 1 pg.)

Mc3349. A-1961
Bp. Alden J. Bell to Mr. Olindo Angelillo
May 3, 1961. Los Angeles, California

The Holy See appreciated the work of the International Water Year but cannot participate at this time. (English 1 pg.)

Mc3350. A-1961
Mr. John T. Amendt to J. Francis Cardinal McIntyre
May 21, 1961. Long Beach, California

Will a church be built on Lewis Street in Garden Grove soon? A house can be purchased if the building of a church will take place. (English 1 pg.) On May 25, 1961, the Cardinal states that there is no immediate need for another church. (English 1 pg.)

Mc3351. A-1961
Mr. Michael Aguilar to Bp. Alden J. Bell
June 14, 1961. Seminole, Texas

Some information is needed about the St. John of God Hospital. (English 1 pg.) On June 17, 1961, the Bishop states that the address can be sent but job information is difficult to send. (English 1 pg.)

Mc3352. A-1961
Mrs. C. Amberg to J. Francis Cardinal McIntyre
June 16, 1961. South Gate, California

The need for Masses, Bible study classes, and some socials for the deaf of the Archdiocese is very great. Can an organization be started to meet this need? (English 4 pgs.)

Mc3353. A-1961
Mr. Richard Arnold to Bp. Timothy Manning
July 15, 1961. Long Beach, California

A complaint is made concerning the acceptance policy of St. Cornelius Parish School. (English 1 pg.) On July 26, 1961, the Bishop suggests that an interview with the Pastor is the best solution to the understanding of the policy. (English 1 pg.)

Mc3354. A-1961
Mr. R. T. Antrim to J. Francis Cardinal McIntyre
September 6, 1961. Redondo Beach, California

The presence of Rev. Edgar Sever, OFM at the burial of Pfc. Raderic Antrim Jr. was a most generous act. The many hours given to restoring the Missions is more than repaid by this kindness. (English 2 pgs.)

Mc3355. A-1961
Mr. Bob Krauch to Mr. Al Flanagan
September 14, 1961. Los Angeles, California

The critic, Mr. Brooks Atkinson, states that O'Neill's play, *The Iceman Cometh,* is a play for mature audiences. Channel 13 is warning viewers that the material is not for children to view. (English 1 pg.)

Mc3356. A-1961
Br. Chistopher Aszelino, OH to Bp. Alden J. Bell
September 17, 1961. Los Angeles, California

A request is made to offer a votive Mass of the Holy Founder on the Profession Day for the Novices and special Indulgences of them when they kiss the Crucifix. (English 1 pg.) On September 19, 1961, the Bishop states that the new rubics would not allow for the substitution of the Sunday Mass. (English 1 pg.)

Mc3357. A-1961
Gregorio Cardinal Agagianian to J. Francis Cardinal McIntyre
October 31, 1961. Rome, Italy

The date for a visit to Los Angeles can not be before December 6 after the closing of the Quinquennial Meeting of the Propagation of the Faith. (English 2 pgs.)

Mc3358. A-1961
Mr. Juvenal Marchisio to J. Francis Cardinal McIntyre
November 2, 1961. New York City, New York

An invitation to attend the American Committee on Italian Migration dinner on December 9 in New York City celebrating the 10th anniversary of its founding. (English 1 pg.) On November 7, 1961, Bishop Manning states that from the appointments on the Cardinal's calendar, it will be impossible for the Cardinal to attend. (English 1 pg.)

Mc3359. A-1961
Mr. John Flanigan to Bp. Timothy Manning
November 15, 1961. St. Louis, Missouri

The sales committee of Anheuser-Busch is most grateful for the invocation at the breakfast and for the challenge given to them. (English 1 pg.)

Mc3360. A-1961
Gregorio Cardinal Agagianian to J. Francis Cardinal McIntyre
December 13, 1961. Rome, Italy

The visit to Los Angeles was an opportunity to visit the American Catholic people and to see the progress made in the Church. The visit to St. John's Seminary was a thrill. (English 2 pgs.)

Mc3361. B-1961
Arbp. Egidio Vagnozzi to Bp. Timothy
Manning
January 13, 1961. Washington, D.C.

The Vatican wishes a statement of gratitude
to be sent to Miss E. Breman for the Christmas
gift of phonograph records for Pope John
XXIII. (English 1 pg.)

Mc3362. B-1961
Rev. Olsin C. Moriarty to Bp. Timothy
Manning
January 23, 1961. Stockton, California

Mr. Robert Bonta is writing a history of the
Church in Stockton and needs the pre-Alemany
Libro de Gabierno. If it is in Los Angeles, please
try to locate Stockton or Fr. Blaine's name between 1850–1851. (English 1 pg.) On February
3, 1961, the Bishop states that no mention is
made of either Stockton or Fr. Blaine.

Mc3363. B-1961
Mrs. M. Bennett to J. Francis Cardinal
McIntyre
January 24, 1961. Santa Barbara, California

A request is made to permit a child to receive
the Sacrament of Confirmation without formal
instruction. The CCD teacher is the reason that
the family left the Catholic school. (English
2 pgs.)

Mc3364. B-1961
Mr. Bruce E. Brant to J. Francis Cardinal
McIntyre
February 10, 1961. Los Angeles, California

A request to be released from the Education
Fund pledge so the contributions can go to the
Seminary Fund. Because blindness prevents
priesthood, the donation to the Seminary is important. (English 2 pgs.)

Mc3365. B-1961
Mr. Paul Malloy to J. Francis Cardinal
McIntyre
February 10, 1961. Santa Monica, California

The estate of Margaret J. Barclay is ready to
close. The stock is divided 1/3 to St. Anne's
Home for the Aged and 2/3 to the Archdiocese.
Should the stock be sold? (English 1 pg.) On
February 16, 1961, the Cardinal states that the
stock should be sold and the distribution made
in cash. (English 1 pg.)

Mc3366. B-1961
Bp. James R. Knox to J. Francis Cardinal
McIntyre
February 25, 1961. New Delhi, India

The Colombian Ambassador, Madam
Leopoldo Borda, will return to Bogota after a
visit in Los Angeles with members of the family.
She would appreciate an interview. (English 1
pg.) On March 15, 1961, the Ambassador
called to say that she is being called back to Co-
lombia. (English 1 pg.)

Mc3367. B-1961
Dr. Harry F. Brown to J. Francis Cardinal
McIntyre
March 3, 1961. Pasadena, California

The Federal Aid to Education Bill is a double
discrimination. The over crowding of the classrooms in the Catholic schools is having a physical and psychological effect on students and
teachers. (English 1 pg.)

Mc3368. B-1961
Mr. Charles Hutchings to Bp. Alden J. Bell
March 21, 1961. Los Angeles, California

The permission for Father Robert F. Tall-
madge, SJ to celebrate Mass in our home for
the anniversary of his sixty years in priestly
ordination is most gratefully received. (English
1 pg.)

Mc3369. B-1961
Bp. Alden J. Bell to Mr. John Barrera
March 29, 1961. Los Angeles, California

The church support expected from each
member is what he can afford. Fr. Quatannena
will discuss this matter with you. (English 1 pg.)

Mc3370. B-1961
Mr. Russell E. Clay to J. Francis Cardinal
McIntyre
April 3, 1961. Los Angeles, California

An invitation is given to meet with Mr. H.
Eames Bishop as the chairman of the Interfaith
Commission on Public Education on April 6 at
12:00 noon. (English 1 pg.) On April, 5 1961,
the Cardinal states that most of the educators
are at conventions. (English 1 pg.)

Mc3371. B-1961
Mr. Henry G. Bodkin to J. Francis Cardinal
McIntyre
April 10, 1961. Los Angeles, California

At the resignation of Msgr. Dignan from the
Board of Directors of Harlon Shoemaker Clinic,
the position is offered to Rev. James B. Clyne.
(English 2 pgs.) On April 20, 1961, Fr. Clyne
states the work being done is good and a large
number of Parochial School children are helped
there. (English 1 pg.)

Mc3372. B-1961
Mr. William Buckley to J. Francis Cardinal
McIntyre
April 18, 1961. New York City, New York

A defense of the policy used to write about the current conditions of the economy of the United States is given. (English 5 pgs.)

Mc3373. B-1961
Rev. Hartford Brookins to Hon Frank Bonelli
April 28, 1961. Los Angeles, California

A site is needed for a new First African Methodist Episcopal Church. Is St. John's Military Academy property available? (English 1 pg.) On May 2, 1961, the Cardinal states that the property of St. John's Military Academy has been sold and there are no other church sites available. (English 1 pg.)

Mc3374. B-1961
J. Francis Cardinal McIntyre to Mr. Shirley Burden
May 2, 1961. Los Angeles, California

The Cardinal states his appreciation for the certificate of 224 shares of Common Stock of I.T.E.K. Corporation. 93 shares will go to St. John's Seminary, 93 shares to the Archbishop's Fund for Charity, and 83 shares to the Church of the Good Shepherd. (English 1 pg.)

Mc3375. B-1961
Mrs. Eleanor Beckmeir to Bp. Alden J. Bell
May 4, 1961. Lawndale, California

Because of the hard work of Fr. Hollinger in the Parish he should be named Pastor. (English 1 pg.) On May 5, 1961, the Bishop states that seniority among the priests determines the Pastors. This policy does not fail to recognize the work being done by Fr. Hollinger. (English 1 pg.)

Mc3376. B-1961
Arbp. John J. Krol to J. Francis Cardinal
McIntyre
May 15, 1961. Philadelphia, Pennsylvania

The death of Bishop Cletus J. Benjamin is announced with a funeral Mass on May 19. (English 1 pg.) On May 19, 1961, the Cardinal expresses shock at the death of the Bishop and promises prayers. (English 1 pg.)

Mc3377. B-1961
Ms. Valerie Bonner to J. Francis Cardinal
McIntyre
June 14, 1961. London, England

A friendly letter commenting on the events in London, examinations in school, and a trip to the United States and Los Angeles on August 15–17. (English 1 pg.) On June 20, 1961, Msgr. Hawkes states that the Cardinal will be out of the city on those dates. (English 1 pg.)

Mc3378. B-1961
Mr. Robert Bonta to Rev. John A. Rawden
July 10, 1961. Stockton, California

Please check the *Libro de Gobierno* again. Many of Archbishop Alemany's entries were not in chronological order. (English 2 pgs.) On July 14, 1961, Fr. states that the book was checked and no record was found. (English 1 pg.)

Mc3379. B-1961
Mrs. Patricia Barrios to Bp. Timothy Manning
August 28, 1961. Los Angeles, California

A plea to assist a mother who wishes to have her daughter in a Catholic High School. Prayers and pleas have not worked. (English 2 pgs.) On August 29, 1961, the Bishop states that hundreds of letters are coming into the office. He has sent the letters to the Superintendent of High Schools. (English 1 pg.)

Mc3380. B-1961
Mr. Max I. Black to Bp. Timothy Manning
September 14, 1961. Van Nuys, California

In order to sell houses in San Fernando Valley some information on new schools and churches is needed. (English 1 pg.) On September 17, 1961, the Bishop sends the projected areas for the new churches. (English 1 pg.)

Mc3381. B-1961
Bp. Timothy Manning to Rev. Joseph Thompson, OFM
September 21, 1961. Los Angeles, California

Please inform Mr. William Butticci that his letter to Pope John XXIII was received. The letter to the Apostolic Delegate will come from the Chancery. (English 1 pg.)

Mc3382. B-1961
Rev. L. K. Parker, O. Praem to Bp. Alden J. Bell
September 30, 1961. Santa Ana, California

Permission is requested to give a lecture to the Cardinal Mindszenty Seminar on October 23, 1961. (English 1 pg.) On October 2, 1961, the Bishop states that the permission is granted and that he is sure that the lecture will be within the bounds of propriety. (English 1 pg.)

Mc3383. B-1961
Rev. Virgil C. Blum, SJ to J. Francis Cardinal
McIntyre
October 24, 1961. Milwaukee, Wisconsin

The Federal Aid to Education discussion is a political not a constitutional issue. The interest must come from the grass roots before it is politically wise to endorse it. Public opinion is a strong encouragement. (English 7 pgs.) On October 28, 1961, the Cardinal states that all suggestions are valuable. (English 1 pg.)

Mc3384. B-1961
Msgr. Benjamin Hawkes to Msgr. Christopher Bradley
November 20, 1961. Los Angeles, California

A friendly letter commenting on the many acts of kindness shown in Rome and that he regrets that another reliquary is not available. (English 1 pg.)

Mc3385. B-1961
Dr. Francis Griffin to J. Francis Cardinal McIntyre
November 20, 1961. New York City, New York

Dr. Francis Browne, Mr. Shirley Burden, Mr. Francis Kanne, and Dr. John Sharpe are to be invested in the Knights of Malta on January 15, 1962 in St. Patrick's Cathedral. (English 1 pg.)

Mc3386. B-1961
Mr. Blase Bonpane to Bp. Timothy Manning
November 22, 1961. Los Angeles, California

The invitation is extended to give the main talk at the Lawyers' Club meeting on December 20, 1961. (English 1 pg.) On November 27, 1961, the Bishop states that he will be very happy to address the lawyers. (English 1 pg.)

Mc3387. B-1961
J. Francis Cardinal McIntyre to Bp. Francis E. Bloy
December 19, 1961. Los Angeles, California

A Christmas message begging the blessings of the Infant Saviour on the Bishop and his people (English 1 pg.) is sent.

Mc3388. B-1961
J. Francis Cardinal McIntyre to Msgr. Christopher Bradley
December 29, 1961. Los Angeles, California

The response from the suggestion of the clergy conference to give a donation to the Seminary Fund is gratefully received. (English 1 pg.)

Mc3389. B-1961
Mr. W. G. Bowman to J. Francis Cardinal McIntyre
December 30, 1960. Chicago, Illinois

An invitation is given to deliver the invocation at the annual convention of Associated Equipment Distributors on February 5, 1961. (English 1 pg.) On January 12, 1961, Msgr. Hawkes states that the Cardinal would deliver the invocation but will be unable to remain for the breakfast. (English 1 pg.)

Mc3390. B-1961
Mrs. Margaret E. Browne to J. Francis Cardinal McIntyre
N.D. Los Angeles, California

A Subscription Note to pay $8,090 toward the building of a Dispensary Building at Don Bosco Technical Institute in memory of William Waldon Gray is enclosed. (English 1 pg.)

Mc3391. C-1961
Mr. Peter Crossan to J. Francis Cardinal McIntyre
N.D. Philadelphia, Pennsylvania

On February 12, 1961, Mr. and Mrs. Patrick Crossan will celebrate their 62nd wedding anniversary. Could the Cardinal send a message and a blessing? (English 1 pg.) On February 7, 1961, the Cardinal sends a prayerful congratulations for 62 years of love. (English 1 pg.)

Mc3392. C-1961
Rev. Edward L. Casey to J. Francis Cardinal McIntyre
February 8, 1961. Stockton, California

The construction of the Chapel for the State Hospital in Stockton is being postponed. A letter to the Governor might help to make the Committee reconsider. (English 2 pgs.)

Mc3393. C-1961
Mr. Bruce Russell to J. Francis Cardinal McIntyre
February 9, 1961. Los Angeles, California

The American Association of Editorial Cartoonists will meet on May 13. An invitation is extended to be present at the dinner and to give the invocation. (English 1 pg.) On February 21, 1961, the Cardinal states that he will be happy to be present and to give the invocation. (English 1 pg.)

Mc3394. C-1961
Bp. John B. Cody to J. Francis Cardinal McIntyre
February 23, 1961. Kansas City, Missouri

The cause of Rev. Luke Etlin, OSB is being opened. If there is any correspondence in the Archdiocesan files it should be returned to the Tribunal. If he gave retreats or missions in the Archdiocese it should be noted. (English 1 pg.)

Mc3395. C-1961
Msgr. Thomas O'Dwyer to J. Francis Cardinal McIntyre
March 7, 1961. Los Angeles, California

The State Committee will rely on Bishop Joseph McGucken's proposal to change the thinking of the Finance Committee and get the allocation of funds for the Chapel in the State Hospital in Stockton. (English 1 pg.)

Mc3396. C-1961
Mr. and Mrs. J. Alvin to Rev. Richard Cotter
March 16, 1961. Granada Hills, California

The Holy Family Retreat Association will enroll the members in the Miraculous Medal as a means of dedicating the Association to the Immaculate Conception. (English 2 pgs.)

Mc3397. C-1961
Mr. Henry Cabirac to J. Francis Cardinal McIntyre
March 29, 1961. New Orleans, Louisiana

A copy of the statement and purpose of the Catholic Council of Human Relations which is taken from the American Bishops Statement of 1958 is enclosed for review. (English 4 pgs.)

Mc3398. C-1961
J. Francis Cardinal McIntyre to Arbp. Martin O'Connor
April 25, 1961. Los Angeles, California

Hon. Vittoria Cervone interviewed Mr. Sherlock. He is unacquainted with the Legion of Decency since he is suggesting things that have been done. (English 1 pg.)

Mc3399. C-1961
Dr. Vincent Carroll D.O, to J. Francis Cardinal McIntyre
April 27, 1961. Laguna Beach, California

The amalgamation of the medical and osteopath doctors will serve the general public better than constant fighting. The two groups would appreciate a statement to this effect. (English 2 pgs.) On May 1, 1961, the Cardinal states that he takes no position in such controversy. (English 1 pg.)

Mc3400. C-1961
Dr. Vincent Carroll D.O. to J. Francis Cardinal McIntyre
May 4, 1961. Laguna Beach, California

The osteopath doctors would be the ones to encourage Loyola University to open a medical school to serve both the doctors and physicians. (English 2 pgs.)

Mc3401. C-1961
Mrs. Mary D. Clark to Msgr. Benjamin Hawkes
May 5, 1961. Pico Rivera, California

A request to have some definite information on current legislation so responsible decisions can be made. (English 2 pgs.) On May 15, 1961, Msgr. states that the Christines is a study club of Catholic women who study current legislation. (English 1 pg.)

Mc3402. C-1961
Mrs. Ann Christensen to J. Francis Cardinal McIntyre
May 5, 1961. Altadena, California

A plea for a more vigorous defense of the Catholic position on moral and social issues in the Catholic press. (English 2 pgs.) On May 10, 1961, Monsignor Hawkes states that the best decision is one based on thought and prayer. (English 1 pg.)

Mc3403. C-1961
Rev. Gerald T. Cahill to J. Francis Cardinal McIntyre
May 18, 1961. Camarillo, California

The Ford Foundation will send matching funds for education purposes. Fr. Thomas Nevin states that several members of his parish are using this method of increasing their donation to the Seminary Fund. (English 1 pg.)

Mc3404. C-1961
Mr. Ernesto V. Cen to J. Francis Cardinal McIntyre
May 23, 1961. Oxnard, California

A request for a special privilege for Rev. Augustin Alvarez to binate on May 30 so he can celebrate the Mass for the deceased members of the Society. (English 1 pg.)

Mc3405. C-1961
Dr. Harry Brickman to Dr. Clifford Cherry
May 25, 1961. Los Angeles, California

The aid given to the Mental Health Departments of Catholic organizations can be increased if the projected allotments will be realized. (English 5 pgs.)

Mc3406. C-1961
Mr. Lawrence Irell to J. Francis Cardinal McIntyre
June 8, 1961. Beverly Hills, California

The allotment for the Youth Education Fund from the Henry Cohn Foundation was not sent last year. This oversight is being satisfied with this check. (English 1 pg.) On June 15, 1961, the Cardinal expresses his gratitude for the donation. (English 1 pg.)

Mc3407. C-1961
Mrs. James L. Calvin to Bp. Timothy Manning
June 8, 1961. Ventura, California

Some help is needed for a 19 year old boy who seems to have doubts about the Doctrine of the Church. (English 1 pg.) On June 19, 1961, the Bishop requests that he talk to the priests of the parish and if this is not satisfactory then he can be referred to some other priest. (English 1 pg.)

Mc3408. C-1961
Msgr. William Johnson to J. Francis Cardinal
McIntyre
June 15, 1961. Los Angeles, California

The Mental Health program under the Short-
Doyle Act gives the advantage of services on an
out-patient basis. The Catholic Welfare uses
these services without making any statement.
(English 2 pgs.)

Mc3409. C-1961
Rev. Thomas J. Carroll to Bp. Alden J. Bell
June 23, 1961. Boston, Massachusettes

A request for permission to speak at the Blind
Veterans Convention and for faculties while in
Los Angeles. (English 1 pg.) On July 3, 1961,
the Bishop states that both requests are given
and Fr. is most welcome in the Archdiocese.
(English 1 pg.)

Mc3410. C-1961
Mr. John Michael Coffey to Msgr. Benjamin
Hawkes
June 29, 1961. Los Padres, California

A friendly letter commenting on the gratitude
he feels and for the confidence and support
given when in need. (English 2 pgs.)

Mc3411. C-1961
Ms. Blanche R. Callender to J. Francis Cardi-
nal McIntyre
N.D. Pasadena, California

Pope John XXIII sent a blessing. Would it be
permitted to print this message in my book?
(English 2 pgs.) On July 12, 1961 Bishop Bell
states that there would be no objection to print
that message in the *Memoirs*. (English 1 pg.)

Mc3412. C-1961
Mr. Thomas Cassidy to J. Francis Cardinal
McIntyre
July 20, 1961. Los Angeles, California

The relic of St. Anastasia, my wife's name
sake, will have a place of honor in our family
for many years. (English 1 pg.)

Mc3413. C-1961
Mr. Irwin C. Chmelir to Bp. Alden J. Bell
August 9, 1961. Wenatchee, Washington

A seminary burse is being planned in honor
of Fr. Duffy. Any information or guidelines
would be most appreciated. (English 1 pg.) On
August 12, 1961, the Bishop suggests writing to
Mr. Lawrence Sork the president of the Serra
Club. (English 1 pg.)

Mc3414. C-1961
Mr. Michael J. Connell to J. Francis Cardinal
McIntyre
October 23, 1961. Los Angeles, California

A donation of $5,000 for the Archbishop to
use for any charity that he desires. (English 1
pg.) On November 2, 1961, the Cardinal states
that he will use the donation for Don Bosco
Technical Institute. (English 1 pg.)

Mc3415. C-1961
Dr. Robert Christensen, DDS to J. Francis Car-
dinal McIntyre
October 26, 1961. Pasadena, California

The article in *The Tidings* by Fr. Healy was
sent to 650 doctors. Many have expressed their
appreciation. (English 1 pg.) On November 2,
1961, the Cardinal states that it is good to
share interests with colleagues. (English 1 pg.)

Mc3416. C-1961
Mr. and Mrs. John Conlin to J. Francis Cardi-
nal McIntyre
November 14, 1961. Los Angeles, California

There is greater need for sermons on Catholic
doctrine in Mass than the need for money. If
Churches were constructed more in keeping
with the neighborhoods, the costs could be reduced. (English 1 pg.)

Mc3417. C-1961
Mr. Michael Strumpf to Pope John XXIII
November 30, 1961. Canoga Park, California

A request to write a special message for the
students at Columbus Junior High School. (English 1 pg.) On January 2, 1961, the Apostolic
Delegate states that the Pope has so many requests that he cannot answer all of them. (English 1 pg.)

Mc3418. C-1961
J. Francis Cardinal McIntyre to Arbp. Romolo
Carboni
December 19, 1961. Los Angeles, California

The copy of the recent pronouncements is
gratefully received and thoughts of you were
prominent when visiting with Cardinal Cicognani and Arbp. Vagnozzi. (English 1 pg.)

Mc3419. D-1961
J. Francis Cardinal McIntyre to Bp. Joseph P.
Dougherty
January 13, 1961. Los Angeles, California

A friendly letter commenting on the recent
visit and enclosing a donation for the diocese.
(English 1 pg.) On January 14, 1961, the
Bishop states that the donation will help to fi-
nance the education of the seminarian in Rome.
(English 1 pg.)

Mc3420. D-1961
Dr. Tirso Del Junco, MD to Bp. Timothy
  Manning
January 27, 1961. Los Angeles, California

A request to establish an organization to help
the Cuban people and assist the refugees. (English 1 pg.) On February 2, 1961, the Bishop
states that the plan can be discussed at any
time. (English 1 pg.)

Mc3421. D-1961
Bp. Joseph P. Dougherty to J. Francis Cardinal
  McIntyre
March 28, 1961. Yakima, Washington

The act of kindness in paying a bill for a Mission Bishop will be repaid in the celebration of
the Mass. (English 1 pg.)

Mc3422. D-1961
Mr. Tom Darnell to Bp. Alden J. Bell
April 6, 1961. Memphis, Tennessee

A request for a picture of St. Vibiana's Cathedral and one of the Main Altar. A picture of
Archbishop John J. Cantwell who was very
popular in Memphis would be most welcome.
(English 2 pgs.)

Mc3423. D-1961
Hon Price Daniel to J. Francis Cardinal
  McIntyre
May 8, 1961. Austin, Texas

A certificate proclaiming the Cardinal as an
honorary citizen of Texas is enclosed (English
1 pg.)

Mc3424. D-1961
Bp. Joseph P. Dougherty to J. Francis Cardinal
  McIntyre
May 25, 1961. Yakima, Washington

Yakima Central Catholic High School will be
dedicated on May 29 and graduation will be
May 30. Could we have a telegram message to
be read on this occasion? (English 2 pgs.) On
May 25, 1961, the Cardinal sends a congratulatory message for the double ceremony. (English
1 pg.)

Mc3425. D-1961
Bp. James P. Davis to Bp. Alden J. Bell
May 25, 1961. San Juan, Puerto Rico

A trip to the Grand Canyon and Yosemite is
being planned with a few days in Los Angeles.
(English 1 pg.) On May 29, 1961, the Bishop
extends the hospitality of the Cathedral rectory
during the Bishop's visit. (English 1 pg.)

Mc3426. D-1961
Mr. Victor Sinclair to J. Francis Cardinal
  McIntyre
June 21, 1961. San Marino, California

An injustice was done to a teacher in the Parish School by dismissing her before anyone
could argue to the contrary. (English 2 pgs.) On
June 30, 1961, Rev. William Fox states that
Mrs. Downey's husband asked her to leave. The
request was granted only after a long discussion. (English pg.)

Mc3427. D-1961
Mr. E. M. Dillhoefer to J. Francis Cardinal
  McIntyre
June 28, 1961. Los Angeles, California

Every effort will be made to interest many
people in Don Bosco Technical Institute. A donation is enclosed from the O'Neill Foundation.
(English 2 pgs.) On June 30, 1961, Bishop
Manning responds to the donation with the
gratitude of the Cardinal for the interest in this
type of education. (English 1 pg.)

Mc3428. D-1961
Rev. Robert E. Brennan to J. Francis Cardinal
  McIntyre
July 9, 1961. Reno, Nevada

Bishop Robert Dwyer's condition is critical
and the doctor expressed a desire to have a lia-
son between the Bishop and the diocese. He is
conscious. (English 2 pgs.) On July 13, 1961,
the Cardinal states that the Bishop's condition
is a shock to the Church. Prayers are being offered for him. (English 1 pg.)

Mc3429. D-1967
Mrs. Mildred Davies to J. Francis Cardinal
  McIntyre
July 14, 1961. Pebble Beach, California

The prayers for the President and his advisors
to be recited for the next three months is a most
timely decision. The insight into the needs of
the people is great. (English 1 pg.)

Mc3430. D-1961
Mr. John Del Zoppo to J. Francis Cardinal
  McIntyre
August 8, 1961. Hollywood, California

Before the destruction of the world takes
place, the leaders of the world ought to meet
and work for the end of wars, all disease, and
poverty. (English 1 pg.)

Mc3431. D-1961
Rev. Robert E. Brennan to Bp. Alden J. Bell
August 19, 1961. Sun Valley, California

For the next ten or twelve weeks, may Fr. McLaughlin request faculties for the Italian American Federation priest who looks upon the parish as headquarters. (English 1 pg.) On August 22, 1961, the Bishop states that he will honor Fr. McLaughlin's requests. (English 1 pg.)

Mc3432. D-1961.
Mrs. Norma Dorr to Pope John XXIII
September 7, 1961 Los Angeles, California

A request to know if a member of the Jewish Faith can become a true Christian. (English 3 pgs.) On October 5, 1961, Bishop Bell states that the Adult Inquiry classes will answer many questions. The Catholic Information Center, the Paulists in Westwood, and the Parish are some of the resources to be used. (English 1 pg.)

Mc3433. D-1961
Rev. Robert E. Brennan to J. Francis Cardinal
    McIntyre
September 8, 1961. Sun Valley, California

Bishop Dwyer will leave Reno for a three month period of rest. I will accompany him to Montreal by train and then by steamer to England. Please continue the prayers. (English 1 pg.)

Mc3434. D-1961
Mrs. Elba Dias de Dufs to J. Francis Cardinal
    McIntyre
September 19, 1961. Santiago, Panama

A request to give a scholarship to a boy in Panama who would like to study at Don Bosco Technical Institute. He would need a home and travel expenses. (Spanish 1 pg.)

Mc3435. D-1961
Ms. Elizabeth Snyder to Bp. Timothy Manning
September 22, 1961. Los Angeles California

An invitation is extended to the dinner honoring Supervisor Ernest Debs for twenty years of public service. (English 1 pg.) On September 25, 1961, the Bishop states that he will be happy to be present. (English 1 pg.)

Mc3436. D-1961
Rev. David Daze, SJ to Bp. Timothy Manning
October 17, 1961. San Jose, California

Permission is requested to celebrate Mass for my mother's 97th birthday on December 6. It will be in her home with all precautions taken. (English 1 pg.) On October 24, 1961, the permission is given and a special birthday greeting is sent from the Cardinal and Bishops. (English 1 pg.)

Mc3437. D-1961
Bp. Hugh A. Donohue to Bp. Timothy
    Manning
October 24, 1961. San Francisco, California

The message of sympathy and the promise of prayers for Archbishop Milty was gratefully received. (English 1 pg.)

Mc3438. D-1961
Mrs. Cecil Davis to J. Francis Cardinal
    McIntyre
November 10, 1961. Pacific Palisades,
    California

A request to know how accurate are the quotes in *What is Morality and How Did It Originate*. (English 1 pg.) On November 20, 1961, Fr. John Sheridan states that he cannot locate any data on the Academy of Bavaria. (English 1 pg.)

Mc3439. D-1961
Ms. Irene Dorias to J. Francis Cardinal
    McIntyre
November 12, 1961. San Pedro, California

A request to have Exposition of the Blessed Sacrament for several hours a day in all of the Churches of the Archdiocese. (English 1 pg.) On November 15, 1961, Rev. John Rawden states that the suggestion will be brought to the Cardinal's attention when he returns. (English 1 pg.)

Mc3440. D-1961
J. Francis Cardinal McIntyre to Mr. Frank S.
    Donant
November 22, 1961. Los Angeles, California

The gracious assistance of Mr. Charles Edmonds made the European phase of the trip to Rome one without any strain. (English 1 pg.)

Mc3441. D-1961
Mr. Robert DeHaven to J. Francis Cardinal
    McIntyre
December 20, 1961. Hollywood, California

The permission to have two children baptized in the Catholic Church is absolutely denied. In a separated family, a father should have the right to deny Baptism for his children. (English 2 pgs.)

Mc3442. D-1961
Mr. Uriel Davis to J. Francis Cardinal
    McIntyre
December 28, 1960. Maitland, Florida

The enclosed vials of pollen tablets should be an aid to your good health. (English 2 pgs.) On January 5, 1961, Msgr. Hawkes states that the doctor regulates the Cardinal's diet and medication. (English 1 pg.)

Mc3443. E-1961
Miss Marie Eckstrom to J. Francis Cardinal
McIntyre
January 9, 1961. Los Angeles, California

A request to intercede for Eileen Eckstrom so
she can be a student at Manhattanville College
in Purchase, New York. (English 1 pg.) On January 12, 1961, the Cardinal requests that
Mother Cora Brady consider Eileen as a student. (English 1 pg.)

Mc3444. E-1961
Mr. Sterling Green to J. Francis Cardinal
McIntyre
January 26, 1961. Los Angeles, California

An invitation to give the invocation on February 24 at the banquet at which engineers will
be honored for their role in the country's development. (English 1 pg.) On February 1, 1961,
the Cardinal states that he will commission
Bishop Alden Bell to give the invocation. (English 1 pg.)

Mc3445. E-1961
Rev. Joseph F. Sharpe to Mrs. Mark Erbach
April 4, 1961. Los Angeles, California

The present bill of Federal Aid to Education
will perpetuate discrimination which the Civil
Rights Movement is trying to correct. (English
1 pg.)

Mc3446. E-1961
Mrs. Edward Egan to J. Francis Cardinal
McIntyre
April 15, 1961. Tustin, California

A strong complaint that St. Cecilia's School
in Tustin is not being built when several other
areas have schools under construction. (English
6 pgs.)

Mc3447. E-1961
Mr. Ernest Ellgner to J. Francis Cardinal
McIntyre
April 17, 1961. Dorchester, Massachusetts

Archbishop Joseph Paracattil of Kerala State,
India, will be in the United States and would
appreciate a visit with the Cardinal and Msgr.
Brouwers. (English 1 pg.) On April 25, 1961,
Msgr. Hawkes states that the Cardinal will not
be in California but Msgr. Brouwers will be
happy to receive the Archbishop. (English 1 pg.)

Mc3448. E-1961
Mr. Earl Blackwell to J. Francis Cardinal
McIntyre
May 16, 1961. Beverly Hills, California

The Embassy Foundation will honor Italy at
the annual Ball and will distribute the proceeds
to Italian Children's Charities in Italy. The following year Mexico will be honored in the
same way. (English 1 pg.)

Mc3449. E-1961
Mrs. Joan Emge to Bp. Alden J. Bell
May 31, 1961. Gardena, California

Will the city of Torrance have a new parish
with a school in the near future? (English 1 pg.)
On June 2, 1961, the Bishop states that the
property on Anza Street near Spencer will be
the site for a parish and school in the very near
future. (English 1 pg.)

Mc3450. E-1961
Bp. Bernardino Echeverria to J. Francis Cardi-
nal McIntyre
July 13, 1961. Ambato, Ecuador

A request to have Rev. Juan Arzube act for
the *Caritas Ecuador* in the Archdiocese. (English 1 pg.) On July 25, 1961, Bishop Bell states
that Fr. Arzube does not wish to be the representative of the *Caritas Ecuador*. (English 1 pg.)

Mc3451. E-1961
Bp. Alonso Escalante, MM to Bp. Timothy
Manning
November 21, 1961. Mexico City, Mexico

Seminaries are a prime necessity for all areas
and since there seem to be many applicants, we
are trying to build a novitiate here. Any help
that can be sent will be appreciated. (English
1 pg.)

Mc3452. E-1961
Mr. Donald Elner to J. Francis Cardinal
McIntyre
N.D. Lakewood, Ohio

A suicide prevention program ought to be established in Los Angeles similar to the one in
Boston. Many lives are saved for God and country. (English 1 pg.)

Mc3453. F-1961
Bp. Joseph T. McGucken to Msgr. Benjamin
Hawkes
January 4, 1961. Sacramento, California

Dr. Leo Farrell, a Knight of St. Gregory, is
living in Downey, California, and is connected
with Rancho Los Amigos Hospital. (English
1 pg.)

Mc3454. F-1961
Bp. Pericle Felici to J. Francis Cardinal
McIntyre
January 30, 1961. Vatican City

Designate a person who can carry the materials of the Ecumenical Council to Los Angeles.
(Latin 1 pg.) On March 6, 1961, the Cardinal
designates Rev. George Schlichte of the North
American College to be the legate. (Latin 1 pg.)

Mc3455. F-1961
Mr. Arthur Hyman to J. Francis Cardinal
McIntyre
February 14, 1961. Los Angeles, California.

Mrs. Albert Free would like to know the Cardinal's favorite charity so it can be properly mentioned in her Will. (English 1 pg.) On February 15, 1961, the Cardinal states that his favorite charity is the Archbishop's Fund for Charity. (English 1 pg.)

Mc3456. F-1961
Sister M. Stanislaus, OSF to Bp. Alden J. Bell
March 17, 1961. Los Angeles, California

A letter of evaluation is needed for Miss Minerva K. Florentino before she can be accepted for the position. (English 1 pg.) On March 20, 1961, the Bishop states that she is a cooperative, willing worker. (English 1 pg.)

Mc3457. F-1961
Mr. Robert Fay to Bp. Timothy Manning
April 11, 1961. Los Angeles, California

A Catholic College education is most important and some assistance will be needed to be able to return to Loyola University or to University of San Diego. (English 2 pgs.) On April 13, 1961, the Bishop explains the situation to the president of University of San Diego. (English 1 pg.)

Mc3458. F-1961
J. Francis Cardinal McIntyre to Mr. George Footz
April 19, 1961. Los Angeles, California

The I.B.M. Corporation matched the donation so generously sent for St. John's Seminary. The added donation is most generous. (English 1 pg.)

Mc3459. F-1961
Mr. Jacques Fortin to Bp. Alden J. Bell
April 25, 1961. Quebec, Canada

Catholic educational opportunities for the children and adults are important before an expected move into the Los Angeles area can be made. (English 1 pg.) On May 1, 1961, the Bishop states the many parishes and schools give a wide background of educational experiences. (English 1 pg.)

Mc3460. F-1961
Mr. Ray Flores to J. Francis Cardinal McIntyre
June 2, 1961. Wilmington, California

The committee requests an interview before organizing a program for the Catholic War Veterans of the area. (English 1 pg.) On June 21, 1961, Msgr. Hawkes states that the Cardinal will be out of the city but Bishop Manning will arrange an interview. (English 1 pg.)

Mc3461. F-1961
Mr. Louis M. Ferro to J. Francis Cardinal McIntyre
August 15, 1961. Oakland, New Jersey

A photo taken at the Salesian Sister's Convent has created speculation. Some see the Face of Christ very similar to the Holy Shroud of Turin on the Tabernacle. (English 2 pgs.)

Mc3462. F-1961
Msgr. Raymond O'Flaherty to J. Francis Cardinal McIntyre
September 21, 1961. Los Angeles, California

Dr. Marion Firor has donated many hours to the Child Guidance Center. A letter of appreciation should be written. (English 1 pg.) On September 25, 1961, the Cardinal expresses his gratitude for the many hours donated to the Center. (English 1 pg.)

Mc3463. F-1961
J. Francis Cardinal McIntyre to Bp. Pericle Felici
October 4, 1961. Los Angeles, California

The annual meeting of the Bishops in Washington, D.C. begins on November 13 and it is a very important meeting; therefore, if possible I will leave Rome on November 12 to be present for the meeting. (English 1 pg.)

Mc3464. F-1961
J. Francis Cardinal McIntyre to Bp. Philip Furlong
November 22, 1961. Los Angeles, California

The priests of Camarillo have a notice that their services at Hamilton Air Force Base are no longer needed. Will a Chaplain be assigned? (English 1 pg.) On November 29, 1961, the Bishop states that no announcement has been made of a change. (English 1 pg.)

Mc3465. F-1961
Rev. Maurice Fitzgerald, CSP to Bp. Alden J. Bell
November 23, 1961. Chicago, Illinois

A convention of priests who are doing the Home Study Apostolate will be held soon. The name of any interested priest could receive an invitation. (English 1 pg.) On November 27, 1961, the Bishop states that a general mailing might be wise to interest priests who are unaware of the program. (English 1 pg.)

Mc3466. G-1961
Mrs. Edith Gardner to J. Francis Cardinal McIntyre
January 8, 1961. Jackson Heights, New York

A friendly letter commenting on past events and asks for a little advanced notice of the next visit to New York. (English 3 pgs.) On January 19, 1961, the Cardinal states that the letter brought many memories. (English 1 pg.)

Mc3467. G-1961
Mr. Joseph Geuting to J. Francis Cardinal
  McIntyre
January 10, 1961. Washington, D.C.

Mr. Simmons will discuss the projects in
which the school children could participate
with Project Hope. The Superintendent of
Schools should be present. (English 1 pg.)

Mc3468. G-1961
Mr. George Gillson to J. Francis Cardinal
  McIntyre
February 6, 1961. San Francisco, California

A statement of the donations to the Archdiocese for the years 1956–1958 is needed by the
State Financial Board. The gold chalice donated
to the Cathedral was listed as a donation. (English 2 pgs.) On February 6, 1961 the Cardinal
listed all donations to the Archdiocese. (English
1 pg.)

Mc3469. G-1961
Mr. Dan Paolo Liggeri to J. Francis Cardinal
  McIntyre
February 14, 1961. Milan, Italy

A request for a letter of recommendation so
that Mr. and Mrs. Wenelin Ganef can obtain
employment. They arrived in Los Angeles in
May 1960, and need a recommendation. (English 2 pgs.)

Mc3470. G-1961
Mr. Daniel Greenwood to J. Francis Cardinal
  McIntyre
March 1, 1961. Los Angeles, California

Catholic University requires a letter of recommendation before allowing one to take a course
in Sacred Theology. Would it be possible to obtain the recommendation? (English 1 pg.)

Mc3471. G-1961
Mr. Dan Gordman to J. Francis Cardinal
  McIntyre
March 29, 1961. Omaha, Nebraska

Beth Israel Humanitarian Award will be
given to Miss Irene Dunne on April 23. As a
friend of hers, may we have a message that can
be read on that event. (English 1 pg.)

Mc3472. G-1961
Bp. Alden J. Bell to Mrs. Priscilla Gonzalez
March 29, 1961. Los Angeles, California

The parish is the one church in which Baptism, First Communion, and Confirmation
should be received. The financial support
should go to the Parish while another Church
can be attended occasionally. (English 1 pg.)

Mc3473. G-1961
Mr. Frederic Gaspard to Bp. Alden J. Bell
April 12, 1961. Winnipeg, Canada

A request to appoint a representative to handle Church Vestments for the company. (English
1 pg.) On April 18, 1961, the Bishop suggested
Mr. C. F. Horan be the representative. (English
1 pg.)

Mc3474. G-1961
Bp. Merlin Guilfoyle to J. Francis Cardinal
  McIntyre
April 14, 1961. San Francisco, California

The biography of Bishop Francisco Garcia
Diego y Moreno by Rev. Francis Weber will be
read with great joy. (English 1 pg.)

Mc3475. G-1961
Mrs. Tito Gomez to Bp. Alden J. Bell
May 1, 1961, Cleveland, Ohio

Before moving into Los Angeles, the degree of
prejudice must be known. (English 1 pg.) On
May 8, 1961, the Bishop states that here one
finds little prejudice. (English 1 pg.)

Mc3476. G-1961
Mr. Murphy Gonsoulin to Bp. Alden J. Bell
May 22, 1961. Los Angeles, California

A complaint that Negro families are being
discriminated against in St. Cecilia's Parish.
(English 1 pg.) On May 27, 1961, the Bishop
states that he will discuss the situation with the
Pastor. (English 1 pg.)

Mc3477. G-1961
J. Francis Cardinal McIntyre to Arbp. Daniel
  Gercke
May 25, 1961. Los Angeles, California

A congratulatory message and a promise of
prayers on June 1 the 60th anniversary of ordination. (English 1 pg.) On June 2, 1961, the
Archbishop states that the 60 years have passed
with great speed and that God has been generous with His natural and supernatural graces.
(English 1 pg.)

Mc3478. G-1961
Mr. John Greeley to Msgr. Benjamin Hawkes
May 26, 1961. San Francisco, California

The meeting with Cardinal McIntyre and Mr.
Laughlin will be most beneficial for both Los
Angeles and San Francisco. (English 1 pg.)

Mc3479. G-1961
Mrs. Nemesic Dixon to Bp. Timothy Manning
May 28, 1961, Colon, Panama

A request to help locate the Leonel Grain family as there has been no contact with the rest of the family in Panama. They should live in Santa Monica. (English 2 pgs.) On May 29, 1961, the Bishop states that he has asked the Pastors to try to locate the family. (English 1 pg.)

Mc3480. G-1961
Mr. Murphy Gonsoulin to Bp. Alden J. Bell
June 9, 1961. Los Angeles, California

The Pastor's conference did not resolve the Negro problem. He does not want to upset the whites in the Parish. A meeting with the Pastor, Bishop and the writer is needed. (English 1 pg.) On June 15, 1961, the Bishop states that the priests' retreats make a meeting difficult. (English 1 pg.)

Mc3481. G-1961
Mrs. Byron Ivancovich to Bp. Francis Green
August 27, 1961. Tucson, Arizona

An expose on the manner of distribution of the food sent by the Bishops' Conference. In Peru the food is sold to the wealthy; In Lima the very poor do not get the food. Some supervision is needed. (English 3 pgs.)

Mc3482. G-1961
Dr. Francis Griffin to J. Francis Cardinal McIntyre
August 27, 1961. Beverly Hills, California

The honor of being Knight Commander of the Order of the Holy Sepulchre must be received in absentia. A trip to Dallas, Texas, is impossible now. (English 1 pg.)

Mc3483. G-1961
Bp. Francis J. Green to J. Francis Cardinal McIntyre
August 30, 1961. Tucson, Arizona

The information given concerning the distribution of the food sent to the Latin American countries must be shared with someone. (English 1 pg.) On September 5, 1961, the Cardinal suggests sending the information to Bishop Swanstrom. Some abuses can be corrected. (English 1 pg.)

Mc3484. G-1961
Mr. Hugh Gaffney to J. Francis Cardinal McIntyre
September 13, 1961. New York City, New York

A friendly letter commenting on the former days and sending snap shots of Bowling on the Green in Central Park. (English 1 pg.) On September 20, 1961, the Cardinal comments that he has to strain to recognize the picture. (English 1 pg.)

Mc3485. G-1961
J. Francis Cardinal McIntyre to Rev. Thomas J. Nevin
October 23, 1961. Los Angeles, California

The letter from Archbishop Arellano concerning Mr. Carlos Gonzalez does not state what assistance he needs. Is it a scholarship or is he a seminarian? (English 1 pg.)

Mc3486. G-1961
Mr. George Gillson to J. Francis Cardinal McIntyre
October 28, 1961. San Francisco, California

There is a new Western Division of the Knights of Malta with Bishop Donohue as the Protector. Many men are worthy to be a Knight of Malta. (English 1 pg.)

Mc3487. G-1961
Msgr. Paul Tanner to J. Francis Cardinal McIntyre
December 21, 1961. Washington, D.C.

Canon Fabre in Lille, France, will screen all students who want to study in the United States. The International High School Program arranges transportation and the host family. (English 1 pg.)

Mc3488. G-1961
Bp. Thomas K. Gorman to J. Francis Cardinal McIntyre
December 21, 1961. Dallas, Texas

The presence of the Cardinal at the Confraternity Congress gave special emphasis to the event. (English 1 pg.)

Mc3489. H-1961
Mr. Charles Herder to J. Francis Cardinal McIntyre
January 16, 1961. Los Angeles, California

Employment by the Archdiocese is an answer to prayer. The Christmas gift and bonus were unexpected. (English 1 pg.)

Mc3490. H-1961
Mr. Norman Topping to J. Francis Cardinal McIntyre
January 17, 1961. Los Angeles, California

The rising cost of medical care makes the conference to be held at U.S.C. a necessity. Meetings will begin at 9:00 and end at 5:00 p.m. (English 1 pg.) On January 20, 1961, the Cardinal states that Msgr. O'Dwyer will attend the meeting since he has had long experiences in the hospital field. (English 1 pg.)

Mc3491. H-1961
Mr. V. M. Haldinger to J. Francis Cardinal
McIntyre
January 23, 1961. Los Angeles, California

Could the priest celebrating the Requiem
Mass give a brief explanation of the ceremony
so that the non-Catholics attending could understand what is happening. (English 1 pg.)

Mc3492. H-1961
Mrs. Maud Havens to Pope John XXIII
February 7, 1961. Fullerton, California

Before the unity of the Christians can take
place everyone will have to return to the simple
faith of the Apostolic Church. Greater discipline
will be needed. (English 2 pgs.)

Mc3493. H-1961
Dr. F. K. Amerongen to Msgr. Benjamin
Hawkes
February 7, 1961. Hollywood, California

Dr. Edward Hayes is nominated as Catholic
physician of the year. The approval of the Chancery Office is needed. (English 1 pg.) On February 16, 1961, Msgr. states that he is happy that
the Catholic physicians recognize an outstanding man. (English 1 pg.)

Mc3494. Mc-1961
Rev. Francis Hurley to J. Francis Cardinal
McIntyre
February 15, 1961. Washington, D.C.

The NCWC news release concerning the Cuban refugee situation in Miami should be sent
to the California Congressman. No provision
for private schools is made. (English 1 pg.)

Mc3495. H-1961
Miss Mary J. Hardy to J. Francis Cardinal
McIntyre
February 25, 1961. Los Angeles, California

The spread of errors and evil is associated
with Free-masonry, Jehoval Witnesses, and
Anti-Christ which were allowed to spread without any checks. (English 12 pgs.)

Mc3496. H-1961
Dr. Edward Hayes to J. Francis Cardinal
McIntyre
March 6, 1961. Monrovia, California

Catholic physicians are needed for the Plaza
Clinic which serves many Mexican families.
(English 1 pg.)

Mc3497 H-1961
Bp. Ralph L. Hayes to J. Francis Cardinal
McIntyre
March 10, 1961. Davenport, Iowa

Mr. Lester C. Bickford, a member of Mary
Star of the Sea Parish, is applying as a Seminarian for the Davenport Diocese. This is his
former home. (English 1 pg.) On March 16,
1961, the Cardinal states that he can understand the desire of the young man to be with his
former classmates. (English 1 pg.)

Mc3498. H-1961
Mr. Robert Harrold to J. Francis Cardinal
McIntyre
March 21, 1961. Canoga Park, California

The hierarchy of America is endorsing the
United World Federalists. Do you endorse it?
(English 1 pg.) On April 3, 1961, Msgr. Paul
Tanner states that all statements will be cleared
with the Bishops before releasing news for the
press. (English 2 pgs.)

Mc3499. H-1961
Rev. Mark Hurley to J. Francis Cardinal
McIntyre
April 24, 1961. San Rafael, California

Information is needed from the Committee of
Mary's Hour so a similar out door celebration
could be held in Golden Gate Park. (English 1
pg.) On April 25, 1961, the Cardinal states that
Rev. John Languille is in charge of Mary's Hour
and will be happy to share all information. (English 1 pg.)

Mc3500. H-1961
Col. James Hunter, USAF to J. Francis Cardi-
nal McIntyre
May 22, 1961 Los Angeles, California

This Colonel of the United States Air Force
stands ready to support and advance the thinking of the Holy Father. (English 1 pg.)

Mc3501. H-1961
Msgr. William Johnson to J. Francis Cardinal
McIntyre
June 2, 1961. Los Angeles, California

The State Department of Social Welfare
Board is bi-partisan so Mr. Hartzer will probably be re-appointed. (English 1 pg.)

Mc3502. H-1961
J. Francis Cardinal McIntyre to Mrs. Annett
Holland
June 5, 1961. Los Angeles, California

The generous donation of 100 shares of Financial Federation stock for St. John's Seminary Fund is received with gratitude. (English
1 pg.)

Mc3503. H-1961
Mrs. Robert Heller to Hon. Barry Goldwater
June 28, 1961. Los Angeles, California

Opposition to Federal Aid to Education preserves the responsibility for the state and local level for the education of the students and reduces additional taxes. (English 1 pg.)

Mc3504. H-1961
Bp. Joseph Hodges to J. Francis Cardinal McIntyre
June 29, 1961. New York City, New York

The Superintendent of Education should be present in Detroit for the Seminar on Catholic School Integration. (English 3 pgs.) On August 2, 1961, the Cardinal states that Los Angeles is tranquil and wants to avoid stimulation. (English 1 pg.)

Mc3505. H-1961
Mrs. Robert Heller to J. Francis Cardinal McIntyre
July 11, 1961. Los Angeles, California

The program for the Archdiocesan Council of Catholic Women is presented for approval with Sister Cecilia as the main speaker in the morning and Rev. Thomas McCarthy in the afternoon. (English 2 pgs.) On July 12, 1961, the Cardinal approves the program. (English 1 pg.)

Mc3506. H-1961
Mr. Ballentine Henley to J. Francis Cardinal McIntyre
July 17, 1961. Los Angeles, California

The dedication service for the incoming freshmen will be September 6. The name of a priest to be on the program is needed. (English 1 pg.) On August 7, 1961, the Cardinal states that Rev. Michael Duffy will be on the program according to Diocesan policy. (English 1 pg.)

Mc3507. H-1961
Mrs. Louis Sims to Mrs. Heller
July 1961. Hollywood, California

The Chaplains Service Corps would like to send a representative to speak to clubs and tell the needs of the Chaplains of the Armed Forces. (English 1 pg.) On August 1, 1961, the Bishop states that the Archdiocese assists the Catholic Chaplains. (English 1 pg.)

Mc3508. H-1961
Rev. James Hastrich to Bp. Timothy Manning
August 5, 1961. Madison, Wisconsin

Any material outlining rules and regulations for Diocesan building would be helpful for the Diocesan committee in Madison to review. (English 1 pg.) On August 10, 1961, the members of the Building Commission are listed. (English 1 pg.)

Mc3509. H-1961
Msgr. Benjamin Hawkes to Col. James Hunter
November 2, 1961. Los Angeles, California

The visit to Offutt Air Force Base was an educational experience and a reassurance of the military preparedness. (English 1 pg.)

Mc3510. I-1961
Mr. James Irving to Rev. John A. Rawden
February 28, 1961. Pasadena, California

Why does the Catholic Church sponsor the protection of wild life societies and legislation? (English 4 pgs.) On March 8, 1961, Fr. states perhaps an inquiry to the office in Washington, D.C. could give an answer. (English 1 pg.)

Mc3511. I-1961
Mr. E. T. Ibbetson to Bp. Timothy Manning
July 26, 1961. Bellflower, California

The presence of the Bishop and the words spoken at the Requiem Mass for the father of the family will be remembered for many years. (English 1 pg.)

Mc3512. J-1961
Mr. Roberto Magallanes to J. Francis Cardinal McIntyre
N.D. Oxnard, California

A request for transportation money to return to Mexico. Because of an automobile accident, employment is now impossible. (Spanish 2 pgs.) On February 15, 1961, Msgr. Johnson states that as soon as medical supervision is over Roberto will be returned to Mexico by the company. (English 1 pg.)

Mc3513. J-1961
Miss Helena Jennings to Bp. Timothy Manning
March 11, 1961. London, England

Is there a possibility of a teaching position during the summer months? A trip is being planned from April to September. (English 2 pgs.) On November 8, 1961, the Bishop states that there are no summer teaching positions under consideration for high school. The three colleges might have an opening. (English 1 pg.)

Mc3514. J-1961
Bp. Alden J. Bell to Catholic Youth Organization
March 22, 1961. Los Angeles, California

Mr. Johansing is recommended for the *Amicus Juvenum* Award because of his unselfish activities for Youth organizations. (English 1 pg.)

Mc3515. J-1961
Mr. Thomas Johnson to Bp. Alden J. Bell
May 22, 1961. Los Angeles, California

The church in Los Angeles needs the assistance of Black people as well as White people. (English 1 pg.) On May 27, 1961, the Bishop states that the situations will be discussed with the Pastors. (English 1 pg.)

Mc3516. J-1961
Mr. Thomas Johnson to Bp. Alden J. Bell
June 10, 1961. Los Angeles, California

The meeting with the Pastor did not solve the race situation and an appointment is necessary. (English 1 pg.) On June 15, 1961, the Bishop states that priest retreats are taking place and another talk will be held with Father. (English 1 pg.)

Mc3517. J-1961
Msgr. William Johnson to J. Francis Cardinal McIntyre
July 13, 1961. Los Angeles, California

The National Conference of Catholic Charities and Catholic Hospital Association are considering a health benefit program for the aged. Congress will probably pass the Forand Bill but a formal statement on the Bill would serve no purpose. (English 1 pg.)

Mc3518. J-1961
Mr. Bob Labonge to J. Francis Cardinal McIntyre
N.D. Los Angeles, California

James Johnson who was accidentally killed is the son of Don Johnson of the Catholic Press Council. (English 1 pg.) On July 20, 1961, the Cardinal expressed his prayerful sympathy to the family. (English 1 pg.)

Mc3519. J-1961
Mr. H. Jett to Bp. Alden J. Bell
October 27, 1961. Palmdale, California

Unfair and unfounded accusations are being made which are ruining reputations and are causing hardships. (English 2 pgs.) On November 8, 1961, Fr. Dachtler states that threats have been made before and that he will talk to Mr. Jett. (English 1 pg.)

Mc3520. J-1961
J. Francis Cardinal McIntyre to Pope John XXIII
N.D. Los Angeles, California

The Clergy, Religious, faithful and the Archbishop feel a distinguished honor is given to be chosen as the Cardinal Legate to the Fifteen hundredth anniversary of the death of St. Patrick. Missionaries have made a great contribution to the Archdiocese. (English 1 pg.)

Mc3521. K-1961
Ms. Carol Karadimas to Pope John XXIII
January 10, 1961. Van Nuys, California

The question of church support in Europe is interesting and some information is needed for the church in the United States. (English 1 pg.) On March 20, 1961, Bishop Bell states that in Germany the Lutheran and Catholic churches are the official churches and receive assistance but the faithful do not support the church. (English 1 pg.)

Mc3522. K-1961
Ms. Marget Kane to Bp. Timothy Manning
January 10, 1961. Los Angeles, California

The recitation of the Rosary during Mass was outlawed by the Vatican in April 1960. Why isn't the legislation carried out in Los Angeles? (English 2 pgs.)

Mc3523. K-1961
Mr. Charles Kelley to J. Francis Cardinal McIntyre
February 10, 1961. Panorama City, California

A formula for scientific living is ready to be put into text books and made available. Would a conference be possible for evaluation. (English 1 pg.)

Mc3524. K-1961
J. Francis Cardinal McIntyre to Arbp. John J. Krol
February 16, 1961. Los Angeles, California

Prayerful congratulations on being named Archbishop of Philadelphia and may your holy predecessors constantly pray for you. (English 1 pg.) On February 23, 1961, the Archbishop expresses his gratitude for the prayers and message. (English 1 pg.)

Mc3525. K-1961
Mrs. Douglas Kauffman to J. Francis Cardinal McIntyre
March 20, 1961. Downey, California

Is it necessary to cover the statue of St. Joseph on his feast day? Flowers were placed at the feet of the purple covered statue. (English 1 pg.) On March 22, 1961, Fr. Rawden states that because the feast was during Passion Time the statues were covered. (English 1 pg.)

Mc3526. K-1961
Mrs. Marian Kimball to J. Fancis Cardinal McIntyre
N.D. New York City, New York

A friendly letter commenting on the lovely medal of Our Lady of the Angels that the Cardinal blessed for her and the desire to return to Rome. (English 2 pgs.) On March 27, 1961, the Cardinal states that he has just returned from Rome and sends a special blessing. (English 1 pg.)

Mc3527. K-1961
Mr. Dan Keavy to J. Francis Cardinal
McIntyre
April 6, 1961. Southampton, England

A request to investigate the working conditions of a daughter who has not written home. (English 1 pg.) On May 19, 1961, Fr. Cummings states that Kathleen is well and busy as a governess and will join the young group in the parish. (English 1 pg.)

Mc3528. K-1961
Countess Mary Young Moore to J. Francis
Cardinal McIntyre
May 1, 1961. Beverly Hills, California

A letter of recommendation for Mr. Francis Kanne to be a Knight of Malta from the Chancery Office. He has done extensive charity donating both time and money. (English 2 pgs.)

Mc3529. K-1961
Arbp. Martin O'Connor to J. Francis Cardinal
McIntyre
May 29, 1961. Rome, Italy

Some information is needed to correct statements made by Mr. Alphonsus Christopher Kelly. The checks that he claims to have sent have never arrived. (English 1 pg.) On June 5, 1961, the Cardinal states that Mr. Kelly is most dependable and worthy of any consideration. (English 1 pg.)

Mc3530. K-1961
Mrs. Helen Koller to Msgr. Patrick Shear
June 19, 1961. El Monte, California

The return to the Baptist Church did not happen from the events of the death of Mr. Koller. My will states that one half of my property will go to the Catholic Church and one half to the Baptist Church. (English 1 pg.)

Mc3531. K-1961
Francis Cardinal Spellman to J. Francis Cardinal McIntyre
June 20, 1961. New York City, New York

A friendly letter commenting on the nomination of Mr. Kanne as a Knight of Malta, the successful results from eye surgery, and the successful birthday message. (English 1 pg.)

Mc3532. K-1961
Mrs. Frank Krok to Rev. John A. Rawden
July 6, 1961. Long Beach, California

At the present time there is no need to have an investigation of the visions. God is asking for love of neighbor. There is no new revelation. (English 1 pg.)

Mc3533. K-1961
Rev. W. J. Kenneally CM to J. Francis Cardinal
McIntyre
July 21, 1961. Camarillo, California

The report of the Middle States Association is very similar to St. John's comment on the lack of a full-time degreed librarian. The comment on psychoanalysts, the discussion on current Biblical problems and the use of tradition in the Seminary are interesting. (English 2 pgs.)

Mc3534. K-1961
Mr. Timothy Keating to J. Francis Cardinal
McIntyre
July 27, 1961. Fall River, Massachusetts

The NCWC has given permission to organize a Catholic Pharmacists Guild. Could the Catholic Pharmacists in Los Angeles be contacted? (English 1 pg.) On August 7, 1961, the Cardinal states that the group in Los Angeles is forming and will cooperate. (English 1 pg.)

Mc3535. K-1961
Rev. Joseph F. Sharpe to Mrs. Glenn Kraft
August 10, 1961. Los Angeles, California

School finance is a difficult problem for many parishes. If someone is given a reduction, the pastor usually has many reasons for this action. (English 1 pg.)

Mc3536. K-1961
Mr. Wilfrid to Bp. Timothy Manning
September 11, 1961. Emery, South Dakota

An appeal is made to have Fr. George Kass reverse his decision to evict the family from the farm that they have worked for over fifty years. (English 1 pg.) On September 22, 1961, the Bishop states that Fr. has delayed his plans in deference to the family. (English 1 pg.)

Mc3537. K-1961
Mr. Patrick James Kirby to Msgr. Patrick
Roche
October 31, 1961. San Gabriel, California

Dr. George Kramer will be honored for his resistance to atheistic Communism if this is wise. (English 1 pg.) On October 26, 1961, Msgr. is requested to assist in getting Mr. Kramer to the meeting. (English 4 pgs.)

Mc3538. K-1961
Rev. W. J. Kenneally, CM to J. Francis Cardinal McIntyre
November 3, 1961. Camarillo, California

Comments on the materials of the Ecumenical Council sent to the Seminary for discussion. Formula *Nova Professionis Fidei* seems to be the most important. (English 3 pgs.)

Mc3539. K-1961
Mr. B. F. Kennedy to Bp. Alden J. Bell
November 30, 1961. Beverly Hills, California

Is *America* an official Catholic magazine and
are the articles approved by an authorized
judge? (English 1 pg.) On December 5, 1961,
the Bishop states that *America* is not an official
Catholic magazine and the article in question is
an editorial and subject to the editor's authority.
(English 1 pg.)

Mc3540. K-1961
Rev. Frederick J. Kass to J. Francis Cardinal
  McIntyre
December 19, 1961. Buena Park, California

A donation of $1,500 for St. John's Seminary
is enclosed in memory of Mr. and Mrs. George
Kass. (English 1 pg.) On December 22, 1961,
the Cardinal expresses his gratitude for the donation to the Seminary. (English 1 pg.)

Mc3541. L-1961
Mrs. Jack Lundberg to Bp. Alden J. Bell
January 16, 1961. Spokane, Washington

Before accepting a position we must know
the school and parish situation in Orange, Anaheim, or Fullerton. On January 20, 1961, the
Bishop sends the names of the parishes and the
fact that most of the schools are crowded. (English 1 pg.)

Mc3542. L-1961
Mrs. Gwendolen D. Lewis to J. Francis Cardi-
  nal McIntyre
February 12, 1961. Santa Barbara, California

To ease the priest shortage could some priests
from Ireland be sent to the Archdiocese for a
period of time until the native priests fill the
need? (English 1 pg.) On February 17, 1961,
the Cardinal states that Ireland has supplied
many priests and Los Angeles is grateful. (English 1 pg.)

Mc3543. L-1961
Mr. Perry Winstead to J. Francis Cardinal
  McIntyre
February 20, 1961. San Bernardino, California

An invitation to attend the Little League
Congress on March 22 as one who is interested
in youth. (English 1 pg.) On February 23, 1961,
the Cardinal states that a trip to Ireland is
scheduled for that time but Fr. John Languille
will give the invocation. (English 1 pg.)

Mc3544. L-1961
Mr. Gerald Lynch to Msgr. Benjamin Hawkes
March 9, 1961. Newport Beach, California

The Ford Foundation Plan matches donations
given to educational institutions as well as the
other companies that have similar programs.
(English 1 pg.) On March 22, 1961, Fr. John
Rawden acknowledges that the material will be
most useful. (English 1 pg.)

Mc3545. L-1961
Rev. Ricardo Lombardi to J. Francis Cardinal
  McIntyre
May 21, 1961. Rome, Italy

The Movement for a Better World will conduct a revised *Pro Ecclesia* course this year in
Rome. Will Los Angeles priests be in the
course? (English 5 pgs.)

Mc3546. L-1961
Mr. T. E. Leavey to J. Francis Cardinal
  McIntyre
June 20, 1961. Los Angeles, California

In honor of the Cardinal's birthday a yearly
scholarship to Don Bosco Technical Institute
will be established. (English 1 pg.) On June 23,
1961, the Cardinal states that he is most grateful for the scholarship. (English 1 pg.)

Mc3547. L-1961
Mrs. Agnes Lank to J. Francis Cardinal
  McIntyre
July 1, 1961. Los Angeles, California

A mailing of Marian literature may increase
devotion to the Blessed Mother which in turn
could help the whole world. (English 3 pgs.) On
July 10, 1961, the Cardinal is happy to increase
devotion to Mary under all titles. (English
1 pg.)

Mc3548. L-1961
Arbp. Robert E. Lucey to J. Francis Cardinal
  McIntyre
August 3, 1961. San Antonio, Texas

Texas will invade Los Angeles in the persons
of the Archbishop and Bishop. A visit to the
Chancery Office is in the plan. (English 1 pg.)

Mc3549. L-1961
Mr. Oscar Lawler to J. Francis Cardinal McIn-
  tyre
August 4, 1961. Beverly Hills, California

The book, *Education of the Founding Fathers,* gives much material for discussion and is
arousing interest. (English 1 pg.)

Mc3550. L-1961
Mr. Joseph Lamb to J. Francis Cardinal
McIntyre
September 14, 1961. New York City, New
York

A friendly letter commenting on the Mass at
the Shrine in Washington, D.C. on the Pope's
birthday, and a request for prayers as cataract
surgery is scheduled. (English 2 pgs.) On September 19, 1961, the Cardinal sends prayerful
sympathy as this is a possibility for him too.
(English 1 pg.)

Mc3551. L-1961
Bp. Alfred Mendes to Mr. Harold Lidin
September 27, 1961. San Juan, Puerto Rico

The quotes in the article violate truth because
additional words were added. At no time was
the Christian Action Party mentioned in the interview either in a positive or negative way. (English 1 pg.)

Mc3552. L-1961
Mr. Joseph Lamb to J. Francis Cardinal
McIntye
November 20, 1961. New York City,
New York

The prayers for the surgery were answered
and with in a week dark glasses will take the
place of bandages. (English 1 pg.) On November 24, 1961, the Cardinal rejoices in the good
news of the surgery. (English 1 pg.)

Mc3553. L-1961
Bp. Francis P. Leipzig to J. Francis Cardinal
McIntyre
December 4, 1961. Baker, Oregon

A report of the missionary journey of the
Bishop in the vast diocese of Baker, Oregon.
(English 7 pgs.) On December 14, 1961, the
Cardinal sends Christmas wishes and a dona-
tion for the Diocese. (English 1 pg.)

Mc3554. L-1961
Mrs. Susan Lakrantz to J. Francis Cardinal
McIntyre
December 6, 1961. Los Angeles, California

If it is the wish of the Cardinal to raise funds
for the Boy's Town of Italy, a committee will be
formed. (English 1 pg.)

Mc3555. L-1961
Mr. David Levitt to J. Francis Cardinal
McIntyre
N.D. Hollywood, California

An appeal to help a member of the armed
forces to be reappointed to the position held before surgery was necessary. (English 1 pg.)

Mc3556. Mc-1961
Arbp. Urban Vehr to Bp. Timothy Manning
January 7, 1961. Denver, Colorado

The presence of many Bishops at the consecration ceremony made the event an added im-
pressive ceremony in Denver. (English 1 pg.)

Mc3557. Mc-1961
Mr. Emmett McGaughey to Msgr. Benjamin
Hawkes
January 19, 1961. Los Angeles, California

The gift to Mr. and Mrs. Power is a Steuben
Glass Bowl and candlesticks as a thank you for
the briefing at S.A.C. (English 1 pg.) On January 24, 1961, Msgr. states that the experience
at S.A.C. holds many memories. (English 1 pg.)

Mc3558. Mc-1961
Rev. F. J. Schwertz to J. Francis Cardinal
McIntyre
February 26, 1961. Wheeling, West Virginia

The death of Bishop Thomas McDonnell is
announced with the funeral Mass on March 2,
1961 at 10:00 a.m. (English 1 pg.)

Mc3559. Mc-1961
Mr. Patrick McCormick to J. Francis Cardinal
McIntyre
March 9, 1961. Los Angeles, California

The whole McCormick family is grateful for
the presence of the Cardinal at the funeral of
Mr. Paul McCormick. He was a man of great
dignity and humility. (English 1 pg.)

Mc3560. Mc-1961
Bp. Joseph T. McGucken to J. Francis Cardinal
McIntyre
March 15, 1961. Sacramento, California

An invitation is given to the dedication of St.
Pius X Junior Seminary and the celebration of
the Diamond Jubilee of the establishment of the
Diocese of Sacramento. (English 1 pg.)

Mc3561. Mc-1961
Msgr. Benjamin Hawkes to Bp. Joseph T.
McGucken
April 5, 1961. Los Angeles, California

The Cardinal will be present for the dedication of St. Pius X Seminary and the celebration
of the Diamond Jubilee of the Diocese. The enclosed booklet will be helpful to the Master of
Ceremonies. (English 1 pg.)

Mc3562. Mc-1961
Bp. elect Vincent McCauley to J. Francis Cardinal McIntyre
April 12, 1961. Notre Dame, Indiana

An invitation is sent to the consecration of Bishop elect Vincent McCauley on May 17 for the new diocese of Fort Portal, Uganda, East Africa. (English 1 pg.) On April 20, 1961, the Cardinal states that a heavy schedule of graduations and ordinations makes May a very busy month. (English 1 pg.)

Mc3563. Mc-1961
Bp. Joseph T. McGucken to J. Francis Cardinal McIntyre
June 13, 1961. Sacramento, California

The State Board of Social Welfare has two Catholics. Mr. Hartzer's term expires soon. He may be reappointed. If there is another who should be considered, then the person should be made known. (English 1 pg.)

Mc3564. Mc-1961
J. Francis Cardinal McIntyre to Mrs. Elsie McBride
June 15, 1961. Los Angeles, California

His many friends and I grieve over the death of Senator McBride. Unchangeable appointments will prevent attendance at the funeral but a Bishop will be present. (English 1 pg.)

Mc3565. Mc-1961
Mrs. Thelma McGrail to Bp. Alden J. Bell
July 1, 1961. Kokomo, Indiana

The time of the Cardinal's Mass on Sunday in the Cathedral is a necessity for planning. (English 1 pg.) On July 3, 1961, the Bishop states that the Cardinal usually celebrates the 10:00 a.m. Mass on Sundays and Holy Days. (English 1 pg.)

Mc3566. Mc-1961
Bp. elect William McNaughton to J. Francis Cardinal McIntyre
July 11, 1961. Maryknoll, New York

An invitation is extended to the consecration of Bishop elect William J. McNaughton on August 24, 1961 at 10:00 a.m. (English 1 pg.) On July 18, 1961, the Cardinal states that staff vacations requires the Cardinal's presence in the Chancery. (English 1 pg.)

Mc3567. Mc-1961
Rev. John McCormick to J. Francis Cardinal McIntyre
July 26, 1961. Whittier, California

The people want the devotion of the Pilgrim Statue initiated in the parish but instructions from the office is needed. (English 1 pg.) On August 1, 1961, the Cardinal states that devotions in the Church is usually best. But use good judgment if the devotion is allowed. (English 1 pg.)

Mc3568. Mc-1961
Mr. T. S. McGinnis to Bp. Timothy Manning
August 20, 1961. Yakima, Washington

The Catholic Travel Guide is published and the 1961 Directory is necessary to update and improve the first edition. (English 1 pg.) On September 5, 1961, the Bishop states that the new Directory will be published in December. (English 1 pg.)

Mc3569. Mc-1961
Rev. Francis Keane to J. Francis Cardinal McIntyre
October 12, 1961. Camarillo, California

Please send an autographed picture to a fifth grade boy, Francis McIntyre, who is in Tucson, Arizona. His teacher will present it to him. (English 1 pg.)

Mc3570. Mc-1961
Francis Cardinal Spellman to J. Francis Cardinal McIntyre
November 9, 1961. New York City, New York

An invitation is extended to the welcome ceremony of the Secetary of State Amelto Cardinal Cicognani in St. Patrick's Cathedral and to the dinner later. (English 1 pg.)

Mc3571. Mc-1961
Mr. C. E. McLean to Bp. Timothy Manning
November 21, 1961. Eugene, Oregon

A Catholic Retirement home is being planned in Eugene, Oregon, and advertisement is needed to allow all of the Catholics to know about it. (English 1 pg.) On November 24, 1961, the Bishop suggests putting an ad in *The Tidings*. (English 1 pg.)

Mc3572. Mc-1961
J. Francis Cardinal McIntyre to Francis Cardinal Spellman
December 1, 1961. Los Angeles, California

A background check is needed for Mr. Harold C. McClellan who will be the chairman of the hospital appeal. (English 1 pg.) On January 6, 1961, Bishop John J. Maguire gives the past and current activities of Mr. McClellan. (English 1 pg.)

Mc3573. M-1961
Msgr. Benjamin Hawkes to Mrs. Elena
Montanari
January 10, 1961. Los Angeles, California

A painting of Pope Pius XII to match the
painting of Pope John XXIII and one of Archbishop John Cantwell will complete the order.
(English 2 pgs.)

Mc3574. M-1961
Rev. Ronald Burt, CSP to Bp. Alden J. Bell
January 19, 1961. Los Angeles, California

The certificates of stock donated by Mrs.
Ann R. Mosby are donated for the Church
Building Fund. (English 1 pg.) Shares of Texaco
and Shell Oil Company stock are also enclosed
as well as shares of International Paper Company. (English 1 pg.)

Mc3575. M-1961
J. Francis Cardinal McIntyre to Msgr. John
Meaney
February 2, 1961. Los Angeles, California

An honorary degree is offered to Miss Irene
Dunne by Hobart and William Smith College,
Geneva, New York. Is there any reason why she
should not accept it? (English 1 pg.) On February 6, 1961, Msgr. states that there is no reason
why the degree should not be accepted. (English
1 pg.)

Mc3576. M-1961
Mrs. John C. Jury to J. Francis Cardinal
McIntyre
February 16, 1961. Hermosa Beach, California

Has the Catholic Church contacts in Kerala,
South India, to assist the sick and starving people? (English 2 pgs.) On February 21, 1961, the
Cardinal states that the Bishop's Relief will send
help if the situation is known. (English 1 pg.)

Mc3577. M-1961
Mrs. Harold Schreuder to Msgr. Benjamin
Hawkes
March 15, 1961. Hollywood, California

The meeting at St. Charles stressed basic
Christian belief, respect for human dignity and
promotion of equal justice for all. (English 1 pg.)

Mc3578. M-1961
Mr. John D. Michel to J. Francis Cardinal
McIntyre
March 21, 1961. Los Angeles, California

The survey of needs of mental health for Los
Angeles County is complete. The need is for a
committee who will help put the findings into
operation. (English 5 pgs.) On March 28, 1961,
the Cardinal states that Msgr. O'Dwyer will
represent the Archdiocese. (English 1 pg.)

Mc3579. M-1961
Mr. Leon Shaw to Bp. Alden J. Bell
March 29, 1961. Mineola, New York

A Will pending in the courts of King County
stipulates a bequest to Mrs. Nell Murphy in Sun
Valley, California. Could the Archdiocese supply
the address. (English 1 pg.) On April 11, 1961,
the Bishop states that Mrs. Murphy died September 11, 1952. Her granddaughter is Mrs. Charles
Dannelly of Eagle Lake, Texas. (English 1 pg.)

Mc3580. M-1961
Mr. R. L. Minckler to J. Francis Cardinal
McIntyre
April 7, 1961. Los Angeles, California

An invitation is extended to accept the nomination to the Board of Governors of the Welfare Federation of Los Angeles. The
Nominating Committee is trying to select the
most capable and respected leaders of the Community. (English 2 pgs.) On April 10, 1961,
Bishop Bell states that he will assume the position. (English 1 pg.)

Mc3581. M-1961
Mrs. Bertha B. Jones to Bp. Alden J. Bell
April 13, 1961. Pasadena, California

Mrs. Mary Moore has no relatives to express
their appreciation for the beautiful Requiem
Mass which was her final wish. (English 1 pg.)

Mc3582. M-1961
Mr. William Maloney to J. Francis Cardinal
McIntyre
April 14, 1961. Los Angeles, California

It is the Company's opinion that the Chancery Office should file the required information
to the State and Federal Governments on its
payments to all staff priests. (English 1 pg.)

Mc3583. M-1961
Dr. Eva Lindemann to J. Francis Cardinal
McIntyre
May 4, 1961. Los Angeles, California

Dr. Franz Meyers of the Upper House of the
Federal Republic of German will be honored at
a dinner on May 19. Dr. and Mrs. Schneider
extend an invitation to be present. (English 1
pg.) On May 12, 1961, the Cardinal regrets
that he has other commitments. (English 1 pg.)

Mc3584. M-1961
Mrs. Louella Parsons to J. Francis Cardinal
McIntyre
May 5, 1961. Los Angeles, California

The interview with Princess Pignatelli received great reviews. A personal interview will
be scheduled on return from the East. (English 1
pg.) On May 10, 1961, the Cardinal comments
on the recent article on Communion in the Examiner. (English 1 pg.)

Mc3585. M-1961
Mr. Walter Matt to J. Francis Cardinal
McIntyre
June 10, 1961. St. Paul, Minnesota

A request for a donation to keep *The Wanderer* capable of performing its work. (English 1 pg.) On June 15, 1961, the Cardinal sends a donation and a letter of congratulations for the work being accomplished. (English 1 pg.)

Mc3586. M-1961
Mr. Cornelis Baen to Miss Karen Molles
June 15, 1961. Los Angeles, California

The first annual Journalism Scholarship of the Catholic Press council of Southern California will be sent to the Catholic College of your choice. (English 1 pg.)

Mc3587. M-1961
Mrs. Cis Mullen to J. Francis Cardinal
McIntyre
June 22, 1961. Co. Monaghan, Ireland

A friendly letter commenting on the Cardinal's recent visit to Ireland and a request to meet Sister Mary Virginia in La Canada. (English 3 pgs.) On July 3, 1961, the Cardinal states that he will be happy to be acquainted with Sister Mary Virginia. (English 1 pg.)

Mc3588. M-1961
Bp. Louis Morrow to Bp. Timothy Manning
July 21, 1961. Williamsbridge, New York

A copy of the Silver Jubilee Edition of *My Catholic Faith* is being sent. It is a twenty-five year dream come to reality. (English 1 pg.)

Mc3589. M-1961
Bp. Louis Morrow to J. Francis Cardinal
McIntyre
July 28, 1961. Krishnagar, India

This copy of *My Catholic Faith* is really a new book. Will the Cardinal recommend the book to the schools and convents and give his blessing to the project. (English 2 pgs.)

Mc3590. M-1961
Msgr. Patrick Dignan to Bp. Alden J. Bell
August 2, 1961. Los Angeles, California

Dr. Knox Mellon is making a study of the negro population growth in Catholic schools and will need the files of the Education Office and CCD records. (English 1 pg.)

Mc3591. M-1961
Mrs. Elena Montanari to Msgr. Benjamin
Hawkes
September 11, 1961. Rome, Italy

The work on the statue of Our Lady of the Angels will continue for the next four months. Please send a deposit for the work. (English 1 pg.)

Mc3592. M-1961
Bp. Timothy Manning to Arbp. Miguel D.
Miranda
October 3, 1961. Los Angeles, California

Bishop Joseph T. McGucken and I will arrive in Mexico City for the Congress and a visit to the Shrine. (English 1 pg.)

Mc3593. M-1961
Msgr. Benjamin Hawkes to Msgr. William
Doheny, CSC
October 6, 1961. Los Angeles, California

The appropriate place for the statue of Our Lady of the Angels will be your decision. The Church of St. Anastasia will lend itself to this statue. (English 1 pg.)

Mc3594. M-1961
Mr. Ernest Williams to J. Francis Cardinal
McIntyre
October 12, 1961. Los Angeles, California

The Americanism Award of the American Legion will be given to Mr. George Murphy. An invitation to the banquet and award is enclosed. (English 1 pg.) On October 19, 1961, the Cardinal sends regrets that he will be in Washington, D.C. on that date. (English 1 pg.)

Mc3595. M-1961
J. Francis Cardinal McIntyre to Bp. Hugh
Donohoe
October 15, 1961. Los Angeles, California

Prayerful sadness and sympathy are extended by the Bishops, priests, and people of Los Angeles on the death of Archbishop John J. Mitty. A friendship of fifty years ends for me. (English 1 pg.)

Mc3596. M-1961
Bp. Alden J. Bell to Rev. Guilebaldo Marquez
October 17, 1961. Los Angeles, California

All of the usual permissions for the right to binate on First Fridays, Wedding Day, and for the days of funerals are still in effect. The special privilege of evening Mass is given to those working with the Mexican laborers. (English 1 pg.)

Mc3597 M-1961
J. Francis Cardinal McIntyre to Rabbi Edgar Magnin
December 19, 1961. Los Angeles, California

A Christmas greeting is sent containing a blessing for all of the faithful. (English 1 pg.)

Mc3598. M-1961
Mr. Bruce Maguire to Bp. Timothy Manning
N.D. Lansing, Michigan

Could some of the prayers of the Mass be eliminated so more reverence could be given to the Sunday Masses. No one ever thought all of the prayers and announcements could be properly said in 50 minutes. (English 1 pg.)

Mc3599. N-1961
Rev. Eugene Burke, CSP to J. Francis Cardinal McIntyre
April 21, 1961. Washington, D.C.

A letter of introduction for Mr. John Noonan who will develop the Natural Law Institute at the University of Notre Dame. (English 1 pg.) On April 25, 1961, the Cardinal states that he is looking forward to meeting Mr. Noonan. (English 1 pg.)

Mc3600. N-1961
Mr. Ken Norwood to Bp. Timothy Manning
July 11, 1961. Los Angeles, California

Given the basic figures of 3,00 to 3,500 people before a parish can be established and 7 to 10 acres of land. Would a larger Church be possible and fewer in number. (English 2 pgs.)

Mc3601. N-1961
J. Francis Cardinal McIntyre to All Pastors
July 28, 1961. Los Angeles, California

Rabbi Max Nussbaum wants a T.V. program that would answer questions directed to a Minister, Priest, or a Rabbi. It is against the policy of the Archdiocese and we cannot cooperate. (English 1 pg.)

Mc3602. O-1961
Msgr. Patrick O'Donoghue to Bp. Timothy Manning
January 20, 1961. Miami, Florida

The Diocese of Miami will need to build churches, schools and convents and could use the booklet used in Los Angeles to help the construction. (English 1 pg.) On January 25, 1961, the Bishop sends the booklets and materials but suggests meetings with the priests and having good discussions. (English 1 pg.)

Mc3603. O-1961
Dr. Bernard O'Loughlin, MD to Msgr. Benjamin Hawkes
January 26, 1961. Los Angeles, California

Taking a family of eight to Ireland for a year will create problems for their schooling. The National University in Dublin might be the biggest problem. (English 1 pg.)

Mc3604. O-1961
Rev. Michael O'Brien to Bp. Timothy Manning
May 9, 1961. San Francisco, California

The Triduum for the Deaf will be from May 12–14 and the hospitality offered is very much appreciated. (English 1 pg.)

Mc3605. o-1961
Arbp. William O'Brady to J. Francis Cardinal McIntyre
May 12, 1961. Saint Paul, Minnesota

An invitation is extended to the consecration of Bishop elect Gerald O'Keefe on July 3 at 3:00 p.m. It will follow the Serra International Convention so many Bishops will be able to remain. (English 1 pg.)

Mc3606. O-1961
Arbp. Martin O'Connor to J. Francis Cardinal McIntyre
May 29, 1961. Rome, Italy

There are fourteen volumes weighing eighty pounds for you. They cannot be mailed or shipped. Someone will have to bring them to Los Angeles. (English 1 pg.) On July 28, 1961, the Cardinal states that the books should be kept in Rome. (English 1 pg.)

Mc3607. O-1961
Mr. E. M. Dillhoefer to J. Francis Cardinal McIntyre
June 28, 1961. Los Angeles, California

The O'Neill Foundation will send a donation to Don Bosco Technical Institute and a smaller donation will come from this office. (English 1 pg.) On June 30, 1961, Bishop Manning expresses the gratitude of the Cardinal for the Foundation's donation. (English 1 pg.)

Mc3608. O-1961
Mrs. Alfred Osterhues to J. Francis Cardinal McIntyre
September 5, 1961. Pasadena, California

A friendly letter commenting on the new building at St. John's Seminary in Camarillo and the new school in Carpenteria. (English 2 pgs.) On September 14, 1961, the Cardinal states that he hopes the Seminary project will justify the generosity of the people of the Archdiocese. (English 1 pg.)

Mc3609. O-1961
J. Francis Cardinal McIntyre to Arbp. Martin
O'Connor
September 19, 1961. Los Angeles, California

Are there additional rooms at the North
American College from November 7 to 12?
Msgr. Hawkes and I will arrive on November 6.
(English 1 pg.) On September 27, 1961, the
Archbishop states that he will have a room and
a car available. (English 1 pg.)

Mc3610. O-1961
Mrs. Lillian Ott to J. Francis Cardinal
McIntyre
October 17, 1961. Los Angeles, California

The contribution to the Anti-Communism
Program at the Hollywood Bowl was outstanding. The presence of the Cardinal would have
added to the importance but Msgr. English did
a great job. (English 1 pg.)

Mc3611. O-1961
J. Francis Cardinal McIntyre to Arbp. Martin
O'Connor
November 21, 1961. Los Angeles, California

The Bishops' Meeting in Washington, D.C.
was successful and a policy of Federal Aid to
Education which leaves no doubt or confusion
is the result. (English 1 pg.)

Mc3612. O-1961
Rev. Aloisius Ogihara to Bp. Timothy
Manning
November 27, 1961. Tokyo, Japan

The work of conversion in Japan will be
strengthened by the new Catholic Center. The
program is outlined and any help available will
be accepted. (English 2 pgs.)

Mc3613. P-1961
Mr. A. C. Pelletier to J. Francis Cardinal
McIntyre
March 1, 1961. South Gate, California

The enclosed certificate for 100 shares of
Purex stock is for Don Bosco Technical Institute
with the hope that support for the school will
continue. (English 1 pg.) On March 6, 1961,
the Cardinal states that the continued support
is great encouragement. (English 1 pg.)

Mc3614. P-1961
Mr. J. F. Prinzing to J. Francis Cardinal
McIntyre
March 17, 1961. Denver, Colorado

Last year attention was given to the fact that
no priest was on the steamship to Hawaii.
Again this year the situation was the same. (English 1 pg.) On March 24, 1961, the Cardinal
states that when asked the Archdiocese tries to
accommodate. (English 1 pg.)

Mc3615. P-1961
Mr. A. C. Pelletier to J. Francis Cardinal
McIntyre
April 18, 1961. South Gate, California

A proxy signature card is enclosed for the
stockholder meeting. (English 1 pg.) On April
20, 1961, the Cardinal states that he is certain
that the proxy card has been signed. (English
1 pg.)

Mc3616. P-1961
Rev. Hildebrand, OSB to Msgr. Benjamin
Hawkes
April 25, 1961. Mt. Angel, Oregon

Is the small shop in Pasadena called Peter Pan
in good standing with the Archdiocese. They
carry some goods for the Gift Shop. (English
1 pg.)

Mc3617. P-1961
Bp. Alden J. Bell to Ms. Anna Pefaur
May 3, 1961. Los Angeles, California

If the name of the parish serving liquor at
parish functions were known, the situation
could be ended. (English 1 pg.) On May 5,
1961, Ms. Pefaur suggests sending out a letter to all parishes to end the practice. (English
1 pg.)

Mc3618. P-1961
Msgr. M. J. Gorges to Bp. Alden J. Bell
May 30, 1961. Coffeyville, Kansas

A young man is in the brig in the Long Beach
Naval Station and needs the assistance of the
Catholic Chaplain. (English 1 pg.) On June 13,
1961, Rev. James Doyle states that he has inter-
viewed the man and will communicate with
Msgr. Gorges. (English 1 pg.)

Mc3619. P-1961
Miss Isabel Piczek to J. Francis Cardinal
McIntyre
September 13, 1961. Los Angeles, California

The windows for the College Seminary Chapel could be a work of inspiration if the work is
given to the right person. (English 1 pg.)

Mc3620. P-1961
Ms. Anna Parker to J. Francis Cardinal
McIntyre
September 27, 1961. New York City,
New York

A plea for assistance and help so a visit to the
hospital can be made and then to the retirement
home. (English 1 pg.) On September 27, 1961,
the Cardinal requests Msgr. Guilfoyle to arrange for a worker to visit Anna. (English 1 pg.)

Mc3621. P-1961
Rev. George Parnassus to J. Francis Cardinal
McIntyre
October 12, 1961. Inglewood, California

How long is a temporary assignment? The
experience as a high school administrator could
be used. (English 1 pg.) On October 18, 1961,
Bishop Bell states that soon a teaching appointment will be made. (English 1 pg.)

Mc3622. P-1961
Bp. Timothy Manning to Msgr. Leo T. Maher
October 24, 1961. Los Angeles, California

Some information is needed to understand
Frederick Pyman who is listed as a Regionary
Bishop. (English 1 pg.) On November 2, 1961,
Msgr. states that the Bishop is a self styled
Bishop and has elevated Monsignors. He has no
police record. (English 1 pg.)

Mc3623. P-1961
Mr. Ernest Phillips to J. Francis Cardinal
McIntyre
November 28, 1961. Los Angeles, California

A request for an interview to discuss a possible plan to arouse interest in giving the people a
new approach to the Gospels. (English 2 pgs.)
On December 15, 1961, the Cardinal states that
he will discuss the plan on December 28. (English 1 pg.)

Mc3624. R-1961
Rev. Thomas Ryan to J. Francis Cardinal
McIntyre
January 15, 1961. Brox, New York

A friendly letter commenting on childhood
memories and asking for prayers for Margaret
who is near death. (English 3 pgs.) On January
19, 1961, the Cardinal states that he will write
to Margaret and pray for her. (English 1 pg.)

Mc3625. R-1961
Mr. Donald E. Ryan to J. Francis Cardinal
McIntyre
January 24, 1961. Rancho Sante Fe, California

The membership in the Knights of Malta is a
great honor and if there is a project that needs
help, call on me. (English 1 pg.)

Mc3626. R-1961
Mr. R. G. Robinson to Bp. Timothy Manning
January 24, 1961. Santa Monica, California

A stronger stand against Communism could
be taken by *The Tidings* and the Bishops. The
Catholics will follow the leadership from the
Bishops. (English 1 pg.)

Mc3627. R-1961
Rev. Francis Koeper, CM to J. Francis Cardi-
nal McIntyre
January 25, 1961. Montebello, California

A request to continue to celebrate Mass at the
home of Mrs. Ann Kavet. Father Richardson requests that the permission be stated. (English 2
pgs.) On January 27, 1961, Fr. Richardson
states that Mrs. Kavet is an unusual lady who
suffers for others and prays constantly. (English
1 pg.)

Mc3628 .R-1961
Mrs. M. S. Raphael to J. Francis Cardinal
McIntyre
March 31, 1961. Los Angeles, California

A suggestion to have all daily Masses at 6:30
and 8:00 and to have evening devotions at 7:45.
Sunday Masses should be hourly. (English 1 pg.)
On April 10, 1961, the Cardinal states that the
time for Masses is for the Pastor to decide. (English 1 pg.)

Mc3629. R-1961
Hon. Ronald Reagan to J. Francis Cardinal
McIntyre
May 24, 1961. Pacific Palisades, California

An invitation to encourage the Catholic
Youth to join the Young Americans for Freedom. Financial contributions would be useful to
have for various activities. (English 1 pg.)

Mc3630. R-1961
Rev. John Languille to J. Francis Cardinal
McIntyre
May 29, 1961. Los Angeles, California

The reply to Mr. Roseman should be negative
as there would be control over the type of fund
raising the Boys Club would have. (English 1
pg.) On June 12, 1961, Fr. Languille states that
the Boys Club work with the Catholic Youth
Organization and a discussion should take place
for the fund raising. (English 1 pg.)

Mc3631. R-1961
Mrs. Elisa Ryan to J. Francis Cardinal
McIntyre
June 15, 1961. Beverly Hills, California

The new ruling in the Archdiocesan schools is
ruining dancing classes. Some remedy should be
considered. (English 1 pg.) On July 14, 1961,
the Cardinal states that there is no new ruling.
Elementary school are not allowed to have
dances. Dancing classes are a parental right.
(English 1 pg.)

Mc3632. R-1961
Mr. Nelson Richardson to Bp. Alden J. Bell
August 11, 1961. Santa Barbara, California

A discussion is necessary on the restricted education given to the clergy on politics, sociology, and economics. (English 1 pg.) On August 14, 1961, the Bishop states that the education is opposite to what is believed. A priest is free to think as he chooses if he does not disagree on fundamental truths. (English 1 pg.)

Mc3633. R-1961
Mr. Lester Recktenwald to J. Francis Cardinal McIntyre
September 13, 1961. Wayne, Pennslyvania

The contract which seems so good will end in June. The terms were never mentioned orally or in writing. (English 1 pg.) On September 18, 1961, the Cardinal states that he regrets the unfortunate experience. (English 1 pg.)

Mc3634. R-1961
Dr. Brendan Rountree to J. Francis Cardinal McIntyre
October 31, 1961. Dun Laoghaire, Ireland

A request to have the Cardinal use his influence to have evening Mass every day in Ireland so more people can go to daily Mass. (English 3 pgs.) On November 6, 1961, Msgr. states that this is a decision for the Irish Bishops and out of the Cardinal's jurisdiction. (English 1 pg.)

Mc3635. R-1961
Rev. Francis Reh to Francis Cardinal Spellman
October 31, 1961. Yonkers, New York

Comments on the questions considered by the Central Preparatory Commission of the Second Vatican Council. (English 2 pgs.)

Mc3636. R-1961
Laurean Cardinal Rugambwa to J. Francis Cardinal McIntyre
December 1, 1961. Bukoba, Tanganyika

The theme, Let us rid Africa of Poverty, Ignorance, and Disease, is the policy of the Interterritorial Episcopal Board of East and Central Africa. Please give it your attention. (English 1 pg.)

Mc3637. R-1961
J. Francis Cardinal McIntyre to Mr. and Mrs. John Rauen
December 8, 1961. Los Angeles, California

A formal invitation to greet Gregory P. Cardinal Agagianian on December 8 at 4:00 p.m. in the Cardinal's residence. (English 1 pg.)

Mc3638. R-1961
Marianne Rubner to J. Francis Cardinal McIntyre
December 15, 1961. Hollywood, California

An antique piece of lace with the insignia of the Knights of Malta is for sale. It is artiscally and historically valuable. (English 1 pg.) On December 21, 1961, the Cardinal states that it is unfortunate that there is no need for such a work of art. (English 1 pg.)

Mc3639. R-1961
Bp. John J. Russell to J. Francis Cardinal McIntyre
December 22, 1961. Richmond, Virginia

An invitation to the consecration of Bishop elect Ernest Unterkaefler on February 22, 1962. (English 1 pg.) On December 29, 1961, the Cardinal states that according to present plans he will be in Rome in February. (English 1 pg.)

Mc3640. S-1961
J. Francis Cardinal McIntyre to Marymount Faculty
January 16, 1961. Los Angeles, California

Mr. Richard Spurney feels that the listening public should have an application of philosophy to every day problems. The Archdiocese could not approve of his presentation as representing the Church or Marymount College due to his inaccuracies. (England 1 pg.)

Mc3641. S-1961
Mr. Mark A. Brady to Francis Cardinal Spellman
February 2, 1961. La Junta, Colorado

Instead of fighting for Federal Aid to Education fight to have the exemption to education raised. (English 1 pg.)

Mc3642. S-1961
Mrs. Richard Snyder to J. Francis Cardinal McIntyre
February 7, 1961. Los Angeles, California

A request to divide St. Joan of Arc Parish and establish a Church within a closer radius. (English 1 pg.) On February 15, 1961, Bishop Manning states that the suggestion will be given attention but cannot promise fulfillment at once. (English 1 pg.)

Mc3643. S-1961
Rev. Cornelius Higgins to Bp. Timothy Manning
February 14, 1961. Sacramento, California

The new Parish of the Presentation will need a professional fund raiser. Mr. Fred Sullivan who has been active in the Little Company of Mary Hospital has applied. (English 1 pg.) On February 20, 1961, the Bishop sends unfavorable comments from Sister Patricia. (English 1 pg.)

Mc3644. S-1961
Mr. Helmut Schmitz to Msgr. Benjamin
Hawkes
February 15, 1961. Gardena, California

A suggestion of a way to make money for the
Seminary is to sell Bishop Fulton J. Sheen's
talks on records and tapes. The one million
Catholics could finance any project. (English 1
pg.) On February 21, 1961, Msgr. states that it
is policy not to make religion a commercial me-
dium. (English 1 pg.)

Mc3645. S-1961
Miss Alfreda Stapinski to Bp. Timothy
Manning
February 17, 1961. San Marino, California

Professional men and women over 40 need a
social group so Catholics can meet others with
similar interests. (English 1 pg.) On February
23, 1961, the Cardinal states that the organization does not have to be Diocesan in scope and
Fr. O'Connor will moderate it. (English 1 pg.)

Mc3646. S-1961
Bp. Timothy Manning to J. Francis Cardinal
McIntyre
March 9, 1961. Los Angeles, California

Miss Judy Serbaroli could make a contribution to the Chapel decorations for the Seminary
Chapel. She feels that she should be in on
the planning from the very beginning. (English
1 pg.)

Mc3647. S-1961
Rev. Anselme Sanniola to Mrs. James E. Moss
March 11, 1961. Lourdes, France

An appeal to obtain names of others who can
contribute to the Shrine at Lourdes. (English 1
pg.) On March 22, 1961, Bishop Bell states that
the Diocese discourages these appeals. (English
1 pg.)

Mc3648. S-1961
Mr. Louis Shawie to J. Francis Cardinal
McIntyre
March 24, 1961. Los Angeles, California

A plan to use all of the unused Church property for apartments for homeless men who in
turn would surrender their pension checks for
the upkeep of the apartments. (English 3 pgs.)

Mc3649. S-1961
Mr. Edward Head to Msgr. John J. Voight
March 30, 1961. New York City, New York

The case of Swart v. Burlington Town School
district should not come to trial. NCWC Legal
Department is asking for withdrawl. (English
1 pg.)

Mc3650. S-1961
J. Francis Cardinal McIntyre to Mr. Emmett
Shipman
April 3, 1961. Los Angeles, California

The collection of prayers reveals A Business-
man's Prayer for your edification. In Rome
Pope John XXIII asked to be remembered. (English 2 pgs.)

Mc3651. S-1961
Mr. Porter Chandler to Francis Cardinal Spell-
man
April 25, 1961. New York City, New York

The cases in state courts which could give un-
friendly decisions to the Church are The Vermont School case, the Zorach case, and the
Alaska school bus law. (English 2 pgs.)

Mc3652. S-1961
Francis Cardinal Spellman to J. Francis Cardi-
nal McIntyre
April 28, 1961. New York City, New York

The Supreme Court of Vermont declared
unconstitutional for towns to pay for children
attending Catholic schools. The case was withdrawn by Bishop Joyce. (English 1 pg.) On
May 2, 1961, the Cardinal states that the case
should be brought to court. Definite principles
must be established. (English 1 pg.)

Mc3653. S-1961
Mr. August Sorce to Msgr. Benjamin Hawkes
N.D. Chula Vista, California

Could money deposited in Rome be turned
over to the North American College and a similar amount be received here. (English 1 pg.) On
May 15, 1961, Msgr. asks the author to come
to the Chancery Office for more details. (English 1 pg.)

Mc3654. S-1961
J. Francis Cardinal McIntyre to Francis Cardi-
nal Spellman
May 20, 1961. Los Angeles, California

The Rosensteil Foundation has legal proceedings between Mr. Rosensteil and Mrs. Louise
Frank. Places on the Board are in dispute. Any
assistance that can be given will be gladly given.
(English 2 pgs.)

Mc3655. S-1961
Mr. Vick Knight to J. Francis Cardinal
McIntyre
June 2, 1961. Los Angeles, California

The talk given to the Archdiocesian Catholic
Women by Mr. W. Cleon Skousen has been incorporated on a long-playing record. Could it
be reviewed in The Tidings? (English 1 pg.)

Mc3656. S-1961
Bp. Joseph T. McGucken to J. Francis Cardinal
McIntyre
June 16, 1961. Sacramento, California

There will be fifteen new Judgeships within
ninety days and many will want endorsements.
It would be good to know which men the Los
Angeles Archdiocese is endorsing. (English 1
pg.) On June 23, 1961, the Cardinal states that
he will write a letter complimenting the person
for aspiring to the office. (English 1 pg.)

Mc3657. S-1961
Dr. John Slawson to J. Francis Cardinal
McIntyre
July 20, 1961. New York City, New York

The Jewish Committee praises the vigorous
statement of Pope John XXIII in the Encyclical
stating the sacred dignity of the individual
and human solidarity and brotherhood. (English
2 pgs.)

Mc3658. S-1961
Fr. Francis Osborne to J. Francis Cardinal
McIntyre
July 26, 1961. Encino, California

The Sisters of Our Lady of Grace Parish no
longer use the home of Mr. and Mrs. Edward
Shipstad. A message of gratitude for the years
the parish used the house should come from the
Chancery Office. (English 1 pg.)

Mc3659. S-1961
Dr. James B. Smith, MD to Msgr. Benjamin
Hawkes
July 31, 1961. Fullerton, California

A request to have the Cardinal Mindszenty
Foundation conduct a four week seminar to
give information to the people who are concerned with Communism. (English 1 pg.)

Mc3660. S-1961
J. Francis Cardinal McIntyre to Francis Cardi-
nal Spellman
August 21, 1961. Los Angeles, California

The application of Dr. Charles Sharpe for
membership in the Knights of Malta is enclosed.
The application is sponsored by Dr. Francis
Griffin and John McCone. (English 1 pg.)

Mc3661. S-1961
Miss Mary M. Stokes to Bp. Timothy
Manning
N.D. Los Angeles, California

A request to be allowed to prepare and receive the Sacrament of Confirmation in Tijuana
with other members of the family. (English 1
pg.) On September 20, 1961, Bishop Manning
states that there is no objection from the Chancery Office. (English 1 pg.)

Mc3662. S-1961
Mrs. Samuel Milby to Bp. Alden J. Bell
October 4, 1961. Erie, Pennsylvania

A young Filipino woman who is an MD, who
did internship in Brooklyn and residency in Buffalo, New York, needs a friend in Los Angeles.
(English 2 pgs.) On November 21, 1961, the
Bishop asks Dr. Nina Salinas to contact Msgr.
O'Dwyer for any assistance that she needs. (English 1 pg.)

Mc3663. S-1961
J. Francis Cardinal McIntyre to Francis Cardi-
nal Spellman
October 10, 1961. Los Angeles, California

Msgr. Hubert Beller has asked me to confer
the robes of Monsignor on the Sunday after the
Bishops' Meeting. (English 1 pg.) On October
13, 1961, the Cardinal states that any function
can be performed in New York at any time.
(English 1 pg.)

Mc3664. S-1961
Dr. Andrew Smatko to J. Francis Cardinal
McIntyre
October 20, 1961. Santa Monica, California

A plan of education to make every Christian
aware of the Communistic methods of infiltrat-
ing public offices and public life is presented.
(English 6 pgs.) On October 24, 1961, the Cardinal states his appreciation of the comments.
(English 1 pg.)

Mc3665. S-1961
Mrs. Richard Stevens to Bp. Alden J. Bell
November 22, 1961. Littleton, Colorado

Mrs. Mary Darling died and was buried in
Los Angeles sometime between 1940–1945.
Any information would be appreciated. (English
2 pgs.) On November 24, 1961, Bishop states
that Mrs. Mary E. Darling was buried from St.
Peter's Church on March 13, 1946. Mrs. Helen
Sine is a surviving relative. (English 1 pg.)

Mc3666. S-1961
Mr. Anton Schmid to J. Francis Cardinal
McIntyre
November 28, 1961. Vancouver, B.C.

The Moral Re-Armament Movement has a
magnetic quality that should have a far reaching
effect. (English 4 pgs.)

Mc3667. S-1961
Arbp. Antonio Samore to J. Francis Cardinal
McIntyre
November 30, 1961. Vatican City

The Sisters at the Orphanage have the donation given in memory of Cardinal Tardini, the
founder of Villa Nazareth. A memento of Cardinal Tardini will follow. (English 1 pg.) On
December 7, 1961, the Cardinal states that the
memento of Cardinal Tardini will be one of his
treasured possessions. (English 1 pg.)

Mc3668. S-1961
Arbp. Lawrence Shehan to J. Francis Cardinal
McIntyre
December 8, 1961. Baltimore, Maryland

The death of Archbishop John Keough is announced with the Funeral Mass on December
14, 1961. (English 1 pg.) On December 12,
1961, the Cardinal states that the prayers of the
Archdiocese accompany the soul of the Archbishop to eternity. (English 1 pg.)

Mc3669. S-1961
Mr. Luke Hart to Rev. Joseph Sharpe
December 12, 1961. Los Angeles, California

The Masonic Ritual was used in the dedication ceremony of Palisades High School giving
the impression that they are the only ones fa-
voring public schools. (English 1 pg.)

Mc3670. S-1961
Mr. Edward Scharfinberger to J. Francis Cardi-
nal McIntyre
December 28, 1961. Ridgewood, New York

Praise for the statement of the Hierarchy on
Need for Personal Responsibility. An essay
which is taken from the statement is enclosed.
(English 1 pg.) On January 5, 1961, the Cardinal expresses his appreciation for the essay. (English 1 pg.)

Mc3671. S-1961
Mr. John C. Sullivan to J. Francis Cardinal
McIntyre
N.D. Los Angeles, California

An appeal for midnight Mass at Christmas
even if some abuse the privilege. Let Christmas
day be a peaceful time for families. (English
1 pg.)

Mc3672. T-1961
Ms. Mary Duren to Bp. Alden J. Bell
February 16, 1961. Los Angeles, California

Please evaluate candidate Alice ChingChang
Tsou for Social Work. (English 1 pg.) On Feb-
ruary 20, 1961, Bishop Bell states that Miss
Tsou worked in In-Take Department and ac-
cepts clients well and is objective in judgment.
(English 1 pg.)

Mc3673. T-1961
Rev. Augustinus Tseu to Msgr. Benjamin
Hawkes
May 29, 1961. Los Angeles, California

The activities of this Chinese priest are teaching at Immaculate Heart College, organizing
the people of North China who do not speak
Cantonize, and trying to convert non-Christian
Chinese. (English 2 pgs.)

Mc3674. T-1961
Bp. Pierre Marie Theas to Whom it may
concern
June 1, 1961. Lourdes, France

The Bishop of Lourdes authorizes Marie de
Vrahnos Baker to solicit and receive donations
for the Sanctuary of Our Lady of Lourdes. (English 1 pg.)

Mc3675. T-1961
Mr. Sam Tattu to J. Francis Cardinal McIntyre
August 30, 1961. Hermosa Beach, California

A plea for some assistance to pay tuition of
$700 at the Institute of Lay Theology at Univer-
sity of San Francisco. (English 1 pg.)

Mc3676. T-1961
Mrs. August Torres to J. Francis Cardinal
McIntyre
September 5, 1961. Coral Gables, Florida

An inquiry into the partial scholarship program at Marymount in Tarrytown, New York,
is requested for Albertina Torres. (English 1
pg.) On September 7, 1961, the Cardinal makes
the request of Mother Brendan McQuillan,
RSHM. (English 1 pg.)

Mc3677. T-1961
J. Francis Cardinal McIntyre to Bp. Enrico
Galeazzi
September 21, 1961. Los Angeles, California

Dr. Tedeschi of the Italian Consul in Los Angeles would appreciate a word to the proper au-
thorities to be transferred to the Hague.
(English 1 pg.) On October 7, 1961, Amleto
Cardinal Cicognani states that it would not be
proper for him to request the transfer. (English
1 pg.)

Mc3678. T-1961
Ms. Mary Taylor to J. Francis Cardinal
McIntyre
November 21, 1961. Alhambra, California

The addresses of Orphanages and Day Care
Centers are needed for the delivery of toys and
the addresses of homes for the elderly for the
delivery of clothing. (English 1 pg.)

Mc3679. V-1961
Miss Barbara Velasco to J. Francis Cardinal
McIntyre
May 20, 1961. Los Angeles, California

How can a Papal Blessing be obtained for a
wedding that will take place in Santa Barbara
Mission? (English 2 pgs.) On June 7, 1961, Fr.
Rawden states that if the Pastor sends the details he will obtain the Blessing. (English 1 pg.)

Mc3680. V-1961
Mr. Carroll VanCourt to Pope John XXIII
August 20, 1961. Los Angeles, California

Sportsmanship must be taught and practiced
in all sports. Is it possible to use the Pope's
name as an endorsement along with other important people to get the message across. (English 2 pgs.)

Mc3681. V-1961
Rev. Raffaele Volta to Bp. Alden J. Bell
December 1, 1961. Madison, Wisconsin

A visit to Los Angeles is being planned from
December 27–31 as a part of the University
Program. Is there a home in which I can stay.
(English 1 pg.) On December 4, 1961, Bishop
Bell offers the Cathedral Rectory. (English
1 pg.)

Mc3682. W-1961
Mr. William Worrilow to Bp. Horace Donegan
January 24, 1961. York, Pennsylvania

The plea for unity is a change from the Gospel message of "I come to bring not peace but
the sword." (English 1 pg.)

Mc3683. W-1961
Mr. Henry F. Withey to Bp. Timothy Manning
January 24, 1961. Sherman Oaks, California

The new library in San Fernando Valley will
have the endorsement of many but the approval
of the Bishop is the one wanted. (English 1 pg.)

Mc3684. W-1961
Rev. Thomas H. McElhatton, OP to J. Francis
Cardinal McIntyre
February 3, 1961. Los Angeles, California

Mr. Lester Wombacher is a good man, a
good organizer but there are many his equal in
this parish and in other parishes. If the nomination is for some awards, then there are others
who also deserve them. (English 1 pg.)

Mc3685. W-1961
J. Francis Cardinal McIntyre to Mr. P. G.
Winnett
February 9, 1961. Los Angeles, California

The $25,000 from the Santa Anita Founda-
tion will be used for Don Bosco Technical Institute. The faculty, students, and Archbishop are
most grateful for the Foundation's donation.
(English 1 pg.)

Mc3686. W-1961
Mrs. E. W. Whittington to Bp. Timothy
Manning
February 28, 1961. Los Angeles, California

A discussion of problems in the Church is
needed. Conscience will not allow silence. (English 1 pg.) On March 8, 1961, the Bishop requests that a telephone call be made for an
appointment. (English 1 pg.)

Mc3687. W-1961
Mr. William Worrilow to Mrs. G. V. Schuler
February 28, 1961. York, Pennsylvania

The subject of rights, civil rights, constitutional rights, legal rights seems to indicate im-
posing your will on others. The question of
mental reservation should be investigated. (English 2 pgs.)

Mc3688. W-1961
Mr. James W. Fifield to J. Francis Cardinal
McIntyre
March 21, 1961. Los Angeles, California

An invitation is extended to give the invocation at the Freedom Club meeting honoring
Robert Welch. (English 1 pg) On March 27,
1961, the Cardinal states that a heavy schedule
prevents his attendance but Msgr. Kenneth
O'Brien will give the invocation. (English 1 pg.)

Mc3689. W-1961
Lt. Vincent Gavin to Bp. Alden J. Bell
March 21, 1961. Baltimore, Maryland

Janis Ann Wiedenhoeft was kidnapped by her
mother. She might be in a Catholic school with
an assumed name. Janis needs medication and a
special diet. Please give the matter special attention. (English 3 pgs.)

Mc3690. W–1961
Msgr. Benjamin Hawkes to Dr. Charles
Westerbeck
March 28, 1961. Inglewood, California

The question raised cannot be incorporated
into the Ecumenical Council at this session but
inquiries can be made among other groups. (English 1 pg.)

Mc3691. W-1961
J. Francis Cardinal McIntyre to Miss Mary
   Waters
April 4, 1961. Los Angeles, California

The property in West Covina can be used by
the Little League on a year to year option.
There can be no bleachers or permanent instal-
lations. (English 1 pg.)

Mc3692. W-1961
Msgr. Patrick Dignan to Msgr. Benjamin
   Hawkes
April 6, 1961. Los Angeles, California

A request for a letter to permit Dr. Paul Win-
kler to use the Vatican Library during the summer in Rome. (English 1 pg.)

Mc3693. W-1961
Miss Ammine Williams to Mr. George H.
   O'Connor
April 25, 1961. Los Angeles, California

It is frustrating being a Catholic woman from
India because Catholics are cold and distant.
There is need for tuition and medicine before
finishing the Master Degree at UCLA. (English
1 pg.) On May 15, 1961, Rev. William Kinney
at UCLA states that invitations are sent to all
foreign students. (English 1 pg.)

Mc3694. W-1961
Rev. Cyril J. Wood to Bp. Alden J. Bell
May 19, 1961. Santa Monica, California

An invitation to the annual Procession and
celebration in honor of St. Anne on July 30, at
3:00 p.m. (English 1 pg.) On May 22, 1961, the
Bishop states that he plans to be present. (English 1 pg.)

Mc3695. W-1961
Bp. elect John Whealon to J. Francis Cardinal
   McIntyre
June 7, 1961. Cleveland, Ohio

An invitation is sent to the consecration of
Bishop elect John Whealon on July 6, 1961, at
10:00 a.m. (English 1 pg.) On June 16, 1961,
the Cardinal states that he regrets that he cannot be present but he will remember the day at
Mass. (English 1 pg.)

Mc3696. W-1961
Mr. Norman Lynn to Bp. Timothy Manning
July 12, 1961. Los Angeles, California

A request to allow the Bishop's name to be
used in fund raising for the Woodcraft Rangers
that serve about 7,000 youngsters in the Lake
Arrowhead Camp area. (English 1 pg.) On July
14, 1961, the Bishop states that it is not possible to use his name. (English 1 pg.)

Mc3697. W-1961
Mr. S. R. Williams to J. Francis Cardinal
   McIntyre
July 12, 1961. Los Angeles, California

Please have the Sisters pin back the cowl of
the Habits so vision will be better when they
are driving. Habits are a hazard on the highways. (English 1 pg.)

Mc3698. W-1961
Mr. William Worrilow to Mr. Norman
   Hemperly
August 1, 1961. York, Pennsylvania

Roman Catholics are being hired in greater
numbers by Public School Boards. By reason of
default and lack of caution, the Catholics will
destroy the public school system. (English 1 pg.)

Mc3699. W-1961
Mr. William Worrilow to Mr. Ray A. Neff
August 3, 1961. York, Pennsylvania

The latest attempt to link Secretary of War
Stanton with the assassination of President Lincoln is another attempt of the Catholic Church
to prevent evidence of the Catholic participation in the conspiracy from being printed. (English 1 pg.)

Mc3700. W-1961
Mr. Harry Wadsworth to Rev. James F. Burke
August 26, 1961. Sante Fe Springs, California

A letter of protest for the financial management of the parish and the method of operation that causes a family to take children out
of the school when other means could have
been made possible for the payment of tuition.
(English 6 pgs.)

Mc3701. W-1961
Mr. William Worrilow to Mr. Roy Larsen
September 1, 1961. York, Pennsylvania

A strong belief that Catholics in Congress
vote the way that the Bishops tell them to vote.
President Kennedy as a Senator can testify to
that statement. (English 1 pg.)

Mc3702. W-1961
J. Francis Cardinal McIntyre to Miss Mary
   Waters
September 6, 1961. Los Angeles, California

Two expensive rings must be added to the
Will to be placed in the category of equipment
for the Archbishop. The Grand Deed for the
disposal of personal property is enclosed. (English 6 pgs.)

Mc3703. W-1961
Rev. Daniel J. Weil to J. Francis Cardinal
McIntyre
N.D. Milwaukee, Wisconsin

An explanation of the coat-of-arms of the
Cardinal would be appreciated for a complete
study of the coat-of-arms of the hierarchy. (English 1 pg.)

Mc3704. W-1961
Mr. Otto Wilhelm to J. Francis Cardinal
McIntyre
N.D. Los Angeles, California

The Mediocre Angels sent previously is ready
for publication but no one has evaluated it. The
papers are undermining the faith of the young
who do not read deeply. (English 5 pgs.)

Mc3705. Y-1961
J. Francis Cardinal McIntyre to Rev. Michael
Bardouil
July 17, 1961. Los Angeles, California

Bishop Eftimois Youakim has permission to
Pontificate at the celebration in honor of St.
Anne. He may stay at the Cardinal's residence.
(English 1 pg.)

Mc3706. Y-1961
Mrs. Robert Yates to J. Francis Cardinal
McIntyre
July 19, 1961. Syracuse, New York

The alert given to the St. Vincent de Paul Society on UNESCO was released by the Associated Press. Keep informing the public. (English
6 pgs.)

Mc3707. Z-1961
Mr. Arnold Zimmerly to Rev. John A. Rawden
January 17, 1961. Sepulveda, California

Council #5007 of the Knights of Columbus
is named after Rev. James Leheny. Some information is needed about his life. (English 1 pg.)
On January 18, 1961, the short biography of
Father is sent. (English 1 pg.)

Mc3708. Z-1961
Mr. David Malloy to Bp. Alden J. Bell
February 9, 1961. Los Angeles, California

The Silver Anniversary of the Musician Post
will provide an opportunity for the religious,
social, and economic leaders to pay tribute to
Dr. Ziegler. (English 1 pg.)

Mc3709. Z-1961
Mr. Uberto Zaccaria to J. Francis Cardinal
McIntyre
August 29, 1961. Los Angeles, California

Mr. Whelen should follow the exhortations
given in his *Tidings* article and recover the
moral tone that made America great. (English
2 pgs.)

Mc3710. Z-1961
Mrs. Robert J. Zick to J. Francis Cardinal
McIntye
November 30, 1961. El Monte, California

The Sacred Heart Lodge Specialized Psychiatric Hospital will have all of the necessary pri-
vacy and possibilities for group interaction. At
a later date could a Bishop bless the Hospital.
(English 1 pg.) On December 7, 1961, Bishop
Bell states that he will be happy to bless the
Hospital. (English 1 pg.)

Listing for the Year
1962

Mc3711. A-1962
Mr. John Annand to J. Francis Cardinal
 McIntyre
April 4, 1962. Los Angeles, California

An invitation to the dinner honoring Mr. and
Mrs. J. Hoffa and to give the invocation to the
occasion. (English 1 pg.) On April 10, 1962, the
Cardinal states that he will be in Washington,
D.C. but Msgr. Truxaw will give the invocation.
(English 1 pg.)

Mc3712. A-1962
J. Francis Cardinal McIntyre to American
 Trust Company
May 14, 1962. Los Angeles, California

Bishop Alden J. Bell will not be able to sign
for the Corporation Sole of Los Angeles. He
will be transferred to Sacramento. (English 1 pg.)

Mc3713. A-1962
Sister Maria Angelica to Bp. Timothy Manning
May 16, 1962. Santo Domingo, Dominican
 Republic

St. Joseph will need a helping hand to build a
new convent for a newly founded cloistered
Carmelite Community. (English 1 pg.)

Mc3714. A-1962
Rev. Marcelino Aguilar to J. Francis Cardinal
 McIntyre
June 7, 1962. La Piedad, Mexico

A request is made for me to come to Los Angeles to Baptize a member of the family and to
visit for a period of time. (Spanish 1 pg.) On
June 16, 1962, Bishop Manning grants the permission for the visit with the stipulation that
permission has been approved by the Bishop of
his Diocese in Mexico. (English 1 pg.)

Mc3715. A-1962
Rev. John B. Thom to Rev. Marcelino Aguilar
August 28, 1962. Los Angeles, California

The two months visit to Los Angeles is agreeable and the hospitality of the rectory near the
relatives can be arranged. (English 1 pg.) On
September 3, 1962, Fr. states that his relatives
live in Montebello. (English 1 pg.)

Mc3716. A-1962
Mother Mary Anselm to J. Francis Cardinal
 McIntyre
September 24, 1962. Rome, Italy

An invitation is extended to visit the Gener-
alate of the Sisters of Notre Dame while in
Rome for the Council. (English 1 pg.)

Mc3717. A-1962
Gregorio Cardinal Agagianian to J. Francis
 Cardinal McIntyre
November 22, 1962. Vatican City

An invitation to a lecture at the Pontifical
University *Urbania*. The subject will be the sig-
nificance of the Council in the history of the
Church. (Italian 1 pg.)

Mc3718. B-1962
Msgr. Hubert Beller to J. Francis Cardinal
 McIntyre
January 6, 1962. Beacon, New York

A letter of congratulations on the 20th anniversary of the consecration as a Bishop. A Mass
will be celebrated on that date. (English 1 pg.)
On January 8, 1962, the Cardinal expresses his
gratitude for the prayers and the remembrances.
(English 1 pg.)

34

Mc3719. B-1962
Msgr. Daniel Sullivan to Bp. Timothy Manning
January 10, 1962. Beverly Hills, California

The enclosed check for $6,000 from Mrs.
Robert Brittingham is for charity in a Mexican
Mission. (English 1 pg.) On January 23, 1962,
$3,000 is sent to Mother Eugenia of Santa
Marta Clinic and $3,000 for Dolores Mission.
(English 1 pg.)

Mc3720. B-1962
Miss Mary E. Waters to J. Francis Cardinal
   McIntyre
February 7, 1962. Los Angeles, California

The title of Mrs. Josephine Brown's property
is being investigated to establish the legal title of
the property. (English 1 pg.)

Mc3721. B-1962
Bp. Timothy Manning to Mrs. Marie Baker
February 15, 1962. Los Angeles, California

The Cardinal does not approve of isolated solicitations for the Lourdes Shrine and therefore
no letter from the Chancery Office will be
given. (English 1 pg.)

Mc3722. B-1962
Bp. Alden J. Bell to Rev. Angel P. Betancourt
February 16, 1962. Los Angeles, California

At the present time there are no unfilled assignments in Los Angeles Archdiocese. Perhaps
an application to the Fresno Diocese or El Paso,
Texas, would be wise. (English 1 pg.)

Mc3723. B-1962
Mr. Frank Brophy to J. Francis Cardinal
   McIntyre
March 16, 1962. Phoenix, Arizona

The extreme right organizations have intelli-
gent, loyal, and devoted Catholics. The Catholic
Press does not see it that way. (English 3 pgs.)

Mc3724. B-1962
Mr. Edward Clancy to Bp. Charles F. Buddy
March 23, 1962. San Diego, California

Is there some explanation for requesting signatures on the initiative for the committee to
combat Communism. Most of the measure is
law or has been declared unconstitutional. (English 1 pg.)

Mc3725. B-1962
Mrs. Consuelo deBonzo to J. Francis Cardinal
   McIntyre
April 23, 1962. Los Angeles, California

The Old Plaza will be the scene of the first
celebration of Senior Citizen Month. It will be
in the tradition of Early California Days. (English 1 pg.) On April 27, 1962, Fr. Louis Bossi
states that it is a civic celebration in the public
square. Benediction will be at the regular time.
(English 1 pg.)

Mc3726. B-1962
Hon. Eugene Biscailuz to J. Francis Cardinal
   McIntyre
April 30, 1962. Los Angeles, California

An invitation to an early California celebration of El Dia de Personas Mayores at the Old
Plaza. (English 1 pg.) On May 16, 1962, the
Cardinal states that unfortunately other commitments are scheduled. (English 1 pg.)

Mc3727. B-1962
Mr. Joseph Biafora to Msgr. Benjamin Hawkes
May 4, 1962. Reseda, California

The Inheritance Tax Appraiser has not sent
the report on the interest on the estate. The tax
is the responsibility of the beneficiaries. (English
1 pg.)

Mc3728. B-1962
J. Francis Cardinal McIntyre to Bank of
   America
May 14, 1962. Los Angeles, California

Bp. Alden J. Bell has been transferred to Sacramento, California, and will no longer sign for
the Archdiocese of Los Angeles. (English 1 pg.)

Mc3729. B-1962
Arbp. Leo Binz to J. Francis Cardinal
   McIntyre
June 22, 1962. St. Paul, Minnesota

The Acta Atque Statuta of the Diocesan
Synod is most gratefully received. (English 1
pg.)

Mc3730. B-1962
Mr. Vito Berardi to J. Francis Cardinal
   McIntyre
June 23, 1962. Inglewood, California

A campaign for modesty in dress ought to begin with a letter from the Cardinal to be read in
all of the Churches of the Archdiocese. (English
1 pg.)

Mc3731. B-1962
Capt. C. R. Bower to J. Francis Cardinal
McIntyre
June 24, 1962. San Francisco, California

The contract made with the Church to rear the children Catholics cannot be kept because the children of navy personnel cannot be accepted in Catholic schools. (English 2 pgs.)

Mc3732. B-1962
Bp. Charles Buddy to J. Francis Cardinal
McIntyre
July 20, 1962. San Diego, California

The Diocese of San Diego will follow the Los Angeles plan of action. The Education Office and the Legal Department of the NCWC have hurt our cause. (English 1 pg.)

Mc3733. B-1962
Bp. Charles F. Buddy to Mr. Andrew Burke
July 26, 1962. San Diego, California

The wording of the Constitutional Amendment could be stronger and more realistic on the need for moral education. (English 1 pg.)

Mc3734. B-1962
Rev. Roger Belanger to J. Francis Cardinal
McIntyre
July 31, 1962. Sherbrooke, Canada

A priest who can speak French, Spanish, and English is available for the Los Angeles Archdiocese. (English 1 pg.) On August 6, 1962, Fr. Rawden states that it is not the policy to accept priests but one may visit and accept a temporary assignment. (English 1 pg.)

Mc3735. B-1962
Mr. C. R. Bower to J. Francis Cardinal
McIntyre
August 30, 1962. San Francisco, California

The intercession of the Cardinal did allow the oldest boy in the family to go to Servite High School but the other children are denied a Catholic education because of military service. (English 2 pgs.)

Mc3736. B-1962
Bp. Charles F. Buddy to J. Francis Cardinal
McIntyre
September 12, 1962. San Diego, California

The opinion of the consulting engineers with reference to the Fire and Safety Code will be helpful to the Chancery Staff and to the Bishop. (English 1 pg.)

Mc3737. B-1962
Bp. Francis E. Bloy to J. Francis Cardinal
McIntyre
September 27, 1962. Los Angeles, California

Msgr. Patrick Dignan presented interesting material to the Ministerial Association about the Vatican Council. Everyone promises prayers. (English 1 pg.) On September 29, 1962, the Cardinal expresses his appreciation for the prayers for the success of the Council. (English 1 pg.)

Mc3738. B-1962
Mr. Andrew Burke to Msgr. Thomas J. Bowe
October 10, 1962. San Francisco, California

There is an envelope with 43,000 Mexican pecos marked Pious Fund. When did the money arrive? Was it 1912? (English 1 pg.) On October 25, 1962, Msgr. states that there is a file concerning the money and the Pious Fund. (English 1 pg.)

Mc3739. B-1962
Rev. Charles Balic, OFM to J. Francis Cardinal
McIntyre
November 24, 1962. Rome, Italy

A volume of Marialogy and the Council is being presented before the discussion to give time for reading and approval. (English 1 pg.)

Mc3740. B-1962
Mr. Steve Broidy to J. Francis Cardinal McIntyre
December 6, 1962. Los Angeles, California

The Radiation Therapy and Nuclear Medicine Wing of the Cedars of Lebanon-Mount Sinai Hospital will be dedicated on January 11. The Board invites the Cardinal to be present. (English 1 pg.) On December 14, 1962, the Cardinal designated Msgr. O'Dwyer to represent the Archdiocese. (English 1 pg.)

Mc3741. B-1962
Arbp. Thomas Boland to J. Francis Cardinal
McIntyre
December 20, 1962. Newark, New Jersey

An invitation is extended to the consecration of Bishop elect John Dougherty and Bishop elect John Costello on January 24, 1963. (English 1 pg.) On December 28, 1962, the Cardinal states that he regrets that his schedule does not allow a trip. (English 1 pg.)

Mc3742. B-1962
Bp. Joseph Blomjous to J. Francis Cardinal
McIntyre
N.D. Mwanza, Tanganyika

The changing role of the mission lands must be seen by the Catholics as native Bishops and Cardinals are appointed. Maybe *Propaganda Fide* can become the world wide planning and world wide coordinator of help to be given to each country. (English 6 pgs.)

Mc3743. C-1962
Mr. Martial Capbern to J. Francis Cardinal
McIntyre
January 4, 1962. Inglewood, California

Dr. Buell Gallagher will be inaugurated as
the first Chancellor of California State Colleges
on April 2, at 11:00 a.m. The Board invites the
Cardinal to give the invocation. (English 1 pg.)
On January 9, 1962, the Cardinal states that he
regrets that another appointment will prevent
his attendance. (English 1 pg.)

Mc3744. C-1962
Ms. Flora Chisholm to Bp. Alden J. Bell
May 3, 1962. Los Angeles, California

The President, Governor and Mayor declared
May to be Senior Citizen Month. All Churches
have been requested to give special attention to
the Senior Citizens. (English 1 pg.)

Mc3745. C-1962
Msgr. James B. Clyne to Bp. Timothy Manning
June 15, 1962. Los Angeles, California

A $1,000 scholarship is offered directly to the
school on the elementary level. There are no
strict conditions to the granting of the scholarship. (English 1 pg.)

Mc3746. C-1962
Mr. William Clark to J. Francis Cardinal
McIntyre
July 6, 1962. Ventura, California

The men of Ventura County would like to
discuss the lay men's role in opposing Atheistic
Communist. (English 1 pg.) On July 18, 1962,
Msgr. Jacobs states that the men want action on
every level. Rev. Charles Miller, CM gave an excellent lecture on Communism. (English 1 pg.)

Mc3747. C-1962
Mr. William Clark to J. Francis Cardinal
McIntyre
August 23, 1962. Oxnard, California

The answer does not reflect the request. We
wish to alert our citizens to the imminent dangers of Communism. (English 1 pg.) On September 7, 1962, Fr. John Rawden suggests a
visit to the Chancery Office the next time business brings him to the city. (English 1 pg.)

Mc3748. C-1962
Dr. Clifford Cherry, MD to J. Francis Cardinal
McIntyre
October 3, 1962. Los Angeles, California

A complete medical record to be taken to
Rome in case a doctor would have to be called
during the session of the Council. (English
2 pgs.)

Mc3749. C-1962 Msgr. James Clyne to J.
Francis Cardinal McIntyre
October 5, 1962. Los Angeles, California

Mr. Crouch accepts the responsibility for everything printed in the Herald-Examiner. He
suggests Letters to the Editor to give another
point of view. (English 1 pg.)

Mc3750. C-1962
Msgr. Michael Costigan to Msgr. Benjamin
Hawkes
October 10, 1962. Rapid City, South Dakota

Father Murray will give his lecture at an Executive Meeting of the club. He has permission
to speak about his Sky Ranch. (English 1 pg.)

Mc3751. C-1962
Richard Cardinal Cushing to Bp. Timothy
Manning
N.D. Boston, Massachusetts

The annual convention of Catholic Nurses
will be held June 7–10 in Boston. A most cor-
dial invitation is extended. (English 1 pg.)

Mc3752. D-1962
Rev. Albert Dumont, OP to J. Francis Cardinal
McIntyre
January 18, 1962. Chicago, Illinois

The Apostolic Delegate announced the establishment of the Leonine Commission. Will
March 8 be a possible meeting date in the
Chancery Office. (English 1 pg.) On February
6, 1962, the Cardinal will welcome the Directors on March 8 at 2:30. (English 1 pg.)

Mc3753. D-1962
Arbp. John F. Deardon to J. Francis Cardinal
McIntyre
March 8, 1962. Detroit, Michigan

The proposed changes that Bp. Fulton J.
Sheen desires to make in the Propagation of the
Faith have received complete disapproval. (En-
glish 1 pg.)

Mc3754. D-1962
Rev. Richard Dwyer to Bp. Alden J. Bell
March 13, 1962. Sacramento, California

Some background information is needed on
the Order of Lazarus and Mr. Alan W. Hazel-
ton, Vice Chancellor of American Bailiwick.
Are they reliable and approved by the Church?
(English 1 pg.) On March 27, 1962, the Bishop
states from the remarks made, the Pastor gives
no assurance of any assistance for the organization. (English 1 pg.)

Mc3755. D-1962
Mr. Ernest E. Debs to J. Francis Cardinal
McIntyre
April 25, 1962. Los Angeles, California

An invitation to give the invocation at the dedication of the Hall of Records on May 18 at 10:30 a.m. (English 1 pg.) On April 30, 1962, the Cardinal states that it will afford him great pleasure to give the invocation. (English 1 pg.)

Mc3756. D-1962
Sister M. Dulcis, OP to J. Francis Cardinal
McIntyre
May 3, 1962. Brooklyn, New York

A family connection through Mary Pelly, your godmother, makes prayers for the success of the Council much easier. (English 2 pgs.) On May 11, 1962, the Cardinal sends the names of the members of the Pelly family and the name of the only living member. (English 1 pg.)

Mc3757. D-1962
Arbp. John F. Deardon to J. Francis Cardinal
McIntyre
June 25, 1962. Detroit, Michigan

The recent Statutes of the Synod of the Archdiocese of Los Angeles will provide guidelines for our Synod when we are ready. (English 1 pg.)

Mc3758. D-1962
Mr. Daniel Donohue to Msgr. Benjamin
Hawkes
October 14, 1962. Rome, Italy

A friendly letter commenting on the arrival in New York and in Rome and the events of the opening of the Vatican Council. (English 1 pg.)

Mc3759. D-1962
J. Francis Cardinal McIntyre to Cardinal de la
Torre
October 20, 1962. Los Angeles, California

Is there a source of information on the *Centro De Estudios Y Reformas Economico Sociales?* Some of the Americans are interested. (English 1 pg.)

Mc3760. D-1962
Mr. Daniel Donohue to Rev. John A. Rawden
N.D. Los Angeles, California

A friendly letter commenting on the pictures taken in Rome and waiting for the return of the Cardinal and his Secretary. (English 2 pgs.)

Mc3761. E-1962
Rev. Ezra Ellis to J. Francis Cardinal McIntyre
January 23, 1962. Whittier, California

Prayers were recited for all Roman Catholics and a collection was taken for the poor. The enclosed check was the amount received. (English 1 pg.) On January 30, 1962, the Cardinal expresses gratitude for the prayers and the generosity of the collection for the poor. (English 1 pg.)

Mc3762. E-1962
Bp. Edward Swanstrom to J. Francis Cardinal
McIntyre
February 3, 1962. New York City, New York

The money from The First Friends Church is in the hands of Fr. Bordelon who helps the people of Leopoldville in the Congo and the poor of Angola. (English 1 pg.) A letter is sent to Rev. Ezra Ellis in Whittier, California. (English 1 pg.)

Mc3763. E-1962
John Cardinal D'Alton to J. Francis Cardinal
McIntyre
October 25, 1962. Armagh, Ireland

A letter of introduction for Professor R. Dudley Edwards of the University College, Dublin is enclosed. (English 1 pg.) On February 21, 1962, Dr. Edwards investigates the possibility of an interview with the Cardinal. (English 1 pg.)

Mc3764. E-1962
Mr. Charles Edmonds to Rev. John A. Rawden
November 21, 1962. Los Angeles, California

Mr. Joseph Boylan will be in Rome on December 7 to escort the Cardinal to Los Angeles. Is there a relic of St. Martin de Porres available? (English 1 pg.)

Mc3765. E-1962
Mr. Clair Engle to J. Francis Cardinal
McIntyre
December 4, 1962. Washington, D.C.

Is the *Congressional Record* serving the purpose for which it is sent? (English 1 pg.) On December 14, 1962, the Cardinal states that a copy is received by *The Tidings* and that is really sufficient. (English 1 pg.)

Mc3766. F-1962
Dr. James Fifield to J. Francis Cardinal
McIntyre
January 2, 1962. Los Angeles, California

Could there be a united front of Catholics, Jews, and Protestants against the growing indecencies and immoralities? (English 1 pg.)

Mc3767. F-1962
J. Francis Cardinal McIntyre to Arbp. Pericle
Felici
January 3, 1962. Los Angeles, California

All of the sessions of the Vatican Council can
be attended. The session from February 17 to
the February 28 and the session from June 10
until the end of the session, I will be present.
The needs of the Archdiocese can be met from
March until June. (English 1 pg.)

Mc3768. F-1962
J. Francis Cardinal McIntyre to Bp. Pericle
Felici
March 19, 1962. Los Angeles, California

The schema on Communications will be dis-
cussed in March when I cannot be present.
Please read the following remarks from the
Hollywood Archbishop. (Latin 7 pgs.)

Mc3769. F-1962
Rev. John Fitzgerald to Bp. Alden J. Bell
April 5, 1962. Long Beach, California

A friendly letter commenting on Bishop Bell's
work in Los Angeles and the regard that the
Junior Clergy has for the Bishop. (English 1 pg.)

Mc3770. F-1962
Mr. Francis Fox to J. Francis Cardinal
McIntyre
April 19, 1962. Los Angeles, California

An invitation is extended to give the invocation at the 35th Annual Conference of Airport
Executives on May 21 at noon. (English 1 pg.)
On April 24, 1962, the Cardinal states that he
cannot attend but Bishop Timothy Manning
will give the invocation. (English 1 pg.)

Mc3771. F-1962
Msgr. Benjamin Hawkes to Rev. William
Forester
June 1, 1962. Los Angeles, California

Arrangements can be made for a car and a
driver for the Cardinal and Fr. John Rawden.
Tell Angelo that Los Angeles is waiting for his
arrival. (English 2 pgs.)

Mc3772. F-1962
Rev. Henry Foltz to Bp. Alden J. Bell
June 27, 1962. Wilmington, Delaware

The recently arrived Acts and Statutes of the
Synod will be a source of inspiration to the Dioceses when we arrive at the Synod. (English
1 pg.)

Mc3773. F-1962
Bp. Frederick Freking to J. Francis Cardinal
McIntyre
June 29, 1962. Salina, Kansas

The history of the Diocese of Salina which
was formerly Concordia is presented in a special edition of the *Register* and a booklet. (English 1 pg.) On July 5, 1962, the Cardinal
expresses his happiness to receive both of the remembrances of seventy-five years of service to
the Church. (English 1 pg.)

Mc3774. F-1962
J. Francis Cardinal McIntyre to Bp. Pericle Felici
September 13, 1962. Los Angeles, California

A correction is needed as Rev. Lawrence Gibson will be my Theologian and assistant in case
impaired hearing will cause difficulty. Please arrange for two ladies to have seats at the Solemn
Pontifical Mass. (English 2 pgs.)

Mc3775. F-1962
J. Francis Cardinal McIntyre to Rev. Guy Fer-
rari, OSB
September 27, 1962. Los Angeles, California

Both Judge William Levit and Judge Joseph
Gorman will be visiting in Rome soon and
would appreciate seeing the Vatican Library
(English 1 pg.) On November 9, 1962, Judge
Levitt and Judge Gorman praised the friendly
spirit of Father Ferrari. (English 1 pg.)

Mc3776. G-1962
Valerian Cardinal Gracias to J. Francis Cardi-
nal McIntyre
March 16, 1962. Rome, Italy

The views of the Episcopal Committee concerning the Propagation of the Faith in the
United States will be given special consideration. (English 1 pg.)

Mc3777. G-1962
Valerian Cardinal Gracias to J. Francis Cardi-
nal McIntyre
April 1, 1962. Bombay, India

Although a general solicitation cannot be
made to all Dioceses at this time, could Los Angeles, California send a donation to the Seminary? (English 1 pg.) On April 10, 1962, the
Cardinal states that the Archdioceses is in a
very heavy debt with a new Seminary and new
Churches. (English 1 pg.)

Mc3778. G-1962
Arbp. Joseph F. Gawlina to J. Francis Cardinal
McIntyre
June 24, 1962. Rome, Italy

A feast day message and a promise of prayers
that St. James will intercede for the Cardinal.
(English 1 pg.) On July 20, 1962, the Cardinal returns the prayerful good wishes. (English 1 pg.)

Mc3779. G-1962
Msgr. Joseph Gorham to J. Francis Cardinal
McIntyre
August 6, 1962. Washington, D.C.

The Civics Clubs will stress "Build Better Local Governments" giving students the incentives
to become active in local activities. (English
1 pg.)

Mc3780. G-1962
Bp. James Griffiths to J. Francis Cardinal
McIntyre
September 3, 1962. New York City, New York

The suggestions of the Liturgical Conference
are submitted to the Bishops before the Vatican
Council will discuss many aspects of the Liturgy. (English 4 pgs.)

Mc3781. G-1962
J. Francis Cardinal McIntyre to Bp. James H.
Griffiths
September 13, 1962. Los Angeles, California

As Secretary of the Liturgical Commission
does this meet with the approval of the Bishops'
Commission? (English 1 pg.) On September 27,
1962, the Bishop states that the report was to
serve as a liaison not as having the consent of
the Bishops. (English 1 pg.)

Mc3782. G-1962
J. Francis Cardinal McIntyre to Msgr. Michael
Galvin
September 19, 1962. Los Angeles, California

During the period when Bishop Timothy
Manning is out of the Archdiocese, the title of
Administrator with the power of the Vicar Gen-
eral will be yours. (English 1 pg.)

Mc3783. G-1962
Arbp. Edward Howard to J. Francis Cardinal
McIntyre
January 31, 1962. Portland, Oregon

A letter of introduction for Judge John F.
Kilkenny who will be in Los Angeles for several
months and will phone for an appointment.
(English 1 pg.) On February 5, 1962, the Car-
dinal states that he will be glad to have the
Judge as a guest for lunch. (English 1 pg.)

Mc3784. H-1962
Bp. Jerome Hannan to J. Francis Cardinal
McIntyre
August 6, 1962. Scranton, Pennsylvania

The Statutes and Acts of the Archdioceses in
the last Synod are written in clear, comprehen-
sive language which will be easily followed.
(English 1 pg.)

Mc3785. H-1962
Mr. John N. Hayes to J. Francis Cardinal
McIntyre
August 22, 1962. Washington, D.C.

Dr. Kamel Said Baladi must leave the United
States for two years; although, the appeals were
made, the answer must be negative. (English
2 pgs.)

Mc3786. H-1962
J. Edgar Hoover to Dr. John E. Granger
September 12, 1962. Washington, D.C.

Prayer is greater than any man made or man
controlled power because prayer is man's greatest mean of tapping the infinite resources of
God. (English 1 pg.)

Mc3787. H-1962
Msgr. Benjamin Hawkes to Rev. John A.
Rawden
October 22, 1962. Los Angeles, California

A letter commenting on the opening activities
of the Council, the ordering of another cassock
for the Cardinal and a request for a Papal Blessing for the five altar boys. (English 2 pgs.)

Mc3788. H-1962
Rev. John A. Rawden to Msgr. Benjamin
Hawkes
October 27, 1962. Vatican City

A letter commenting on the fees for the Cardinal's car, the purchase of the *Pontificale Ro-
manum*, a totum brievary. Bishop Manning
celebrated his sixteenth anniversary of consecration with a dinner. (English 2 pgs.)

Mc3789. H-1962
Msgr. Benjamin Hawkes to Rev. John A.
Rawden
November 8, 1962. Los Angeles, California

A friendly letter commenting on Bishop Manning's arrival home, the purchasing being done
in Rome, and the need to be careful of colds.
(English 2 pgs.)

Mc3790. H-1962
Rev. John A. Rawden to Msgr. Benjamin
Hawkes
November 15, 1962. Vatican City

A friendly letter commenting on the packages
being mailed, the cheers that Cardinal Cicognani received when he asked for St. Joseph's
name to be included in the Canon of the Mass,
the Cardinal's Mass at St. Anastasia on November 25 and the blessing of the statue. (English
1 pg.)

Mc3791. H-1962
Msgr. Benjamin Hawkes to Rev. John A. Rawden
November 17, 1962. Los Angeles, California

A friendly letter commenting on the reaction of Cardinal Larraona to St. Vibiana remaining in Los Angeles, and the arrival of *Paritus,* as well as the additional purchases that are needed for the Seminary. (English 1 pg.)

Mc3792. H-1962
Rev. John A. Rawden to Msgr. Benjamin Hawkes
November 25, 1962. Vatican City

A friendly letter commenting on the Papal audience of the American Bishops, the dinner in honor of the Cardinal, and the Thanksgiving dinner at the North American College. (English 1 pg.)

Mc3793. I-1962
Ms. Mary Iwanicki to J. Francis Cardinal McIntyre
January 27, 1962. Canoga Park, California

A request to establish a Cardinal Mindszenty Study Club according to the Foundation Rules. (English 1 pg.) On January 31, 1962, the Cardinal states that the only organizations approved by the Archdiocese are strictly spiritual and under the direction of the Pastor. (English 1 pg.)

Mc3794. I-1962
Msgr. Michael Ivanko to Msgr. Benjamin Hawkes
July 3, 1962. Cleveland, Ohio

Some information is needed about the retirement plan for the priests in Los Angeles as Cleveland is about to organize one. (English 1 pg.) On July 6, 1962, there is no retirement plan. When a priest has permanent disability the Archdiocese provides. (English 1 pg.)

Mc3795. J-1962
J. Francis Cardinal McIntyre to Msgr. Anthony Jacobs
July 31, 1962. Los Angeles, California

Mr. Bernard Loughman approves of the lecture to be given on Communism. The other Grand Knight will assist. (English 2 pgs.)

Mc3796. J-1962
Msgr. William Johnson to J. Francis Cardinal McIntyre
October 3, 1962. Los Angeles, California

The Foundation for International Cooperation works with Mr. and Mrs. Ned Taylor placing foreign students in Catholic homes to give the students a balanced view of American family life. (English 2 pgs.) On October 4, 1962, the Cardinal asks Msgr. Roche to use his best judgment on the matter. (English 1 pg.)

Mc3797. K-1962
Rev. Thomas Kelly to Bp. Timothy Manning
January 4, 1962. Los Angeles, California

The book, *The Church and the Change,* stresses the need for priests to take leadership in civic, governmental, and social affairs. There is not too much new in it. (English 1 pg.)

Mc3798. K-1962
J. Francis Cardinal McIntyre to Mr. Patrick Kirby
January 23, 1962. Los Angeles, California

Msgr. Anthony Brouwers is very interested in the Uganda Martyrs, therefore, your suggestions will be sent to him. (English 1 pg.)

Mc3799. K-1962
Rev. W. J. Kenneally, CM to J. Francis Cardinal McIntyre
June 2, 1962. Camarillo, California

The brochures for the coming Council are being returned with comments. Some add nothing new, so there are no comments. (English 1 pg.)

Mc3800. K-1962
Rev. Francis L. Kennedy to J. Francis Cardinal McIntyre
June 25, 1962. Jefferson City, Missouri

Pope John XXIII is anxious for the Cause of Pope Pius IX to go through as quickly as possible. He asks prayers and donation for the Cause. (English 1 pg.)

Mc3801. K-1962
Rev. John Cavanaugh to Mr. Charles Keating
August 23, 1962. Cincinnati, Ohio

The campaign for decent literature and motion pictures is finding a good audience in Catholic colleges and high schools. (English 1 pg.)

Mc3802. K-1962
Rev. W. C. Kenneally, CM to J. Francis Cardinal McIntyre
September 27, 1962. Camarillo, California

Comments on the use of the vernacular in the Liturgy of the Mass are enclosed. If English is to be used let it be at Ordination, or in the Breviary. (English 2 pgs.)

Mc3803. K-1962
J. Francis Cardinal McIntyre to Rev. John A. Kucingis
October 4, 1962. Los Angeles, California

The cooperation of the parish with Bishop Vincent Brizgys gives great hope to the Lithuanian people. (English 1 pg.)

Mc3804. K-1962
Rev. W. J. Kenneally, CM to J. Francis Cardinal McIntyre
December 24, 1962. Camarillo, California

A friendly letter commenting on the talks given at the first session of the Council, the introduction of some vernacular in the Liturgy. The name of Margaret E. Murphy will be added to the list of benefactors. (English 1 pg.)

Mc3805. K-1962
J. Francis Cardinal McIntyre to Msgr. John Kavanaugh
December 27, 1962. Los Angeles, California

A friendly letter commenting on the death of Rev. John Flynn and the interesting tales that will be given to the class at the next reunion. (English 1 pg.)

Mc3806. L-1962
Arbp. Robert E. Lucey to J. Francis Cardinal McIntyre
April 23, 1962. San Antonio, Texas

The picture of the Bishops taken at Archbishop McGucken's enthronement is excellent. The Archbishop is an honor to the great Archdiocese of Los Angeles. (English 1 pg.)

Mc3807. L-1962
Mr. T. E. Leavey to Msgr. Benjamin Hawkes
April 24, 1962. Los Angeles, California

The Foundation will sponsor Fred and John Balak at St. John's Seminary. Please send an invoice when the money is due. (English 1 pg.) On April 30, 1962, Msgr. states that the Archdiocese appreciates the wonderful kindness of the Foundation. (English 1 pg.)

Mc3808. L-1962
Bp. Francis Leipzig to Bp. Timothy Manning
May 12, 1962. Baker, Oregon

Rev. Thomas Scanlan will preach for the Diocese of Baker on June 10, 17, 24. Could he make one of the Priests' Retreats? (English 1 pg.) On May 14, 1962, the Bishop states that the retreat beginning on June 18 would be the most convenient. (English 1 pg.)

Mc3809. L-1962
Mr. Edward Foley to Msgr. Benjamin Hawkes
July 2, 1962. Santa Barbara, California

Is there a possibility that the cardinal could request that Mr. Mark Lansburgh be permitted to see the old Vatican manuscripts? (English 1 pg.) On July 9, 1962, Msgr. states that unless there is a definite research project no request will be made. (English 1 pg.)

Mc3810. L-1962
Mr. Mark Lansburgh to Msgr. Benjamin Hawkes
July 12, 1962. Santa Barbara, California

My present position is the Consultant in Rare Books and Manuscripts at the University of California. The research project is Irish and Spanish manuscripts of the 7-10 century. (English 1 pg.) On July 17, 1962, the Cardinal requests Archbishop O'Connor to arrange for Mr. Lansburgh to do the research. (English 1 pg.)

Mc3811. L-1962
Mr. Irving R. Levine to J. Francis Cardinal McIntyre
September 3, 1962. Rome, Italy

The news department of the National Broadcasting Company will want to film the area where the Bishops are living and to have a half-hour interview. (English 1 pg.) On September 25, 1962, Fr. states that the Cardinal will arrive in Rome on October 9 and if time permits he will be available for the interview. (English 1 pg.)

Mc3812. L-1962
Bp. Vincent Brizgys to J. Francis Cardinal McIntyre
September 11, 1962. Brooklyn, New York

The Lithuania Catholic Religious Aid Inc. sends assistance to priests and nuns as well as vestments and religious articles. Could a priest be appointed to assist in the Archdiocese? (English 1 pg.) On September 27, 1962, Bp. Edward Swanstrom states that the Bishops' Relief makes an annual grant to the organization (English 1 pg.)

Mc3813. Mc-1962
Mr. John F. McCarthy to J. Francis Cardinal McIntyre
January 29, 1962. San Rafael, California

The time given to counsel and advice is greatly appreciated. Your copy of the Sign magazine is in my office. (English 1 pg.)

Mc3814. Mc-1962
J. Francis Cardinal McIntyre to All Priests
February 6, 1962. Los Angeles, California

During the Lenten season a talk or two should be given on the Ecumenical Council and prayers should be offered for the work and success of the Council. (English 2 pgs.)

Mc3815. Mc-1962
Mr. Ray McCarthy to Bp. Alden J. Bell
February 9, 1962. New York City, New York

A request to know the Bishop's plans for accommodations in Rome during the first session of the Council and all transactions for accommodations. (English 12 pgs.)

Mc3816. Mc-1962
Mr. Harold McClellan to J. Francis Cardinal McIntyre
February 15, 1962. Los Angeles, California

The schedule of events for the dedication of Dodger Stadium is enclosed. Please indicate what part the Cardinal can have in the ceremonies. (English 1 pg.) On April 9, 1962, the Cardinal states the Invocation, the Blessing of the Flag, and the Pledge of Allegiance. (English 1 pg.)

Mc3817. Mc-1962 Arbp. John Krol to J. Francis Cardinal McIntyre
June 27, 1962. Philadelphia, Pennsylvania

An invitation is extended to the consecration of Bishop elect Gerald McDevitt on August 1, 1962. (English 1 pg.) On July 9, 1962, the Cardinal states that it will be impossible to leave the Archdiocese in early August. (English 1 pg.)

Mc3818. Mc-1962
Msgr. Benjamin Hawkes to Arbp. Joseph T. McGucken
July 17, 1962. Los Angeles, California

Mrs. Marie deVrahnos Baker has no permission to collect for the Lourdes Shrine in Los Angeles. She was given permission for one collection. (English 1 pg.)

Mc3819. Mc-1962
Mr. Mark Robinson to J. Francis Cardinal McIntyre
July 31, 1962. Los Angeles, California

Rev. McQuillan cannot preach at the Red Mass but Rev. Charles Casassa will be at Good Shepherd Church on September 19. (English 1 pg.)

Mc3820. Mc-1962
Mr. H. J. McMains to J. Francis Cardinal McIntyre
September 11, 1962. New York City, New York

RCA is sending a Guaranteed Account card allowing messages to be sent without the necessity of foreign cash. The message will be sent quickly and easily. (English 1 pg.) On September 18, 1962, the Cardinal expresses his appreciation for the card. (English 1 pg.)

Mc3821. Mc-1962
Arbp. Joseph T. McGucken to J. Francis Cardinal McIntyre
September 25, 1962. San Francisco, California

There are only two claims unsettled, so is this a good time to re-open the Pious Fund claim with Mexico? (English 2 pgs.) On September 28, 1962, the Cardinal states that the whole Pious Fund is a maze but it can be discussed in Rome. (English 1 pg.)

Mc3822. Mc-1962
Arbp. Joseph T. McGucken to J. Francis Cardinal McIntyre
September 28, 1962. San Francisco, California

The need for the tax exemption for rectories and convents should be tried in a smaller area so the opposition will not be so strong. (English 1 pg.)

Mc3823. M-1962
Bp. Timothy Manning to Miss Norma Marcus
January 23, 1962. Los Angeles, California

The donation for the College Seminary will be used to buy one of the Sacred Vessels which will be a fitting remembrance. (English 1 pg.)

Mc3824. M-1962
Mr. Karl Mangoian to Msgr. Benjamin Hawkes
February 5, 1962. Lakewood, California

Two pictures of Cardinal Agagianian and Cardinal McIntyre are for the Cardinal and yourself. (English 1 pg.) On February 6, 1962, Msgr. states that the pictures are excellent. (English 1 pg.)

Mc3825. M-1962
Bp. Timothy Manning to J. Francis Cardinal McIntyre
February 23, 1962. Los Angeles, California

A friendly letter commenting on Archbishop Joseph T. McGucken's appointment, the funeral of Archbishop O'Brien with Bishop Bell in attendance, and the property available in Fullerton. (English 1 pg.)

Mc3826. M-1962
Bp. elect Leo T. Maher to J. Francis Cardinal McIntyre
March 19, 1962. San Francisco, California

An invitation is extended to the consecration of Bishop elect Leo Maher on April 29 as the first Bishop of the new Diocese of Santa Rosa. (English 1 pg.) On March 23, 1962, the Cardinal states that a new Church is being blessed and ordinations will take place on the following day. (English 1 pg.)

Mc3827. M-1962
Msgr. Arcadio Marinas to J. Francis Cardinal McIntyre
April 3, 1962. Bronx, New York

A report on the conditions of the Seminaries in Cuba and a message of gratitude for the assistance given. (English 1 pg.)

Mc3828. M-1962
Mr. Antonio Mortensen to J. Francis Cardinal
McIntyre
April 14, 1962. Quito, Equador

The *Cruzada Social* will try to break the circle of poverty by setting up production stations, one for the production of toys, one for fruits and timber, one for preserves and marmalades. (English 4 pgs.)

Mc3829. M-1962
J. Francis Cardinal McIntyre to Bp. Timothy
Manning
July 23, 1962. Los Angeles, California

A friendly letter commenting on the weather conditions in Los Angeles and the latest communication that Rome does not expect all Auxiliary Bishops at the Council full time. (English 1 pg.)

Mc3830. M-1962
Bp. Timothy Manning to J. Francis Cardinal
McIntyre
November 9, 1962. Los Angeles, California

A friendly letter commenting on the transfer of Bishop Mora's body to Calvary Cemetery and the removal of Bishop Amat's body from the Cathedral. (English 2 pgs.)

Mc3831. M-1962
Rev. John B. Thom to Rev. Charles Miller, CM
November 28, 1962. Los Angeles, California

A transfer will take place for the feast of St. Patrick to March 18 because the Sunday is always celebrated. St. Didacus will be celebrated as the Universal Church celebrates it and Mother Cabrini's feast will be the one celebrated. (English 1 pg.)

Mc3832. M-1962
Bp. Timothy Manning to All Priests
December 4, 1962. Los Angeles, California

Cardinal McIntyre will return to Los Angeles International Airport on December 9 at 10:00 p.m. Many priests will want to welcome him home from this historic occasion. (English 1 pg.)

Mc3833. N-1962
Bp. Timothy Manning to Rev. Joseph Nagy
January 31, 1962. Los Angeles, California

The indult from the Sacred Consistorial Congregation prolongs your residence in Los Angeles for one year. (English 1 pg.)

Mc3834. N-1962
Mr. Benjamin Norris to Bp. Alden J. Bell
February 6, 1962. Washington, D.C.

The hospitality granted to the foreign educators made a most favorable impression on them and did contribute to their understanding of American life. (English 1 pg.)

Mc3835. N-1962
Mr. Cyril C. Nigg to J. Francis Cardinal McIntyre
July 19, 1962. Los Angeles, California

A meeting for the representatives of the four Catholic colleges in Los Angeles could accomplish a better understanding among the colleges. (English 1 pg.) On July 23, 1962, the Cardinal states that he will arrange the meeting at his residence. (English 1 pg.)

Mc3836. N-1962
Mrs. Harold Norris to Msgr. Benjamin Hawkes
July 21, 1962. Milton, Indiana

The picture of Mrs. John Dennis McVay must be returned to her parents. Information about her is still needed. (English 1 pg.) On August 3, 1962, Msgr. states that the family moved from Glendale and it seems to be impossible to trace them. (English 1 pg.)

Mc3837. N-1962
J. Francis Cardinal McIntyre to Mr. Cyril C. Nigg
July 24, 1962. Los Angeles, California

The formation of a joint committee of alumni, sympathizers and student should be in the form of an analysis of potential persons and foundations. One of the sisters should have this position. (English 1 pg.)

Mc3838. N-1962
Mr. Richard Nell to J. Francis Cardinal McIntyre
August 1, 1962. Santa Barbara, California

What role is the educated Catholic layman going to have in the Council? There are arrangements that can be made for TV coverage of the Pontifical Liturgy as well as other activities. (English 2 pgs.) On August 17, 1962, Fr. states that at the present time the CCD would be the best place for the layman. (English 1 pg.)

Mc3839. N-1962
Rev. Gerard Nathe, OSB to Rev. John B. Thom
October 23, 1962. Los Angeles, California

A request is made for the necessary delegation for absolving from ex-communication one who joined another religion and now wishes to return to the Catholic Church. (English 1 pg.) On October 26, 1962, the faculties are given. (English 1 pg.)

Mc3840. O-1962
Arbp. Patrick O'Boyle to J. Francis Cardinal
McIntyre
April 6, 1962. Washington, D.C.

The Legal Department of the NCWC states
that the basic educational requirements are the
same for public and private schools and that
private schools should receive support for everything except the teaching of religion. (English 3 pgs.)

Mc3841. O-1962
Arbp. Martin O'Connor to J. Francis Cardinal
McIntyre
April 15, 1962. Vatican City

There is additional room for theology students for the next scholastic year. Please nomi-
nate the candidates soon. (English 1 pg.)

Mc3842. O-1962
Rev. David Orozco to J. Francis Cardinal
McIntyre
June 5, 1962. Guadalajara, Mexico

A request is made for faculties while visiting
in Los Angeles from July 10 to August 10. (English 1 pg.) On June 7, 1962, Msgr. Hawkes
states that the permission is given and asks Fr.
to call at the Chancery Office on his arrival.
(English 1 pg.)

Mc3843. O-1962
Rev. M. Oliva A. Pbro to J. Francis Cardinal
McIntyre
June 8, 1962. Tepic, Mexico

A request to visit in Los Angeles as a Silver
Jubilee present. (Spanish 1 pg.) On June 25,
1962, Msgr. Hawkes states that the permission
is granted for a visit if the Bp. has given his approval. (English 1 pg.)

Mc3844. O-1962
Rev. Pablo M. Orozco to J. Francis Cardinal
McIntyre
N.D. Jalisco, Mexico

A request to visit Los Angeles during the
month of August. The Bishop has granted his
permission. (Spanish 1 pg.) On June 29, 1962,
Msgr. Hawkes states that Los Angeles is happy
to grant permission for the visit. (English 1 pg.)

Mc3845. O-1962
J. Francis Cardinal McIntyre to Arbp. Patrick
O'Boyle
July 6, 1962. Los Angeles, California

The vote will not be sent as the plan, as it is
now finalized, was not presented to the Bishops
at the November meeting nor does it follow the
policy of the Bishops. (English 4 pgs.)

Mc3846. O-1962
J. Francis Cardinal McIntyre to Arbp. Patrick
O'Boyle
August 9, 1962. Los Angeles, California

The American hierarchy should appoint a
spokesman for any point that would represent
the American viewpoint. Theologians can be
sent the material or consulted at home and in
Rome. (English 1 pg.)

Mc3847. O-1962
J. Francis Cardinal McIntyre to Arbp. Patrick
O'Boyle
August 10, 1962. Los Angeles, California

Mr. Luke Hart, the Supreme Knight of the
Knights of Columbus, has made an interesting
statement in the NCWC's news sheet about
Federal aid to education. (English 1 pg.)

Mc3848. O-1962
J. Francis Cardinal McIntyre to Msgr. Thomas
O'Dwyer
August 21, 1962. Los Angeles, California

In White Memorial Hospital, does everyone
who is registered as a Catholic see a priest?
Does everyone who is on the serious list see a
priest? (English 1 pg.) On August 29, 1962, Fr.
Dessert assured the Cardinal that a priest would
be available from St. Mary's Parish to give service to the hospital. (English 1 pg.)

Mc3849. O-1962
Msgr. Benjamin Hawkes to Arbp. Martin
O'Connor
September 8, 1962. Los Angeles, California

The travel arrangements are for the Cardinal,
Rev. John Rawden, Rev. Larry Gibson, and Mr.
Daniel Donohue to arrive in Rome on October
9 at 10:10 a.m. (English 1 pg.)

Mc3850. O-1962
J. Francis Cardinal McIntyre to Arbp. Martin
O'Connor
September 15, 1962. Los Angeles, California

Could the sitting room of the suite be used
for a common room for Cardinals Cushing, Ritter and myself or for a Chapel for Mass at different times? (English 1 pg.)

Mc3851. O-1962
Dr. Joseph O'Connor, MD to J. Francis Cardi-
nal McIntyre
October 5, 1962. Los Angeles, California

The two most important ways to have a community wide participation in the oral polio immunization is by the press and the Church. *The
Tidings* has promised a story on the program.
An announcement from the pulpit on the necessity of the immunization will be the second
phase. (English 1 pg.)

Mc3852. O-1962
Rev. Henry J. O'Brien to J. Francis Cardinal
McIntyre
December 29, 1961. Hartford, Connecticut

An invitation is extended to the dedication of
the new Cathedral on May 23, 1962. (English 1
pg.) On January 9, 1962, the Cardinal states
that his schedule will not permit any trips except to the Council and to the Bishops' Meeting. (English 1 pg.)

Mc3853. P-1962
Mr. Virgil Pinkley to J. Francis Cardinal
McIntyre
January 9, 1962. Indio, California

To take time from the very busy schedule to
visit Mrs. Pinkley was appreciated by the entire
family. Praise is due to St. Vincent Hospital
likewise. (English 1 pg.)

Mc3854. P-1962
Mr. Reuben Parson to J. Francis Cardinal
McIntyre
January 10, 1962. Norwalk, California

Why is the Church hesitant to organize anti-
communistic activities? St. John of God Parish
in Norwalk is an exception to the rule. (English
1 pg.) On January 16, 1962, the Cardinal states
that the Church preaches doctrine. The lay people can organize the other types of activities.
(English 1 pg.)

Mc3855. P-1962
Mr. & Mrs. Joseph Patin to J. Francis Cardi-
nal McIntyre
April 6, 1962. Norwalk, California

A request to investigate the possibility of a
Catholic wedding for a couple. The girl is 15
and the man is 20. A baby will be born in May.
(English 3 pgs.) On April 22, 1962, Fr. Burke
states that the wedding is almost a superstitious
act so that the baby will be healthy. (English
2 pgs.)

Mc3856. P-1962
The Papal Knights to J. Francis Cardinal
McIntyre
May 14, 1962. Los Angeles, California

A burse of $10,675 for the Archbishop's
Charities is presented at the first dinner for the
Papal Knights. (English 4 pgs.)

Mc3857. P-1962
Bp. Ernest Primeau to J. Francis Cardinal
McIntyre
May 22, 1962. Washington, D.C.

NCWC will have an office in Rome to be of
service to the Bishop. Religious Orders will
have available specialists in Theology, Scripture,
Canon Law, and Liturgy. (English 2 pgs.)

Mc3858. P-1962
Bp. Timothy Manning to Mr. Irving W. Parker
September 19, 1962. Los Angeles, California

Mr. Michael Shadow's application at the University was rejected. Could special consideration be given? (English 1 pg.) On September
25, 1962, Mr. Parker states because the application was so late and the classes are crowded,
the answer is still negative. (English 1 pg.)

Mc3859. P-1962
Antonio Cardinal Piolanti to J. Francis Cardi-
nal McIntyre
October 23, 1962. Rome, Italy

An invitation is extended to participate at the
opening of the Pontifical University *Lateranense*
for the scholastic year 1962–1963 on October
28. The University is named for Pope John
XXIII. (Italian 1 pg.)

Mc3860. P-1962
Rev. John B. Thom to Rev. Michael Pawelek
October 25, 1962. Los Angeles, California

The Archdiocese would be happy to provide
an ecclesiastical assignment if a rescript is issued
in the norm of the Apostolic Constitution. (English 1 pg.)

Mc3861. P-1962
Mr. Carlo G. Paluzzi to J. Francis Cardinal
McIntyre
November 6, 1962. Rome, Italy

An invitation is extended to attend the reception at the *Presidenza Centrale* to honor an outstanding alumni, Giuseppe Rossi. (Italian 1 pg.)

Mc3862. R-1962
Jose Cardinal Rivera to J. Francis Cardinal
McIntyre
January 27, 1962. Guadalajara, Mexico

An announcement of the Golden Jubilee of
ordination celebration in Mexico is sent. (English 1 pg.) On March 7, 1962, the Cardinal
promised prayers on the occasion. (English
1 pg.)

Mc3863. R-1962
J. Francis Cardinal McIntyre to Rev. Harold
Ring, SJ
February 8, 1962. Los Angeles, California

A request to investigate the note of Rev.
Fletchinger concerning the smear campaign
against Orthodox clergy and laity in the city.
(English 1 pg.)

Mc3864. R-1962
Mr. Russell Rock to J. Francis Cardinal
McIntyre
February 19, 1962. Little Rock, Arkansas

A request to be ordained in Los Angeles so
relatives and friends can attend the ordination
and First Mass. (English 4 pgs.) On March 12,
1962, Bishop Guilfoyle states that he can arrange the ordination on April 8, in San Francisco. (English 1 pg.)

Mc3865. R-1962
Bp. Timothy Manning to Msgr. William Reilly
May 11, 1962. Los Angeles, California

The forms for the annual reports from the
parishes and also from the schools are enclosed
with a hope that they will be helpful. (English
1 pg.)

Mc3866. R-1962
J. Francis Cardinal McIntyre to Mr. and Mrs.
John Rauen
June 27, 1962. Los Angeles, California

The generous gift will be used for Don Bosco
Technical Institute and prayers are assured for
the good health and happiness of the donors.
(English 1 pg.)

Mc3867. R-1962
J. Francis Cardinal McIntyre to Hon. Dean
Rusk
August 13, 1962. Los Angeles, California

A request to intercede with the Immigration
Department to allow Dr. Kamel Said Michel
Baldi to remain in the United States and serve
at Queen of Angeles Hospital. (English 1 pg.)

Mc3868. R-1962
Rev. Patrick Roche to Rev. John A. Rawden
November 12, 1962. Los Angeles, California

The pictures of the Papal Audience are excellent and the press releases show the preparatory
work done for each session. (English 1 pg.)

Mc3869. R-1962
Rev. John Rawden to J. Francis Cardinal
McIntyre
November 17, 1962. Vatican City

Rev. Daniel Lazzarato feels that the American
matrimonial cases do not give enough information on which the Tribunal can base a judgment. (English 1 pg.)

Mc3870. R-1962
Rev. Antonio Riolout to J. Francis Cardinal
McIntyre
December 3, 1962. Rome, Italy

An invitation to visit the Pontifical University
to see the proficiency of the studies at the University. (Italian 1 pg.)

Mc3871. R-1962
J. Francis Cardinal McIntyre to Mr. and Mrs.
John Rauen
December 31, 1962. Los Angeles, California

The treasured volumes will be given to St.
John's Seminary Library. (English 1 pg.)

Mc3872. S-1962
Rev. Victor Savaria to Msgr. Benjamin Hawkes
January 8, 1962. Montreal, Canada

Are the Diocesan Offices in Los Angeles in
one building? What number of personnel is at-
tached to each office? A new building is being
planned and the best use of the building is being investigated. (English 1 pg.)

Mc3873. S-1962
Mr. Robert Spriggs to J. Francis Cardinal
McIntyre
February 12, 1962. Mundelein, Illinois

For a debate, some ideas could be shared on
the importance of the role of the Junior Seminary in today's world. (English 1 pg.)

Mc3874. S-1962
Msgr. Kenneth O'Brien to Mrs. Helen
Saufnauer
March 3, 1962. Los Angeles, California

Title Insurance and Trust Company provides
a service to search estates. A Chain of Title
Guarantees list all recorded instruments of a
parcel in Los Angeles and they might have a
survey of the San Juan Bautista area likewise.
(English 1 pg.)

Mc3875. S-1962
J. Francis Cardinal McIntyre to Francis Cardi-
nal Spellman
April 4, 1962. Los Angeles, California

The Legal Department of the NCWC will remove the foundation for the appeal for basic
principles. What lay leadership does the Committee want? (English 2 pgs.)

Mc3876. S-1962
Rev. Albert Nevins to Rev. John Donovan
June 17, 1962. New York City, New York

A rebuttal to the talk given at the 89th Annual National Conference on Social Welfare is
enclosed. The quotes are a distortion as there
was no attack on the conservative position. (English 2 pgs.) On June 22, 1962, Bishop John
Comber, MM states that he is surprised at the
reaction to the lecture. (English 1 pg.)

Mc3877. S-1962
Giuseppe Cardinal Pizzardo to Francis Cardinal Spellman
June 23, 1962. Rome, Italy

The Holy See will never interfere on matters of civil rights and University teaching. Yet everyone knows that the Church has laws pertaining to Ecclesiastic and Religious matters. (English 2 pgs.)

Mc3878. S-1962
Francis Cardinal Spellman to Guiseppe Cardinal Pizzardo
July 2, 1962. New York City, New York

The American Catholic Colleges and Universities are known by everyone as Catholic and are chartered by the States to give degrees. A new charter by the Holy See could jeopardize the other Charter. (English 2 pgs.)

Mc3879. S-1962
Rev. Luis A. Sanchez to J. Francis Cardinal McIntyre
August 7, 1962. Zacatecas, Mexico

A request is made to visit for a few days in Wilmington, California, with my parents. (Spanish 1 pg.) On August 10, 1962, Bishop Timothy Manning states that the Archdiocese will welcome Fr. for a visit. (English 1 pg.)

Mc3880. S-1962
J. Francis Cardinal McIntyre to Msgr. George Scott
August 20, 1962. Los Angeles, California

The proposal made by Mr. Charles K. Chapman show that he does not understand that the Church borrows money but does not loan money. (English 1 pg.)

Mc3881. S-1962
Mr. Cheou-Kang-Sie to J. Francis Cardinal McIntyre
September 21, 1962. Rome, Italy

An invitation to a reception on Chinese National Day at the Grand Hotel in Rome on October 10 at 6:00 p.m. (English 1 pg.) On September 27, 1962, the Cardinal states that there is some doubt about his arrival time. (English 1 pg.)

Mc3882. S-1962
Arbp. Antonio Samore to J. Francis Cardinal McIntyre
December 29, 1962. Rome, Italy

The generous donation given to Villa Nazareth in memory of Cardinal Tardini is appreciated. (English 1 pg.)

Mc3883. S-1962
Dr. James B. Smith, MD to J. Francis Cardinal McIntyre
December 30, 1962. Fullerton, California

The Cardinal Mindszenty Foundation has authorized a Fullerton Affiliate. We will distribute literature to the new Study Groups being formed. (English 1 pg.) On January 4, 1962, the Cardinal states that he hopes the Holy Spirit will bless the undertaking. (English 1 pg.)

Mc3884. T-1962
Rev. Armando Trindade to Msgr. Benjamin Hawkes
January 31, 1962. Karachi, Pakistan

A request is made to be able to reside in a parish near Loyola University in order to take advantage of an offered scholarship. (English 1 pg.) On February 5, 1962, Msgr. states that a parish will be made available but please indicate arrival plans. (English 1 pg.)

Mc3885. T-1962
Bp. John E. Taylor to Bp. Timothy Manning
April 25, 1963. Stockholm, Sweden

An appeal for some financial help to pay the current debts so that the long time debts can be taken into operating expenses. (English 1 pg.) On April 30, 1962, the Bishop sends a personal donation to pay the immediate debts. (English 1 pg.)

Mc3886. T-1962
Bp. Bernard T. Topel to J. Francis Cardinal McIntyre
June 29, 1962. Spokane, Washington

The retreat given by Rev. Michael Sheahan to the priests of the Diocese did more good for their souls than other retreats. (English 1 pg.) On July 9, 1962, the Cardinal states that the comments implement the esteem in which Fr. is held in Los Angeles. (English 1 pg.)

Mc3887. T-1962
Msgr. Paul Tanner to J. Francis Cardinal McIntyre
August 3, 1962. Washington, D.C.

NCWC will supply altar breads and wine for Masses in Rome. Most of the needs of the Bishops will have to be brought to Rome. (English 1 pg.)

Mc3888. T-1962
Msgr. Paul Tanner to J. Francis Cardinal McIntyre
September 5, 1962. Washington, D.C.

The bells of all Churches should ring for ten minutes at the beginning of the Council. The annual report of the NCWC should be brought to Rome. The addresses of all Bishops in Rome will be ready as well as the addresses of all theologians. (English 1 pg.)

Mc3889. T-1962
Msgr. Paul Tanner to J. Francis Cardinal
McIntyre
October 3, 1962. Washington, D.C.

Pope John XXIII praises the ideals which
have characteristically animated the American
hierarchy. All priests may celebrate Mass from
Midnight October 10 to October 11 for the
opening of the Council. (English 1 pg.)

Mc3890. U-1962
Rev. John Urban to J. Francis Cardinal
McIntyre
May 7, 1962. Beverly Hills, California

False advertising of Papal Blessings is being
used in Tijuana, Mexico. This commercializes a
religious article and adds confusion to the general public. (English 2 pgs.)

Mc3891. V-1962
J. Francis Cardinal McIntyre to Arbp. Edigio
Vagnozzi
January 31, 1962. Los Angeles, California

Interest in the Ecumenical Council is alive in
Los Angeles. The Theological Conference, articles in The Tidings, and special prayers are being offered for the success of the Council.
(English 2 pgs.)

Mc3892. V-1962
Arbp. Diego Venini to J. Francis Cardinal
McIntyre
May 29, 1962. Vatican City

The source of the Papal Blessings advertised
in Los Angeles has not been discovered. In case
it should be attempted again, please try to find
the connection in Rome. (English 1 pg.)

Mc3893. V-1962
Arbp. Edigio Vagnozzi to Msgr. Paul Tanner
June 8, 1962. Washington, D.C.

No decision has been made for priests in
Rome to participate in the opening session of
the Ecumenical Council. (English 1 pg.)

Mc3894. V-1962
Rev. William S. Vita to J. Francis Cardinal
McIntyre
August 6, 1962. Los Angeles, California

NCWC News Bureau cannot issue press
cards. A proper application to the Vatican Press
Bureau is being sent with pictures and all necessary identification. The Villa Nazareth will be
my residence. (English 2 pgs.)

Mc3895. V-1962
Arbp. Egidio Vagnozzi to J. Francis Cardinal
McIntyre
August 7, 1962. Washington, D.C.

The Schemeta of the first session of the
Council will be delivered with a receipt for the
Holy See. All dress regulations are enclosed.
(English 2 pgs.) On August 13, 1962, the
Cardinal acknowledges the delivery of the
Schemeta. (English 1 pg.)

Mc3896. W-1962
Mr. Thomas White to J. Francis Cardinal
McIntyre
January 3, 1962. Bell, California

The City of Bell needs a Church and there is
property available for a Church, Rectory and
school. (English 1 pg.) On January 12, 1962,
Msgr. Galvin states that other parish would suf-
fer if another parish were started. (English
1 pg.)

Mc3897. W-1962
Rev. Michael Walsh to Msgr. Benjamin
Hawkes
January 4, 1962. Newcastle, England

A request is made to visit in Los Angeles and
to have faculties while visiting. (English 1 pg.)
On April 6, 1962, Bishop Bell states that the
Archdiocese will be happy to extend faculties
while visiting in Los Angeles for two months.
(English 1 pg.)

Mc3898. W-1962
Rev. Joseph Ward to J. Francis Cardinal
McIntyre
January 16, 1962. Prince Albert, Canada

Is there a printed form to instruct the laity
when to stand, sit, or kneel at Low Mass, High
Mass, Pontifical Mass and Requiem Mass? (English 1 pg.)

Mc3899. W-1962
Rev. Francis J. Weber to J. Francis Cardinal
McIntyre
April 7, 1962. Washington, D.C.

The attention and suggestions given to the article for The Catholic Youth Encyclopedia are
deeply appreciated. A copy of the article is enclosed. (English 6 pgs.)

Mc3900. W-1962
J. Francis Cardinal McIntyre to Arbp. Martin
O'Connor
May 28, 1962. Los Angeles, California

A letter of introduction for Fr. Francis J. Weber, the Archivist of the Los Angeles Archdiocese is enclosed. (English 1 pg.)

Mc3901. W-1962
Rev. John Ward to J. Francis Cardinal McIntyre
June 1, 1962. Los Angeles, California

Comments on the *Schema* on Matrimony with recommendations to formulate a course stressing the spiritual preparations for marriage are enclosed. (English 4 pgs.)

Mc3902. W-1962
Bp. Timothy Manning to Armstrong Circle Theater
September 27, 1962. Los Angeles, California

The documentary on Bishop James E. Walsh made every American proud of this hero of faith and freedom. (English 1 pg.)

Mc3903. W-1962
Sr. Rose Virginia Waring to J. Francis Cardinal McIntyre
November 21, 1962. Rome, Italy

An invitation is extended to a reception to be given on November 28 for all of the Bishops of the Council by the Sisters of the Good Shepherd. (English 1 pg.)

Mc3904. Y-1962
Mr. Richard Young to J. Francis Cardinal McIntyre
February 20, 1962. Rome, Italy

Is there a hospital that could care for a wheel-chair patient to give a husband a break from constant care? (English 1 pg.) On Septem-ber 18, 1962, Fr. Rawden states that suggestions were made but the present arrangement seems to be best. (English 1 pg.)

Mc3905. Z-1962
Mrs. Robert J. Zick to J. Francis Cardinal McIntyre
February 20, 1962. El Monte, California

Sacred Heart Lodge Specialized Psychiatric Hospital would like a picture of the Cardinal for the main hall. (English 1 pg.)

Mc3906. Z-1962
Hon. J. Howard Ziemann to J. Francis Cardinal McIntyre
March 21, 1962. Los Angeles, California

A Mass will be celebrated at noon on May 27 as a part of the *El Dia de los Personas Mayores* celebration. (English 1 pg.) On March 26, 1962, the Cardinal states that commitments make it impossible for him to attend. (English 1 pg.)

Mc3907. Z-1962
J. Francis Cardinal McIntyre to Mr. B. C. Ziegler
August 14, 1962. Los Angeles, California

Two new cemeteries have been purchased recently. What type of loans would be available on these properties. (English 1 pg.)

Listing for Year
1963

Mc3908. A-1963
J. Francis Cardinal McIntyre to Senor Jose
Alemany
January 10, 1963. Los Angeles, California

The body of Bishop Francis Mora is in the
Mausoleum of Calvary Cemetery with the bod-
ies of Bishop Thomas Conaty, Archbishop John
Cantwell and where mine will be. (English
1 pg.)

Mc3909. A-1963
Rev. Alexander Humphrey to J. Francis Cardi-
nal McIntyre
January 29, 1963. Los Angeles, California

The American Catholic Sociological Society
wishes to hold its annual meeting at Loyola
University from August 23–25 and invites the
Cardinal to give the invocation on August 25.
(English 1 pg.)

Mc3910. A-1963
J. Francis Cardinal McIntyre to Rev. Alexander
Humphrey
February 9, 1963. Los Angeles, California

The American Catholic Sociological Society is
most welcome to come to the Archdiocese. Submit the names of the proposed speakers for consideration. (English 1 pg.)

Mc3911. A-1963
Bp. Leo Arkfeld, SVD to J. Francis Cardinal
McIntyre
March 25, 1963. Wewak, New Guinea

A request to assist with Confirmations during
January, February, and March 1964. (English 2
pgs.) On May 9, 1963, the Cardinal states that
it is not certain that the Archdiocese will need
additional help. (English 1 pg.)

Mc3912. A-1963
Msgr. Benjamin Hawkes to Bp. Josip Arnerik
May 3, 1963. Los Angeles, California

On receipt of the documents required by
Canon 117 #2, Rev. Felix Diomartich will be
incardinated into the Archdiocese of Los Angeles. (English 1 pg.)

Mc3913. A-1963
Miss Carole Alberts to J. Francis Cardinal
McIntyre
June 4, 1963. Los Angeles, California

Enter the name of Pope John XXIII for Beatification and Canonization while you are in
Rome for elections. (English 1 pg.)

Mc3914. A-1963
Rev. Paul Ayoub to J. Francis Cardinal
McIntyre
August 22, 1963. Buffalo, New York

A pamphlet, A Latin Patriarchate of Jerusalem, is a subject that might be brought to the
Vatican Council. Latin priests in the Holy Land
are a necessity. (English 1 pg.)

Mc3915. A-1963
Mrs. Melinda Akard to J. Francis Cardinal
McIntyre
August 27, 1963. Los Angeles, California

Use your influence to bring an end to the
priests marching in the Civil Rights demonstrations. We can do more good quietly than by all
of the demonstrations. (English 1 pg.)

Mc3916. A-1963
Rev. Samuel R. Allison to Msgr. Benjamin
Hawkes
September 24, 1963. Beverly Hills, California

Could a priest be assigned to be on a panel,
Our Judeo-Christian Heritage What We Have
in Common on October 9 at 12:15? (English
1 pg.)

Mc3917. A-1963
Msgr. John C. Abbing to J. Francis Cardinal McIntyre
October 7, 1963. Rome, Italy

An invitation is extended to the dedication of the Ohio Building of Boys' Town of Rome. 250 citizens of Ohio will come to Rome for the dedication. (English 1 pg.)

Mc3918. A-1963
Dear Abby to Rev. John B. Thom
N.D. Los Angeles, California

Can a Baptism be invalidated and another Baptism be performed if the father of the child did not give his consent? (English 1 pg.) On October 25, 1963, Fr. states that a Baptism that was validly administered cannot be invalidated. (English 1 pg.)

Mc3919. B-1963
J. Francis Cardinal McIntyre to Msgr. James T. Booth
January 4, 1963. Los Angeles, California

Could the Pastor or Social Worker call on a friend from New York and offer some assistance or advice. (English 1 pg.) On January 7, 1963, Msgr. states that the Pastor of St. Kieran's is in contact. (English 1 pg.)

Mc3920. B-1963
J. Francis Cardinal McIntyre to Mr. Curtis Bourland
January 8, 1963. Los Angeles, California

The generous gift to Don Bosco Technical Institute is most encouraging to the Administration and to the Chancery. (English 1 pg.)

Mc3921. B-1963
Mr. Frank Doherty to J. Francis Cardinal McIntyre
January 11, 1963. Los Angeles, California

A request for an interview with Mr. Balfour to explain the necessity for an overhead ramp for the children crossing the off ramp from La Tijera Boulevard. There is a signal and the children can be taught to use it. (English 3 pgs.)

Mc3922. B-1963
Mr. Paul Butler to J. Francis Cardinal McIntyre
January 19, 1963. Little Silver, New Jersey

A request for a copy of a sermon or talk that could be included in a book, *Great Catholic Sermons*. (English 2 pgs.) On February 1, 1963, the Cardinal sends a sermon entitled, What is Law. (English 1 pg.)

Mc3923. B-1963
Ms. Margaret Bradley to J. Francis Cardinal McIntyre
February 5, 1963. New York City, New York

A request to verify employment in the Chancery Office of New York before the social security and withholding records were kept. (English 1 pg.) On February 21, 1963, the Cardinal states that he remembers the years of service in the Office of the Propagation of the Faith. (English 1 pg.)

Mc3924. B-1963
Mr. Robert Burns to J. Francis Cardinal McIntyre
February 19, 1963. Pasadena, California

The text *God's Plan for Us* gives the CCD teacher material that is vital and approaches the real needs of the student. (English 1 pg.) On February 20, 1963, the Cardinal states that it is good to have a good text. (English 1 pg.)

Mc3925. B-1963
Rev. Harley A. Baker to Rev. John A. Rawden
March 26, 1963. Juneau, Alaska

The Bishop is happy to have a copy of the book, *The Theology of Christian Perfection* and the members of the staff are grateful for the California experience for the Bishop. (English 1 pg.)

Mc3926. B-1963
Ms. Agnes Biddle to Bp. Timothy Manning
March 28, 1963. Garden Grove, California

Your beautiful example as a member of the Legion of Mary gives strength and courage to many who grow discouraged. (English 1 pg.)

Mc3927. B-1963
Mrs. H. F. Beavers to J. Francis Cardinal McIntyre
April 15, 1963. Los Angeles, California

The Pope seems to be misinformed concerning the United Nations if he thinks this a great peace keeping force. Your Easter message was more to the point. (English 1 pg.)

Mc3928. B-1963
Mr. Frank Brophy to Mr. Frank Hanighen
April 19, 1963. Phoenix, Arizona

Inroads are being made against the Catholic Church by the liberals who seem to want to destroy the Church as it is now. (English 1 pg.)

Mc3929. B-1963
Mrs. Aida Boccanera to Rev. John B. Thom
April 23, 1963. Miami, Florida

Is the job market very difficult for one who
can speak, write and take dictation in English
and Spanish? (English 1 pg.) On April 29, 1963,
Fr. states that a bi-lingual secretarial position is
available now. (English 1 pg.)

Mc3930. B-1963
Rev. William G. Butler to Bp. Timothy
    Manning
N.D. San Jose, California

A request is made for me to preside at the
first graduation of Marymount Junior School in
Santa Barbara on June 2, 1963. (English 1 pg.)
On April 30, 1963, the Bishop states that the
Cardinal is most happy to grant the permission.
(English 1 pg.)

Mc3931. B-1963
Ms. Mary Ellen Blinn to Bp. Timothy
    Manning
May 22, 1963. Santa Barbara, California

The gratitude of the family must be expressed
for the privilege of having Mass in our home so
that Mother could assist at Mass for the first
time in twenty-five years. (English 1 pg.)

Mc3932. B-1963
Mr. Anthony Berardi to Bp. Timothy Manning
May 24, 1963. Inglewood, California

The details of donating one's body to a medical school after death are needed. (English 1
pg.) On May 27, 1963, the Bishop states that
precautions must be taken to assure reverence
to the body. Ecclesial burial can be given. (English 1 pg.)

Mc3933. B-1963
Bp. Vladimiro Boric to Bp. Timothy Manning
May 26, 1963. Punta Arenas, Chile

From the poorest section of Chile, a request
is made for donations or Mass stipends. (English 1 pg.) On June 27, 1963, the Bishop sends
a donation and asks for one Mass to be celebrated. (English 1 pg.)

Mc3934. B-1963
Mrs. H. F. Beavers to Rev. John Thom
May 29, 1963. Los Angeles, California

The Pope and Bishops stressing the goodness
of the United Nations are being led by false
promises. Only God can bring peace in His own
good time. (English 1 pg.)

Mc3935. B-1963
Mr. Walter Brooks to J. Francis Cardinal
    McIntyre
June 14, 1963. Santa Ana, California

The courage that Pope John XXIII gave to
the world is being used in a small way in the
college classes being taught in Santa Ana. Elect
someone who will carry on his work. (English
1 pg.)

Mc3936. B-1963
Mr. Martin Ostrow to Msgr. Benjamin
    Hawkes
June 18, 1963. Los Angeles, California

An invitation is extended to honor Sy Bartlett
for his movie, A Gathering of Eagles, a picture
dedicated to the devotion of the men of the Air
Force. (English 1 pg.) On June 21, 1963, Msgr.
send regrets as he will be on retreat. (English
1 pg.)

Mc3937. B-1963
Mr. Walter Boland to Bp. Timothy Manning
July 12, 1963. Inglewood, California

It is necessary to have a discussion of a situation in which spirits are causing great unhappi-
ness. (English 1 pg.) On July 18, 1963, the
Bishop asks that a physical examination take
place before the discussion. (English 1 pg.)

Mc3938. B-1963
Mr. Danotolo Belluii to J. Francis Cardinal
    McIntyre
July 13, 1963. Milan, Italy

The Gallery of Sacred Contemporary Art has
available a statue of Pope John XXIII and a volume of the Ecumenical Council documents.
(Italian 1 pg.)

Mc3939. B-1963
Mr. Ralph Boryszewski to J. Francis Cardinal
    McIntyre
July 15, 1963. Rochester, New York

A recent court decision could make the separation of powers of Congress a rule of the past
if people are not aware of what is happening.
(English 2 pgs.)

Mc3940. B-1963
Mr. Irving G. Breyer to J. Francis Cardinal
    McIntyre
July 19, 1963. San Francisco, California

A copy of the talk given to the San Francisco
Board of Education is enclosed and a test case
to abolish a song sung in many schools because
it refers to God. (English 8 pgs.)

Mc3941. B-1963
Mr. Andrew Burke to Arbp. Joseph T. McGucken
July 24, 1963. San Francisco, California

When the United States government settles the Chamizal matter, it is time to press Mexico to make payments on the Pious Fund. The Senators of the Pacific Coast ought to make the statements. (English 2 pgs.)

Mc3942. B-1963
Mr. Richard Berlin to J. Francis Cardinal McIntyre
July 24, 1963. New York City, New York

A recording of the last public appearance of Pope John at the Beatification of Mother Seton is enclosed. (English 1 pg.) On July 27, 1963, the Cardinal expresses his appreciation for the gift. (English 1 pg.)

Mc3943. B-1963
J. Francis Cardinal McIntyre to Bp. Charles Buddy
July 27, 1963. Los Angeles, California

The splendid presentation of doctrine in your new book makes it one of exceptional value. (English 1 pg.)

Mc3944. B-1963
Mr. William E. Barrett to J. Francis Cardinal McIntyre
August 6, 1963. Washington, D.C.

For the new biography of Pope Paul VI any clippings, manuscripts, or anecdotes shared with the Cardinal is requested. All materials will be returned. (English 1 pg.) On August 12, 1963, the Cardinal states that he had nothing that would be of general interest. (English 1 pg.)

Mc3945. B-1963
Bp. Charles Buddy to J. Francis Cardinal McIntyre
August 7, 1963. San Diego, California

An invitation is extended to preside at the Liturgical Reception for Bishop Furey on September 12, 1963. (English 1 pg.) On August 10, 1963, the Cardinal accepts the invitation to preside at the reception but I must return to Los Angeles later in the day. (English 1 pg.)

Mc3946. B-1963
Mrs. Catherine Braun to J. Francis Cardinal McIntyre
August 11, 1963. Los Angeles, California

Please give the enclosed money to any Bishop at the Council who has to depend on charity. (English 1 pg.) On August 13, 1963, the Cardinal expresses his gratitude for the thoughtfulness of the donation and will carry out the assignment. (English 1 pg.)

Mc3947. B-1963
Mr. J. J. Brandlin to J. Francis Cardinal McIntyre
August 13, 1963. Los Angeles, California

The integration problems can be settled by a calm, realistic, patient policy such as the article in the *Times* indicates. (English 2 pgs.) On August 16, 1963, the Cardinal expresses his appreciation for the message. (English 1 pg.)

Mc3948. B-1963
Rev. John B. Thom to Msgr. Francis Brown
August 21, 1963. Los Angeles, California

Los Angeles Archdiocese is integrated in parishes, schools, and institutions with an amiable relationship with the growing population. (English 1 pg.)

Mc3949. B-1963
J. Francis Cardinal McIntyre to Mrs. Margaret Browns
August 26, 1963. Los Angeles, California

The donation to the Youth Education Fund and to Don Bosco Technical Institute are deeply appreciated and an encouragement to us. (English 1 pg.)

Mc3950. B-1963
Bp. Charles Buddy to J. Francis Cardinal McIntyre
August 30, 1963. San Diego, California

An invitation to give the principle address at the luncheon following the Liturgical Reception on September 12. (English 1 pg.) On August 31, 1963, the Cardinal states that the dignity of the address belongs to the Bishop. Congratulations to the Bishop will come at the end. (English 1 pg.)

Mc3951. B-1963
Mr. Emmet E. Blaes to Msgr. Benjamin Hawkes
September 20, 1963. Wichita, Kansas

The estate of Marie Trimper cannot be settled until the entire estate can be evaluated. Could the legal counsel investigate the remaining property for a true evaluation. (English 3 pgs.) On September 25, 1963, Msgr. states that a copy of the letter went to the Realtor and the letter to the legal counsel. (English 1 pg.)

Mc3952. B-1963
Mr. Forest Barber to Rev. John Sheridan
November 4, 1963. Long Beach, California

Could a Marian Knight of the Teutonic Order march with the Knights of St. Gregory and the Knights of Malta. (English 1 pg.) On December 7, 1963, the Cardinal states when an occasion arises for another guard of honor, your position will be remembered. (English 1 pg.)

Mc3953. B-1963
Mr. Robert Barker to J. Francis Cardinal
McIntyre
November 12, 1963. New York City, New
York

Mr. Shirley Burden's contribution to the
Archbishop's Fund for Education is 190 shares
of Allied Chemical Corporation stock with the
credit given to Good Shepherd Parish. (English
1 pg.) On November 14, 1963, Msgr. sends a
message of gratitude for the assistance given to
the schools. (English 1 pg.)

Mc3954. B-1963
Mr. Anthony Borsa to J. Francis Cardinal
McIntyre
December 12, 1962. Gyor, Kassuth

A request to give some assistance to a son liv-
ing in Los Angeles and attending University of
Southern California. On January 10, 1963, Rev.
Felix Doherty states that Tony is an active
member of the Newman Club of the University.
(English 1 pg.)

Mc3955. C-1963
Rev. Francis J. Case to Bp. Alden J. Bell
January 5, 1963. Rochester, New York

Are newly ordained priests obliged to pledge
to remain away from liquor? When was the
pledge inaugurated? (English 1 pg.) On January
8, 1963, Fr. states that young priests are encouraged at Tonsure to abstain from liquor for
five years after ordination. The pledge is not
imposed. (English 1 pg.)

Mc3956. C-1963
Mr. Louis R. Cross to Rev. John Rawden
February 8, 1963. Los Angeles, California

A request is made to handle the Diocesan Accounts as the Santa Clara Cemetery accounts
are handled. (English 1 pg.) On February 11,
1963, Fr. states that our few investments are
handled very satisfactorily. (English 1 pg.)

Mc3957. C-1963
Mr. Norman Chandler to J. Francis Cardinal
McIntyre
February 14, 1963. Los Angeles, California

The Cavalier Magazine is not being sent by
this office and an apology is being offered for
such literature to enter your home. (English 1
pg.) On February 10, 1963, the Cardinal states
that Msgr. Hawkes destroyed the magazine and
the apology is accepted and understood. (English 1 pg.)

Mc3958. C-1963
Mr. Edward Carroll to J. Francis Cardinal
McIntyre
February 18, 1963. Chicago, Illinois

A professional search team is available to
present qualified candidates for almost any position. (English 1 pg.) On February 21, 1963,
the Cardinal states that he is not in need at the
present time but the information will be kept
on file. (English 1 pg.)

Mc3959. C-1963
Arbp. John P. Cody to J. Francis Cardinal
McIntyre
March 1, 1963. New Orleans, Louisiana

The first edition of the Clarion Herald is being sent with the prayer that this will be one
means to have better informed Catholics. (English 1 pg.) On March 12, 1963, the Cardinal
states that it is an auspicious beginning and
sends prayers for success. (English 1 pg.)

Mc3960. C-1963
Mr. Reginald E. Carles to J. Francis Cardinal
McIntyre
March 11, 1963. Hollywood, California

A request for the name of the Abbot of the
Trappist Monastery in Utah so arrangements
can be made for a retreat. (English 1 pg.)

Mc3961. C-1963
Mrs. William Walsh to J. Francis Cardinal
McIntyre
March 14, 1963. Camarillo, California

The presence of Mr. John Cogley at the Catholic Library Association meeting and at Immaculate Heart College should be questioned.
(English 1 pg.)

Mc3962. C-1963
Mr. Walker Cisler to J. Francis Cardinal
McIntyre
March 19, 1963. Detroit, Michigan

The gift of The Theology of Christian Perfection is appreciated and especially the trouble
that was taken to obtain it. (English 1 pg.)

Mc3963. C-1963
Mr. John Cogley to J. Francis Cardinal
McIntyre
March 25, 1963. Santa Barbara, California

A copy of Natural Law and Modern Society
is being sent for examination and discussion.
(English 1 pg.)

Mc3964. C-1963
Mrs. Frank Clark to Alfredo Cardinal
Ottaviani
April 10, 1963. Altadena, California

If the investigation concerning Montreal can
become active, a decision can be made and the
law suit settled. (English 5 pgs.) On April 22,
1963, Fr. Thom states that the Cardinal cannot
act on the case and neither can the Archdiocese.
(English 1 pg.)

Mc3965. C-1963
Mr. Andre Regla to Msgr. Benjamin Hawkes
N.D. Los Angeles, California

Mrs. Morning Carty is donating this fine lace
table cloth to the Archdiocese. (English 1 pg.)
On April 11, 1963, the Cardinal states that the
table cloth will be treasured and used on the
Cardinal's table for special occasions. (English
1 pg.)

Mc3966. C-1963
Arbp. Romolo Carboni to J. Francis Cardinal
McIntyre
April 23, 1963. Lima, Peru

An update on the conditions and needs of the
priests in Peru. The information is accurate
coming from the Bishops and not guess work.
(English 1 pg.)

Mc3967. C-1963
Mr. John Congdon to J. Francis Cardinal
McIntyre
N.D. Stanford, California

Permission is requested to be Best Man in a
wedding that will take place in an Episcopal
Church. (English 1 pg.) On April 24, 1963,
Msgr. Hawkes grants the permission and sends
a special blessing to the Bride and Groom. (English 1 pg.)

Mc3968. C-1963
Sister Benedict, SCU to J. Francis Cardinal
McIntyre
April 28, 1963. St. Louis, Missouri

Those who object to Mr. John Cogley speaking at the Catholic Library Association ought to
read the latest encyclical. (English 1 pg.)

Mc3969. C-1963
J. Francis Cardinal McIntyre to Arbp. Romolo
Carboni
May 3, 1963. Los Angeles, California

The statistics concerning Peru are most encouraging. Would a priest or Community of
Sisters apply directly to the Bishop of the area?
(English 1 pg.) On May 10, 1963, the Archbishop states that the lines of authority are the
same as in the United States. The Sisters of
Mary Mother of God have a house and a school
in Peru. (English 1 pg.)

Mc3970. C-1963
J. Francis Cardinal McIntyre to Mr. C. E. Cord
May 15, 1963. Los Angeles, California

A new and larger school is needed on Detroit
Street. Would you consider an exchange of land
for the lots on Detroit so that a larger school
would be possible? (English 1 pg.)

Mc3971. C-1963
Mr. R. Corbett to J. Francis Cardinal McIntyre
May 16, 1963. Sepulveda, California

A Pastor would have more time for his
priestly duties if he could hire an accountant either on a full-time or part-time basis. (English 1
pg.) On June 3, 1963, the Cardinal states that
many Pastors have taken this step. (English
1 pg.)

Mc3972. C-1963
Mr. Richard Cashin to J. Francis Cardinal
McIntyre
May 22, 1963. Detroit, Michigan

Can a Catholic actively conduct fund raising
campaigns for a non-Catholic cause? (English 1
pg.) On May 27, 1963, the Cardinal suggests
asking the local Bishop since there may be some
unusual circumstances. (English 1 pg.)

Mc3973. C-1963
Mrs. John M. Cunningham to J. Francis Car-
dinal McIntyre
May 28, 1963. Santa Barbara, California

Can the UNICEF collection be taken
throughout the school where the principals are
willing to collect it? (English 1 pg.) On June 4,
1963, the Cardinal states that the schools are
being over loaded with demands so all solicitations are restricted. (English 1 pg.)

Mc3974. C-1963
Rev. Philip Conneally, SJ to Bp. Timothy
Manning
June 20, 1963. Los Angeles, California

A copy of the talk given on the morality of
cooperation with Communists Fronts is enclosed. It is still in rough draft and needs re-
working. (English 13 pgs.)

Mc3975. C-1963
Amleto Cardinal Cicognani to J. Francis Cardi-
nal McIntyre
June 27, 1963. Vatican City

Pope Paul VI conveys his gratitude for the donation to defray the expenses of Vatican Council II and extends his Apostolic Blessing to the
Archdiocese. (English 1 pg.)

Mc3976. C-1963
Amleto Cardinal Cicognani to J. Francis Cardinal McIntyre
June 27, 1963. Vatican City

The formal announcement is made that the Second Session of the Vatican Council will begin September 29, the feast of St. Michael the Archangel. (Latin 1 pg.)

Mc3977. C-1963
Mr. William Consedine to Arbp. Joseph T. McGucken
July 22, 1963. Washington, D.C.

This is the time to call on friendly influences in Congress to press for the settlement of the Pious Fund. Keep the settlement of the Chamizal matter and the Pious Fund together. (English 2 pgs.) On July 24, 1963, the Archbishop states that he is happy that someone is pressing the situation. (English 1 pg.)

Mc3978. C-1963
Msgr. Francis Connell, CSSR to J. Francis Cardinal McIntyre
July 26, 1963. Washington, D.C.

The theological and juridical views of the Church-State Relations are being sent for your review and discussion later. It is prepared at the request of the Apostolic Delegate. (English 3 pgs.)

Mc3979. C-1963
Mr. Gonzaleo Cano to J. Francis Cardinal McIntyre
July 31, 1963. Los Angeles, California

There are race relation problems in Los Angeles and the Catholic Church ought to exert leadership in setting forth moral principles. (English 2 pgs.) On August 1, 1963, the Cardinal suggests an article that could offer some solutions to the problem. (English 1 pg.)

Mc3980. C-1963
J. Francis Cardinal McIntyre to Amleto Cardinal Cicognani
August 20, 1963. Los Angeles, California

A well qualified priest should be in charge of the press releases of the Council so that newsmen could print facts rather than unofficial comments. (English 2 pgs.)

Mc3981. C-1963
Mr. William Brangham to J. Francis Cardinal McIntyre
August 30, 1963. Seal Beach, California

An invitation is extended to the luncheon honoring Mr. Ross Cortese at the Beverly Hilton on September 26. (English 1 pg.) On September 5, 1963, the Cardinal states that he will be departing for Rome on that date. (English 1 pg.)

Mc3982. C-1963
Mr. Ross Cortese to J. Francis Cardinal McIntyre
September 5, 1963. Seal Beach, California

A donation to the Archdiocese is enclosed and a desire for a possible church site in the future. (English 1 pg.) On September 6, 1963, Msgr. Benjamin Hawkes states that the donation will be used for the Youth Education Fund. (English 1 pg.)

Mc3983. C-1963
Mr. Jack Lawson to J. Francis Cardinal McIntyre
September 6, 1963. Los Angeles, California

Mr. Gene Cowles will be the Executive Editor of the *Valley Times Today*. A letter of congratulations would be helpful. (English 1 pg.) On September 10, 1963, the Cardinal recalls former kindnesses and looks forward to continued relations. (English 1 pg.)

Mc3984. C-1963
Amleto Cardinal Cicognani to J. Francis Cardinal McIntyre
September 18, 1963. Vatican City

The appointment of Archbishop Martin O'Connor to be responsible for all press releases should be good for the future relationships with the Press. (English 1 pg.)

Mc3985. C-1963
Hon. Thomas Commins to J. Francis Cardinal McIntyre
September 24, 1963. Rome, Italy

An invitation is extended to attend the reception for all of the Irish Bishops attending the Second Session of the Council on September 29 from 5:00 to 7:30 p.m. (English 1 pg.)

Mc3986. C-1963
Ms. Miriam Clark to J. Francis Cardinal McIntyre
September 25, 1963. Ontario, California

A request is made for an audience with the Pope while visiting in Rome. (English 1 pg.) On September 26, 1963, Msgr. states that it is the policy to apply through one's Bishop. (English 1 pg.)

Mc3987. C-1963
Mr. Stuart Cuthbertson to The Chancery Office
October 10, 1963. Glendale, California

Could readings be suggested to understand the teaching of the Church on *a priori* judgements. Encyclicals, pronouncements or authoritative statements could be used. (English 2 pgs.) On October 15, 1963, Fr. Thom suggests a visit to the Chancery Office for a discussion. (English 1 pg.)

Mc3988. C-1963
Mr. Earle Holsapple to J. Francis Cardinal
McIntyre
November 7, 1963. New York City, New York

The Budenz Fund of the Archbishop Cushing
Charity Fund will be used entirely for Louis Budenz. (English 1 pg.) On December 10, 1963,
the Cardinal requests that a donation be sent to
the Fund. (English 1 pg.)

Mc3989. C-1963
Arbp. Thomas Cooray to J. Francis Cardinal
McIntyre
November 18, 1963. Rome, Italy

A request is made for Rev. Mervyn Fernando
to work in the Diocesan Marriage Tribunal during the summer months so he can gain some experience. (English 2 pgs.)

Mc3990. C-1963
Mr. Philip J. Callan to J. Francis Cardinal
McIntyre
December 1, 1963. Rochester, New York

A donation that can be used for any Archdiocesan project is enclosed. (English 1 pg.) On
December 9, 1963, Msgr. Benjamin Hawkes
states that the money will be used for the Youth
Education Fund. (English 1 pg.)

Mc3991. C-1963
Rev. William Atwill to J. Francis Cardinal
McIntyre
N.D. Los Angeles, California

Mr. James M. Chavez has worked each year
on the Guadalupe Procession. A letter of appreciation from the Cardinal would be most pleasing. (English 1 pg.)

Mc3992. D-1963
Mrs. E. A. Dondero to J. Francis Cardinal
McIntyre
N.D. Long Beach, California

Before another Education Drive begins, a reminder is sent that the Lakewood area is ready
for a high school. (English 1 pg.) On January 8,
1963, the Cardinal states that a high school in
that area is high on the priority list. (English
1 pg.)

Mc3993. D-1963
Mrs. Frank DenBeste to *The Tidings*
January 14, 1963. Alhambra, California

The name of a Catholic attorney is needed so
a Will can be written to donate all of the property to a Catholic institution. (English 1 pg.)
On January 18, 1963, the name of Miss Mary
Waters is sent since she represents the Archdiocese. (English 1 pg.)

Mc3994. D-1963
Mr. Lawrence C. deLongue to Rev. John A.
Rawden
N.D. Claremont, California

Are the requirements to be a Knight of Malta
written? This is a goal that is important to me.
(English 1 pg.) On January 16, 1963, Fr.
Strange states that Mr. deLongue is a student at
Claremont College. (English 1 pg.)

Mc3995. D-1963
Bp. Angelo Dell'Acqua to J. Francis Cardinal
McIntyre
January 16, 1963. Vatican City

A formal invitation from the Pope for the
opening of the second session of the Vatican
Council II is sent to all participants. (Italian
1 pg.)

Mc3996. D-1963
Msgr. William McDonald to J. Francis Cardi-
nal McIntyre
January 24, 1963. Washington, D.C.

Cardinal Konig agrees that Dr. Heinrich
Drimmel should be honored by a Doctor of
Law Degree by the Catholic University. The entire Board must agree to the granting of the degree. (English 6 pgs.)

Mc3997. D-1963
J. Francis Cardinal McIntyre to Msgr. Patrick
Dignan
February 1, 1963. Los Angeles, California

The press release of the use of the vernacular
in the Liturgy seems premature. A commentary
on the *Ordo* will be published. (English 2 pgs.)

Mc3998. D-1963
Mr. D. E. Davis to Bp. Timothy Manning
February 10, 1963. Riverside, California

Could an interview be arranged to discuss
lending to churches which is the topic of my
thesis. (English 1 pg.) On February 13, 1963,
the Bishop states that most of the borrowing is
from your employer. There is nothing else that
can be told. (English 1 pg.)

Mc3999. D-1963
Bp. Raymond Lane, MM to J. Francis Cardi-
nal McIntyre
March 13, 1963. Los Angeles, California

A letter of introduction for Mrs. Ellis Dillon
who is giving a series of lectures on Ireland.
(English 1 pg.) On March 21, 1963, Mrs. Dillon requests the names of schools and organizations that might want to hear the lecture.
(English 1 pg.)

Mc4000. D-1963
Mr. Dennis Karzog to J. Francis Cardinal
 McIntyre
May 1963. Santa Barbara, California

A copy of *The Reporter* of the Direct Relief
Organization is enclosed. It outlines the needs
of the people in various areas of the world. (English 5 pgs.)

Mc4001. D-1963
Mr. Dennis Karzog to J. Francis Cardinal
 McIntyre
June 11, 1963. Santa Barbara, California

Any help that can be given is appreciated if it
can transport food and utensils over seas. (English 2 pgs.) On August 11, 1963, the Cardinal
states that the best resources would be Catholic
Relief Services. (English 1 pg.)

Mc4002. D-1963
Ms. Jean Davis to J. Francis Cardinal
 McIntyre
July 5, 1963. Los Angeles, California

The opportunity to report adequately on the
election of Pope Paul VI would have been impossible without your help. I am most grateful.
(English 1 pg.)

Mc4003. D-1963
Mrs. Francis Donahue to Msgr. Benjamin
 Hawkes
July 20, 1963. Long Beach, California

What is the Church's official attitude towards
any Catholic joining the YMCA or YWCA (English 1 pg.) On July 24, 1963, Msgr. states that
the Y is a religious organization and membership must be measured by that standard. (English 1 pg.)

Mc4004. D-1963
Mr. Larry Distel to Rev. John A. Rawden
July 30, 1963. Santa Ana, California

Could an interview be arranged to outline
how parishes are planned, methods used to fix
boundaries, and assign personnel. (English 1
pg.) On August 16, 1963, Fr. O'Connor suggests the interview for a newspaper article. (English 1 pg.)

Mc4005. D-1963
Mary B. D'Ambrosia to J. Francis Cardinal
 McIntyre
September 23, 1963. Los Angeles, California

A new plan for Evangelization is being sent
to Pope Paul VI and the plan can be discussed
at any time that is convenient. (English 28 pgs.)
On September 25, 1963, Fr. states that the Car-

dinal is very busy immediately before departing
for Rome. (English 1 pg.)

Mc4006. D-1963
Mrs. H. F. Davenport to Rev. John A. Rawden
October 8, 1963. Orange, California

Could information be obtained on The
Church and Integration for a class. (English 1
pg.) On October 11, 1963, Fr. sends the editorial on the subject from *The Tidings* with the
hope that the material will be helpful. (English
1 pg.)

Mc4007. D-1963
Rev. John B. Thom to Msgr. Donald Doxie
October 25, 1963. Los Angeles, California

The Canonical Visitation and Confirmation
usually are accomplished at the same visit. The
Bishop reviews financial and sacramental
records and other items formulated by the Archdiocese. (English 1 pg.)

Mc4008. D-1963
Rev. Edoardo Dhanis, SJ to J. Francis Cardinal
 McIntyre
November 5, 1963. Rome, Italy

The Gregorian University invites the members
of the Commission of the Vatican Council considering The Bishops and Diocesan Regulations
and Sacramental Discipline to meet on November 10. (Italian 1 pg.)

Mc4009. D-1963
Mr. J. M. Downey to Bp. Timothy Manning
November 6, 1963. Los Angeles, California

With so many changes in the Liturgy taking
place since the Council began, could Los Angeles return to having Midnight Mass on Christmas? (English 1 pg.)

Mc4010. D-1963
Msgr. William Doheny to Msgr. Benjamin
 Hawkes
November 9, 1963. Rome, Italy

The reprinting of the booklet on St. Anastasia
Church is necessary. The price in Italy is high
but if the color plates are in Los Angeles, the
price could be less. (English 1 pg.)

Mc4011. D-1963
Mrs. Kathryn Downey to J. Francis Cardinal
 McIntyre
November 27, 1963. South Gate, California

The article in *Cosmopolitan,* "Have Public
Schools Had It?" and Letters to the Editor in
the December issue should be read carefully.
(English 1 pg.)

Mc4012. D-1963
Mrs. Robert Demers to J. Francis Cardinal
 McIntyre
December 9, 1963. Veneta, Oregon

Why are the encyclicals allowed to go out of
print? The world needs this information. (English 1 pg.)

Mc4013. D-1963
Mr. George Doderlein to J. Francis Cardinal
 McIntyre
December 12, 1963. Sylmar, California

The Catholic position on Racial Justice must
be stated and practiced as the whole country
needs to know our philosophy. Don't endorse a
law unless it is good but make a public statement. (English 6 pgs.)

Mc4014. D-1963
Mr. M. E. Dwight to J. Francis Cardinal
 McIntyre
N.D. Des Moines, Iowa

An appeal to have the Cardinal speak out on
the rights of the individual in politics and society during the Fourth of July celebrations is
made. (English 6 pgs.)

Mc4015. E-1963
Mrs. Dorothy Enright to J. Francis Cardinal
 McIntyre
January 24, 1963. Garden Grove, California

The weekly sermons are on Doctrine but the
terminology is beyond the average parishioner.
Could an advertising copy writer work with the
priest to sell the Product (English 1 pg.) On January 30, 1963, Bishop Manning states that
much depends on the priest but the idea will be
considered. (English 1 pg.)

Mc4016. E-1963
Mr. Zoe Eberhart to J. Francis Cardinal
 McIntyre
January 30, 1963. Huntington Beach,
 California

Could you send a medal of Our Lady of the
Angels for my son's airplane. Many members of
his crew are Catholics. (English 1 pg.) On January 31, 1963, the Cardinal sends two medals
one for the plane and one for the mother. (English 1 pg.)

Mc4017. E-1963
Mrs. Dorothy Enright to J. Francis Cardinal
 McIntyre
February 2, 1963. Garden Grove, California

An outline showing the Blessed Virgin's plan
in the salvation of mankind is enclosed. A special commission has been given to me to make
Mary's position known. (English 1 pg.) On Feb-

ruary 5, 1963, the Cardinal states that the
Council will address the position of the Blessed
Virgin. (English 1 pg.)

Mc4018. E-1963
J. Francis Cardinal McIntyre to Msgr. Ben-
 jamin Hawkes
April 15, 1963. Los Angeles, California

The Esty Company should not send the organ
to Rome but should send a letter to the Pope
who will probably place the organ in his name
in one of the new Churches. (English 1 pg.)

Mc4019. E-1963
Msgr. Edward Connors to Mr. Guyon Earle
April 16, 1963. New York City, New York

The high schools and elementary schools
could use copies of *Quest for Happiness*. That
means 220,000 copies and the office can not be
responsible to distribute them. (English 1 pg.)

Mc4020. E-1963
J. Francis Cardinal McIntyre to Rev. Newman
 Eberhardt
November 7, 1963. Vatican City

Did past Councils discuss similar movements
to give Bishops power in Regional matters? (English 1 pg.) On November 7, 1963, Fr. states
that the history of the Regional meetings have
been forced to rely on Rome due to wars and
politics. To avoid nationalism, the Pope should
confirm all decisions. (English 1 pg.)

Mc4021. E-1963
Sister Mary Esther, RSM to J. Francis Cardinal
 McIntyre
November 8, 1963. Rome, Italy

The Center for a Better World is sponsoring a
one or two day retreat for the American Bishops
at the Center in Rome. (English 2 pgs.)

Mc4022. F-1963
Dr. James Fifield to J. Francis Cardinal
 McIntyre
February 18, 1963. Los Angeles, California

Legislation is being introduced in Sacramento
to tax all homes for the aged. Msgr. O'Dwyer
surely has the details. (English 1 pg.) On February 20, 1963, the Cardinal states that he will
ask the representatives to give a report on the
bill. (English 1 pg.)

Mc4023. F-1963
Mrs. Marino Fragiacomo to Catholic Committee
April 15, 1963. Portland, Oregon

Is there any place that can assist in sending a
person to Trieste, Italy, to visit parents who are
ill. (English 1 pg.) On April 18, 1963, Fr. Thom
states that the request is beyond the help given
by the Archdiocese. (English 1 pg.)

Mc4024. F-1963
J. Francis Cardinal McIntyre to Bp. Pericle
Felici
June 11, 1963. Los Angeles, California

The formal request is made to replace Rev.
Lawrence Gibson with Rev. W. J. Kenneally,
C.M. as assistant for the Second Session of the
Council. (Latin 1 pg.)

Mc4025. F-1963
Bp. Joseph L. Federal to J. Francis Cardinal
McIntyre
July 17, 1963. Salt Lake City, Utah

A case involving the Diocese is being tried in
the Orange County Court with Mr. Robert
Hickson representing the Diocese. (English
1 pg.)

Mc4026. F-1963
Rev. Stephen Hoeller to Mr. Thomas Fairbanks
July 28, 1963. Hollywood, California

The reply to Canonical Document contained
no insults and no further replies will be given to
letters of complaint. (English 1 pg.)

Mc4027. F-1963
Rev. John A. Rawden to Msgr. William For-
ester
September 10, 1963. Rome, Italy

The driver, Salvatore Romano, from Hiar Service, could be the Cardinal's driver again for
this session. The same insurance policy should
be arranged. (English 1 pg.)

Mc4028. F-1963
J. Francis Cardinal McIntyre to Francis Cardi-
nal Spellman
September 13, 1963. Los Angeles, California

Mr. Fugozi of the Vatican Pavilion wants
more advertising done for the World's Fair and
to have the Archdiocese a part of the travel
agency. (English 1 pg.)

Mc4029. F-1963
Mr. Kenneth Fraine to Bp. Timothy Manning
October 25, 1963. Long Beach, California

A sorority at Lakewood High School is sponsored by the YWCA. At no time are the members subjected to Y teaching. May a Catholic
girl join the sorority? (English 1 pg.) On October 29, 1963, the Bishop states that there is apparently no objection. (English 1 pg.)

Mc4030. F-1963
Mrs. Jerry Fairbanks to Bp. Timothy Manning
November 9, 1963. Los Angeles, California

The side altar to Our Lady of Guadalupe is
not complete at the Shrine. Much more information should be given concerning the apparitions to the people of the United States and
especially in the Archdiocese. (English 2 pgs.)

Mc4031. F-1963
Bp. Pericle Felici to All Bishops of the Council
November 21, 1963. Vatican City

So the work of the Council can move more
quickly, the number on each Commission will
be increased to thirty. The names of the new
members can be collected on a single sheet. (English 2 pgs.)

Mc4032. F-1963
Mr. Ellis Flint to Bp. Timothy Manning
December 19, 1963. Santa Ana, California

Is the new parish for Huntington Beach to be
built on Edinger and Warner Avenues? (English
1 pg.) On December 23, 1963, the Bishop states
that the information is incorrect and no definite
site has been determined. (English 1 pg.)

Mc4033. F-1963
Ms. Roberta Falkenstein to J. Francis Cardinal
McIntyre
December 20, 1962. Los Angeles, California

An investigation should be held concerning
the statements made by Rev. Edward Henriques
in a sermon at Precious Blood Parish. He
caused confusion among the people. (English 1
pg.) On January 16, 1963, Fr. Henriques states
that the statements made can be found in any
theology book. (English 1 pg.)

Mc4034. G-1963
Mr. Henry W. Barley to J. Francis Cardinal
McIntyre
January 4, 1963. Beverly Hills, California

While reading *Letters from Rome,* the
thought came that the Archdiocese would be interested in Garden of the World. Is an appointment possible? (English 1 pg.) On January 7,
1963, Fr. states that the Cardinal will notify
him in advance when it is convenient. (English
1 pg.)

Mc4035. G-1963
Mr. Richard Grant to J. Francis Cardinal
McIntyre
January 11, 1963. Los Angeles, California

The further the Russian scientists advance in
science the more they increase their interest in
religion. Science will be complete when it be-
comes a colleague of religion. (English 1 pg.)

Mc4036. G-1963
Mr. David Gibler to Bp. Timothy Manning
January 21, 1963. Jamaica, New York

With interest in Christian unity, could a Baptist receive Holy Communion or would it be worthless. (English 1 pg.) On January 24, 1963, the Bishop suggests a talk with the local Bishop or the Pastor of the parish. (English 1 pg.)

Mc4037. G-1963
Hon. Anacleto Gianni to J. Francis Cardinal McIntyre
January 26, 1963. Rome, Italy

The President of the Department of Agriculture, Industry and Commerce is presenting a gift to all of the Cardinals of the Council. Cardinal Spellman will send it. (Italian 1 pg.) On January 30, 1963, Cardinal Spellman states the gift will be sent directly from Rome. (English 1 pg.)

Mc4038. G-1963
Mr. M. E. Gibbens to J. Francis Cardinal McIntyre
February 4, 1963. Denver, Colorado

Why could not a method of birth control be introduced into India to prevent the starvation of children. Everything changes, why not this? (English 3 pgs.)

Mc4039. G-1963
J. Francis Cardinal McIntyre to Bp. Francis Gleeson
February 9, 1963. Los Angeles, California

A trip to Fairbanks, Alaska, for the installation would be most interesting but there are too many needs in Los Angeles. (English 1 pg.)

Mc4040. G-1963
Mr. A. G. Lorenzo to J. Francis Cardinal McIntyre
April 3, 1963. Detroit, Michigan

An invitation is given to view the exhibit, The Turning Wheel, a history of transportation before it opens to the general public on May 1. (English 1 pg.) On April 10, 1963, the Cardinal states that a previous commitment will prevent attendance. (English 1 pg.)

Mc4041. G-1963
Mr. George Gerard to J. Francis Cardinal McIntyre
April 6, 1963. Inglewood, California

Could a statement be made in *The Tidings* to explain the Archdiocesan policy of designating the speakers who will be allowed to speak or lecture in the area. The Fr. Kueng-UCLA affair raises the question. (English 2 pgs.)

Mc4042. G-1963
Mr. B. LeRoy Gordon to J. Francis Cardinal McIntyre
April 17, 1963. Middlesex, England

Father Schiro from Albania could minister to the Italian-Albanians who have no church in Southern California. (English 1 pg.) On April 24, 1963, the Cardinal states that the Byzantine Church of Los Angeles is active and so are most of the other Eastern Rites. (English 1 pg.)

Mc4043. G-1963
Hon. Eduardo Toda to J. Francis Cardinal McIntyre
April 25, 1963. Los Angeles, California

On May 31, could a Mass be celebrated in the Plaza Church or the Cathedral for the anniversary of Junipero Serra's birth and then a wreath of flowers be placed at the foot of the statue in the Square? (English 3 pgs.)

Mc4044. G-1963
Mr. John Gavin to J. Francis Cardinal McIntyre
April 25, 1963. Beverly Hills, California

On May 30 dignitaries of the Latin American States will be in Los Angeles when the Mayor will be in Spain for the 250th anniversary of the birth of Junipero Serra. Could a Mass be celebrated with an invitational breakfast following? (English 2 pgs.)

Mc4045. G-1963
J. Francis Cardinal McIntyre to Mr. John Gavin
May 2, 1963. Los Angeles, California

The Consul of Spain chose May 31 for the celebration of a Solemn Mass *Coram Pontifice* with a sermon by Bishop Timothy Manning. The Franciscan and Claretian Fathers will be the ministers of the Mass. A civic function will follow at 10:30. (English 2 pgs.)

Mc4046. G-1963
Bp. Timothy Manning to Mr. James Gepson
June 6, 1963. Los Angeles, California

The plans of Swift and Company to commemorate the long years of service, stirs us to commemorate the years of service to the parish and other organizations. (English 1 pg.)

Mc4047. G-1963
J. Francis Cardinal McIntyre to Arbp. Daniel Gercke
July 15, 1963. Los Angeles, California

A message of admiration for the forty years in the Episcopacy and the harvest being reaped from the early years of sowing. (English 1 pg.)

Mc4048. G-1963
Mr. Edward Gaffney to J. Francis Cardinal
  McIntyre
July 15, 1963. Sacramento, California

House of Representative Resolution #628 expresses the pleasure of the House in the election
of Pope Paul VI and his desire to bring peace to
the world. (English 1 pg.)

Mc4049. G-1963
Mr. Don Gift to J. Francis Cardinal McIntyre
August 12, 1963. Los Angeles, California

An organization, Los Angeles at Home, will
meet tourists and introduce them to families
with like interests. The host family is a volun-
teer family and will designate the amount of
time available. Could a priest be assigned to the
organization? (English 7 pgs.)

Mc4050. G-1963
Rev. Fissore Giacomo to Msgr. Benjamin
  Hawkes
August 16, 1963. Rome, Italy

There is a vacant residence that can be rented
for priests or Bishops at the Council. Archbishop Martin O'Connor suggested that I send
the message to the Bishops. (English 1 pg.)

Mc4051. G-1963
Mr. Elmer Griffin to J. Francis Cardinal
  McIntyre
August 27, 1963. Beverly Hills, California

Judge Thomas Coakley should be the Attorney General of California and can be if the
Catholics will back him at election time. (English 1 pg.)

Mc4052. G-1963
J. Francis Cardinal McIntyre to Hon. Anacleto
  Gianni
September 26, 1963. Los Angeles, California

The memorial gift for the Cardinals attending
the Council is a beautiful gift of a memorable
occasion. (English 1 pg.)

Mc4053. G-1963
Dr. Vincent Gerty, MD to J. Francis Cardinal
  McIntyre
December 16, 1963. Pasadena, California

The election to the Knights of Malta is a
great honor and won by your generous approval. A donation to the Youth Education
Fund is enclosed. (English 1 pg.)

Mc4054. H-1963
Mr. John Haidinger to J. Francis Cardinal
  McIntyre
January 24, 1963. Torrance, California

A funeral is an excellent time to explain the
Rosary and the Mass to non-Catholics so they
can participate in both devotions. (English
1 pg.)

Mc4055. H-1963
Rev. Samuel L. Hall to Msgr. Benjamin
  Hawkes
February 19, 1963. Whittier, California

The lecture on the Vatican Council and the
answers to many questions was good for St.
Stephen's Episcopal Church. (English 1 pg.)

Mc4056. H-1963
Rev. John A. Hardon, SJ to J. Francis Cardinal
  McIntyre
February 23, 1963. Kalamazoo, Michigan

An evaluation of having a priest teach Religion in a State University is enclosed. This is
not for publication. (English 13 pgs.) On March
7, 1963, the Cardinal states that there are several comments that would not allow publication. (English 1 pg.)

Mc4057. H-1963
Ms. Marie B. Hall to J. Francis Cardinal
  McIntyre
February 27, 1963. Los Angeles, California

The definition of true democracy must be
known before there can be peace and world and
family democracy established. (English 14 pgs.)

Mc4058. H-1963
Mrs. Mildred Hunt to J. Francis Cardinal
  McIntyre
March 9, 1963. Redondo Beach, California

An example of the type of literature that is
being sent to Catholics should receive Archdiocesan attention. (English 1 pg.)

Mc4059. H-1963
Arbp. Joseph Hurley to J. Francis Cardinal
  McIntyre
April 5, 1963. St. Augustine, Florida

Preparations are being made to celebrate the
400th anniversary of the founding of St. Augustine by an illuminated Cross, A Beacon of
Faith, to mark the place of American origin.
(English 1 pg.)

Mc4060. H-1963
Mr. Vincent Huppe to J. Francis Cardinal
McIntyre
April 5, 1963. Albuquerque, New Mexico

The Institute of Lay Theology would equip
me for the work of teaching and assisting in the
parish. Could a loan or a scholarship be arranged? (English 1 pg.) On April 11, 1963, the
Cardinal states that the Diocese or Parish for
whom the work is intended should arrange the
scholarship. (English 1 pg.)

Mc4061. H-1963
Msgr. John Rawden to Msgr. George Hopkins
April 30, 1963. Los Angeles, California

A Msgr. O'Grady phones concerning a divorce proceeding. Suspicion makes us question
his identity. (English 1 pg.) On May 1, 1963,
Msgr. states that there is no Msgr. O'Grady in
the Archdiocese. (English 1 pg.)

Mc4062. H-1963
Paul Cardinal S. Henriquez to J. Francis Cardi-
nal McIntyre
May 9, 1963. Santiago, Chile

At Notre Dame University, I will celebrate the
Baccalaureate Mass and receive the Doctor of
Law Degree. Then I will visit in the United
States. (English 1 pg.)

Mc4063. H-1963
Miss Jane Hoey to J. Francis Cardinal
McIntyre
May 16, 1963. New York City, New York

Genevieve Caufield's new book The Kingdom
Within, will be sent at her request. Many hon-
ors are coming to her. (English 1 pg.) On June
4, 1963, the Cardinal states that the work Miss
Caufield does for others is outstanding. (English
1 pg.)

Mc4064. H-1963
Ms. Mary Haedge to J. Francis Cardinal
McIntyre
June 1963. San Francisco, California

The last line of the Pledge of Allegiance
should never be changed and the nation should
come to a greater awareness of what "under
God" means. (English 2 pgs.)

Mc4065. H-1963
Msgr. Benjamin Hawkes to J. Francis Cardinal
McIntyre
June 12, 1963. Los Angeles, California

Our insurance company asked to be relieved
and a new carrier is being obtained. A new
County Code is published and some of our

buildings do not meet the Code. A new student
accident policy will be carried by our present
carrier. (English 3 pgs.)

Mc4066. H-1963
Mr. Meyer Hessel to Msgr. Benjamin Hawkes
June 13, 1963. St. Louis, Missouri

If the address of Raymond Harvey is available
ask him to contact the law office for an inheritance. (English 1 pg.) On June 17, 1963, Msgr.
comments that there is no central file in the
Archdiocese. (English 1 pg.)

Mc4067. H-1963
Msgr. Benjamin Hawkes to J. Francis Cardinal
McIntyre
June 20, 1963. Los Angeles, California

The Standard Oil Company lease for the
Chester Place property has two agreements, a
subsurface oil and gas lease and a drill site
agreement. The agreement will run from this
date for seven years or until the Oil Company
terminates it. (English 2 pgs.)

Mc4068. H-1963
Mr. V. Lawrence Hodges to J. Francis Cardinal
McIntyre
June 28, 1963. Pasadena, California

Is nudism condemned by the Church under
limited conditions as modern nudism is practiced. (English 1 pg.) On July 3, 1963, Fr. Thom
quotes Scripture and the encyclicals to answer
the question. (English 2 pgs.)

Mc4069. H-1963
Mrs. Grace Higgins to Pope Paul VI
July 19, 1963. Glendale, California

There is great need for unity among all faiths
but some Catholics are impossible to understand how they live their faith. No one can live
near them. (English 4 pgs.) On August 30,
1963, Fr. states that the accusations are unfounded and are being brought to court in October. (English 1 pg.)

Mc4070. H-1963
Msgr. Benjamin Hawkes to J. Francis Cardinal
McIntyre
October 8, 1963. Los Angeles, California

The death of Fr. Dosithea Trudel in Duarte
and the burial in Calvery Cemetery and the
death of Fr. Obermair who was retired were
Msgr. O'Dwyer's responsibility. Fr. Clyne was
ill before your departure and Fr. Donal Gearty
went home to Ireland. The Pelletier property is
still in discussion state. (English 2 pgs.)

Mc4071. H-1963
Mrs. Edward Herron to *Newsweek*
October 10, 1963. Manhattan Beach, California

The author of the article on parochial schools ought to listen to the parents who want to place their children in Catholic grade schools. Even non-Catholics are asking for the privilege. (English 2 pgs.)

Mc4072. H-1963
Msgr. Benjamin Hawkes to J. Francis Cardinal McIntyre
October 15, 1963. Los Angeles, California

The check for the Morgan account is cleared, the pictures of the Papal audience are beautiful; the Christmas Party is well underway; Confirmation tours are beginning, and the news of the Fremont property is good. (English 2 pgs.)

Mc4073. H-1963
Msgr. Benjamin Hawkes to J. Francis Cardinal McIntyre
October 16, 1963. Los Angeles, California

The news of Bishop elect Ward is well received; a temporary accountant for Don Bosco Technical is necessary; the mortgage on the Pelletier property will be assumed; the C.Y.O. and Catholic Alumni Club will incorporate. (English 3 pgs.)

Mc4074. H-1963
Msgr. Benjamin Hawkes to J. Francis Cardinal McIntyre
October 18, 1963. Los Angeles, California

The Vocation Guidance Committee is being reactivated against Fr. Gibson's wishes since he had the program scheduled. Many hidden items are included in this. (English 2 pgs.)

Mc4075. H-1963
Msgr. Benjamin Hawkes to J. Francis Cardinal McIntyre
October 22, 1963. Los Angeles, California

The new ring will be fitted and engraved for Bishop elect Ward and the chain will be ready when the Cross comes from Rome. The financial settlement can be made with Tustin and to Ziegler. Mr. Joseph Klupar will be in the Chancery Office to study the Archdiocesan policy. (English 3 pgs.)

Mc4076. H-1963
Msgr. Benjamin Hawkes to J. Francis Cardinal McIntyre
October 28, 1963. Los Angeles, California

Msgr. Gross wants to know about the building on Seventh and Ardmore; the Vocation Committee is settled, Bishop Ward's invitations will be sent to Rome. (English 1 pg.)

Mc4077. H-1963
Mrs. Helen Huff to J. Francis Cardinal McIntyre
November 2, 1963. Corona Del Mar, California

A good change in the Liturgy would be to introduce some music. (English 1 pg.) On November 5, 1963, Msgr. states that the suggestion will be brought to the Cardinal's attention. (English 1 pg.)

Mc4078. H-1963
Msgr. Benjamin Hawkes to J. Francis Cardinal McIntyre
November 14, 1963. Los Angeles, California

The Wilshire property will be negotiated. The death of Msgr. Edmond O'Donnell will move Fr. Thomas O'Connell to be Administrator. The Seminary and Cemetery property must be more clearly defined. (English 1 pg.)

Mc4079. H-1963
Msgr. Benjamin Hawkes to J. Francis Cardinal McIntyre
November 20, 1963. Los Angeles, California

The Mass of consecration is progressing nicely as well as the luncheon following the Mass. The Youth Education Fund is increased by $10,000 and everyone is delighted with the news about Msgr. Rawden. (English 2 pgs.)

Mc4080. H-1963
Msgr. Benjamin Hawkes to J. Francis Cardinal McIntyre
November 24, 1963. Los Angeles, California

For President Kennedy's memorial the Archdiocesan schools will be closed on Monday, a special Pontifical Requiem Mass will be celebrated at St. Vincent's Church at 9:00 a.m. on Monday, and evening Masses will be permitted on Saturday and Monday. (English 2 pgs.)

Mc4081. H-1963
J. Francis Cardinal McIntyre to Msgr. Benjamin Hawkes
N.D. Vatican City

Bishop McQuaid would like copies of the reports from San Francisco and Fr. Kenneally's and Msgr. Dignan's comments. Dan and Bernardine Donohue are in Rome. (English 2 pgs.)

Mc4082. I-1963
J. Francis Cardinal McIntyre to U.S. Department of Justice
January 25, 1963. Los Angeles, California

Mr. Angelo Idda is employed under the first preference quota. He has his visa and asks if he should have it in his possession. (English 1 pg.)

Mc4083. I-1963
Dr. J. M. De los Reyes, MD to J. Francis Cardinal McIntyre
March 14, 1963. Los Angeles, California

An invitation is extended to give the invocation at the International College of Surgeons Congress on April 25. (English 1 pg.) On March 22, 1963, Msgr. Rawden asks Msgr. Truxaw to represent the Cardinal. (English 1 pg.)

Mc4084. I-1963
Msgr. John A. Rawden to Bp. Miguel Ibarra
March 23, 1963. Los Angeles, California

Msgr. Laubacher as Assistant Director of the Propagation of the Faith has the request. You will hear directly from him. (English 1 pg.)

Mc4085. I-1963
Msgr. James T. Booth to Msgr. Benjamin Hawkes
April 10, 1963. San Diego, California

Would Los Angeles have any objections to giving Mr. John J. Irwin a Papal Honor? (English 1 pg.) On April 15, 1963, the Cardinal states that any honor that the Bishop wishes to give him is agreeable to the Archdiocese. (English 1 pg.)

Mc4086. I-1963
Bp. Timothy Manning to Mr. Lawrence Irell
June 25, 1963. Los Angeles, California

The generous donation to the Youth Education Fund on the Cardinal's birthday is gratefully received. The Cardinal will celebrate in Rome. (English 1 pg.)

Mc4087. I-1963
Mrs. Edward DePatie to J. Francis Cardinal McIntyre
August 6, 1963. North Hollywood, California

Shipstads and Johnson is giving a benefit performance of the Ice Follies for Rancho San Antonio on September 8. Would you allow pictures to be taken for publicity. (English 1 pg.)

Mc4088. J-1963
Mr. Flor Perez Jimenez to J. Francis Cardinal McIntyre
January 23, 1963. Miami Beach, Florida

As a defender of Human Rights, help release Marco Perez Jimenez from the Miami prison. (English 2 pgs.) On January 25, 1963, the Cardinal asks Msgr. Paul Tanner for some background information. (English 1 pg.)

Mc4089. J-1963
Msgr. Paul Tanner to J. Francis Cardinal McIntyre
February 5, 1963. Washington, D.C.

The Jimenez case is now on appeal to the Supreme Court. Intervening on his behalf would be a very delicate decision. (English 1 pg.) On February 11, 1963, the Cardinal appreciated the information. (English 1 pg.)

Mc4090. J-1963
Ms. Marcella Jackson to J. Francis Cardinal McIntyre
May 7, 1963. Fullerton, California

A group of unmarried Catholics over thirty wish to form a club similar to Stalpar Club. Is there a priest available to be the Chaplain? (English 1 pg.) On May 11, 1963, it is suggested to become a branch of the Stalpar and not another club. (English 1 pg.)

Mc4091. J-1963
Mr. Hugh Jennings to Pope Paul VI
July 9, 1963. Los Angeles, California

Why should a family be separated in death because some members are Catholic and others are not? Could a priest consecrate a plot of land in any cemetery? (English 1 pg.)

Mc4092. K-1963
J. Francis Cardinal McIntyre to Mr. Alfonso Kelly
January 25, 1963. Los Angeles, California

The property of Mono Camp Tract Number 2 being deeded to the Archdiocese of Los Angeles is a most generous expression of friendliness. The money realized from this project will educate future priests for the Archdiocese. (English 1 pg.)

Mc4093. K-1963
Hon. Hans. R. Kiderlen to J. Francis Cardinal McIntyre
January 29, 1963. Los Angeles, California

An invitation is extended to the Cardinal for a luncheon honoring the Ambassador of the Federal Republic of Germany on March 1. (English 1 pg.)

Mc4094. K-1963
Bp. Vincent Brizgys to J. Francis Cardinal McIntyre
February 22, 1963. Chicago, Illinois

American-Lithuanians will be asked to contribute to a chapel in the National Shrine in Washington, D.C. (English 1 pg.) On March 5, 1963, Rev. John Kucingis, states that the parish cannot solicit funds for the Chapel of Our Lady of Siluva because of other commitments. (English 1 pg.)

Mc4095. K-1963
Rev. W. J. Kenneally, CM to J. Francis Cardinal McIntyre
March 7, 1963. Camarillo, California

Comments on the schema *Cura Animarum*. Much could be handled by a *manuale episcoparum* which could be supplemented in various countries. (English 2 pgs.)

Mc4096. K-1963
Rev. W. J. Kenneally, CM to J. Francis Cardinal McIntyre
March 27, 1963. Camarillo, California

Comments on the relationship between Church and State which the Cardinal adapted are sent to Msgr. Paul Tanner on April 2, 1963. (English 2 pgs.)

Mc4097. K-1963
J. Francis Cardinal McIntyre to Msgr. Paul Tanner
April 2, 1963. Los Angeles, California

If we stick to principles, the practical application of Church-State relations can be left to the individual nations. We must remain friendly with all nations. (English 1 pg.)

Mc4098. K-1963
Capt. Charles Kelly to J. Francis Cardinal McIntyre
April 7, 1963. Philippines

The decision to study at Beda Pontifical College in Rome is most satisfactory. There is a possibility that a two year program of twenty-four-months could be arranged in the Philippines. (English 4 pgs.)

Mc4099. K-1963
Rev. John Kerr, SJ to Bp. Timothy Manning
May 15, 1963. Limerick, Ireland

A message of gratitude for the generosity shown to Mungret Seminary. The new extension is complete giving much needed facilities. (English 1 pg.)

Mc4100. K-1963
Ms. Violet Kapalko to Rev. John Thom
May 20, 1963. Cleveland, Ohio

A letter from a religious in Sun Valley, California, is most distressing. Could there be some information of this community. (English 1 pg.) On May 24, 1963, Fr. states that there is no religious community in the Archdiocese by this title or at this address. (English 1 pg.)

Mc4101. K-1963
Rev. W. J. Kenneally, CM. to J. Francis Cardinal McIntyre
June 1, 1963. Camarillo, California

Comments on the United States' position of separation of Church and State and the philosophy of Pope Leo XIII that should prevail is being sent. (English 2 pgs.)

Mc4102. K-1963
Rev. W. J. Kenneally, CM to J. Francis Cardinal McIntyre
July 2, 1963. Camarillo, California

Comments on the Schema on Relationship of Church and State with the outline and statements that will be used at the next session. (English 5 pgs.)

Mc4103. K-1963
Mr. Thomas Kelly to Bp. Timothy Manning
July 7, 1963. Long Beach, California

Why does the Church remain silent in the racial crisis and the Yugoslavian earthquake? We are an international Church and we need leadership. (English 1 pg.)

Mc4104. K-1963
Mr. William Keith to J. Francis Cardinal McIntyre
July 26, 1963. Los Angeles, California

The stock certificates of market value of $5,000 should be assigned to Don Bosco Technical Institute. (English 1 pg.) On July 29, 1963, the Cardinal states that he will keep the stock for the present but will assign the value to the Institute. (English 1 pg.)

Mc4105. K-1963
Mr. Edward Kennedy to J. Francis Cardinal McIntyre
August 2, 1963. Los Angeles, California

A letter of recommendation is needed if the office of Vice Supreme Master of the Junipero Serra Council of the Knights is to be filled. (English 1 pg.)

Mc4106. K-1963
Mr. Joseph Keener to J. Francis Cardinal McIntyre
October 5, 1963. Charleston, South Carolina

Any information on the Catholic Council on Civil Liberties is needed for an interview that is being held. (English 1 pg.) On October 14, 1963, the Cardinal states that much of his information cannot be given, so it is better for him to say nothing. (English 1 pg.)

Mc4107. K-1963
Mrs. Herbert Kalmus to J. Francis Cardinal
McIntyre
November 26, 1963. Los Angeles, California

Mr. Howe has a ruby fashioned into an *Ecce Homo* that should belong to a Cardinal. The description is enclosed. (English 4 pgs.) On December 10, 1963, the Cardinal states that the price of such a treasure would make it prohibitive. (English 1 pg.)

Mc4108. K-1963
Mr. John Keuter to Bp. Timothy Manning
December 3, 1963. Lebanon, Ohio

Why do Catholic institutions hire non-Catholics when Catholics are available for the work? A credit manager or a public relations man is available for work in any part of the world. (English 2 pgs.) On December 6, 1963, the Bishop states that the Chancery Office cannot provide work opportunities. (English 1 pg.)

Mc4109. K-1963
Mr. Herbert Kandel to J. Francis Cardinal
McIntyre
December 6, 1963. Wilmington, California

The Civitas Club of Wilmington is in need of a Chaplain. Our civic service is directed to CYO, Mahan House, Neighborhood Youth Center, and Schiemaker School. (English 1 pg.)

Mc4110. K-1963
Dr. William Kroger MD to J. Francis Cardinal
McIntyre
N.D. Los Angeles, California

The two books, *Philosophy of God,* and *Makers of the Modern Mind,* will make enjoyable reading. (English 1 pg.)

Mc4111. L-1963
Rev. Alvin LaFeir to Bp. Timothy Manning
January 14, 1963. Agana, Guam

Typhoon Karen has destroyed 98% of the buildings including our Church, school, convent, and rectory. Any donation will be useful. (English 1 pg.) On March 13, 1963, the Bp. sends a donation. (English 1 pg.)

Mc4112. L-1963
Rev. John Languille to J. Francis Cardinal
McIntyre
January 29, 1963. Los Angeles, California

Mr. Dean Rusk has invited Sister Celine Vasquez to participate in the Department of State Foreign Policy Conference. (English 1 pg.) On February 1, 1963, the Cardinal states it would be better for the Director to join Msgr. Dignan at the meeting. (English 1 pg.)

Mc4113. L-1963
Msgr. William Doheny, CSC to J. Francis Cardinal McIntyre
February 2, 1963. Vatican City

A letter of introduction for Hon. Giovanni Leone whose son needs specialized care and surgery in Los Angeles. (English 1 pg.) On March 16, 1963, the Cardinal states that the family can return to Italy soon because the son is progressing well. (English 1 pg.)

Mc4114. L-1963
Mrs. M. L. Lehman to J. Francis Cardinal
McIntyre
February 16, 1963. San Francisco, California

Please intercede to have Dan Lehman accepted in USF, Santa Clara, or Seattle University. His future is at stake. (English 2 pgs.) On February 19, 1963, the Cardinal requests Archbishop McGucken to become interested in the problem. (English 1 pg.)

Mc4115. L-1963
Mr. Dan Sweeney to Msgr. John Rawden
February 18, 1963. Pasadena, California

An invitation to have Cardinal McIntyre speak at the Lions Club luncheon on March 29 or April 19. (English 1 pg.) On February 20, 1963, Msgr. states that due to previous commitments, the Cardinal has asked Msgr. North to speak at the luncheon. (English 1 pg.)

Mc4116. L-1963
Mr. Oscar Lawler to J. Francis Cardinal
McIntyre
February 23, 1963. Beverly Hills, California

The copy of Lincoln's Proclamation setting aside April 30 as a day of fasting and prayer will be a cherished possession. (English 1 pg.)

Mc4117. L-1963
Bp. Francis Leipzig to Bp. Timothy Manning
March 7, 1963. Baker, Oregon

Must a Bishop always celebrate a Pontifical Mass or may he celebrate a Solemn High Mass with two priests. (English 1 pg.) On March 11, 1963, the Bishop states that he and Bishop Bell have permission to sing a *Missa Contata* with no attendants. (English 1 pg.)

Mc4118. L-1963
Mrs. Jerry Lujan to J. Francis Cardinal McIntyre
March 19, 1963. Los Angeles, California

A portion of the promised donation for a young man who is studying for the priesthood is enclosed. (English 1 pg.) On March 22, 1963, the Cardinal states that the donation is an encouragement to the priests of the Archdiocese. (English 1 pg.)

Mc4119. L-1963
Bp. Francis Leipzig to Rev. John Thom
April 13, 1963. Baker, Oregon

Could the number of candidates for Confirmation for the period that I was in Los Angeles be calculated so a report can be given to the Diocese. (English 1 pg.) On April 16, 1963, Fr. states that the number was 5,301. (English 1 pg.)

Mc4120. L-1963
Mr. Thomas Locraft to Msgr. Benjamin Hawkes
April 27, 1963. Bethesda, Maryland

A request for information of a parish in High Grove, California, that would have records dating before 1915. (English 1 pg.) On May 2, 1963, Msgr. states that the information was sent to the San Diego Diocese since the parish is in that Diocese. (English 1 pg.)

Mc4121. L-1963
Mr. Victor Johnson to J. Francis Cardinal McIntyre
N.D. Trinidad, BWI

Is there a Mr. Whitey Lee registered in the telephone book or voter registration list? He was in Trinidad in 1921 and moved to Los Angeles. (English 2 pgs.) On May 16, 1963, Fr. states that he had found a Whitey Lee in Los Angeles. (English 1 pg.)

Mc4122. L-1963
Rev. Jesus Lash to Bp. Timothy Manning
May 18, 1963. Navarra, Spain

A request is made for Mass stipends to help build apartments for the poor. We are in the process of building 400 more apartments. (English 1 pg.)

Mc4123. L-1963
Mrs. Carlos Prietto to J. Francis Cardinal McIntyre
May 31, 1963. Los Angeles, California

The *Las Damas Pan Americanas* has pledged to financially support the California Adoption Center. The young debutantes will work for the Holy Family Adoption Agency. (English 1 pg.)

Mc4124. L-1963
Mr. Walter Trask to J. Francis Cardinal McIntyre
June 3, 1963. Los Angeles, California

Could a priest be assigned as our Chaplain at our luncheon meetings and be a member of the Club? A paid membership can be obtained. (English 2 pgs.) On July 5, 1963, the Cardinal states that Rev. John Sheridan could be the Chaplain filling the requirements. (English 1 pg.)

Mc4125. L-1963
Mrs. Kitty Lane to J. Francis Cardinal McIntyre
June 4, 1963. Los Angeles, California

When in Rome, a period of relaxation would be a visit to the home of Mr. and Mrs. J. Caffery. He was the Ambassador to Brazil, France and Egypt and has interesting tales to tell. (English 1 pg.)

Mc4126. L-1963
J. Francis Cardinal McIntyre to Mr. Joseph Lamb
August 5, 1963. Los Angeles, California

The pictures of the Vatican are splendid and it is good to have them in the News. (English 1 pg.) On August 9, 1963, Mr. Lamb states that an accident is making life rather difficult at the present time. (English 1 pg.)

Mc4127. L-1963
Rev. Giorgio LaRira to J. Francis Cardinal McIntyre
August 8, 1963. Rome, Italy

A history of the devotion to the Blessed Mother that has been in Italy and especially Florence is enclosed. The dedication of the world to the Immaculate Heart of Mary could bring peace to the world. (Italian 3 pgs.)

Mc4128. L-1963
Mr. Paul Lockwood to Msgr. Benjamin Hawkes
August 9, 1963. Los Angeles, California

The discussion should be on the renewal of the Missionary spirit, the necessity of human relations, and the aims of Vatican II. (English 2 pgs.)

Mc4129. L-1963
Mr. Robert Liberty to J. Francis Cardinal McIntyre
August 16, 1963. Glendora, California

The desire to become a priest is still dominant in my life and the next step must be taken even if some difficulties do exist. (English 8 pgs.) On August 29, 1963, the Cardinal states to continue to follow the advice of the Pastor of the parish. (English 1 pg.)

Mc4130. L-1963
Mr. Sam Weiss to Rev. John Thom
August 21, 1963. Los Angeles, California

Dr. David Lieber will be the president of the University of Judaism. A letter of congratulations from the Cardinal that can be reproduced is desired. (English 10 pgs.) On September 12, 1963, the Cardinal congratulates Dr. Lieber and expresses his confidence in the extension of the good work of the University. (English 1 pg.)

Mc4131. L-1963
Mrs. Kitty Lynch to Bp. Timothy Manning
September 12, 1963. Co. Cork, Ireland

As an Irish mother, I worry about a girl working as a nurse in the Good Samaritan Hospital in Los Angeles. Please contact her. (English 2 pgs.) On October 11, 1963, the Bishop states that an invitation is extended to come to the Chancery Office. (English 1 pg.)

Mc4132. L-1963
Mr. Andrew Landay to Bp. Timothy Manning
September 17, 1963. Santa Monica, California

Three suggestions for the Vatican Council would be to have the readings at Mass follow the Scriptures and not repeat the same reading at each daily Mass during the week; Give a visible sign of peace at Mass; and the introduction of the Divine Office in the parish Churches. (English 1 pg.)

Mc4133. L-1963
J. Francis Cardinal McIntyre to Bp. Francis Leipzig
September 19, 1963. Los Angeles, California

There will be need for additional help for the Confirmations scheduled from January 19 to February 9. If this fits into your schedule, please let us know. (English 1 pg.) On September 21, 1963, the Bishop states that the time schedule is satisfactory. (English 1 pg.)

Mc4134. L-1963
Dr. David Lieber to J. Francis Cardinal McIntyre
September 30, 1963. Los Angeles, California

As president of the University of Judaism, I will attempt to transmit cultural and spiritual values to the students of the Jewish heritage. (English 1 pg.)

Mc4135. L-1963
Mrs. Margaret Linn to J. Francis Cardinal McIntyre
October 3, 1963. Toledo, Ohio

Please vote to leave the Mass in Latin but increase the Scripture classes for the laity. (English 2 pgs.)

Mc4136. L-1963
Rev. Edward Lynch, SJ to J. Francis Cardinal McIntyre
October 9, 1963. Rome, Italy

Vatican Radio can assist with the communication of the Cardinal and his faithful of the Archdiocese. The studio is available at *Petriano* daily. (English 1 pg.)

Mc4137. L-1963
Mr. Paul Landsowne to Bp. Timothy Manning
November 27, 1963. Los Angeles, California

Could a dispensation be received for the banquet to be held on Friday, March 20. The menu is meat for the main course. (English 1 pg.) On November 29, 1963, the Bishop grants the dispensation but suggests a choice ought to be available. (English 1 pg.)

Mc4138. L-1963
Mrs. Ann LeCocq to Bp. Timothy Manning
December 7, 1963. Tujunga, California

Would you be available when a 89 year old convert dies to celebrate the Requiem Mass? Arrangements have been made with the Pastor. (English 4 pgs.) On December 20, 1963, the Bishop assures both mother and daughter a special remembrance in his Mass. (English 1 pg.)

Mc4139. L-1963
Miss Florence Lyons to J. Francis Cardinal McIntyre
December 9, 1963. Los Angeles, California

The Western Edition of the *New York Times* has the text of the United Nations Delegation on the elimination of religious discrimination. (English 1 pg.)

Mc4140. L-1963
Mr. T. E. Leavey to J. Francis Cardinal McIntyre
December 12, 1963. Los Angeles, California

The honor of being elected to the Knights of Malta is appreciated by one who sees more short-comings than good qualities in his personality. (English 1 pg.)

Mc4141. L-1963
Mr. Charles Luckman to J. Francis Cardinal McIntyre
December 1963. Los Angeles, California

Our Christmas gift is a donation to the Child Guidance Clinic in the name of the Company. (English 1 pg.) On December 26, 1963, the Cardinal sends his blessings to the Company for their charity. (English 1 pg.)

Mc4142. Mc-1963
Msgr. Patrick Roach to *The Tidings*
January 21, 1963. Los Angeles, California

A revised biography of James Francis Cardinal McIntyre is printed in *The Tidings* (English 6 pgs.)

Mc4143. Mc-1963
Mr. William McKesson to J. Francis Cardinal
McIntyre
February 4, 1963. Los Angeles, California

An invitation is extended to give the invocation at the National District Attorney's Association Meeting on March 13 at 7:30 p.m. (English 2 pgs.) On February 11, 1963, the Cardinal states that he is looking forward to greeting the District Attorney Association. (English 1 pg.)

Mc4144. Mc-1963
Bp. Thomas McCarty to J. Francis Cardinal
McIntyre
February 4, 1963. Rapid City, South Dakota

An invitation is extended to the Solemn Blessing and Dedication of the new Cathedral on May 7 at 10:00 a.m. (English 1 pg.) On February 8, 1963, the Cardinal states that so many absences from the Chancery Office makes it impossible for him to attend. (English 1 pg.)

Mc4145. Mc-1963
J. Francis Cardinal McIntyre to Arbp. Joseph
T. McGucken
February 11, 1963. Los Angeles, California

The decrease in the membership of N.E.A. in Los Angeles is interesting as is the increase in the membership in San Diego. (English 1 pg.)

Mc4146. Mc-1963
Francis Cardinal Spellman to J. Francis Cardinal McIntyre
April 15, 1963. New York City, New York

The *ad limina* visit in 1964 will be dispensed but the *quinquennial* report should be submitted. Please tell the Ordinaries. (English 1 pg.)

Mc4147. Mc-1963
Mrs. James McElwee to J. Francis Cardinal
McIntyre
April 15, 1963. Coral Gables, Florida

Some attention should be paid to the literature given to high school students to read and more attention ought to be paid to the anti-Communistic activities. (English 2 pgs.)

Mc4148. Mc-1963
Mrs. Mary McHale to J. Francis Cardinal
McIntyre
April 29, 1963. Camarillo, California

A watch guard should be placed on our government involvement with the Communists and the takeover of so many countries by the Russians. (English 4 pgs.)

Mc4149. Mc-1963
Rev. John Languille to J. Francis Cardinal
McIntyre
July 16, 1963. Los Angeles, California

Notes taken at the Community Service Organization which works for the civil rights of the Mexican Americans are enclosed. The race relations of the Mexican and Negro was stressed. (English 4 pgs.)

Mc4150. Mc-1963
Arbp. Joseph T. McGucken to J. Francis Cardinal McIntyre
July 19, 1963. San Francisco, California

Mr. Burke feels that the Pious Fund claims should be brought forth before the money and land question is settled. (English 1 pg.) On July 25, 1963, the Cardinal states that he is the best informed on the subject, and the Bishops will follow any suggestion. (English 1 pg.)

Mc4151. Mc-1963
Arbp. Joseph T. McGucken to J. Francis Cardinal McIntyre
July 26, 1963. San Francisco, California

The psychological timing must be considered to either press for payment of the Pious Fund or drop it. There will be a Conference on Religion and Race in September in San Francisco. (English 1 pg.)

Mc4152. Mc-1963
J. Francis Cardinal McIntyre to Rev. W. J.
Kenneally, CM
August 6, 1963. Los Angeles, California

Comments on the First Chapter of the Schema of The Bishops and the Government of the Diocese is enclosed for discussion. (English 10 pgs.)

Mc4153. Mc-1963
Rev. Harry McKnight to J. Francis Cardinal
McIntyre
August 8, 1963. Los Angeles, California

The Church Federation of Los Angeles has adopted a five point program to aid in the current race relation problem. (English 1 pg.) On August 12, 1963, Fr. Thom replies by sending the editorial of *The Tidings* and the opposition of the Cardinal to demonstrations. (English 1 pg.)

Mc4154. Mc-1963
J. Francis Cardinal McIntyre to All of the
Faithful
September 24, 1963. Los Angeles, California

A plea for prayers for the Second Session of the Vatican Council so the inspiration of the Holy Spirit will be upon the members of the Council. (English 1 pg.)

Mc4155. Mc-1963
Mr. Neil McLaughlin to Msgr. Thomas
O'Dwyer
November 14, 1963. Long Beach, California

A new 300 bed hospital will be opened in
January. Many of the patients will be Catholics
and will need the assistance of a Chaplain (English 1 pg.) On November 19, 1963, Msgr.
states that the priests in Holy Innocents Parish
will act as Chaplains. (English 1 pg.)

Mc4156. Mc-1963
Mr. Gary MacEoin to J. Francis Cardinal
McIntyre
November 17, 1963. Rome, Italy

A request for an interview so the syndicated
column can have material from the Council that
will be relevant to the faithful of the United
States. (English 1 pg.)

Mc4157. Mc-1963
J. Francis Cardinal McIntyre to Bp. Timothy
Manning
N.D. Vatican City

The announcement of Bishop elect John
Ward as Auxiliary Bishop of Los Angeles is
confirmed. The date and arrangements for consecration could be November 30 or December
12. St. Timothy Parish could be his if the Consultors agree. (English 2 pgs.)

Mc4158. Mc-1963
J. Francis Cardinal McIntyre to Delegates of
the Council
N.D. Los Angeles, California

Clarification of the position of relationship
between the Church and State is made for the
members of the committee. (English 5 pgs.)

Mc4159. Mc-1963
J. Francis Cardinal McIntyre to Delegates of
the Council
N.D. Los Angeles, California

Remarks on the proposed statements of De
Relationibus Inter Ecclesiam et Statum are en-
closed for discussion (English 4 pgs.) The entire
Schema of De Ecclesia et Statum. (Latin 7 pgs.)

Mc4160. Mc-1963
Ms. Margaret McEvoy to Msgr. Benjamin
Hawkes
N.D. Los Angeles, California

A certificate for 100 shares of Pepsi Cola
stock is enclosed which is transferred to the Cardinal for the education of a young man to the
priesthood. (English 1 pg.) On December 26,
1963, the Cardinal expresses his gratitude for
the generous gift to the Seminary. (English 1 pg.)

Mc4161. Mc-1963
Mrs. Mary McEvans to J. Francis Cardinal
McIntyre
N.D. Hollywood, California

Examples of hand bills being distributed near
Hollywood High School by Carl McIntyre who
was an official spectator at the Vatican Council
are sent for the Cardinal's attention. (English
7 pgs.)

Mc4162. M-1963
Mr. Mortimer Mears to J. Francis Cardinal
McIntyre
January 5, 1963. Seal Beach, California

The residents of Leisure World want a simple
Church of their own or be allowed to belong to
St. Anne's Parish and not St. Hedwig's (English
3 pgs.) On January 9, 1963, the Parish designa-
tion was given serious consideration, however,
any Parish can be attended. (English 1 pg.)

Mc4163. M-1963
Mrs. Sonia Miller to J. Francis Cardinal McIntyre
January 9, 1963. Whittier, California

An expressed desire to know the Church's position on the John Birch Society since Cardinal
Cushing and some priests seem to endorse it.
(English 5 pgs.) On February 18, 1963, the
Cardinal states that the Society has no Church
affiliation and must be judged on its own merits. (English 1 pg.)

Mc4164. M-1963
Mrs. Margaret Manning to J. Francis Cardinal
McIntyre
January 15, 1963. Co. Cork, Ireland

A message of gratitude for the beautiful Rosary that came from the Cardinal and for all
of the kindnesses shown to the Bishop. (English
1 pg.)

Mc4165. M-1963
Bp. Timothy Manning to Rev. Arnold Paroline
January 16, 1963. Los Angeles, California

Would a retroactive salary for the apartment
house managers be within consideration.
$2,400 is needed for the down payment on a
house. (English 1 pg.) On January 21, 1963, Fr.
states that a retroactive salary would be unjust
and would bring an outcry from the parish.
(English 2 pgs.)

Mc4166. M-1963
Rev. John Languille to Bp. Timothy Manning
February 25, 1963. Los Angeles, California

The Lay Institute called Missionaries of Peace
work as Chaplains to the armed forces. They
have the approbation of the Archbishops and
Bishops but must be called Friends of the Sol-
diers to accommodate the laws in Mexico. (English 2 pgs.)

Mc4167. M-1963
Rev. Francis J. Weber to Mr. Robert E. Moore
March 4, 1963. Los Angeles, California

The title and regulations concerning the water rights to the Los Angeles River dating from the Spanish land-grant period to the present are presented for your information. (English 3 pgs.)

Mc4168. M-1963
Rev. Urban to Msgr. John Rawden
March 7, 1963. Los Angeles, California

Mr. Ben Mindenberg requests a letter of introduction to solicit funds for the production of a movie based on the importation of narcotics from China. He was told that this is not our policy. (English 1 pg.)

Mc4169. M-1963
J. Francis Cardinal McIntyre to Paul Cardinal Marella
March 8, 1963. Los Angeles, California

Comments on De Episcopis et Diocecesium Regimine are enclosed and a favorable comment on Manuale Episcorporum is being sent. (English 4 pgs.)

Mc4170. M-1963
Bp. Egidio Vagnozzi to J. Francis Cardinal McIntyre
March 28, 1963. Washington, D.C.

Dr. Rudolf Ludwig Mossbauer is a candidate for the Pontifical Academy of Science. Is some background information available? (English 1 pg.) On April 8, 1963, the Cardinal states that the Dr. received the Nobel Prize in Physics and is a professor at California Institute of Technology. He is a good Catholic. (English 1 pg.)

Mc4171. M-1963
Mr. Philip Menninger to J. Francis Cardinal McIntyre
April 9, 1963. Topeka, Kansas

The Menninger Quarterly is being sent to keep abreast with psychiatric topics. (English 1 pg.) On April 15, 1963, the Cardinal states that he appreciates the kindness of sending the Quarterly. (English 1 pg.)

Mc4172. M-1963
Mr. Anthony Magzio to Msgr. Benjamin Hawkes
April 12, 1963. Los Angeles, California

Could a cousin who is a Religious be assigned to come to the United States and be in the Archdiocese. (English 1 pg.) On April 15, 1963, Msgr. suggests that the family work through the Religious Community. (English 1 pg.)

Mc4173. M-1963
J. Francis Cardinal McIntyre to Paul Cardinal Marella
April 15, 1963. Los Angeles, California

Comments on the Schemata are enclosed. (English-Latin 4 pgs.) On April 18, 1963, Archbishop Vagnozzi thanks the Cardinal for his viewpoints and expresses concern for the NCEA meeting. (English 1 pg.)

Mc4174. M-1963
Mrs. J. E. Manning to Msgr. John Rawden
April 22, 1963. Burbank, California

Why does the Archdiocese neglect homes for the elderly when all other religions seem to have enough money to build and staff them? (English 1 pg.)

Mc4175. M-1963
Mrs. Eva Masciotra to J. Francis Cardinal McIntyre
April 23, 1963. Burbank, California

An invitation is extended to attend the wedding of the oldest daughter on May 11 at 12:00 noon. (English 2 pgs.) On May 17, 1963, Mrs. Masciotra states that the greatest honor paid to the family was having the Cardinal present for the wedding. (English 1 pg.)

Mc4176. M-1963
Mr. Theodore Mala to J. Francis Cardinal McIntyre
May 1963. Los Angeles, California

A note of profound gratitude for all that is being done for the Church and the people of the Archdiocese. (English 1 pg.)

Mc4177. M-1963
Mr. Ettore Masina to J. Francis Cardinal McIntyre
May 21, 1963. Milano, Italy

If the text or summary of your interventions at the Council are available, they can be printed in the forthcoming book. (English 1 pg.) On May 31, 1963, the Cardinal states that the policy of not giving any publicity to comments is being followed. (English 1 pg.)

Mc4178. M-1963
Mr. W. E. Martin to J. Francis Cardinal McIntyre
May 22, 1963. Los Angeles, California

Could some one give advice and help to the clergy in public speaking, microphone techniques, and voice projection so the Sunday sermon could fulfill its role. (English 2 pgs.)

Mc4179. M-1963
Mrs. Adelaide Marcoux to Msgr. Benjamin
   Hawkes
June 21, 1963. Long Beach, California

A legal refutation should be brought to assure the right to call upon God for assistance in
preserving the Union. (English 2 pgs.)

Mc4180. M-1963
Bp. Timothy Manning to J. Francis Cardinal
   McIntyre
June 24, 1963. Los Angeles, California

The priests' retreat was a success and was
strengthened by the election of the new Pope.
The Donohue Memorial could be the chapel in
connection with the new high school near St.
Bernardine's Parish or the chapel area at the
Junior Seminary. (English 1 pg.)

Mc4181. M-1963
Bp. John Maguire to All priests
July 11, 1963. New York City, New York

Cardinal Spellman's message against discrimination is to be read at all Masses. (English 6 pgs.)

Mc4182. M-1963
Mr. W. E. Martin to J. Francis Cardinal McIntyre
July 29, 1963. Los Angeles, California

Could the old Catholic Truth Society be revived to monitor newspapers, magazine, and
now talk shows that release so much false information on the air. (English 2 pgs.)

Mc4183. M-1963
Dr. George Merkle, MD to J. Francis Cardinal
   McIntyre
August 11, 1963. Carlsbad, California

Why are Cardinals and Archbishops silent
when some left wing priests get all of the publicity. It seems that they are the spokesmen for
the Church. (English 1 pg.)

Mc4184. M-1963
Mr. E. Morrison to J. Francis Cardinal
   McIntyre
August 14, 1963. Pomona, California

Could a circular church be built at St. Madeline's Parish so the congregation would be
closer to the altar and more attentive at Mass?
(English 2 pgs.)

Mc4185. M-1963
Bp. Timothy Manning to J. Francis Cardinal
   McIntyre
August 16, 1963. New York City, New York

Cardinal Spellman agrees with the Charter
of the NAACP and agrees that the demonstrations are not fulfilling the purpose. Washington
seems to be upset over the signature of Bishop
McGuire. (English 1 pg.) On September 14,
1963, the Bishop remarks on his mother's
health and the trip to Lourdes. (English 1 pg.)

Mc4186. M-1963
Miss Laura Moore to J. Francis Cardinal
   McIntyre
August 16, 1963. New York City, New York

A *Tribute to Pope John XXIII* by Morris
West is enclosed. Perhaps you missed this when
you were in Rome. (English 2 pgs.) On August
19, 1963, the Cardinal states his appreciation
for the article and for the *Time* magazine. (English 1 pg.)

Mc4187. M-1963
J. Francis Cardinal McIntyre to Bp. Timothy
   Manning
September 16, 1963. Los Angeles, California

Bishop Furey is in San Diego and seems to be
well received. There is need for more land in
Santa Monica, and Msgr. Brouwer's condition
is cause for concern. (English 1 pg.)

Mc4188. M-1963
Dr. A. J. Murrieta, MD to J. Francis Cardinal
   McIntyre
September 23, 1963. Los Angeles, California

The Los Angeles Medical Association would
like to invite Bishop Fulton J. Sheen to address
our convention. (English 1 pg.) On September
26, 1963, the Cardinal gives the permission but
states that the Bishop will probably be in Rome
for the Council but extend the invitation. (English 1 pg.)

Mc4189. M-1963
Mr. Albert Martin to Msgr. Benjamin Hawkes
October 10, 1963. Los Angeles, California

The question of individual rights and the
common good is being discussed and various
opinions are suggested. Another view is needed.
(English 3 pgs.) On October 17, 1963, Fr.
Thom distinguishes between natural rights and
civil rights and the necessity to provide for the
common good. (English 1 pg.)

Mc4190. M-1963
Bp. Timothy Manning to J. Francis Cardinal
   McIntyre
October 16, 1963. Los Angeles, California

The return trip from Rome was peaceful, the
Council of Catholic Women luncheon is over,
Fr. Furber of the Missionaries of the Holy Spirit
asks if two of the Seminarians can visit St.
John's Seminary during their vacation in Mex-
ico. (English 1 pg.)

Mc4191. M-1963
Bp. Timothy Manning to J. Francis Cardinal
McIntyre
October 21, 1963. Los Angeles, California

The consultors who were available agree that
Bishop elect Ward should be offered St. Timothy's. The Bishop elect appreciated the offer and
would like to continue as *Vice officialis*. (English 2 pgs.)

Mc4192. M-1963
Mr. O'Neill Martin to Msgr. Benjamin
Hawkes
October 25, 1963. San Diego, California

Mercy Hospital extension will depend on the
signature of the quitclaim granting the lots to
Bishop Charles Buddy of San Diego, a Corporation Sale. This parcel of land was not included
when the Diocese was formed. (English 2 pgs.)
On November 6, 1963, Msgr. states the claim is
signed and notorized. (English 1 pg.)

Mc4193. M-1963
Bp. Timothy Manning to J. Francis Cardinal
McIntyre
October 25, 1963. Los Angeles, California

The School Board will meet as will the Building Commission to study Divine Savior Church.
All of the plans were accepted if the approval is
given. There is property available on Main
Street in Ventura next to the Church. (English
1 pg.)

Mc4194. M-1963
Bp. Timothy Manning to J. Francis Cardinal
McIntyre
October 31, 1963. Los Angeles, California

The proposal of Msgr. McNicholas is enclosed for consideration. The School Board
meeting went smoothly and the Sisters of St. Joseph will be approached about the Lakewood
School. (English 1 pg.)

Mc4195. M-1963
Bp. Timothy Manning to J. Francis Cardinal
McIntyre
November 8, 1963. Los Angeles, California

No action was taken on the Wilshire Boulevard Cathedral property but the latest version is
enclosed. The Vincentian Fathers want a drive
for the new Novitiate building in Santa Barbara. The convent for the Holy Family Sisters is
not ready to go to the Building Commission.
(English 1 pg.)

Mc4196. M-1963
J. Francis Cardinal McIntyre to Bp. Timothy
Manning
November 13, 1963. Vatican City

Mary Waters must be our attorney and not a
party to the Wilshire Boulevard deal. The Vincentian proposal will be discussed. The subject
of the Regional Conferences is meeting with
some success. (English 2 pgs.)

Mc4197. M-1963
Mr. Cibin Michelangelo to J. Francis Cardinal
McIntyre
November 24, 1963. Rome, Italy

An invitation is extended to a program prepared by the students of Villa Nazareth for all
of the Bishops of the Council. (English 2 pgs.)
On November 26, 1963, because of President
Kennedy's death, the program has been cancelled. (English 1 pg.)

Mc4198. M-1963
J. Francis Cardinal McIntyre to Bp. Timothy
Manning
N.D. Vatican City

The St. Teresa's property must be examined
for the value of the land and the use that can be
made of the buildings. The invitations have arrived but probably not too many Bishops will
be able to attend. (English 2 pgs.)

Mc4199. M-1963
J. Francis Cardinal McIntyre to Bp. Timothy
Manning
N.D. Rome, Italy

The Ventura property is good, but the Commission ought to have a hand in Divine Savior
especially the altar, pews, confessional. We will
go to Naples during the break and Archbishop
McGucken to Ireland. (English 2 pgs.)

Mc4200. M-1963
J. Francis Cardinal McIntyre to Bp. Timothy
Manning
N.D. Vatican City

As soon as Msgr. Dolan and Msgr. O'Dwyer
know, make the announcement that Bishop
elect Ward will go to St. Timothy's. Tell Msgr.
Dignan and Msgr. Galvin that they will have
consideration. The Bishop elect will continue as
Vice officialis. (English 2 pgs.)

Mc4201. M-1963
Mr. Joseph Nealon to Msgr. John Rawden
February 10, 1963. North Hollywood,
California

The teachings of the Church concerning labor
unions should be made known to all parishio-
ners. (English 1 pg.)

Mc4202. N-1963
Mr. John Northrop to J. Francis Cardinal
  McIntyre
March 5, 1963. Santa Barbara, California

An invitation is extended to speak at the
Channel City Club on the Vatican Council or
any subject that the Cardinal wishes. (English 1
pg.) On March 19, 1963, Rev. O. B. Cook appeals for the Cardinal to come at his convenience. (English 1 pg.)

Mc4203. N-1963
Mrs. William Noonan to J. Francis Cardinal
  McIntyre
March 8, 1963. Los Angeles, California

The members of the Supreme Court are being
given a copy of the Susskind letter and a letter
of response. (English 4 pgs.)

Mc4204. N-1963
Mr. August Kettmann to J. Francis Cardinal
  McIntyre
April 23, 1963. Los Angeles, California

The National Broadcasting Company will
host a luncheon to discuss President Kennedy's
National Police Week. It is an effort to restore
respect for law and authority. (English 2 pgs.)
On April 25, 1963, the Cardinal states that
Msgr. Johnson will attend the luncheon. (English 1 pg.)

Mc4205. N-1963
Mrs. Abigail Notterman to J. Francis Cardinal
  McIntyre
June 26, 1963. Adelanto, California

Could the kissing of the Bishop's ring be
changed to a hand shake and a bow. (English 1
pg.) On June 27, 1963, Father state that the
veneration is a profession of faith and an indul-
gence is received by kissing the ring. (English
1 pg.)

Mc4206. N-1963
Dr. Louis Nash, MD to Rev. Francis Keane
July 5, 1963. Camarillo, California

As the first permanent Catholic Chaplain at
the State Hospital, the patients, relatives, and
staff have received great care and an example of
selfless devotion. (English 2 pgs.) On July 11,
1963, the Cardinal states that Fr. Keane has a
permanent home at St. Alphonsus and the Parish has a Pastor of exceptional talent. (English
1 pg.)

Mc4207. N-1963
Mr. L. L. Callaway to J. Francis Cardinal
  McIntyre
July 22, 1963. New York City, New York

The *Newsweek* Magazine will try to uncover
what the American Negro wants, thinks, and
hates which may differ from what the others
think. (English 2 pgs.) On August 5, 1963, the
Cardinal states that the issue of the magazine
covering the racial question is most helpful.
(English 1 pg.)

Mc4208. N-1963
Mr. Arthur Nie to Bp. Timothy Manning
August 12, 1963. Los Angeles, California

As a government official, it would be interesting to speak to the Holy Name Society and furnish some facts. (English 1 pg.)

Mc4209. N-1963
Mr. Richard Mathison to J. Francis Cardinal
  McIntyre
August 30, 1963. Los Angeles, California

The September 28 issue of *Newsweek* will
cover the Vatican Council and each Bishop is
asked to respond to the following questions. An
hour's interview may be necessary. (English
1 pg.)

Mc4210. O-1963
Rev. John Languille to J. Francis Cardinal
  McIntyre
January 11, 1963. Los Angeles, California

Mrs. Orcutt, a generous supporter of the
Guadalupe Youth Center, will celebrate 90
years of life. A letter to her will be appreciated.
(English 1 pg.) On January 17, 1963, the Cardinal states that prayers will be offered on her
anniversary. (English 1 pg.)

Mc4211. O-1963
Mr. Fergus O'Rourke to J. Francis Cardinal
  McIntyre
March 5, 1963. Co Cork, Ireland

Trinity College, Dublin, Ireland, receives en-
dowments for Biological Research. A contribution could be made to stimulate Biological
research in Ireland. (English 1 pg.) On March
13, 1963, the Cardinal states that a meeting
could take place if travel time is correct. (English 1 pg.)

Mc4212. O-1963
Ms. Pam Osborne to Msgr. Benjamin Hawkes
April 18, 1963. Beverly Hills, California

A critique is requested for the article, Republican Principles Found in the New Testament.
(English 6 pgs.) On April 22, 1963, Msgr. states
that the quotations used to establish the principles of the Republican party would serve no
purpose for the Party. (English 1 pg.)

Mc4213. O-1963
Arbp. Martin O'Connor to J. Francis Cardinal
McIntyre
April 30, 1963. Rome, Italy

An invitation to reside at the North American
College during the second session of the Vatican
Council is sent to the Cardinal. (English 1 pg.)
On May 13, 1963, the Cardinal offers to take
any room available but not the best. (English
1 pg.)

Mc4214. O-1963
Rev. Cornelius Dougherty to J. Francis Cardi-
nal McIntyre
June 24, 1963. Starke, Florida

The Florida Catholic remembered Msgr. Edward Pace on the 25th anniversary of his death
April 26, 1963. (English 1 pg.) On July 12,
1963, the Cardinal states that he is happy that
Msgr. Pace is remembered. He was an authority
at Catholic University. (English 1 pg.)

Mc4215. O-1963
Mrs. Evelyn O'Hara to J. Francis Cardinal
McIntyre
July 26, 1963. Torrance, California

A Novena of the Family Rosary should be inaugurated in the Archdiocese for peace and the
fulfillment of the Council's Decrees. (English 1
pg.) On August 2, 1963, Msgr. states that it is
the wish of the Cardinal and will be begun
soon. (English 1 pg.)

Mc4216. O-1963
Rev. Patrick O'Rourke to Bp. Timothy
Manning
December 2, 1963. Camden, New Jersey

For a short period, permission is given to
work with the St. Patrick Fathers in Sao Paulo,
Brazil. A memento in a Mass will be appreciated. (English 1 pg.)

Mc4217. O-1963
Mr. Charles Oberhelman to J. Francis Cardinal
McIntyre
December 16, 1963. Los Angeles, California

If no changes are made by the Council, how
will unity of all Faiths be achieved? Will infall-
ability be discussed? (English 3 pgs.)

Mc4218. P-1963
Mr. Daniel Petruzzi to J. Francis Cardinal
McIntyre
January 2, 1963. Houston, Texas

An article on the role that Religion and Ethics can have in business is necessary for a company publication. (English 1 pg.) On January 3,
1963, the Cardinal states that due to pressure of
time such an article is impossible. (English
1 pg.)

Mc4219. P-1963
Mr. P. L. Penny to J. Francis Cardinal
McIntyre
January 7, 1963. Santa Maria, California

Is the Archdiocese any closer to an announcement for a Catholic High School in the Santa
Maria area? Every other group is expanding.
(English 2 pgs.) On January 17, 1963, the Cardinal states that the new school should be ready
to open in September 1964. (English 1 pg.)

Mc4220. P-1963
Mr. Pietro Patti to J. Francis Cardinal
McIntyre
February 12, 1963. Rome, Italy

Is it possible to receive some information
about Joseph Patti who had cancer surgery
about two months ago. Letters have not been
answered. (Italian 1 pg.) On February 21, 1963,
the Cardinal asks Fr. Ring, SJ to visit the
brother and to respond to Rome. (English 1 pg.)

Mc4221. P-1963
Mr. Robert Piser to J. Francis Cardinal
McIntyre
February 14, 1963. Rome, Italy

Good reporting of the Council is necessary if
the Catholic public will receive and understand
the workings of the Council. The price to
America is $15,000. The distribution of the
money is enclosed. (English 4 pgs.)

Mc4222. P-1963
Mr. Frank Pryor to Bp. Timothy Manning
February 19, 1963. West Covina, California

What is the thinking behind the dislike of
having the Confirmation Class wear robes? A
simple garment could alleviate many problems
of proper dress. (English 2 pgs.) On February
25, 1963, the Bishop asks the Pastor to give the
information available. (English 1 pg.)

Mc4223. P-1963
J. Francis Cardinal McIntyre to Mr. Edwin
Pauley
February 21, 1963. Los Angeles, California

Would it be possible for you as a Regent of
the University of California to meet with Msgr.
Joseph Sharpe concerning the proposed changes
in the accreditation of high schools? (English
1 pg.)

Mc4224. P-1963
Bp. Jesus Palacios to J. Francis Cardinal
McIntyre
March 14, 1963. Oaxaca, Mexico

A request is made to be placed on the Missionary collection program. Rev. Antonio Sanchez is studying the CCD Program and the Catholic Schools in Los Angeles. (Spanish 1 pg.) On March 25, 1963, the Cardinal states that all of the parishes are assigned for this year but a donation is enclosed for the assistance needed. (English 1 pg.)

Mc4225. P-1963
Mr. H. E. Gali to J. Francis Cardinal McIntyre
March 15, 1963. Seattle, Washington

The project at Providence Hospital is not complete and money should not be paid. (English 1 pg.) On March 22, 1963, the Cardinal states that there is not enough information to make a decision. (English 1 pg.)

Mc4226. P-1963
Rev. Francis Parrish, SJ to Msgr. John Rawden
March 26, 1963. Los Angeles, California

The Soul Assurance Plan is incorporated in the Apostleship of Prayer and the League of the Sacred Heart. A new organization would confuse people. (English 2 pgs.) On April 5, 1963, Msgr. suggests that Mary Ortmann meet with Fr. Parrish. (English 1 pg.)

Mc4227. P-1963
Msgr. John Rawden to Bp. Jesus Palacios
April 9, 1963. Los Angeles, California

Rev. Antonio Sanchez is assigned to Santa Teresita Parish and the Archdiocese will endorse the petition for him to remain during the summer months. (English 1 pg.)

Mc4228. P-1963
Mr. F. W. Petersen to J. Francis Cardinal McIntyre
June 4, 1963. Altadena, California

A proposal is made to have a modest memorial Chapel in Rome where all Christians can pray in unity under the leadership of Pope John XXIII (English 1 pg.) On June 11, 1963, Msgr. Hawkes states that he has copies of the sketches of the Chapel and will bring them to the Cardinal's attention on his return from Rome. (English 1 pg.)

Mc4229. P-1963
Mr. A. C. Pellitier to J. Francis Cardinal McIntyre
November 6, 1963. Lakewood, California

A donation of $15,000 and 500 shares of stock are enclosed for Don Bosco Technical Institute. (English 1 pg.) On November 9, 1963, Bishop Manning expresses the gratitude of the Cardinal and his own for the donation. (English 1 pg.)

Mc4230. P-1963
Mr. Gemisco Pope to J. Francis Cardinal McIntyre
December 9, 1963. Hawthorne, California

If hate movements are condemned by the Church, how can any parish accept donations from such societies as the John Birch Society? (English 1 pg.)

Mc4231. P-1963
Rev. Raymond Pelly to J. Francis Cardinal McIntyre
December 16, 1963. Co. Tipperary, Ireland

A friendly letter commenting on the activities of the Council and a visiting priest from Los Angeles who is in Ireland. (English 1 pg.) On January 4, 1963, the Cardinal expresses gratitude for the hospitality shown to Fr. Pierse. (English 1 pg.)

Mc4232. Q-1963
Rev. Martin Quigley to J. Francis Cardinal McIntyre
April 18, 1963. New York City, New York

A copy of *Catholic Action in Practice* is being sent. It is a practical handbook for clergy and laity. (English 1 pg.)

Mc4233. Q-1963
Rev. Hugh Quinn to Msgr. Benjamin Hawkes
May 13, 1963. El Paso, Texas

A con man is widening his practice and priests ought to be warned. He often impersonates a priest and collects money. (English 1 pg.) On May 16, 1963, Msgr. states that the gentleman has been in Los Angeles and the alarm has been sounded. (English 1 pg.)

Mc4234. Q-1963
Mr. John R. Quirk to J. Francis Cardinal McIntyre
May 17, 1963. Los Angeles, California

A long discourse on graft and unfair practices that are being used by the members of the government and various companies and even the Catholic Church. Some of the material is being sent to Rome. (English 6 pgs.)

Mc4235. R-1963
Mr. Bernard Durand to J. Francis Cardinal McIntyre
January 7, 1963. White Plains, New York

Mr. Martin D. Ryan will be inducted into the Knights of Malta on January 14 of St. Patrick's Cathedral. (English 1 pg.) On January 11, 1963, the Cardinal sends congratulations and states that another Mediterranean conquest is his. (English 1 pg.)

Mc4236. R-1963
Hon. Dean Rusk to J. Francis Cardinal McIntyre
January 14, 1963. Washington, D.C.

An invitation is extended to attend the Regional Foreign Policy Conference in Los Angeles on February 13. (English 2 pgs.) On January 22, 1963, the Cardinal states that he has commitments that he cannot break but that he will send a representative to the Conference. (English 1 pg.)

Mc4237. R-1963
Mrs. Dorothy Rowan to J. Francis Cardinal McIntyre
March 4, 1963. Los Angeles, California

Is there a retirement age for priests? Some of the priests are so feeble that it is difficult for them to say Mass. Is it the policy for retirement to be a time of ease and peace? (English 1 pg.)

Mc4238. R-1963
Mr. Michael Reyes to Msgr. Benjamin Hawkes
March 15, 1963. Camaguey, Cuba

A plea for help to care for and support two children ages 10 and 8. (Spanish 1 pg.) On March 28, 1963, Fr. Salazar states that if the parish priest will write a letter on Church stationery, some help can be given. (English 1 pg.)

Mc4239. R-1963
Msgr. John Rawden to Ronald Printing Corporation
April 17, 1963. Los Angeles, California

The name of the individual who ordered 2,500 copies of Quest for Happiness is needed. (English 1 pg.)

Mc4240. R-1963
J. Francis Cardinal McIntyre to Ernesto Cardinal Ruffini
April 30, 1963. Los Angeles, California

A defense of the position taken in regard to Rev. Hans Kung at Loyola University is needed. Two local theologians gave opinions of the texts of the lecture. (Latin 5 pgs.)

Mc4241. R-1963
Miss Carol Rondeau to Msgr. Benjamin Hawkes
April 30, 1963. Sierra Madre, California

Could a priest or a parish use a Chalice and Paten? (English 1 pg.) On May 2, 1963, Msgr. states that Santa Teresita Church and its Missions or a newly ordained priest may be able to use a chalice. (English 1 pg.)

Mc4242. R-1963
Mr. William Ross to J. Francis Cardinal McIntyre
May 28, 1963. Los Angeles, California

There is a campaign to have all bells, chimes, and carillions in the nation rung at the same time 11:00 PDT. It will be the message to Let Freedom Ring. (English 1 pg.) On June 11, 1963, the Cardinal states that the bells and carillions will not be silent on July 4. (English 1 pg.)

Mc4243. R-1963
Mr. William Ross to J. Francis Cardinal McIntyre
June 25, 1963. Los Angeles, California

The Supreme Court is making it impossible for prayer to be a part of public school education. Maybe an amendment would be possible to correct this unjust situation. (English 1 pg.)

Mc4244. R-1963
Mr. Charles Ramirez to J. Francis Cardinal McIntyre
July 13, 1963. Los Angeles, California

The donor of the Apologetic Award became known when the award arrived. I am most grateful for the award and for the education that the Archdiocese makes available. (English 1 pg.)

Mc4245. R-1963
J. Francis Cardinal McIntyre to Mr. Bruce Russell
August 1, 1963. Los Angeles, California

The cartoon The Headless Rider interested me as does your positions on many issues. (English 1 pg.)

Mc4246. R-1963
Paul Revere Association to J. Francis Cardinal McIntyre
August 27, 1963. New Orleans, Louisiana

Urgent work is needed to block the booby trap of the Eisenhower Good Reservations Clause. (English 1 pg.)

Mc4247. R-1963
J. Francis Cardinal McIntyre to Msgr. Patrick
Ryan
September 17, 1963. Los Angeles, California

While in Los Angeles to address the Archdi-
ocesan Council of Catholic Women, both Msgr.
Roche and Msgr. Sharpe will confer with you.
(English 1 pg.)

Mc4248. R-1963
Mr. Martin Ryan to J. Francis Cardinal
McIntyre
November 4, 1963. White Plains, New York

The highlight of the retirement dinner was
the cablegram from Vatican City. There are
some needs in the office so complete retirement
will not be for several months. (English 1 pg.)

Mc4249. R-1963
Mr. Marion deVelder to J. Francis Cardinal
McIntyre
November 8, 1963. New York City, New York

An invitation is extended to participate in
Religion in American Life Program on January
8 and 9 in Harriman, New York. (English 2
pgs.) On December 10, 1963, the Cardinal
states that he is incapable of participating due
to the very heavy schedule of the Archdiocese.
(English 1 pg.)

Mc4250. R-1963
Mrs. Mary J. Roelle to Msgr. Benjamin
Hawkes
N.D. Covina, California

A request for information on the procedure
to donate human organs after death. (English 1
pg.) On November 19, 1963, Msgr. states that
it is licit morally to donate one's organs but at
the conclusion of the use, the body must be buried. (English 1 pg.)

Mc4251. R-1963
Rev. James Richardson, CM to J. Francis Car-
dinal McIntyre
December 4, 1963. Camarillo, California

Observations when the vernacular can be jus-
tifiably be used in the recitation of the Divine
Office and still retain the use of the Latin. (English 4 pgs.)

Mc4252. R-1963
Ms. Muriel Rizzo to J. Francis Cardinal
McIntyre
December 11, 1963. Los Angeles, California

As a tribute to Pope John and President
Kennedy, the Catholics ought to spearhead the
Civil Rights Movement under the leadership of
the hierarchy. (English 2 pgs.)

Mc4253. R-1963
Rev. Lawrence Gibson to Bp. Victor Reed
December 16, 1963. Los Angeles, California

Is there another way to read the Breviary in
English? Paragraph 101 does not apply at the
present time. (English 1 pg.)

Mc4254. R-1963
Ms. Hilda Burns to J. Francis Cardinal
McIntyre
December 19, 1963. New York City, New
York

January 5 is This Nation Under God Sunday
according to the *Readers Digest* working with
the World Council of Churches. What will the
Catholics do? (English 1 pg.)

Mc4255. S-1963
Mr. Florian DeDonato to Bp. Timothy Man-
ning
January 7, 1963. Los Angeles, California

The Better Humanity League is not incorporated and must be a new organization or a
cover-up for some promotion. (English 2 pgs.)
On January 8, 1963, the Bishop states that
since information is so scarce, it is better to refrain from contact. (English 1 pg.)

Mc4256. S-1963
Miss Lolita Savage to J. Francis Cardinal
McIntyre
N.D. Beverly Hills, California

A request for a picture that can be used for
the program of the Mardi Gras Ball which will
raise money for the retreat house. (English 1
pg.) On January 9, 1963, the Cardinal states
that he is happy to send the picture. (English
1 pg.)

Mc4257. S-1963
Mr. Peter Schmid to J. Francis Cardinal
McIntyre
January 12, 1963. Downey, California

Priests should be shouting from the pulpits
the evils of Communism and should leave the
other topics for the politicians. (English 1 pg.)
On January 17, 1963, the Cardinal states that
discrimination is unjust and all children should
share in tax money. (English 1 pg.)

Mc4258. S-1963
Miss Elizabeth Scott to Bp. Timothy Manning
January 22, 1963. Long Beach, California

As a staunch Catholic why would reading the
Upper Room be harmful? I read the suggested
Scripture from a Catholic Bible. (English 8 pgs.)
On January 25, 1963, Fr. Vandenberg agrees
that the *Upper Room* would do Miss Scott no
harm. (English 1 pg.)

Mc4259. S-1963
Bp. Egidio Vagnozzi to J. Francis Cardinal
  McIntyre
January 22, 1963. Washington, D.C.

A request for some information on the capability of Mr. Gerard Sherry to be the editor of the Catholic newspaper. (English 1 pg.) On January 30, 1963, the Cardinal states that he cannot evaluate the editor but adds, does it not seem that a priest should be the editor? (English 1 pg.)

Mc4260. S-1963
Miss L. Schmitz to Rev. John Sheridan
February 8, 1963. Los Angeles, California

Could a downtown hotel be turned into a home for working girls who would do missionary work in the area after working hours and help people return to the Faith. (English 1 pg.) On February 16, 1963, Fr. suggests that the plan be talked over with the priests of the area. (English 1 pg.)

Mc4261. S-1963
Mr. T. W. Conway to J. Francis Cardinal
  McIntyre
February 9, 1963. Las Vegas, New Mexico

Dr. Singh has a medical background and could practice if he could qualify in California. Could the Archdiocese help? (English 1 pg.) On February 18, 1963, the Cardinal requests Catholic Welfare to investigate the requirements. (English 1 pg.)

Mc4262. S-1963
Julius Cardinal Dopfner to J. Francis Cardinal
  McIntyre
March 20, 1963. Berlin, Germany

An explanation and defense of Professor H. Schlier's teachings of the New Testament and his portrayal of the Christ of Faith and the Christ of History. (Latin 6 pgs.)

Mc4263. S-1963
Rev. William Kenneally, CM to J. Francis Cardinal McIntyre
April 4, 1963. Camarillo, California

In fairness to Professor Schlier, no comment should be made until the article is read and studied. Opinions should not be based on reviews of the article. (English 1 pg.)

Mc4264. S-1963
Francis Cardinal Spellman to J. Francis Cardinal McIntyre
April 9, 1963. New York City, New York

Suggestions for the revision of Canon Law should be sent succinctly and in Latin. (English 1 pg.)

Mc4265. S-1963
Msgr. Maurice Sheehy to J. Francis Cardinal
  McIntyre
April 11, 1963. Cedar Rapids, Iowa

The Military Chaplains are meeting in Pasadena May 14–16. Is a visit at that time a possibility. (English 1 pg.) On April 18, 1963, the Cardinal states that if Msgr. will tell him the free time available, a luncheon will be prepared. (English 1 pg.)

Mc4266. S-1963
J. Francis Cardinal McIntyre to Francis Cardinal Spellman
April 16, 1963. Los Angeles, California

Bishop John J. Ward made a survey of the United States, Hawaii, Bahama Islands and Mexico which will give static. He will be in New York for the Canon Law Society of America Meeting. (English 1 pg.)

Mc4267. S-1963
Rev. Ferdinand Slejzer to Msgr. Benjamin
  Hawkes
April 22, 1963. Camp Pendleton, California

The U.S. Marine Corps sent orders for over seas duty on May 1. Gratitude for the faculties of the Archdiocese and for the help of the priests in San Clemente must be expressed. (English 1 pg.)

Mc4268. S-1963
Judge Irving Hill to J. Francis Cardinal
  McIntyre
April 26, 1963. Los Angeles, California

The Papal announcement during Easter celebration that statements derogatory to the Jews will be eliminated from the Liturgy was received with joy. Let us follow the Papal command and live in truth, justice and love. (English 1 pg.)

Mc4269. S-1963
Mrs. William Snider to Bp. Timothy Manning
May 26, 1963. Dayton, Kentucky

Is it possible to have a Catholic priest perform a marriage in a wedding chapel in West Covina? (English 1 pg.) On May 26, 1963, the Bishop states that no priest is authorized to perform weddings in the Chapel and they do not do so. (English 1 pg.)

Mc4270. S-1963
J. Francis Cardinal McIntyre to Mrs. Harry H.
  Spearman
May 29, 1963. Los Angeles, California

Your donation will help to build a church in the Orient through the Propagation of the Faith. It will be dedicated to the memory of the members of the family. (English 1 pg.)

Mc4271. S-1963
Rev. Blase Schumacher to Mr. Mario Salas
June 14, 1963. Montebello, California

It is understood that when the family moves out of the parish, the child moves out of the school. In this way a new child can enter the parish school. (English 1 pg.)

Mc4272. S-1963
Arbp. Gerald P. Sigaud to J. Francis Cardinal McIntyre
July 31, 1963. Rio de Janeiro, Brazil

An appeal to petition the Commission of Extraordinary Affairs to study the Catholic Social Doctrine so a definite teaching of the Church can be formulated. (English 4 pgs.)

Mc4273. S-1963
Mr. James W. Scott to J. Francis Cardinal McIntyre
August 1, 1963. San Francisco, California

The integrity of the Supreme Court is in question from the statements in the *San Francisco Chronicle*. Some public statement ought to be made to clarify your position. (English 2 pgs.)

Mc4274. S-1963
Mrs. Rose Corrigan to J. Francis Cardinal McIntyre
August 5, 1963. San Juan Capistrano, California

Is the book *Blessed Mother Goose* by Frank Scully suppose to be giving the Catholic direction or ridicule? (English 1 pg.)

Mc4275. S-1963
Mr. Ed Kelly to Francis Cardinal Spellman
August 15, 1963. New York City, New York

The Catholic Church should never endorse the racial march on Washington, D.C. More harm is done to the negro cause by the march than the good that came from it. (English 1 pg.)

Mc4276. S-1963
J. Francis Cardinal McIntyre to Francis Cardinal Spellman
August 23, 1963. Los Angeles, California

The National Social Action Convention and the Catholic Civil Liberties Union will meet in Dayton. Some attention ought to be given to the Civil Liberties Union. (English 2 pgs.)

Mc4277. S-1963
Mr. John Schroeder to Rev. John Thom
N.D. LaHabra, California

Is it lawful for a Catholic to donate his body to science? (English 1 pg.) On August 26, 1963,

Fr. states that it is lawful but after the scientific study is finished, the body must be buried. (English 1 pg.)

Mc4278. S-1963 J. Francis Cardinal McIntyre to Francis Cardinal Spellman
September 10, 1963. Los Angeles, California

The peaceful demonstration in Washington, D.C. is spoken of as peace for a day. maybe some type of legislation will be passed. (English 1 pg.)

Mc4279. S-1963
J. Francis Cardinal McIntyre to Francis Cardinal Spellman
September 18, 1963. Los Angeles, California

Could the Pope be prevailed upon to sit for a portrait by Mr. Alex Clayton for the Vatican Pavilion. After the World's Fair, the portrait will come to St. John's Seminary. (English 1 pg.)

Mc4280. S-1963
Mr. Earl Schneider to J. Francis Cardinal McIntyre
N.D. Los Angeles, California

Where does one find a philosophy of Christianity? Billy Graham has won converts for the Catholic Church but the Church does not recognize him. (English 1 pg.) On October 7, 1963, Fr. Thom suggests a conversation with the priest at Our Lady Chapel but gives basic logical reasons. (English 2 pgs.)

Mc4281. S-1963
Rev. Joseph Sharpe to J. Francis Cardinal McIntyre
October 29, 1963. Los Angeles, California

The Vocation Committee will use the Education Office and Fr. Gibson will conduct his program without hindrance. The Superintendents met in Canada and the desire to have the Superintendents a part of NCWC did not materialize. (English 2 pgs.)

Mc4282. S-1963
Hon. de Souza-Gomes to J. Francis Cardinal McIntyre
November 20, 1963. Rome, Italy

The Brazilian Embassy will have a special *Te-Deum* on Thanksgiving Day at the *Domus Mariae* to which all of the American Bishops are invited. (English 1 pg.)

Mc4283. S-1963
Abbe Pierre Vermont to Bp. Timothy Manning
December 2, 1962. Geneva, Switzerland

Could some information be obtained about
the Better Humanity League of Los Angeles. Is
it a sect or a racket? (English 1 pg.) On December 12, 1962, the Bishop requests information
from the California Intelligence Bureau. (English 1 pg.)

Mc4284. T-1963
Rev. Francis Keane to J. Francis Cardinal
   McIntyre
January 9, 1963. Camarillo, California

Dr. Tiangco came from the Philippines and
must return for two years before permanent residence status can be obtained. A letter to the
Immigration Department might change this.
(English 1 pg.) On January 17, 1963, the Cardinal states that in the past an appeal has been
unsuccessful. (English 1 pg.)

Mc4285. T-1963
Rev. Francis Keane to J. Francis Cardinal
   McIntyre
January 23, 1963. Camarillo, California

Dr. Tiangco might receive a waiver if he appeals to the Secretary of State or the Department of Health and Welfare. (English 2 pgs.)
On January 31, 1963, the Cardinal states that
he does not usually make these requests. (English 1 pg.)

Mc4286. T-1963
Mr. Alfred Parisi to J. Francis Cardinal McIntyre
February 4, 1963. Mt. Vernon, New York

A long history of the Wallace and Thorn estates and the final disposition of the Thorn estate is given. (English 5 pgs.) On February 15,
1963, the Cardinal states that his knowledge of
Mrs. Thorn was limited to business transactions. (English 1 pg.)

Mc4287. T-1963
J. Francis Cardinal McIntyre to Msgr. Paul
   Tanner
March 11, 1963. Los Angeles, California

The Administrative Board has no power to
speak for the American Bishops. Any matter
can be submitted to the Bishops before an announcement is made. (English 2 pgs.)

Mc4288. T-1963
J. Francis Cardinal McIntyre to Hon. Eduardo
   Toda
April 19, 1963. Los Angeles, California

With regret the invitation to attend the 250th
anniversary of Fr. Junipero Serra's birth cannot
be accepted. Msgr. Raymond O'Flaherty will
represent the Archdiocese. (English 2 pgs.)

Mc4289. T-1963
Mrs. Rosie Taylor to Msgr. Benjamin Hawkes
April 19, 1963. Los Angeles, California

Detailed information is needed for the family
tree study of the Urquidez family. Records
should be at the Plaza Church. (English 1 pg.)
On April 25, 1963, Fr. Bossi, CM states that all
of the information available has been given to
Mrs. Taylor. (English 1 pg.)

Mc4290. T-1963
Mr. Manuel Iribarne to J. Francis Cardinal
   McIntyre
April 1, 1963. Madrid, Spain

An invitation to the events commemorating
the 250th anniversary of the birth of Junipero
Serra in Petra, Mallorca, from May 29–June 4
is sent. The entire proposed program is enclosed. (English 5 pgs.)

Mc4291. V-1963
Mr. Patrick Burns to Msgr. Benjamin Hawkes
April 19, 1963. Los Angeles, California

The Volunteers of America would be honored
to have Cardinal McIntyre give the invocation
and attend the luncheon in June. A date agreeable to him will be agreeable to us. (English 2
pgs.) On April 22, 1963, Msgr. Johnson states
that the Volunteers of America is an old and
honored organization. (English 1 pg.)

Mc4292. T-1963
Mrs. Roy S. Talum to Rev. John B. Thom
May 16, 1963. Los Angeles, California

A series of pictures of the mysteries of the
Rosary is available to promote the family Rosary. The blessing of the Chancery is requested
for the success of the project. (English 2 pgs.)
On May 22, 1963, the Bishop states that an
oral blessing can be given but nothing in writing. (English 1 pg.)

Mc4293. T-1963
Mrs. Gracia Tessier to J. Francis Cardinal
   McIntyre
December 19, 1963. Glendale, California

Resistance to some of the suggested changes
by the Vatican Council is praiseworthy. Unity of
religions will be by faith and prayer and sacrifice. (English 1 pg.)

Mc4294. V-1963
Arbp. Edigio Vagnozzi to Msgr. Paul Tanner
March 11, 1963. Washington, D.C.

Giuseppe Cardinal Pizzardo comments on the
wealth of material sent to the Pope attesting the
interest in the Vatican Council and the Pope
conveys his Apostolic Blessings to all concerned.
(English 3 pgs.)

Mc4295. V-1963
J. Francis Cardinal McIntyre to Arbp. Egidio Vagnozzi
April 5, 1963. Los Angeles, California

A copy of the memorandum concerning Fr. Hans Kung's speaking engagement in Los Angeles is given for review. (English 4 pgs.)

Mc4296. V-1963
Arbp. Egidio Vagnozzi to J. Francis Cardinal McIntyre
April 18, 1963. Washington, D.C.

Your comments on the Schemata *De Episcopis and Dioecesium Regimine* are in accord with the thinking of others. (English 1 pg.)

Mc4297. W-1963
Mr. Michael Welsh to Bp. Alden J. Bell
January 8, 1963. Philadelphia, Pennsylvania

Statistical information is needed of the number of Catholics and Protestants in each area Santa Monica, Pasadena, etc. (English 1 pg.) On January 16, 1963, Msgr. states that Catholics are 17% or 18% of the total population. (English 1 pg.)

Mc4298. W-1963
Mrs. William Walsh to Msgr. Joseph Sharpe
January 31, 1963. Camarillo, California

Is any Catholic high school using the kit, *Reading for Understanding?* It is being removed from the Camarillo School District by Catholic demand. (English 1 pg.) On February 1, 1963, Msgr. states that no Catholic high school is using that kit. (English 1 pg.)

Mc4299. W-1963
Mr. Gordon Wood to Bp. Timothy Manning
February 21, 1963. Los Angeles, California

An invitation is extended to give the invocation at the opening of the new building for the Food and Drug Administration on March 15 at 11:00 a.m. (English 2 pgs.) On March 1, 1963, the Bishop states that he will be very happy to give the invocation. (English 1 pg.)

Mc4300. W-1963
Mr. Egon Bittner to Rev. John Sheridan
March 16, 1963. Riverside, California

Explain why Franz Werfel was given a Catholic burial without conversion. What theological authority can be cited to support the dispensation? (English 1 pg.)

Mc4301. W-1963
Rev. Emmanuel Muessiggang to Bp. Timothy Manning
April 4, 1963. Santa Barbara, California

Rev. Cyril Fischer, OFM was a good friend of Franz Werfel and asked him if he wanted Baptism. The answer was that he did not want to offend the Jews. (English 1 pg.)

Mc4302. W-1963
Mr. Arthur Potts to Mr. Olin Wellborn III
May 2, 1963. Los Angeles, California

The need for an increase of qualified social welfare workers is acute and a planning commission is being formed to address the issue. (English 4 pgs.) On May 6, 1963, Mr. Wellborn asks for an appointment to discuss the situation. (English 1 pg.)

Mc4303. W-1963
Rev. Anthony Wouters to Bp. Timothy Manning
June 19, 1963. Washington, D.C.

Prayers are requested for the canonization of the Uganda Martyrs. The Church needs to be told that heroes and holiness belong to every race and in every age. (English 2 pgs.) On July 2, 1963, the Bishop sends a donation for the cause of the Uganda Martyrs. (English 1 pg.)

Mc4304. W-1963
Miss Dorothy Watson to J. Francis Cardinal McIntyre
July 18, 1963. Charlottesville, Virginia

The Supreme Court did not outlaw God. The decision forbids the State from proscribing prayer as an official act. (English 2 pgs.)

Mc4305. W-1963
Mr. James Walton to J. Francis Cardinal McIntyre
August 1, 1963. Cleveland, Ohio

The chief work of the Vatican Council ought to be the increase of prayer and penance and then everything else will fall into place. (English 2 pgs.)

Mc4306. W-1963
Arbp. Luigi Raimondi to J. Francis Cardinal McIntyre
August 10, 1963. Mexico City, Mexico

Mr. Emile Valton who is allegedly a school mate of the Pope might have some interesting historical material with him. He is presently living in Los Angeles. (English 1 pg.) On August 28, 1963, the Cardinal states that the individual is unknown at the address given. (English 1 pg.)

Mc4307. W-1963
Rev. Manuel Alves to Msgr. Benjamin Hawkes
August 27, 1963. Los Angeles, California

Mrs. Lullia Washington has designated St. Patrick's Parish as the recipient in her will. Now a Mr. and Mrs. A. J. Spill claim a relationship. Should the police be informed? (English 1 pg.)

Mc4308. W-1963
Dr. Edward Wiater, MD to J. Francis Cardinal
   McIntyre
September 3, 1963. Long Beach, California

Is there anything that a layman could do to encourage the Sisters to open a school similar to St. Coletta here in California? (English 1 pg.) On September 13, 1963, the Cardinal states that the Joseph P. Kennedy Center in Santa Monica is the only center in Los Angeles. (English 1 pg.)

Mc4309. W-1963
Mrs. Clark Wiedmann to J. Francis Cardinal
   McIntyre
September 14, 1963. Palos Verdes, California

The placement of the Church and school will completely destroy the character of the deed restricted neighborhood. There is plenty of space in nearby areas. (English 2 pgs.) On September 17, 1963, Msgr. states that there will be no restricting of the view. (English 1 pg.)

Mc4310. W-1963
Rev. Leo F. Fey, SJ to Msgr. Benjamin Hawkes
October 25, 1963. San Francisco, California

Is there a school for cerebral palsy children in Los Angeles? (English 1 pg.) On October 30, 1963, Msgr. states that St. Vincent's Home in Santa Barbara might be able to take the child. (English 1 pg.)

Mc4311. W-1963
Rev. Arnold Paroline, OFM to Bp. Timothy
   Manning
December 6, 1962. Los Angeles, California

For twenty-five years Roger Wagner has conducted work shops, choirs, and has trained many choir directors in the West. Would the Archdiocese consider an honor for him? (English 1 pg.)

Mc4312. W-1963
Mrs. Gertrude Wilson to Msgr. Benjamin
   Hawkes
December 11, 1962. San Gabriel, California

Because the pastor of St. Anthony's Church told the people to vote "NO" the annexation vote was defeated. (English 1 pg.) On December 27, 1963, Fr. James J. Glennon states that a message was placed in the bulletin but that no statement was made from the altar at Mass. (English 3 pgs.)

Mc4313. W-1963
Mr. James McCarthy to J. Francis Cardinal
   McIntyre
December 17, 1963. Washington, D.C.

The Catholic War Veterans want to give an award to John Wayne for Americanism. Is he a person of good character? (English 1 pg.) On December 27, 1963, the Cardinal states that John Wayne is not personally known by me but his first wife was an outstanding Catholic. (English 1 pg.)

Mc4314. W-1963
Mrs. Clare Wilson to J. Francis Cardinal
   McIntyre
December 20, 1963. Los Angeles, California

Why isn't Midnight Mass allowed in Los Angeles when it is permitted in so many Dioceses? (English 2 pgs.) On December 27, 1963, Fr. states that the Pastors recommend and support the present policy. (English 1 pg.)

Mc4315. Y-1963
Mrs. Richard Esbenshade to Rev. John Thom
August 30, 1963. Pasadena, California

A Tri-Faith Symposium will be held in October for youth giving them an opportunity to express respect for every individual and Catholic participation is needed. (English 2 pgs.) On September 3, 1963, Fr. states that another program is operating along the same lines. (English 1 pg.)

Mc4316. Y-1963
Ms. Maria Ysasi to J. Francis Cardinal
   McIntyre
November 15, 1963. Plasencia, Spain

For a lady who is ill in a sanitorium, a picture and a medal could bring happiness and relief. Please pray for her recovery. (Spanish 1 pg.)

Mc4317. Z-1963
Mrs. Dominic Zappa to J. Francis Cardinal
   McIntyre
April 2, 1963. Los Angeles, California

Catholic Welfare will not loan us enough money to pay debts and this is causing stress and worry. (English 3 pgs.) On April 5, 1963, Msgr. Johnson states that the loan would lessen the welfare's ability to help other people. (English 1 pg.)

Mc4318. Z-1963
Sister M. Zenda to Gen. Dwight D. Eisenhower
May 10, 1963. Los Angeles, California

A message of great importance must be delivered by you to the President of the United States. (English 1 pg.) On June 1963, Sister states that perhaps Senator Knowland can bring the message when he comes to Los Angeles. (English 1 pg.)

Mc4319. Z-1963
J. Francis Cardinal McIntyre to Mrs. Mary
   Zabrowski
July 10, 1963. Los Angeles, California

Lt. William Reese wishes to extend special greetings and in his name there are some medals for the members of the family. (English 1 pg.)

Mc4320. Z-1963
Rev. Thomas O'Donnell, CSC to Msgr. Benjamin Hawkes
August 22, 1963. Notre Dame, Indiana

General Robert Schulz requests an investigation of Sister Zenda. If she is a religious, the letters are to be stopped. (English 1 pg.) On August 28, 1963, Msgr. states that the lady is definitely not a religious and the letters can be disregarded. (English 1 pg.)

Listing for the Year
1964

Mc4321. A-1964
Dr. Joseph Nillo, MD to Msgr. Benjamin
  Hawkes
N.D. Norfolk, Virginia

A request for information where a Radiologist can serve who is not qualified to practice in the United States. (English 1 pg.) On January 7, 1964, Msgr. asks Dr. John Aiken to supply any information that is available. (English 1 pg.)

Mc4322. A-1964
Mr. Fred Hyman to J. Francis Cardinal
  McIntyre
February 7, 1964. Los Angeles, California

The Ambassador Hotel is now under new management and will again be the finest Old World hotel in Los Angeles. (English 1 pg.) On February 15, 1964, the Cardinal extends best wishes for a successful administration. (English 1 pg.)

Mc4323. A-1964
Mrs. Melinda Akard to J. Francis Cardinal
  McIntyre
March 26, 1964. Canoga Park, California

Why does a good and caring Pastor forbid a chapter of the Cardinal Mindszenty Society to be organized in the parish? Some feel a moral obligation to be informed. (English 4 pgs.) On March 31, 1964, the Cardinal states that each Pastor must follow his best judgment. (English 1 pg.)

Mc4324. A-1964
J. Francis Cardinal McIntyre to
  Mr. & Mrs. R. Auth
June 3, 1964. Los Angeles, California

I am most grateful for the beautiful floral decoration which accompanied the statue of the Blessed Mother on the anniversary of my ordination. (English 1 pg.)

Mc4325. A-1964
Mr. Frederick Wayne to Msgr. Benjamin
  Hawkes
September 3, 1964. Richmond, Virginia

The burial of Gracie Allen from an Episcopal Church so her Jewish husband can be buried next to her is a disgrace to the Catholic Church. (English 1 pg.) On September 11, 1964, Msgr. states that George Burns was told that he could be buried next to Gracie. (English 1 pg.)

Mc4326. A-1964
Rev. Tullio Andreatta to J. Francis Cardinal
  McIntyre
September 5, 1964. San Ysidro, California

The example of Christ-like attitude and brotherly love toward Father DuBay is a lesson for all clergy and laity. (English 2 pgs.) On September 10, 1964, the Cardinal expresses his appreciation for the letter. (English 1 pg.)

Mc4327. A-1964
Mr. Joseph Alvin to J. Francis Cardinal
  McIntyre
September 26, 1964. Los Angeles, California

Should not Mary be presented and explained to all people as a loving, helpful mother and not as a rival to Jesus or as a goddess. (English 5 pgs.)

Mc4328. A-1964
Msgr. Benjamin Hawkes to Rev. John Acton
October 7, 1964. Los Angeles, California

When the opportunity presents itself, correct the false rumors concerning the funeral of Gracie Allen. (English 1 pg.) On October 13, 1964, Fr. states that he will try to correct the false impressions. (English 1 pg.)

Mc4329. A-1964
Arbp. Egidio Vagnozzi to Msgr. Benjamin Hawkes
December 9, 1963. Washington, D.C.

Could some information be given concerning the present residence of Mr. Gaetano Anelli? (English 1 pg.) On January 14, 1964, Msgr. states that after several investigations the last known record was September 1962 and that his present residence is unknown. (English 1 pg.)

Mc4330. B-1964
Msgr. Franco Brambilla to Bp. Timothy Manning
January 3, 1964. Washington, D.C.

A movie producer, Mr. Eric Ballard, requests a Papal audience for the principal actors of a movie being made in Rome. (English 1 pg.) On January 15, 1964, the Bishop states that after investigation no one knows the gentleman. (English 1 pg.)

Mc4331. B-1964
Msgr. Benjamin Hawkes to Rev. Charles Burns, OMI
January 6. 1964. Los Angeles, California

Please accept the appointment as Chaplain of the Civic Service Club of Wilmington. (English 1 pg.) On July 9, 1964, Fr. states that the Civitan Club is not well known nor well attended. The Optimist Club requests a Chaplain and seems to be more deserving. (English 2 pgs.)

Mc4332. B-1964
Bp. Alden J. Bell to J. Francis Cardinal McIntyre
January 6, 1964. Sacramento, California

The expenditures of the Public Relations Committee are enclosed and the need for a permanent secretary is evident. (English 2 pgs.)

Mc4333. B-1964
Mr. Steven Balch to J. Francis Cardinal McIntyre
January 8, 1964. Los Angeles, California

The benefits of participating in a dialogue Mass with the priest out weighs the difficulty of educating the laity. (English 1 pg.)

Mc4334. B-1964
Msgr. John Rawden to J. Francis Cardinal McIntyre
January 9, 1964. Los Angeles, California

Mr. Ernest Berry, the owner of the land in Palos Verdes that the Diocese is buying, died. A letter of condolence to his wife would be advantageous. (English 1 pg.)

Mc4335. B-1964
J. Francis Cardinal McIntyre to Bp. Alden J. Bell
January 10, 1964. Los Angeles, California

Archbishop McGucken is trying to arrange a meeting of all California Bishops. The matter of a full time secretary will be a topic for discussion. (English 1 pg.)

Mc4336. B-1964
Mr. Allen Blitstein to J. Francis Cardinal McIntyre
January 19, 1964. Minneapolis, Minnesota

May a priest witness a wedding of a Catholic and Jewish couple and have them promise to rear the children in both faiths? (English 2 pgs.)

Mc4337. B-1964
Rev. Darby Betts to Msgr. Jon Rawden
January 21, 1964. Oakland, California

Could the early records of Santa Barbara Mission be used to find the birthdate of Juan Castro Campbell and the given name of Alicia's father. The date would be between 1840–1860. (English 1 pg.)

Mc4338. B-1964
Mrs. Lucienna Biggs to Bp. Timothy Manning
January 24, 1964. Hollywood, California

On February 2 at 4:00 p.m. a choral and organ concert will be held in memory of Mr. Richard Biggs at Blessed Sacrament Church. Four members of the family have parish choirs. (English 1 pg.)

Mc4339. B-1964
Rev. Francis Weber to Rev. Eugene Gilb
January 27, 1964. San Fernando, California

The life of Rev. Francisco DeJesus Sanchez. OFM is the central figure in Helen Hunt Jackson's novel *Ramona*. He traveled in California giving Retreats and Missions. (English 1 pg.)

Mc4340. B-1964
Rev. Maynard Geiger to Rev. Eugne Gilb
January 9, 1964. Santa Barbara, California

The records at Santa Barbara Mission are the records of Baptism and deaths of the Mission Indians. The Presidio Chapel records are at Our Lady of Sorrows Parish. The priest referred to in the letter is Fr. Francisco Sanchez, OFM. (English 2 pgs.)

Mc4341. B-1964
Mr. Joseph Jenks to J. Francis Cardinal
McIntyre
January 29, 1964. Belmont, Massachusetts

A weekly bulletin can be printed without
charge. It is for the benefit of the Archdiocese
to have this new concept of Sunday bulletins.
(English 1 pg.) On February 7, 1964, the Cardinal states that there are several such organizations in the West. (English 1 pg.)

Mc4342. B-1964
Mr. E. Richard Barnes to California Legislators
February 5, 1964. San Diego, California

Instead of rehabilitating juveniles, the flood
of indecent and immoral literature ought to be
prevented from causing the delinquency in the
youth. (English 6 pgs.)

Mc4343. B-1964
J. Francis Cardinal McIntyre to Bp. Michael
Browne
February 14, 1964. Los Angeles, California

The point of *juridica* on the Commission's
material is entirely unsatisfactory. The arguments are prepared in English and will be trans-
lated into Latin. (English 1 pg.)

Mc4344. B-1964
Rev. Gerald Brynda to Rev. Eugene Gilb
March 4, 1964. Tucson, Arizona

Is hospitality possible at the Cathedral rectory while investigating the CYO Organization?
(English 1 pg.) On March 9, 1964, Fr. states
that all arrangements are made at the Cathedral. (English 1 pg.)

Mc4345. B-1964
Mr. Robert Aultz to J. Francis Cardinal
McIntyre
March 5, 1964. San Fernando, California

Bullock's Department Stores arranges for an
Easter service for employees from 9:15 to 9:50.
Could a priest give a 15 minute address at this
special season? (English 1 pg.) On March 10,
1964, the Cardinal requests Msgr. Meade to
participate in the Easter Service. (English 1 pg.)

Mc4346. B-1964
Mr. Dan Baedeker to J. Francis Cardinal
McIntyre
March 11, 1964. Oakland, California

Some members of the diocese would like to
have the following items presented to the Vatican Council. The role of the Deacon should be
reestablished, there should be freedom of worship for all of the world and the list of forbidden books should be changed. (English 4 pgs.)

Mc4347. B-1964
Mr. Robert McDonald to J. Francis Cardinal
McIntyre
Mary 4, 1964. Sacramento, California

The California Council of American Indians
desires to form a 12 man Indian Council and
request assistance from non-Indian leaders to
attain their goal. (English 2 pgs.) On May 6,
1964, the Cardinal requests Bishop Bell to get
some definite information on the Council. (English 1 pg.)

Mc4348. B-1964
Bp. Alden J. Bell to J. Francis Cardinal
McIntyre
May 11, 1964. Sacramento, California

Mr. McDonald requested $2,500 from the
Chancery and when he learned about the annual collection for the Negro and Indian Missions he wanted to know where the fund was
kept. He is unknown in Sacramento. (English
1 pg.)

Mc4349. B-1964
J. Francis Cardinal McIntyre to Bp. Leo Byrne
June 2, 1964. Los Angeles, California

The bank has requested verification of you as
the Apostolic Administrator of the Diocese of
Wichita. (English 1 pg.) On June 5, 1964, the
Bishop expresses his appreciation for the favorable statements made. (English 1 pg.)

Mc4350. B-1964
Dr. Francis Brown to Committee on Judiciary
June 3, 1964. Washington, D.C.

This is the time to recognize individual rights
and the Church-State separation principle. It is
time to move toward true neutrality in education. (English 2 pgs.)

Mc4351. B-1964
Mr. Gerald Brauer to J. Francis Cardinal
McIntyre
June 19, 1964. Chicago, Illinois

Summaries of the discussions held by Cardinal Suenens and the seminarians are enclosed.
The Divinity School of the University of Chicago will try to encourage continued dialogue
between Catholics and Protestants. (English
1 pg.)

Mc4352. B-1964
Mrs. Mary Burroughs to J. Francis Cardinal
McIntyre
June 19, 1964. Los Angeles, California

A request for permission to have a wedding
ceremony in San Juan Capistrano Mission in
late July. (English 1 pg.) On June 25, 1964, the
Cardinal states that the pastor will help with
the arrangements with Msgr. Russell. (English
1 pg.)

Mc4353. B-1964
Rev. William Barry to J. Francis Cardinal
McIntyre
June 25, 1964. Claremont, California

The Inter-Cultural Council of Claremont
agrees that Archbishop Roberts' invitation
should be postponed but others were most ve-
hement that he should be given the invitation.
(English 1 pg.)

Mc4354. B-1964
Bp. Charles Buddy to J. Francis Cardinal
McIntyre
June 25, 1964. San Diego, California

A message of support and understanding is
given while so many attacks are being hurled
against the office and person of the Cardinal.
San Diego is anticipating the Cardinal's presence at the Golden Jubilee celebration. (English
2 pgs.)

Mc4355. B-1964
Mr. W. A. Bushman to Mr. Ed Sovatkin
June 29, 1964. Los Angeles, California

The list of articles needed at St. Luke's Hospital in Nigeria are enclosed. Send the articles
to Catholic Medical Bureau in New York and
the bill to Los Angeles. (English 4 pgs.)

Mc4356. B-1964
Rev. William Barry to J. Francis Cardinal
McIntyre
July 3, 1964. Claremont, California

Archbishop Roberts accepted the Pomona
Fair Housing Council's invitation to speak on
July 22. (English 1 pg.) On July 9, 1964, the
Cardinal states that the Archbishop is not qual-
ified to speak about conditions in California.
(English 1 pg.)

Mc4357. B-1964
Mrs. Mary Burton to Bp. Timothy Manning
July 11, 1964. Corona DelMar, California

The appointment of a guardian is needed for
Mrs. Mary Konecny so her person and property
will be protected. (English 2 pgs.) On July 21,
1964, the Bishop states that Mary Waters, attorney for the Archdiocese, will give the necessary guardianship papers. (English 1 pg.)

Mc4358. B-1964
Rev. Virgil Blum, SJ to Msgr. Benjamin
Hawkes
July 20, 1964. Milwaukee, Wisconsin

A request is made to participate in a subscription T.V. program on church-state relations
on the school tax issue. (English 1 pg.) On July
30, 1964, Msgr. states that the permission is
granted and extends good wishes. (English
1 pg.)

Mc4359. B-1964
Bp. George Bernarding to Bp. Timothy
Manning
July 25, 1964. Mt. Hagen, New Guinea

The harvest in New Guinea is ready to be
brought into the Church but the building of a
church is needed. Many of the natives are of the
stone age civilization and can contribute nothing. (English 1 pg.) On August 12, 1964, the
Bishop sends a donation for the new church.
(English 1 pg.)

Mc4360. B-1964
Msgr. Kenneth O'Brien to Msgr. Hugh Quinn
July 29, 1964. Los Angeles, California

Mr. and Mrs. R. A. Barrows want to donate
land to Fr. Zuniga or to his parish if the Diocese is willing to accept the land. The documents will be given to a Notary and sent to the
Chancery. (English 1 pg.)

Mc4361. B-1964
Mr. Tom Bowen to Bp. Timothy Manning
August 18, 1964. Pacific Palisades, California

An offer to sell the concrete vault business to
the cemeteries so that all of the necessary activities can be carried on in one place. (English 3
pgs.) On September 18, 1964, the Bishop states
that it would not be to the interest of the Archdiocese to buy the enterprise. (English 1 pg.)

Mc4362. B-1964
Rev. John Languille to J. Francis Cardinal
McIntyre
August 26, 1964. Los Angeles, California

Bishop Bosa will organize the United Cubans
in Exile within the Catholic Cuban Center. He
stresses unity with the local Church and is
happy that so many Cuban children are in Parish schools. (English 2 pgs.)

Mc4363. B-1964
J. Francis Cardinal McIntyre to Hon. Louis
Burke
September 3, 1964. Los Angeles, California

The Spirit should direct the appointment to
the Supreme Court of the State to one who has
spent himself in legal ethics and social relations.
(English 1 pg.) On September 4, 1964, Mr.
Burke states that the letter will be treasured
whether the appointment is received or not.
(English 1 pg.)

Mc4364. B-1964
Sister M. Brigid to Bp. Timothy Manning
September 24, 1964. Mongu, North Rhodesia

An appeal is made for a donation for a teacher
training school in Mongu. The need for teachers is as great as our need for funds. (English 1
pg.) On October 13, 1964, the Bishop sends a
donation for the training school. (English 1 pg.)

Mc4365. B-1964
Mr. Leonard Branowetz to J. Francis Cardinal McIntrye
October 12, 1964. Wichita, Kansas

Is a copy of the address given at Mt. St. Mary's available? A similar address must be given on October 20, in Kansas. (English 1 pg.)

Mc4366. B-1964
Fr. Henry Bell to J. Francis Cardinal McIntyre
October 17, 1964. Kaduna, Nigeria

Conditions in Africa are improving but the challenges and uncertainties of the emerging countries add to the missionary stress. The generosity of Los Angeles is appreciated. (English 1 pg.)

Mc4367. B-1964
Mrs. Edward Berryman to Msgr. Benjamin Hawkes
November 1, 1964. South Gate, California

A protest is made to the materials being distributed at various Churches after Masses. A reprint of the El Rodeo of *The Tidings* and the use of the material to abolish the Rumford Forced Housing Act is necessary. (English 3 pgs.) On November 4, 1964, Msgr. states that no one can control the papers handed out at Churches. (English 1 pg.)

Mc4368. B-1964
Rev. Alfred Boeddeker, OFM to J. Francis Cardinal McIntyre
November 11, 1964. Dominican Republic

An invitation is extended to the Mariological and Marian Congresses in the Dominican Republic from March 18–25, 1965. This city has the oldest Cathedral in this hemisphere. (English 1 pgs.)

Mc4369. B-1964
Mr. Vito Berardi to J. Francis Cardinal McIntyre
November 11, 1964. Los Angeles, California

Is it fair for parishes to sell religious articles Sunday after Sunday and deprive a legitimate business man from making a living? (English 1 pg.) On November 18, 1964, the Cardinal requests the Pastors not to sell religious articles except at the time of Missions. (English 1 pg.)

Mc4370. B-1964
Mr. David Bland to J. Francis Cardinal McIntyre
November 28, 1964. Los Angeles, California

A letter of opposition to the attacks on the Archbishop by the so-called Catholic press. The emerging layman is doing more harm than good. (English 1 pg.) On December 1, 1964, the Cardinal states that it is difficult to comprehend the reasoning that stimulates the attacks. (English 1 pg.)

Mc4371. B-1964
Mr. Frank Berling to Pope Paul VI
December 2, 1964. Los Angeles, California

The donation of the *Tiara* to the poor is a step in the right direction of getting rid of the ostentatious robes setting the priests apart from the people. (English 1 pg.)

Mc4372. B-1964
Mrs. Beatrice Ballesteros to J. Francis Cardinal McIntyre
December 21, 1964. Los Angeles, California

The first copy of the *Memorare Recordings* is enclosed. It may cause some people to think. (English 1 pg.)

Mc4373. C-1964
Mr. William Clinton to J. Francis Cardinal McIntyre
January 27, 1964. Bloomington, Illinois

A message must be given to Philip O'Brien that his younger brother has died. (English 2 pgs.) On February 17, 1964, Fr. states that Mr. O'Brien no longer lives at the address given and his present residence is unknown. (English 1 pg.)

Mc4374. C-1964
Mr. John W. Cove to Mr. James Hoffa
February 5, 1964. Kingston, New York

Copies of the Constitution should be given to every school age child and this in turn will strike terror in the hearts of the Leftists. (English 1 pg.)

Mc4375. C-1964
Bp. Alden J. Bell to Hon. Winslow Christian
February 6, 1964. Sacramento, California

The California Bishops are concerned about the report of the statewide system of city and county birth control clinics. The conscience of the individual must be respected. (English 1 pg.)

Mc4376. C-1964
Mrs. John Chaffey to J. Francis Cardinal
McIntyre
February 7, 1964. Fullerton, California

There must be a definite statement made on
the Rumford Act and state that it is or is not a
sin to vote for the Act. (English 1 pg.) On February 15, 1964, Fr. Suggests a talk with a priest
about the matter of the Act. (English 1 pg.)

Mc4377. C-1964
Mrs. R. F. Christopher to Msgr. Benjamin
Hawkes
February 11, 1964. Los Angeles, California

What is the official title of the Archdiocese to
have a valid mention in a Will? Is there an hon-
est lawyer that can handle the will? (English 1
pg.) On February 13, 1964, Msgr. Gross states
that he will contact Mr. Christopher. (English
1 pg.)

Mc4378. C-1964
Mr. Lee Fortner to J. Francis Cardinal
McIntyre
February 13, 1964. Los Angeles, California

An invitation is extended to give the invocation at the Credit Managers Association Convention on May 18. (English 1 pg.) On
February 18, 1964, the Cardinal states that he
will be happy to give the invocation. (English
1 pg.)

Mc4379. C-1964
Bp. Warren Boudreaux to J. Francis Cardinal
McIntyre
February 14, 1964. New Iberia, Louisiana

Mr. Patrick Caffery has been elected to the
House of Representatives from Louisiana. He is
the cousin of Ambassador Caffery. (English 1 pg.)

Mc4380. C-1964
Rev. James Carney to Bp. Timothy Manning
March 19, 1964. Vancouver, B.C.

The general plan used by the Building Commission would be useful for Archbishop
Johnson. (English 1 pg.) On April 7, 1964, the
Archbishop sends the outline of the procedures
and the composition of the Board. (English
1 pg.)

Mc4381. C-1964
Mrs. E. Geier to Msgr. Benjamin Hawkes
March 22, 1964. Long Island, New York

Before property can be sold, Mary Callahan
must be located to furnish the papers. Several
addresses are enclosed for this purpose. (English
1 pgs.) On April 1, 1964, Msgr. states that the
address in El Monte must have five numerals
and the other addresses are in the Archdiocese
of San Francisco. (English 1 pg.)

Mc4382. C-1964
Mr. Charles Carter to J. Francis Cardinal
McIntyre
March 30, 1964. Long Beach, California

Could an interview be arranged to discuss a
plan to legalize gambling to end the profits by
the underworld in drugs and prostitution. (English 2 pgs.) On April 10, 1964, the Cardinal
states that the Church is interested in the problems but with other solutions. (English 1 pg.)

Mc4383. C-1964
Mr. William Consedine to Arbp. Joseph
McGucken
April 20, 1964. Washington, D.C.

This is the time to demand payment of the
Pious Fund before the elections in Mexico and
when Mr. Thomas Mann of the Inter American
Affairs Office is in favor. (English 2 pgs.)

Mc4384. C-1964
Miss Cynthia Cooley to Rev. Eugene Gilb
April 20, 1964. Loma Linda, California

Could Rev. Robert Webster be on a panel to
discuss common beliefs held by many religions
and to determine the goal for cooperation
among all religions. (English 1 pg.) On April
23, 1964, Fr. states that it is not the policy to
have priests on this type of a panel. (English
1 pg.)

Mc4385. C-1964
Bp. Timothy Manning to Arbp. M. Joseph
Lemieux
April 30, 1964. Los Angeles, California

A letter of recommendation is required for
Hubert Carnero who wants to study at the
Medical School of Catholic University of Ot-
tawa. (English 1 pg.) On May 6, 1964, the
Archbishop states that he will forward the letter
to the Rector. (English 1 pg.)

Mc4386. C-1964
Mr. Thomas Carroll to J. Francis Cardinal
McIntrye
May 15, 1964. Sacramento, California

Answers to the questionnaire concerning the
relationship between the Division of Highways
and the Chancery Office will give some guidelines for the future. (English 2 pgs.)

Mc4387. C-1964
Mr. Phillip Callan to J. Francis Cardinal
McIntyre
May 28, 1964. Rochester, New York

The yearly gift of $2,597 is sent to be used in whatever need that arises. (English 1 pg.) On June 9, 1964, the Cardinal states that the most pressing need is the maternity clinic which must be expanded. (English 1 pg.)

Mc4388. C-1964
Mr. Ted Curley to Bp. Timothy Manning
June 1, 1964. Rome, Italy

The walk through the Roman streets of the first and third century and the visit to St. Peter's tomb is an unforgettable experience. (English 1 pg.)

Mc4389. C-1964
Miss Kathleen Cahill to J. Francis Cardinal
McIntyre
June 29, 1964. Co. Galway, Ireland

A gift of Waterford Glassware is being sent but the gift of a visit to Our Lady of Knock for your intentions is the one that is important. (English 1 pg.)

Mc4390. C-1964
Mr. Bert S. Cross to J. Francis Cardinal
McIntyre
August 10, 1964. St. Paul, Minnesota

An invitation is extended to the Bing Crosby Golf Tournament sponsored by 3M Company. (English 1 pg.) On August 13, 1964, the Cardinal states that previous commitments will make attendance impossible. (English 1 pg.)

Mc4391. C-1961
Arbp. Thomas Connolly to Bp. Timothy
Manning
August 24, 1964. Seattle, Washington

A welcome to Seattle for the Episcopal Silver Jubilee celebration is sent with the program of events for this occasion. (English 2 pgs.)

Mc4392. C-1964
Bp. Louis Callignon, OMI to J. Francis Cardinal McIntyre
September 1, 1964. Lowell, Massachusetts

A plea for assistance to the Church in Haiti which was partially destroyed by hurricane Flora and the Cleo. (English 1 pg.) On September 4, 1964, the Cardinal states that he is sending a token gift that will relieve in some measure the devastation. (English 1 pg.)

Mc4393. C-1964
Rev. P. Coffey, SJ to Bp. Timothy Manning
October 8, 1964. Los Angeles, California

This added generosity to Mungret Seminary obligates us to pray more feverently for the Bishop and for Los Angeles. (English 1 pg.)

Mc4394. C-1964
Rev. Clifford Craft to Msgr. Benjamin Hawkes
October 6, 1964. Malibu, California

The new parish *Handbook* will be ready for the Open House in November. At that time all of the questions will be answered. (English 1 pg.)

Mc4395. C-1964
Mr. J. A. Curran to J. Francis Cardinal
McIntyre
October 20, 1964. Pasadena, California

The Pope's welcome of Sukarno brings questions to many minds. Surely the Pope knows the man's record. (English 1 pg.) On October 22, 1964 the Cardinal states that as the head of State the Pope must receive other heads of State. (English 1 pg.)

Mc4396. C-1964
Rev. Charles Casassa, SJ to Mr. L. E.
Timberlake
November 20, 1964. Los Angeles, California

It is a matter of justice that the Blue Diamond Pit be submitted to arbitration. It could serve as an example to all that ethical concepts do have force in society. (English 1 pg.) Letters of Judge White and Msgr. O'Dwyer are enclosed.

Mc4397. D-1964
Rev. Al Dineen to J. Francis Cardinal McIntyre
January 18, 1964. New York City, New York

A friendly letter commenting on the Dr. Tom Dooley Foundation Mass that was celebrated in traditional style. (English 1 pg.) On January 21, 1964, the Cardinal states that a remembrance in the Mass is made often and today especially. (English 1 pg.)

Mc4398. D-1964
Rev. Eugene Gilb to Mr. Emery Drake
January 22, 1964. Los Angeles, California

Every parish will have the privilege of an evening Mass during Lent if that is the desire of the parish. (English 1 pg.)

Mc4399. D-1964
Mr. Phil DesMarteau to J. Francis Cardinal
McIntyre
February 3, 1964. Van Nuys, California

The silence of the Catholic Chancery Office in the racial question and the housing act does not give the leadership that the laity needs. (English 1 pg.)

Mc4400. D-1964
J. Francis Cardinal McIntyre to Rev. Patrick
McGoldrick
February 6, 1964. Los Angeles, California

A conversation with Mr. Des Marteau might
help him to see the difference between purely
political issues and the moral issues on the bal-
lot. (English 1 pg.)

Mc4401. D-1964
Mrs. Jean Des Marteau to J. Francis Cardinal
McIntyre
February 15, 1964. North Hollywood,
California

The Human Relations Council was forbidden
from meeting at the Parish Hall. This organization strives to promote the dignity of every person. (English 1 pg.)

Mc4402. D-1964
Msgr. Benjamin Hawkes to Rev. Michael
Gormally
February 21, 1964. Los Angeles, California

Explain to Mrs. Des Marteau that the Human Relations Council is trying to promote political convictions under ecclesiastical approval.
(English 1 pg.)

Mc4403. D-1964
Mrs. James Doyle to Bp. Timothy Manning
February 7, 1964. Huntington Beach,
California

Will the new parish be formed from Westminster and Huntington Beach area? 2,000 children are in CCD classes and there is a full
parish school. (English 1 pg.) On March 3,
1964, the Bishop states that the Chancery Office is aware of the number of people in this
and in other areas. (English 1 pg.)

Mc4404. D-1964
Mr. George Daderlein to Rev. John Thom
March 6, 1964. Sylmar, California

There is a need for the clergy to speak out in
all of the parishes concerning the racial policy
of the Church and Diocese. (English 1 pg.)

Mc4405. D-1964
Rev. Francis Dowd, CSSR to Bp. Timothy
Manning
March 31, 1964. Whittier, California

The new Chapel should be ready for the dedication ceremony on May 30. Would it be possible to have Mass at 10:30 on that date?
(English 1 pg.) On April 7, 1964, the Bishop
states that he will reserve that date and time for
the Mass. (English 1 pg.)

Mc4406. D-1964
Mr. William Doheny to J. Francis Cardinal
McIntyre
April 11, 1964. Fort Lauderdale, Florida

Major solicitations for funds can be discussed
now that the tax situations allow greater generosity. (English 1 pg.) On April 15, 1964, the
Cardinal asks that a meeting be arranged when
it is convenient for everyone. (English 1 pg.)

Mc4407. D-1964
Mr. Frank Doherty to J. Francis Cardinal
McIntyre
April 21, 1964. Los Angeles. California

Could The Tidings print the entire talk given
by the Pope and the Cardinal instead of editori-
alizing the talk. (English 1 pg.) On April 23,
1964, the Cardinal states that many speeches
are long and that tends to discourage readers
(English 1 pg.)

Mc4408. D-1964
J. Francis Cardinal McIntyre to Miss Dorothy
Day
May 4, 1964. Los Angeles, California

Your latest book is being read with much interest. It is good that the Catholic Worker continues under such energetic direction. (English
1 pg.)

Mc4409. D-1964
Mr. Frederick Dockweiler to J. Francis Cardi-
nal McIntyre
May 5, 1964. Los Angeles, California

The excellent editorial in the Herald/
Examiner on the gradual loss of religion in the
country should be printed in The Tidings. (English 1 pg.)

Mc4410. D-1964
Mr. Anson Hoyt to J. Francis Cardinal
McIntyre
May 11, 1964. Los Angeles, California

An appeal is sent for a donation to the Direct
Appeal Foundation that gives assistance to all in
need. (English 1 pg.) On May 25, 1964, Msgr.
Johnson states that the work of the Direct Appeal Foundation is worthy of a donation. (English 1 pg.)

Mc4411. D-1964
Mr. Frank Doherty to J. Francis Cardinal
McIntyre
June 12, 1964. Los Angeles, California

California has the greatest guarantee of rights
for the individual of any state. The legal rights
of all businesses are clearly stated and the pen
alty for the violation of these rights are definite.
(English 1 pg.)

Mc4412. D-1964
Mr. Leigh Battson to Msgr. Benjamin Hawkes
July 2, 1964. Beverly Hills, California

A request for the Cardinal to write a letter of
recommendation for Lucy Doheny to attend the
Catalina School in Monterey. (English 1 pg.)
On July 9, 1964, the Cardinal requests a special
consideration for Lucy Doheny. (English 1 pg.)

Mc4413. D-1964
Rev. Edward Cassidy to J. Francis Cardinal
McIntyre
August 30, 1964. New York City, New York

The Catholic Worker has a fitting tribute to
the Cardinal written by Dorothy Day. The
Catholic Worker sold the farm owned on Staten
Island. (English 1 pgs.)

Mc4414. D-1964
Bp. Timothy Manning to Sister M. Sacred
Heart
September 3, 1964. Los Angeles, California

Mrs. Gertrude Dunne has worked for the
American Cancer Society and now wants to
work with children. If she can be of service,
contact her directly. (English 1 pg.) The same
letter sent to Sister Francis, Sister Frederica, Sister Benigna.

Mc4415. D-1964
Mrs. Mary Dingle to Bp. Timothy Manning
September 8, 1964. Whitter, California

The scroll given with the Pro Ecclesia et Pontifice Medal was taken from the car. Would a
duplicate be possible? (English 1 pg.) On September 14, 1964, the Bishop requests Fr. Gilb
to investigate the possibility of a duplicate while
in Rome. (English 1 pg.)

Mc4416. D-1964
Ms. Mary D'Ambrosia to J. Francis Cardinal
McIntyre
September 10, 1964. Los Angeles, California

A plan for the New World Community and
an Encyclical letter on Christian Unity with a
message for Pope Paul VI is enclosed. (English
12 pgs.)

Mc4417. D-1964
Rev. Francis Dowd, CSSR to Bp. Timothy
Manning
September 20, 1964. Whittier, California

The dedication of the Chapel must be postponed again until November 21. If this date is
impossible for your presence, Msgr. O'Dwyer
might be able to officiate. (English 1 pg.) On
September 28, 1964, the Bishop states that he
will be at the Council on that date. (English
1 pg.)

Mc4418. D-1964
Mr. James Moran to Bp. Timothy Manning
September 24, 1964. Los Angeles, California

An invitation is extended to be on the special
planning committee for the County Board of
Supervisors Prayer Breakfast. (English 1 pg.) On
September 29, 1964, the Bishop states that he is
willing to cooperate in the Prayer Breakfast.
(English 1 pg.)

Mc4419. D-1964
Mr. Warren Dorn to Bp. Timothy Manning
September 30, 1964. Los Angeles, California

A short meeting of the participants for the
Prayer Breakfast will be October 8 to outline
each area of participation. (English 1 pg.) On
October 2, 1964, The Bishop requests Fr. Languille to attend the meeting. (English 1 pg.)

Mc4420. D-1964
Mr. J. K. Doolan to J. Francis Cardinal
McIntyre
October 14, 1964. Los Angeles, California

A friendly letter commenting on the concern
held for the Cardinal's health, and the proposed
trip to France with a visit to Lisieux. (English
1 pg.)

Mc4421. D-1964
J. Francis Cardinal McIntyre Memo
October 14, 1964. Los Angeles, California

The outside contracts with St. John's Hospital are in default and Irene Dunne feels that she
needs counsel other than legal. Mr. Hagerty
from New York is the suggested person and is
acceptable to Irene Dunne. (English 7 pgs.)

Mc4422. D-1964
Mr. Frank Doherty to J. Francis Cardinal
McIntyre
November 30, 1964. Los Angeles, California

A request is made to have a member of the
Chancery Office give the Invocation at Judge
Evelle Younger's installation as District Attor-
ney. (English 1 pg.) On December 1, 1964, the
Cardinal states that Msgr. Joseph Truxaw will
be happy to give the invocation. (English 1 pg.)

Mc4423. D-1964
Mr. Edward Diaz to J. Francis Cardinal
McIntyre
December 9, 1964. Williams AFB, Arizona

A request to bless the St. Christopher Medal
for an airman from Whittier. (English 1 pg.) On
December 15, 1964, Fr. states that the Cardinal
sends his blessing for the men on the base ac-
companying the blessed medal. (English 1 pg.)

Mc4424. D-1964
Rev. Gommar DePauw to J. Francis Cardinal
McIntyre
December 9, 1964. Emmitsburg, Maryland

Comments are made on the *Saturday Evening
Post*'s article on the Cardinal and the label of
conservative. (English 1 pg.) On December 17,
1964, Fr. Gilb comments that the article was
conspicuous for its inaccuracies. (English 1 pg.)

Mc4425. D-1964
Arbp. Egidio Vagnozzi to J. Francis Cardinal
McIntyre
December 17, 1964. Washington, D.C.

Mr. DeVille's work contains statements that
can lead to unorthodox conclusions and inter-
pretations. Contact Mr. DeVille and explain the
wisdom of having his work on the Shroud
within the limits of orthodoxy. (English 1 pg.)

Mc4426. D-1964
Mr. Milner Clary to Msgr. Benjamin Hawkes
December 18, 1964. Los Angeles, California

The Probation Department will open a new
facility in Sylmar. Could a Catholic priest be assigned to assist these young people? (English 1
pg.) On December 22, 1964, Msgr. asks Fr.
William Duggan to come to the Chancery Office to discuss the proposal. (English 1 pg.)

Mc4427. D-1964
Mrs. Maud Darland to J. Francis Cardinal
McIntyre
N.D. Los Angeles, California

The union of all Faiths in love could be
strengthened by prayer, especially by praying the
Lord's Prayer together. (English 2 pgs.)

Mc4428. D-1964
Mr. Emery Drake to J. Francis Cardinal
McIntyre
N.D. Los Angeles, California

A request is made to have an evening Mass
daily in centrally located Churches to have
Communion services in the evening for those
who cannot attend morning Mass. (English
1 pg.)

Mc4429. D-1964
Mr. and Mrs. Roy Doty to Bp. Timothy
Manning
N.D. Long Beach, California

Conscience demands that we speak out
clearly against racism and *de facto* racism. (English 1 pg.)

Mc4430. E-1964
Ms. Dorothy Enright to Bp. Timothy Manning
May 4, 1964. Garden Grove, California

The Vatican Council ought to define the
word Christian and put Mary in her proper
place in the role of salvation. (English 2 pgs.)

Mc4431. E-1964
Mr. John W. Edwards to J. Francis Cardinal
McIntyre
N.D. Hawthorne, California

Is there an explanation for dispensations
from fasting on Ember days when a social affair
is taking place? (English 1 pg.) On June 1,
Msgr. states that it is better to grant a dispensation than to have people with a disturbed conscience. (English 1 pg.)

Mc4432. E-1964
Mr. John Hart to J. Francis Cardinal McIntyre
August 26, 1964. Los Angeles, California

An Easter parade and pageant is being
planned. Fr. Urban requests a Catholic layman
to serve on the Executive Board. (English 1 pg.)

Mc4433. E-1964
Mr. John Eberle to Msgr. Benjamin Hawkes
September 1, 1964. Oklahoma City, Oklahoma

Copies of articles from *The Oklahoma Cou-
rier* attacking the Cardinal and advocating a
priests' union are enclosed. (English 1 pg.) On
September 3, 1964, Msgr. states that the material will be brought to the Cardinal's attention.
(English 1 pg.)

Mc4434. E-1964
Mr. Norman Elliott to Hon Edmund Brown
October 8, 1964. Los Angeles, California

A request to be given consideration for the
position of Judge in the Los Angeles Municipal
Court. (English 1 pg.) On October 9, 1964,
Mrs. Elliott request that the Cardinal write a
letter of recommendation to the governor. (English 1 pg.)

Mc4435. E-1964
Mr. Leif Erickson to J. Francis Cardinal
McIntyre
N.D. Lake Arrowhead, California

The work toward unity among all religions is
becoming more evident. (English 3 pgs.)

Mc4436. F-1964
Mrs. Elmira Feliz to Bp. Timothy Manning
January 23, 1964. Sherman Oaks, California

All priests must realize that women must wear slacks at times when it is appropriate dress for the work they do. (English 1 pg.) On January 28, 1964, the Bishop states that opinions of others should not disturb anyone. (English 1 pg.)

Mc4437. F-1964
Ms. Kathryn Fitzgerald to Msgr. Benjamin Hawkes
January 24, 1964. Englewood Cliff, New Jersey

The questionnaire related to Church spending needs to be returned so a true picture can be projected. If an educated guess can be sent, that will suffice. (English 1 pg.) On January 31, 1964, Msgr. states that the requested data will not be furnished. (English 1 pg.)

Mc4438. F-1964
J. Francis Cardinal McIntyre to Bp. Francis Furey
February 5, 1964. Los Angeles, California

The educational meeting was excellent and if needed both Sister Mary Patrick, OP and Sister Mary Benigna, OSF can be actively placed on the committee. (English 1 pg.)

Mc4439. F-1964
Mr. and Mrs. W. Frame to Alfredo Cardinal Ottaviani
February 14, 1964. Savannah, Georgia

An illustration of how good people can be drawn into the Communistic trap is the National Council of Catholic Women working with the Foreign Policy Association in Latin America. (English 3 pgs.)

Mc4440. F-1964
Mr. John J. Ford to J. Francis Cardinal McIntyre
February 25, 1964. Los Angeles, California

A request for a letter of recommendation to the University of Dublin, Dublin, Ireland, so Stephen Ford can study Irish literature. (English 1 pg.) On March 3, 1964, Mr. Michael Tierney states that he thinks there will be little difficulty for Stephen. (English 1 pg.)

Mc4441. F-1964
Mr. Raymond Frazier to Rev. Joseph Thompson
March 8, 1964. Los Angeles, California

Every citizen has the Constitutional right of freedom of Religion but the 350 prisoners at the Cardinal's Mass were forced to attend. It is degrading to the Church to use force. (English 1 pg.)

Mc4442. F-1964
Mrs. Mary Fonda to J. Francis Cardinal McIntyre
March 27, 1964. Pasadena, California

I send a tribute of praise for retaining the Church for the Gospel message and not turning the Church into the political arena. (English 2 pgs.) On March 31, 1964, the Cardinal states that the Church will continue to refrain from speaking on political issues. (English 1 pg.)

Mc4443. F-1964
Dr. David Hubbard to J. Francis Cardinal McIntyre
May 19, 1964. Pasadena, California

The forthright and clear presentation of the Catholic position by Dr. John Christopher and Msgr. Patrick Dignan was appreciated by the students of Fuller Theological Seminary. (English 1 pg.)

Mc4444. F-1964
Mr. James Tynion to Francis Cardinal Spellman
May 26, 1964. New York City, New York

The application of Mr. John Ford for the Knights of Malta has been given by Rev. Edward Carney, OSA. (English 1 pg.) On June 18, 1964, the Cardinal states that the application must be approved by the Bishop and be presented by the Bishop. (English 1 pg.)

Mc4445. F-1964
Mr. Bernard Flynn to J. Francis Cardinal McIntyre
July 1, 1964. Los Angeles, California

The great privilege of having the Cardinal celebrate the Nuptial Mass for the former lay missionary in Africa will never be forgotten. A donation for some charity is enclosed. (English 1 pg.) On July 9, 1964, the Cardinal states that the privilege of the Mass is his. (English 1 pg.)

Mc4446. F-1964
Mr. Brian Fitzpatrick to J. Francis Cardinal
McIntyre
July 5, 1964. Fullerton, California

Is the address of the White Fathers available so one can send rosaries and other items to the Missions? (English 1 pg.) On July 7, 1964, Fr. states that the Los Angeles address is the only one available but all further information can be obtained from there. (English 1 pg.)

Mc4447. F-1964
Mrs. Odelia Chidester to Bp. Timothy
Manning
August 3, 1964. Los Angeles, California

Good example was given by Fr. Nocero and his ushers to take the First Aid training course in case there is an emergency in church. (English 1 pg.)

Mc4448. F-1964
Mr. Elmer P. Friel to J. Francis Cardinal
McIntyre
August 25, 1964. Los Angeles, California

For building schools and churches and for shepherding your flock with such care, you are remembered in prayer. (English 1 pg.)

Mc4449. F-1964
Mr. Louis Fourmier to J. Francis Cardinal
McIntyre
September 1, 1964. San Diego, California

A plea to speak more frequently against divorce and the many evils coming from divorces. (English 2 pgs.)

Mc4450. F-1964
Mr. John J. Foley to J. Francis Cardinal
McIntyre
September 7, 1964. Yonkers, New York

A request to write a letter of congratulations to be read at the testimonial dinner celebrating the 45 years of priesthood of Msgr. Edward Betowski. (English 1 pg.)

Mc4451. F-1964
J. Francis Cardinal McIntyre to Bp. John
Fearns
November 2, 1964. Los Angeles, California

A request is made to send the arguments used for making English mandatory for Sunday Masses and to have the Act of Contrition recited before or after entering the confessional. (English 1 pg.)

Mc4452. F-1964
Mr. Frank Fitzsimons to J. Francis Cardinal
McIntyre
November 9, 1964. Brooklyn, New York

A friendly letter commenting on the prayers offered and the need for the Cardinal to rest. Mention of former classmates is a part of the news. (English 2 pgs.) On November 18, 1964, the Cardinal states that it is always good to hear from former classmates. (English 1 pg.)

Mc4453. F-1964
J. Francis Cardinal McIntyre to Arbp. Pericle
Felici
November 24, 1964. Los Angeles, California

A request is made for the materials given to the hierarchy attending the *Aula*. A note that the NCWC NewsSheet gives a poor presentation of the Council. (English 1 pg.)

Mc4454. F-1964
Miss Maria Galvanauskas to Msgr. Benjamin
Hawkes
February 19, 1964. Chicago, Illinois

How many Churches in Los Angeles have Exposition of the Blessed Sacrament every day? This information is needed so a definite location can be made. (English 1 pg.) On February 27, 1964, the Plaza Church has Exposition daily but many parishes have Nocturnal Adoration. (English 1 pg.)

Mc4455. F-1964
Mr. Robert Gleeson to J. Francis Cardinal
McIntyre
February 22, 1964. Palmdale, California

St. Mary's Parish has 25 acres of land which could be the location for the new high school instead of the site chosen. (English 2 pgs.) On February 28, 1964, the Bishop states it is judicious to locate the high school between the two communities. (English 1 pg.)

Mc4456. F-1964
Rev. Eugene Gilb to Mr. Frank Seaver
February 26, 1964. Los Angeles, California

The Cardinal regrets that he cannot attend the Goldwater dinner. The exact date for the return from the Vatican Council is uncertain. (English 1 pg.)

Mc4457. G-1964
J. Francis Cardinal McIntyre to Miss Griffiths
February 27, 1964. Los Angeles, California

The death of Bishop Griffiths is a loss to New York, the Military Ordinariate, and the Administrative Board of Bishops. (English 1 pg.)

Mc4458. G-1964
Bp. Francis J. Green to J. Francis Cardinal
   McIntyre
March 26, 1964. Tucson, Arizona

The whole Diocese of Tucson owes a debt of
gratitude to the Cardinal for presiding at the funeral of Archbishop Daniel Gercke. (English
1 pg.)

Mc4459. G-1964
Mr. Joseph Galea to J. Francis Cardinal
   McIntyre
April 23, 1964. Los Angeles, California

On May 31, the Catholics from Malta request a Mass at the Cathedral to celebrate the
independence of Malta. Could the Knights of
Malta be present? (English 1 pg.) On May 4,
1964, the Cardinal asks for the request to be
made to Msgr. Roche at the Cathedral. (English
1 pg.)

Mc4460. G-1964
Msgr. John Sheridan to Msgr. Benjamin
   Hawkes
May 26, 1964. Los Angeles, California

The enclosed donation is given for one of the
Seminaries in memory of her husband Francois
Galameau. (English 1 pg.) On May 27, 1964,
Msgr. asks that the name of the family be re-
corded on the list of benefactors of the Semi-
nary. (English 1 pg.)

Mc4461. G-1964
Mr. and Mrs. B. Gorman to J. Francis Cardi-
nal McIntyre
June 12, 1964. Garden Grove, California

Prayers of gratitude are being offered for
your wise and prudent leadership in the Archdiocese. (English 1 pg.) On June 16, 1964, the
Cardinal expresses gratitude for the prayers and
for the donation to the Youth Education fund.
(English 1 pg.)

Mc4462. G-1964
Mrs. J. M. Gallinger to Bp. Timothy Manning
June 27, 1964. Portland, Oregon

An appeal is made to join a Novena to Fr.
Junipero Serra for a cure of a two year old boy
who does not have a very good chance to sur-
vive. (English 4 pgs.)

Mc4463. G-1964
Mr. Patrick Borman to J. Francis Cardinal
   McIntyre
July 2, 1964. Chicago, Illinois

The Vatican Council should modernize the
wording of "May the Body of the Lord which I
have eaten and Thy Blood which I have drunk"
to less cannibalistic words. (English 1 pg.) On
July 9, 1964, the Cardinal states that the words
of the priest are "Body of Christ." (English 1
pg.)

Mc4464. G-1964
Ms. Eileen Schaeffler to J. Francis Cardinal
   McIntyre
July 24, 1964. Loveland, Ohio

Grailville is sponsoring the English theologian, Rev. Charles Davis, to discuss practical
problems and arrive at concrete suggestions for
solutions. The presence of the Cardinal would
be most welcome. (English 1 pg.)

Mc4465. G-1964
Dr. Alfred Graves, MD to J. Francis Cardinal
   McIntyre
July 28, 1964. Long Beach, California

A request for permission to give every seminarian a copy of None Dare Call It Treason to
halt the spread of Communism. (English 1 pg.)
On August 13, 1964, the Cardinal states that a
few copies of the book could be made available
to all of the students. (English 1 pg.)

Mc4466. G-1964
Msgr. Joseph Gorham to J. Francis Cardinal
   McIntyre
August 20, 1964. Washington, D.C.

Politics Is Your Business is the theme for the
Civic Clubs for this election year. The goal is to
prepare our youth for Christian citizenship.
(English 1 pg.)

Mc4467. G-1964
Arbp. Egidio Vagnozzi to Msgr. Benjamin
   Hawkes
October 12, 1964. Washington, D.C.

Some information is needed to locate Guiseppe Gelmini for his relatives in Rome. (English 1 pg.) On November 16, 1964, Msgr.
states that Guiseppe does live and work in Los
Angeles and a priest will visit him to request
that he write to his family. (English 1 pg.)

Mc4468. G-1964
Mr. John E. Galway to Pope Paul VI
December 12, 1964. Santa Monica, California

Los Angeles Archdiocese has two large cemeteries both very distant from Santa Monica.
Catholics ought to be allowed to be buried in
non-secterian cemeteries and have a priest bless
the ground and have graveside services. (English
2 pgs.)

Mc4469. G-1964
Mr. Albert Goodman to J. Francis Cardinal
McIntyre
December 24, 1963. Montrose, California

The need for retirement homes is increasing,
and now such a facility is available. Why does
the Archdiocese hesitate? (English 1 pg.) On
January 2, 1964, the Cardinal states that such
facilities are available as Leisure World in Seal
Beach and Laguna Beach. (English 1 pg.)

Mc4470. G-1964
Dr. Arthur Greenburg to J. Francis Cardinal
McIntyre
N.D. New York City, New York

A questionnaire is enclosed to assess the effect of media in our lives. A representative will
call first to arrange an interview. (English 1 pg.)

Mc4471. G-1964
Mr. Harry Harvey to J. Francis Cardinal
McIntyre
February 24, 1964. Torrance, California

An invitation is extended to give the invocation at the benefit for the Children's Hospital.
(English 1 pg.) On February 28, 1964, the Cardinal states that previous appointments will
prevent him from attending this worthy benefit.
(English 1 pg.)

Mc4472. G-1964
Mr. Vernon Hunt to J. Francis Cardinal
McIntyre
March 11, 1964. Los Angeles, California

An invitation to give the invocation opening
the California Judges Conference on September
28 at the Internation Hotel is enclosed. (English
1 pg.) On March 24, 1964, the Cardinal regrets
that he cannot attend the Conference since he
will be in Rome. (English 1 pg.)

Mc4473. H-1964
Mr. Jude Hourihan to J. Francis Cardinal
McIntyre
March 19, 1964. Washington, D.C.

A request is made for a Bible to be used for
prayer. (English 1 pg.) On March 31, 1964, Fr.
states that the Bible will be sent from the Bor-
romeo Guild. (English 1 pg.)

Mc4474. H-1964
Mr. Homer Hinman to J. Francis Cardinal
McIntyre
April 10, 1964. Los Angeles, California

An invitation is extended to give the invocation at the Kiwanis International Convention
on July 2, 1964 at the Sports Arena. (English 1
pg.) On April 14, 1964, the Cardinal regrets
that he cannot be present but Msgr. Patrick
Roche, Rector of the Cathedral and publisher
of The Tidings will give the invocation. (English
1 pg.)

Mc4475. H-1964
J. Francis Cardinal McIntyre to Mr. Richard
Herman
May 27, 1964. Los Angeles, California

Mr. Herman is interested in knowing the attitude of the Catholics towards Mr. Rockefeller's marital status from a moral standpoint.
Since the attitude of the Church is so well
known, any statement would be construed as
political propaganda. (English 1 pg.)

Mc4476. H-1964
Mr. Frank Hogan to Bp. Timothy Manning
May 29, 1964. Mt. Western, California

To relieve racial tension, the Cardinal ought
to build a high school and a new Church in the
black section of the city. More Negro priests
and sisters ought to be solicited for Los Angeles. St. Francis Hospital ought to be investigated
by the Chancery Office. (English 1 pg.)

Mc4477. H-1964
Mr. Kenneth Hines to J. Francis Cardinal
McIntyre
June 12, 1964. Anaheim, California

The Masons' third annual Public Observance
of the Constitution of the United States celebration will be held on September 18 in Anaheim.
An invitation is extended to greet the Catholics
of the area. (English 1 pg.) On June 25, 1964,
the Cardinal states that he regrets that he cannot be present. (English 1 pg.)

Mc4478. H-1964
Mrs. G. Allen Hancock to J. Francis Cardinal
McIntyre
July 7, 1964. Santa Maria, California

A birthday donation for Don Bosco Technical
Institute is enclosed. The parish is busy and
Msgr. is in the hospital. (English 1 pg.) On July
15, 1964, the Cardinal expresses his appreciation for the birthday donation. (English 1 pg.)

Mc4479. H-1964
J. Francis Cardinal McIntyre to Mrs. Allen
Hancock
August 21, 1964. Los Angeles, California

The very generous donation to the Franciscan
Sisters for a new hospital in Santa Maria will
give an important message to the people of the
city. (English 1 pg.) On September 2, 1964,
Mrs. Hancock state that it is a privilege to share
one's blessings. (English 1 pg.)

Mc4480. H-1964
Msgr. Benjamin Hawkes to J. Francis Cardinal
McIntyre
September 22, 1964. Los Angeles, California

Mr. O'Malley will donate seven lots across
from San Conrado Mission. The money to put
some shrubbery in front of St. Anastasia is
ready for Fr. Gilb to negotiate the work to be
done. Dr. Cherry agrees with the treatment pre-
scribed by the doctors. (English 2 pgs.)

Mc4481. H-1964
Mr. Joseph Hupp to Pope Paul VI
September 22, 1964. Los Angeles, California

As the head of the Church, could you give
some information to a Mormon student to answer questions of Peter's position as "rock" and
some information on relics. (English 1 pg.)

Mc4482. H-1964
Mr. J. H. Hoeppel to J. Francis Cardinal
McIntyre
October 4, 1964. Los Angeles, California

A solution to the Federal Aid to education argument is to allow a $1,000 tax exemption for
parents who have children in private schools
and thus prevent a double taxation. (English 2
pgs.)

Mc4483. H-1964
J. Francis Cardinal McIntyre to Mr. Henry
Haggerty
October 7, 1964. Los Angeles, California

A plea to talk to and give advice to the New
York attorney in the transaction concerning St.
John's Hospital. Miss Irene Dunne will be contacting the office. (English 2 pgs.) On October
15, 1964, Mr. Haggerty states that Cinerama
will be able to withstand their financial difficulty. (English 1 pg.)

Mc4484. H-1964
Bp. Phillip Hannan to Bp. Timothy Manning
November 24, 1964. Washington, D.C.

Any interventions on the schema "De Matri-
monii Sacramento" should be sent immediately.
The form enclosed may be used or a more personal one may be sent. (English 2 pgs.)

Mc4485. H-1964
Dr. A. L. Henrichsen, MD to Bp. Timothy
Manning
December 22, 1964. Van Nuys, California

The teachings, traditions, and customs of the
Catholic Church would be helpful to a psychia-
trist who is dealing with Catholic patients. Is
such a book available? (English 1 pg.) On
December 29, 1964, the Bishop asks Msgr.
O'Dwyer to contact the doctor and to inquire
about materials. (English 1 pg.)

Mc4486. H-1964
Ms. Rosemary Hurd to J. Francis Cardinal
McIntyre
December 30, 1964. Los Angeles, California

When the new translation for the prayers said
at the end of the Requiem Mass are introduced
could the reference to Hell fires be eliminated?
(English 1 pg.) On January 4, 1964, Fr. Thom
states that attention is being paid to the transla-
tions. (English 1 pg.)

Mc4487. J-1964
Rev. Eugene Gilb to Mrs. Agnes Jones
January 30, 1964. Los Angeles, California

The obligation to attend the Eastern Rite
Church is first an obligation unless it is a great
inconvenience to fulfill the obligation. (English
1 pg.)

Mc4488. J-1964
J. Francis Cardinal McIntyre to Mr. Maurice
Jones
April 10, 1964. Los Angeles, California

Verbum Dei High School seems to be doing
well and the extended lots have changed the appearance of the area. (English 1 pg.)

Mc4489. J-1964
Sister M. Julia, CSJ to J. Francis Cardinal
McIntyre
April 25, 1964. Weston, Massachusetts

The change of the reading habits of many
Catholic students and theological students will
place the responsibility of the choice of books
on the individual. (English 2 pgs.)

Mc4490. K-1964
Mr. Robert Knauf to J. Francis Cardinal
McIntyre
January 2, 1964. Long Beach, California

Could a Diocesan wide fund raiser be organized to make Loyola a first class University
and co-educational? (English 1 pg.) On January
7, 1964, the Cardinal states that there are three
women's colleges and a co-educational institution could bankrupt them. (English 1 pg.)

Mc4491. K-1964
Rev. Edward Keller, CSC to J. Francis Cardinal
McIntyre
January 8, 1964. Notre Dame, Indiana

A Mass was celebrated on the anniversary of
your elevation to the College of Cardinals. The
United States needs you. (English 1 pg.) On January 17, 1964, the Cardinal states his appreciation for the Mass and the remembrance of the
anniversary. (English 1 pg.)

Mc4492. K-1964
J. Francis Cardinal McIntyre to Mr. C. A.
Korkowski
January 31, 1964. Los Angeles, California

The beautiful conference table and chairs for
the Consultors' room are appreciated as is all of
the furniture given to various institutions. (English 1 pg.)

Mc4493. K-1964
Mr. George Kish to Msgr. Benjamin Hawkes
February 10, 1964. New York City, New York

The letter of reference for Dr. John Kelly, MD
must include his stability and his ability to im-
provise. The over-seas hospitals cannot provide
everything the Dr. has in the United States. (English 1 pg.)

Mc4494. K-1964
J. Francis Cardinal McIntyre Memo
February 11, 1964. Los Angeles, California

Rabbi Solomon Kleinman and Rabbi Balfour
Brickner need a better understanding from a religious viewpoint of the theological differences.
A Catholic representative could be present if the
group desires it. Neither can understand Federal
Aid to education as a discrimination. (English 1
pg.)

Mc4495. K-1964
Ms. Josephine Kelly to J. Francis Cardinal
McIntyre
N.D. Sun City, California

A request is made to locate a Catholic nurs-
ing home where a lady can live until death. (English 2 pgs.) On May 19, 1964, Msgr. Johnson
states that perhaps Marycrest Manor could accommodate her but Mrs. Kenna could do some
investigation. (English 1 pg.)

Mc4496. K-1964
Msgr. Benjamin Hawkes to Mr. W. A.
Bushman
June 6, 1964. Los Angeles, California

A list of instruments which are needed at St.
Luke's Hospital in East Nigeria is enclosed. If
any of these are available, Dr. Kelly could take
them next month. (English 1 pg.)

Mc4497. K-1964
Mr. Daniel W. Klein to J. Francis Cardinal
McIntyre
June 22, 1964. San Francisco, California

A copy of the letter sent to Archbishop
McGucken in which the writer comments on
the fact that discrimination is a moral offense
and it is impossible to legislate morality. Silence
on the issue of the Housing Act is necessary to
allow everyone to follow his conscience. (English 7 pgs.)

Mc4498. K-1964
Rev. William Kenneally, CM to J. Francis Car-
dinal McIntyre
June 24, 1964. Camarillo, California

An invitation is extended to rest and relax in
the quiet of St. John's Seminary where a rest is
guaranteed. (English 1 pg.)

Mc4499. K-1964
Miss Madeline Kane to J. Francis Cardinal
McIntyre
August 6, 1964. Hooksett, New Hampshire

A request is made to initiate a coordinated
Religion program throughout the Catholic high
schools and CCD Programs. (English 3 pgs.)
On August 7, 1964 a letter of recommendation
from Sister Mary Colman RSM is sent. (English
5 pgs.)

Mc4500. K-1964
Rev. Donald Montrose to J. Francis Cardinal
McIntyre
August 19, 1964. Los Angeles, California

There is no one way to teach Religion or one
set of text books better than another. The religion teachers will be motivated to do the best
job possible with Fr. Hughes as the Religion Director. (English 2 pgs.)

Mc4501. K-1964
Arbp. John Krol to J. Francis Cardinal
McIntyre
September 8, 1964. Philadelphia, Pennsylvania

A report is ready on the maximum use of radio and television by the Church. A discussion
and a decision will be made at the annual Bishops' Meeting. (English 1 pg.)

Mc4502. K-1964
Mr. R. S. Lawson to Bp. Timothy Manning
September 28, 1964. San Francisco, California

A request for permission to serve meat at the
final banquet of the Kraft Foods Convention.
(English 1 pg.) On September 29, 1964, the
Bishop requests that the announcement be made
of the dispensation before the dinner is served.
(English 1 pg.)

Mc4503. K-1964
J. Francis Cardinal McIntyre to Mr. Alfonso
Kelley
November 25, 1964. Los Angeles, California

The magnificent specimen of Thanksgiving
plumage will be roasted and served for our dinner. We are most appreciative of your kindness.
(English 1 pg.)

Mc4504. K-1964
The Staff to J. Francis Cardinal McIntyre
N.D. Los Angeles, California

The death of Mr. Vincent Keating is a loss to
the Church by his example; to the Community
that another good man is gone; to the Newspaper by having one less strong, forthright man.
(English 5 pgs.)

Mc4505. L-1964
J. Francis Cardinal McIntyre   Memo
January 20, 1964. Los Angeles, California

Miss Kitty Lane desires to raise $25,000 and
engage Mr. Romeiro to make a bust of Pope
John XXIII and present it to Washington, D.C.
A definite refusal was given since it seems to be
a promotion for Romeiro. (English 1 pg.)

Mc4506. L-1964
Mr. William Lewis to Bp. Timothy Manning
February 27, 1964. Los Angeles, California

Advice and assistance is needed to seek a solution to a marriage problem. (English 3 pgs.)
On March 2, 1964, the Bishop asks to call for
an appointment. (English 1 pg.)

Mc4507. L-1964
Mr. Sven Lokrantz to J. Francis Cardinal
McIntyre
March 26, 1964. Los Angeles, California

A donation of $3,000 is enclosed from the es-
tate of Miss Marguerite Winston. (English 1
pg.) On March 30, 1964, the Cardinal expresses his prayerful gratitude for the donation.
(English 1 pg.)

Mc4508. L-1964
Bp. Luigi Bettazzi to J. Francis Cardinal
McIntyre
May 6, 1964. Bologna, Italy

An invitation is extended to send a message
for the celebration of the Golden Jubilee of Giacomo Cardinal Lercaro. (Italian 1 pg.) On
June 1, 1964, the Cardinal congratulates the
Cardinal on attaining the Golden Years in the
priesthood. (English 1 pg.)

Mc4509. L-1964
Mr. Walter Laband to J. Francis Cardinal
McIntyre
May 26, 1964. Covina, California

Could weekly newsbriefs be sent to the Archdiocese and be printed in *The Tidings* so we can
know what is happening in the Council? (English 1 pg.) On June 9, 1964, the Cardinal expresses his appreciation for the suggestion and
will send newsbriefs. (E 1 pg.)

Mc4510. L-1964
Mr. Richard Lescoe, MD to Msgr. Benjamin
Hawkes
July 6, 1964. Torrance, California

The Los Angeles County Medical Association
will print a *Handbook* listing pertinent information for all religions. The Catholic Hospital
Code will be printed. If any other suggestions
came to mind, please send them. (English 1 pg.)

Mc4511. L-1964
Mr. Josef V. Lombardo to J. Francis Cardinal
McIntyre
July 11, 1964. New York City, New York

The book, *Michelangelo's Pieta,* will appear
at the Vatican Pavillion. Each Cardinal will
have a copy bound in red leather with his coat-
of-arms. Could some one from the Chancery
Office send the coat-of-arms of the Cardinal
and the Bishops.

Mc4512. L-1964
Msgr. John Languille to J. Francis Cardinal
McIntyre
August 26, 1964. Los Angeles, California

The CYO will be most willing to cooperate
with the October celebration of Our Lady of
Fatima. It will be best to have the children meet
in their own parish for the Mass and Rosary
and not transport them to a central place. (English 2 pgs.)

Mc4513. L-1964
Rev. Riccardo Lombardi, SJ to J. Francis Car-
dinal McIntyre
August 28, 1964. Rome, Italy

An announcement is made of a retreat for all
Bishops from September 18–20 before the session of the Council. (English 1 pg.)

Mc4514. L-1964
Arcadio Cardinal Larraona to J. Francis Cardi-
nal McIntyre
September 11, 1964. Rome, Italy

The revised material for the third session of
the Council is enclosed for study. (Italian 1 pg.)

Mc4515. L-1964
Mr. Oscar Lawler to Bp. Timothy Manning
September 18, 1964. Los Angeles, California

The Chamber of Commerce of Los Angeles
conveys wishes for a speedy recovery for the
Cardinal and the safe return to Los Angeles.
(English 1 pg.)

Mc4516. L-1964
Bp. Edward Lawton to Msgr. Benjamin
   Hawkes
October 13, 1964. Charlestown, Massachusetts

A request is made to spend some time in Los
Angeles before visiting the Dominicans in Mexico, Texas, and Louisiana. (English 2 pgs.) On
October 21, 1964, Msgr. states that the Cardinal and the household will be most happy to
welcome the Bishop to Los Angeles. (English
1 pg.)

Mc4517. L-1964
Mr. Charles Luckman to J. Francis Cardinal
   McIntyre
December 21, 1964. Los Angeles, California

In place of the usual Christmas gifts, the
Charles Luckman Associates will donate money
to the Child Guidance Clinic. (English 1 pg.)

Mc4518. Mc-1964
Mr. Constantine McGuire to J. Francis Cardi-
   nal McIntyre
January 4, 1964

The present plans are to spend thirty or forty
days in Bogota, then go to the University of
Freiburg and Milan, before coming to the Pacific Coast. (English 1 pg.) On January 10,
1964, the Cardinal comments that he will await
the visit to the Pacific Coast. (English 1 pg.)

Mc4519. Mc-1964
Bp. Timothy Manning to Dr. Harry McKnight
January 10, 1964. Los Angeles, California

The Cardinal expects to be called to Rome
for a Committee Meeting so a lecture could not
be scheduled at the present time. (English 1 pg.)

Mc4520. Mc-1964
Mr. William McGlone to J. Francis Cardinal
   McIntyre
January 26, 1964. La Grange, Illinois

Some sanity ought to remain in the Church
and atheism, agnosticism, and communism
ought to be attacked and not other Catholics.
(English 1 pg.)

Mc4521. Mc-1964
Bp. elect Charles McLaughlin to J. Francis
   Cardinal McIntyre
January 29, 1964. Raleigh, North Carolina

An Invitation is extended to the consecration
on April 15 at the Cathedral in Greensboro,
North Carolina. (English 1 pg.) On February 7,
1964, the Cardinal states that his Easter calendar will prevent attendance. (English 1 pg.)

Mc4522. Mc-1964
Mr. Maytor McKinley to J. Francis Cardinal
   McIntyre
March 23, 1964. Los Angeles, California

The outstanding work being done by the Vatican Council deserves a token of respect and
admiration. Please remember mother in your
prayers. (English 1 pg.)

Mc4523. Mc-1964
Arbp. Joseph T. McGucken to J. Francis Cardi-
   nal McIntyre
April 28, 1964. San Francisco, California

Mr. William Consedine feels this is the best
time to press for the payment of the Pious Fund.
We could ask for two million dollars and not
settle for less than one million. (English 1 pg.)

Mc4524. Mc-1964
J. Francis Cardinal McIntyre
MEMORANDUM
April 30, 1964. Los Angeles, California

The Council is timely and has stimulated the
spiritual impulses of all people of the world. It
has timely urged the people to seek basic reasons for religion. (English 1 pg.)

Mc4525. Mc-1964
J. Francis Cardinal McIntyre to Arbp. Joseph
   T. McGucken
April 30, 1964. Los Angeles, California

It is my opinion to give the Pious Fund eternal rest in the past tense. It is noteworthy that
Montezuma Seminary as the beneficiary is not
an attraction. (English 1 pg.)

Mc4526. Mc-1964
Arbp. Joseph T. McGucken to Francis Cardinal
   McIntyre
May 4, 1964. San Francisco, California

The Mexican Diplomat reopened the case of
the Pious Fund. Most of the Bishops would be
satisfied with a lump sum settlement. (English
1 pg.)

Mc4527. Mc-1964
Arbp. Joseph T. McGucken to J. Francis Cardinal McIntyre
May 21, 1964. San Francisco, California

The Church will not press for payment but the State Department could settle for a lump sum. There will be no reference made to the Church so the reaction to the Church in Mexico will be unaffected. (English 1 pg.)

Mc4528. Mc-1964
Mr. Frank MacDonald to Msgr. Benjamin Hawkes
August 13, 1964. Hollywood, California

A long letter sent to various Senators and newspapers giving his views on the racial question in Los Angeles and his reaction to the demonstrations against the Cardinal. (English 5 pgs.)

Mc4529. Mc-1964
J. Francis Cardinal McIntyre to All Priests
August 25, 1964. Los Angeles, California

The Catholic press announces the use of the vernacular in the *Collectio Rituum*. The Altar Missals should be ready for the First Sunday in Advent. (English 4 pgs.)

Mc4530. Mc-1964
Ms. Rose McCarthy to Bp. Timothy Manning
September 21, 1964. Hollywood, California

Some work as assistant in theater and publicity would allow me to return my talents to the Lord. (English 1 pg.) On September 22, 1964, the Bishop states that he has alerted Msgr. John Languille. (English 1 pg.)

Mc4531. Mc-1964
J. Francis Cardinal McIntyre to Bp. Timothy Manning
November 5, 1964. Los Angeles, California

A family letter commenting on the election of the President and senators, the unfortunate comments of Archbishop McGucken. Schema No 13 has some press coverage but the election is too important. (English 3 pgs.)

Mc4532. Mc-1964
Mrs. James McElwee to J. Francis Cardinal McIntyre
November 14, 1964. Coral Gables, Florida

The world looks for complicated solutions to the defeat of Communism when they have the Rosary which could be in everyone's hands. (English 3 pgs.)

Mc4533. Mc-1964
Msgr. Benjamin Hawkes to J. Francis Cardinal McIntyre
November 24, 1964. Los Angeles, California

The law pertaining to Catholic Hospitals is one which needs wide knowledge and complete coverage. (English 1 pg.)

Mc4534. Mc-1964
Amleto Cardinal Cicognani to Arbp. E. Clarizio
November 25, 1964. Vatican City

The Fourth Mariological Congress will provide help for the poor with the construction of the new villages and the donation of $10,000 by the Pope. (English 1 pg.)

Mc4535. Mc-1964
Msgr. Benjamin Hawkes to Mr. Neil McCarthy
November 30, 1964. Los Angeles, California

The donation of $1,000 to Dolores Mission School in memory of Ellen McCarthy will assist with the rehabilitation work. (English 1 pg.)

Mc4536. M-1964
J. Francis Cardinal McIntyre to Mr. Robert Magdlen
January 18, 1964. Los Angeles, California

The generous donation of 165 shares of Schur-Kon Company stock is appreciated and will be used for the education of the priests. (English 1 pg.)

Mc4537. M-1964
Mr. Harold Marlowe to J. Francis Cardinal McIntyre
January 21, 1964. Los Angeles, California

An invitation is extended to join with prominent industrial, civic, and political leaders to honor Senator Muskie. (English 1 pg.)

Mc4538. M-1964
Paul Cardinal Marella to J. Francis Cardinal McIntyre
February 4, 1964. Vatican City

A special session of the Commission will be called March 3 to 13 to discuss the work done on the revision of the documents before presentation to the Council. (Latin 2 pgs.)

Mc4539. M-1964
J. Francis Cardinal McIntyre to Paul Cardinal Marella
February 15, 1964. Los Angeles, California

The importance of the plenary session is evident. I will arrive on March 2 with Fr. Eugene Gilb. (English 1 pg.)

Mc4540. M-1964
J. Francis Cardinal McIntyre to Mr. James Matthew
February 15, 1964. Los Angeles, California

The copy of *An Historical Pilgrimage* gives excellent pictures of St. Vibiana's Cathedral and Pope Paul VI. (English 1 pg.)

Mc4541. M-1964
Mrs. Dorothy Marchesano to Bp. Timothy Manning
February 19, 1964. Thousands Oaks, California

An equal stress ought to be placed on the importance of men on Father's Day as the Church does for women on Mother's Day. (English 2 pgs.) On March 2, 1964, the Bishop states that it is edifying to speak so well of sons and sons-in-law. (English 1 pg.)

Mc4542. M-1964
Mr. Ross Montgomery to J. Francis Cardinal McIntyre
February 20, 1964. Los Angeles, California

Modern architecture will be dated soon. A Cathedral should generate the stability and sanctity in which the Church is steadfast. (English 2 pgs.)

Mc4543. M-1964
J. Francis Cardinal McIntyre to Paul Cardinal Marella
February 24, 1964. Los Angeles, California

The question of *Juridica* is left dangerously undecided. An argument is prepared for the meeting. (English 1 pg.)

Mc4544. M-1964
Mrs. Laura Moore to J. Francis Cardinal McIntyre
March 13, 1964. New York City, New York

A friendly letter commenting on the changes in the Church made by Vatican Council and physical conditions of aging. (English 4 pgs.) On April 27, 1964, the Cardinal states that the changes are not as radical as some people anticipated. (English 1 pg.)

Mc4545. M-1964
Bp. John J. Maguire to J. Francis Cardinal McIntyre
April 2, 1964. New York City, New York

An invitation is extended to the celebration of the Silver Jubilee of Cardinal Spellman's tenure as Archbishop of New York. (English 1 pg.) On April 9, 1964, the Cardinal states that Mary's Hour on May 3 and a scheduled talk on May 5 makes a trip to New York impossible. (English 1 pg.)

Mc4546. M-1964
J. Francis Cardinal McIntyre to Msgr. Harry C. Meade
April 3, 1964. Los Angeles, California

A special medal commemorating the Pope's visit to the Holy Lands is enclosed for Mr. Leslie Miller. (English 1 pg.)

Mc4547. M-1964
Mr. Gene Handsaker to J. Francis Cardinal McIntyre
April 23, 1964. Los Angeles, California

The Associated Press is writing an article on Rabbi Magnin and requests a statement of esteem that can be published. (English 1 pg.) On April 25, 1964, the Cardinal states the influence that Rabbi Magnin has exerted in the life of the city has been salutary and productive. (English 1 pg.)

Mc4548. M-1964
Mr. Robert Mauro to J. Francis Cardinal McIntyre
April 25, 1964. Long Branch, New Jersey

A request is made to add the name of the Cardinal to an ad in the New York Times for a Constitutional Amendment to clarify the First Amendment. (English 1 pg.)

Mc4549. M-1964
Mr. Francis Montgomery to The Los Angeles *Times*
May 20, 1964. Los Angeles, California

The article in the Los Angeles *Times* is in error. The Human Relations Council has no connection with the Catholic Church. (English 1 pg.)

Mc4550. M-1964
Mr. Thomas Morris to Msgr. John Rawden
June 19, 1964. Fullerton, California

Could the hand lettered parchments of Papal Blessing sold in Rome be sold in the Archdiocese? (English 1 pg.) On July 13, 1964, Msgr. states that the Pastor must give a recommendation before the parchments are signed by an official at the Vatican. (English 1 pg.)

Mc4551. M-1964
Bp. Timothy Manning to J. Francis Cardinal McIntyre
September 21, 1964. Los Angeles, California

The good news of your return to the North American College brings happiness to the people. Many letters and calls promise prayers. Everything is peaceful in Los Angeles. (English 1 pg.)

Mc4552. M-1964
Miss Yara Muro to J. Francis Cardinal
McIntyre
October 28, 1964. San Gabriel, California

A request is made for permission to get married in the Chapel at Maryvale. As a Cuban refugee this is the only Chapel or Church I know. (English 2 pgs.) On November 2, 1964, Fr. Gilb suggests that a contact with the Pastor of St. Anthony's Church should be made and then let the Office know the answer. (English 1 pg.)

Mc4553. M-1964
Bp. Timothy Manning to J. Francis Cardinal
McIntyre
November 9, 1964. Rome, Italy

The document on the Church is ready for promulgation; the schema on the Missions was ripped apart; the newly authorized concelebrated Mass will be celebrated for the consecration of Bishop-elect O'Herlihy. (English 4 pgs.)

Mc4554. M-1964
Mr. Myron S. Fox to Msgr. Benjamin Hawkes
December 7, 1964. Beverly Hills, California

This donation of $2,000 given by Suzanne Mary Mauer is for Dolores Mission and Santa Teresita Church. (English 1 pg.) On December 10, 1964, Msgr. states that the Pastors of both parishes are most grateful. (English 1 pg.)

Mc4555. M-1964
Msgr. Benjamin Hawkes to Mr. Hugh Maguire
December 11, 1964. Los Angeles, California

The information on *Enlightened Giving* and the *Engineer's Suggestions to the Clergy* are valuable and will be shared with the ordination class. (English 1 pg.)

Mc4556. M-1964
Mr. Vincent Murtha to J. Francis Cardinal
McIntyre
December 14, 1964. Yonkers, New York

A request is made for information on the Ecumenical Movement and changes in the Liturgy for a paper to be submitted to Columbia University. (English 1 pg.) On December 10, 1964, the Cardinal suggest the *Catholic News* in New York has all of the information. (English 1 pg.)

Mc4557. N-1964
Mr. Hans Ries to J. Francis Cardinal McIntyre
June 1, 1964. Beverly Hills, California

An invitation to attend the Memorial Service for Jawaharlal Nehru at the Greek Theatre on June 7, at 6:30 is enclosed. (English 1 pg.) On June 2, 1964, the Cardinal states that due to a previous engagement, Msgr. O'Sullivan will represent the Archdiocese. (English 1 pg.)

Mc4558. N-1964
Mrs. Teresa Nelson to Msgr. Benjamin Hawkes
July 23, 1964. La Puente, California

The letters from Bishop Amat High School and St. Joseph's School stating that the tuition was paid in full by Msgr. Hawkes is beyond any words of appreciation. Prayers of gratitude are offered. (English 1 pg.)

Mc4559. N-1964
Msgr. Joaquin Nabuco to J. Francis Cardinal
McIntyre
December 21, 1963. Rio de Janeiro, Brazil

The books on the Liturgy are ready for publication. May I ask for your donation to match Cardinal Ritter's. (English 1 pg.) On January 3, 1964, the Cardinal states that Cardinal Ritter exceeded his expectations but the check is enclosed. (English 1 pg.)

Mc4560. O-1964
Mr. Fergus O'Rourke to J. Francis Cardinal
McIntyre
January 9, 1964. Co. Cork, Ireland

A plea for funds to continue to work on biological research projects. (English 6 pgs.) On January 21, 1964, the Cardinal states that when he speaks with the colleges he will mention his name. A donation for the work is enclosed. (English 1 pg.)

Mc4561. O-1964
Arbp. Patrick O'Boyle to J. Francis Cardinal
McIntyre
January 22, 1964. Washington, D.C.

If there are any suggestions, alterations, additions, or suppressions for "*DeScholis Catholicis*" please send them so the thinking of the American Bishops can be heard. (English 4 pgs.)

Mc4562. O-1964
Rev. Harley Baker to Msgr. Benjamin Hawkes
February 5, 1964. Juneau, Alaska

Bishop O'Flanagan will arrive in Los Angeles on February 15 on Western Air Lines. Arrangements for hospitality have not been made. (English 1 pg.)

Mc4563. O-1964
J. Francis Cardinal McIntyre to Arbp. Martin
O'Connor
February 14, 1964. Los Angeles, California

A separate and special session of the Committee of Cardinal Marella will meet on March 3–13. I will arrive on March 2. (English 1 pg.) On February 17, 1964, the Archbishop states that the North American College will be waiting. (English 1 pg.)

Mc4564. O-1964
J. Francis Cardinal McIntyre to Arbp. Patrick
O'Boyle
February 15, 1964. Los Angeles, California

Comments on *De Scholis Catholicis* are limited to the United States and these have no place in the Council. The following ideas on the Natural Law are enclosed. (English 5 pgs.)

Mc4565. O-1964
Mr. Ernest O'Brien to Bp. Timothy Manning
March 8, 1964. New York City, New York

A request to join the novena to Mother Seton for a cure of cancer is sent. This could be the miracle that is needed for canonization. (English 2 pgs.) On March 12, 1964, the Bishop states that the intention will be remembered in prayer. (English 1 pg.)

Mc4566. O-1964
Bp. Dermot O'Flanagan to J. Francis Cardinal
McIntyre
March 17, 1964. Juneau, Alaska

For the most generous donation for the Diocese of Juneau, for the gracious hospitality, and for the complete set of Episcopal Robes, I am most grateful. (English 2 pgs.)

Mc4567. O-1964
Rev. Aloysius Ogihara, SJ to Bp. Timothy
Manning
March 19, 1964. Toyko, Japan

There is one priest convert from the Orthodox Church and there is a possibility of another priest soon. Please continue to pray for the work of the Church of Japan. (English 1 pg.) On March 31, 1964, the Bishop sends a gift for the great work of the Church in Toyko. (English 1 pg.)

Mc4568. O-1964
Bp. Dermot O'Flanagan to Msgr. Benjamin
Hawkes
April 20, 1964. Juneau, Alaska

The Good Friday earthquake and seismic waves ruined two churches; Seward and Valdez suffered major damage. All hospitals and schools survived. (English 1 pg.)

Mc4569. O-1964
Mr. Gilbert Oddo to Bp. Timothy Manning
May 21, 1964. Guadalajara, Mexico

The Catholic University of Mexico in Guadalajara ITESO has Jesuits Priests in Administration and needs continual support. (English 2 pgs.)

Mc4570. O-1964
J. Francis Cardinal McIntyre to Arbp. Patrick
O'Boyle
May 22, 1964. Los Angeles, California

A questionnaire from *Ave Maria* Magazine is a potential for unfair misinterpretations and criticism. Some action should be taken by the Bishops' Board. (English 5 pgs.) On June 4, 1964, the Archbishop states that if the Board took any action, the cry would be censorship. (English 1 pg.)

Mc4571. O-1964
Mr. Leon Ohanesian to J. Francis Cardinal
McIntyre
August 20, 1964. Los Angeles, California

An offer to donate property valued at $300,000 to the Archdiocese is planned. (English 3 pgs.) On August 29, 1964, the Cardinal asks to call Fr. Gilb for an appointment. (English 1 pg.)

Mc4572. O-1964
J. Francis Cardinal McIntyre to Mr. John
O'Melveny
November 4, 1964. Los Angeles, California

The additional three acres of land for St. Vincent de Paul Boys' Camp will enhance the summer program. Both the Society and the Cardinal are grateful. (English 1 pg.)

Mc4573. O-1964
Mr. Harold Henry to Mrs. Daniel O'Brien
December 1, 1964. Los Angeles, California

The City Council voted down the Human Relation Council and joined with the County. The Council was seen as a first step to harass the Police Department. (English 1 pg.)

Mc4574. O-1964
Msgr. Francis Ott to Msgr. John Rawden
November 4, 1964. San Diego, California

Could the date for the canonical permission for petitioning for divorce be given and the cause for the authorization for permanent separation be made known. This will help me in my guidance. (English 1 pg.)

Mc4575. O-1964
Mr. Trave O'Hearn to J. Francis Cardinal
McIntyre
December 9, 1964. Davenport, Iowa

The youth of America are proud of a Catholic leader who is willing to preserve the Constitution of the United States. (English 1 pg.)

Mc4576. P-1964
Mr. Hal Phillips to J. Francis Cardinal
McIntyre
January 27, 1964. Los Angeles, California

Are there definite ways that the communication media can help to improve the moral standard of the public? (English 1 pg.)

Mc4577. P-1964
J. Francis Cardinal McIntyre to Mr. Virgil
Pinkley
February 3, 1964. Los Angeles, California

Prayerful condolences are extended on the death of Mrs. Pinkley and prayers of comfort and consolation for the family. (English 1 pg.) On February 5, 1964, Mr. Pinkley requests greater understanding among all members of the Christian faiths and greater attention to the decrees of the Council. (English 2 pgs.)

Mc4578. P-1964
Mr. Peter Pitchess to J. Francis Cardinal
McIntyre
February 26, 1964. Los Angeles, California

The presence of the Cardinal at the dedication of the new Chapel added greatly to the solemnity of the event. Pictures of the event are enclosed. (English 1 pg.)

Mc4579. P-1964
Mr. Peter Pitchess to J. Francis Cardinal
McIntyre
June 4, 1964. Los Angeles, California

Is a copy of the statement to the Supreme Court concerning prayer in public school and public gatherings available? Right-thinking people must applaud the statement. (English 1 pg.)

Mc4580. P-1964
Mr. Leon Paul to J. Francis Cardianl McIntyre
June 23, 1964. Jackson Heights, New York

The Edith Stein Guild is interested in the forthcoming statement from the Council on the Jewish people. Could Pope John's love be extended to all and condemn anti-semitism? (English 2 pgs.)

Mc4581. P-1964
Chief William Parker to J. Francis Cardinal
McIntyre
September 17, 1964. Los Angeles, California

The presentation of the Medal of Valor was a special occasion for the Police Department. Knowing the problems and dangers confronting the police will make communication with the Department possible. (English 1 pg.)

Mc4582. P-1964
Mr. Patrick Powers to J. Francis Cardinal
McIntyre
October 5, 1964. Los Angeles, California

The message of condolence was received with heartfelt gratitude. The illness in Rome was the occasion of special prayers for the Cardinal. (English 1 pg.)

Mc4583. P-1964
Mrs. G. Pries to Bp. Timothy Manning
November 2, 1964. Los Angeles, California

Gilbert Pries requests a letter of recommendation for Loyola University. His greatest desire is to become a priest. (English 2 pgs.) On December 3, 1964, the Bishop states that a letter will be sent to Loyola University but no decision has been made to admit a blind student to the Seminary. (English 1 pg.)

Mc4584. P-1964
Mr. William Barth to Msgr. Benjamin Hawkes
November 5, 1964. Los Angeles, California

Pepsi Cola Company is presenting 1000 documentary records to the public and private schools entitled, Adventures in Negro History. (English 1 pg.)

Mc4585. P-1964
Mrs. Helen Pickett to J. Francis Cardinal
McIntyre
November 25, 1964. Los Angeles, California

A committee of Catholic women is being formed to work on the celebration of California's 200th birthday. The information for the committee is enclosed. (English 1 pg.) On December 1, 1964, the Cardinal states that the Catholic women's colleges are an excellent place to gather members. (English 1 pg.)

Mc4586. P-1964
Mrs. Jeanne Prepen to J. Francis Cardinal
McIntyre
N.D. Venice, California

Could a series of talks be given on the Mystical Body so Catholics could understand their responsibility towards all races and nationalities. (English 2 pgs.)

Mc4587. P-1964
Msgr. Stanislaus Pereira to J. Francis Cardinal
McIntyre
N.D. Bombay, India

An appeal is made for donations to help build a Temple to God in honor of Our Lady of the Rosary in Bombay. (English 1 pg.)

Mc4588. Q-1964
Mr. G. Harold Quinton to J. Francis Cardinal
McIntyre
April 20, 1964. Los Angeles, California

The meeting with His Highness Otto Von
Hapsburg was an occasion to hear an authoritative discussion on Europe, Near and Far East, and Africa. (English 1 pg.)

Mc4589. Q-1964
Mrs. Emma Quigley to Bp. Timothy Manning
April 30, 1964. Los Angeles, California

The Sunday after Ascension Thursday would
be an excellent time to introduce the prayer for
charity to all. Conchita Chapman understands
the appeal and will help to spread the idea. (English 6 pgs.)

Mc4590. R-1964
Mr. Maurice Norcop to Bp. Timothy Manning
January 11, 1964. Los Angeles, California

Mrs. Rose Roy, a long time member of the
Archdiocese and a founder of many Diocesan
organizations, is now old and ill. Could some
type of honor be given to her to make the last
months of her life happy? (English 2 pgs.) On
January 23, 1964, the Bishop states that Mrs.
Roy will be honored in some way. (English
1 pg.)

Mc4591. R-1964
J. Francis Cardinal McIntyre to Mr. W. S.
Rosecrans
January 20, 1964. Los Angeles, California

Since illness prevented the investiture of the
Knights of Malta in New York, a ceremony will
be held in any Church or my Chapel at your
convenience. (English 1 pg.)

Mc4592. R-1964
Joseph Cardinal Rivera to J. Francis Cardinal
McIntyre
March 2, 1964. Guadalupe, Mexico

An invitation is extended to the centenary of
the Archdiocese of Guadalajara which will be
celebrated with the Eucharistic Congress. (English 1 pg.) On March 5, 1964, Bishop Manning states that the invitation will be given to
the Cardinal on his return from Rome. (English
1 pg.)

Mc4593. R-1964
Rev. James Richardson, CM to J. Francis Cardinal McIntyre
March 6, 1964. Los Angeles, California

The requirements of the Constitution on the
Liturgy are enclosed with emphasis on the reading of the Divine Office in English (English
1 pg.)

Mc4594. R-1964
Msgr. John Rawden to Miss K. Rasinger
March 12, 1964 Los Angeles, California

The Cardinal acknowledges with great pleasure the book on the life of Emperor Charles I
of Austria. (English 1 pg.)

Mc4595. R-1964
J. Francis Cardinal McIntyre to Joseph Cardinal Rivera
March 23, 1964. Los Angeles, California

With regret, the invitation to attend the Eucharistic Congress in Guadalajara must be declined. (English 1 pg.)

Mc4596. R-1964
J. Francis Cardinal McIntyre to Arbp. Thomas
Roberts, SJ
June 11, 1964. Los Angeles, California

Postpone the speaking engagements in the
Archdiocese lest further confusion results. (English 1 pg.) On January 23, 1964, the Archbishop states that the speaking engagements are
on *Pacem in Terris* with a view to ecumenism.
(English 1 pg.)

Mc4597. R-1964
Msgr. George Rice to J. Francis Cardinal
McIntyre
July 9, 1964. San Diego, California

Prayers are being offered for continued
strength against the false accusations being
made against you. (English 1 pg.) On July 16,
1964, the Cardinal states that he appreciates
the confidence. (English 1 pg.)

Mc4598. R-1964
Mr. Hugh Rafferty to J. Francis Cardinal
McIntyre
August 7, 1964. Kenosha, Wisconsin

Mr. Drew Pearson states that the Cardinal is
in favor of Proposition 14. Please give your decision. (English 1 pg.) On August 8, 1964, the
Cardinal states he follows the traditional teaching of dignity of all human beings and the
responsibility to respect that dignity. (English
2 pgs.)

Mc4599. R-1964
Ms. Carrie Jones to J. Francis Cardinal
McIntyre
August 15, 1964. Los Angeles, California

Should the advice of an unbiased real estate
broker be needed, this list of American Society
of Real Estate Counselors can be of assistance.
(English 1 pg.)

Mc4600. R-1964
Arbp. Antonio Rocco to J. Francis Cardinal
  McIntyre
August 20, 1964. Buenos Aires, Argentina

A letter of introduction for Dr. Anselmo Ramon Hernandez and Dr. Luis Hernandez who are studying in the United States is enclosed. (English 1 pg.)

Mc4601. R-1964
Arbp. Joseph Raya to J. Francis Cardinal
  McIntyre
September 8, 1964. Birmingham, Alabama

A copy of the promised *Missal of the Byzantine Rite* is enclosed. (English 1 pg.) On September 18, 1964, Msgr. states that the Missal will be given to the Cardinal on his return from Rome. (English 1 pg.)

Mc4602. R-1964
J. Francis Cardinal McIntyre to Mrs. Charles
  Ridder
October 21, 1964. Los Angeles, California

Prayerful condolences are sent to the family on the death of Charles, a loyal member of the Knights of Malta. His death ends a long friendship and one blessed by many joys. (English 1 pg.)

Mc4603. R-1964
Msgr. Patrick Roche to J. Francis Cardinal
  McIntyre
October 26, 1964. Los Angeles, California

The book on the Council by Mr. Sugrue should be acknowledged with gratitude. It has some inadequacies but any book would have. (English 1 pg.) On October 29, 1964, the Cardinal states to Mr. Whitney that Mr. Sugrue has fulfilled an enormous task. (English 1 pg.)

Mc4604. R-1964
Msgr. John Rawden to Msgr. Benjamin
  Hawkes
October 29, 1964. Vatican City

Please send a copy of the ceremonies of a Consecration of a Bishop. The copy of the *Congregation of Rites* for Bishop Ward is enclosed. (English 1 pg.)

Mc4605. R-1964
Rev. Harry Rasmussen to Msgr. Benjamin
  Hawkes
November 2, 1964. Turin, Italy

A message of appreciation for the quick reply to the statement of faculties in Los Angeles. The American workers appreciate a Mass in English. (English 1 pg.)

Mc4606. R-1964
Mr. Lorenzo Renzoni to J. Francis Cardinal
  McIntyre
December 16, 1964. Los Angeles, California

An offer to sell three large paintings of the late 15th and 16th centuries for about $500 a piece is made. (English 1 pg.) On December 29, 1964, the Cardinal states that he has no place for them at the present time but will keep the possibility in mind. (English 1 pg.)

Mc4607. R-1964
Joseph Cardinal Ritter to J. Francis Cardinal
  McIntyre
December 29, 1964. St. Louis, Missouri

A request to send a letter to the Secretariat for Christian Unity on the wording of the text. The present text would seem best to retain. (English 2 pgs.)

Mc4608. S-1964
Mrs. Henrietta Schleppey to Msgr. Benjamin
  Hawkes
January 9, 1964. Seal Beach, California

Is there some method of locating Professor Ernst Wolfram in Canoga Park? (English 1 pg.) On January 13, 1964, Msgr. suggests contacting the Pastor who might know the gentleman or have some leads for a method of locating him. (English 1 pg.)

Mc4609. S-1964
Ms. Mary Pechance to Rev. Eugene Gilb
January 12, 1964. Los Angeles, California

Mr. Edmundo Stockins will arrive on January 23 and would be interested in giving illustrated lectures. Could hospitality with Catholic families be arranged? (English 2 pgs.)

Mc4610. S-1964
J. Francis Cardinal McIntyre Memo
January 17, 1964. Los Angeles, California

Mr. Mendel Silberberg asks to accept an invitation to go to Israel. If the opportunity presents itself when I am next in Rome, the visit will be considered. (English 1 pg.)

Mc4611. S-1964
Richard Cardinal Cushing to J. Francis Cardinal McIntyre
February 10, 1964. Brighton, Massachusetts

Mr. Edward Sheehan is delegated by the *Saturday Evening Post* to write an article on the Catholic Church in the United States. He will not quote unless given permission. (English 1 pg.)

Mc4612. S-1964
Mr. Harry Shepherd to J. Francis Cardinal
McIntyre
February 11, 1964. Long Beach, California

The series on *Church and State* and *First Amendment* are being sent for your reading and comments. (English 1 pg.) On February 27, 1964, the Cardinal states that the present legislation changes the controversy over Constitutionality. (English 1 pg.)

Mc4613. S-1964
J. Francis Cardinal McIntyre to Francis Cardinal Spellman
February 19, 1964. Los Angeles, California

Mr. Dan Donohue wants $5,000 sent to the Vatican Pavilion in the World's Fair. The collection is being gathered now in Los Angeles. (English 1 pg.) On February 24, 1964, the Cardinal states that Cardinal Marella will bless the Pavilion on April 19. (English 1 pg.)

Mc4614. S-1964
Mr. Roland Seidler to J. Francis Cardinal
McIntye
February 24, 1964. Los Angeles, California

Is there an area in the Archdiocese that needs additional help? Is there a person who can direct me? (English 1 pg.) On February 27, 1964, the Cardinal states upon return from Rome, several projects will be presented. (English 1 pg.)

Mc4615. S-1964
Mr. Arthur Sutton to J. Francis Cardinal
McIntyre
March 27, 1964. Claremont, California

Could Monsignor Roach speak to the Claremont Community Church of Seventh-day Adventists. The group would be interested in Vatican II and establishing some communication with the contemporary Catholic Church. (English 1 pg.)

Mc4616. S-1964
J. Francis Cardinal McIntyre to Francis Cardinal Spellman
April 9, 1964. Los Angeles, California

With regret, Bishop Maguire's invitation to your Silver Jubilee must be declined. The annual event of Mary's Hour is on May 3 and a lecture on May 5 in Pomona must be given priority. My daily prayers will continue for peace and joy. (English 1 pg.)

Mc4617. S-1964
Mr. John Simons to J. Francis Cardinal
McIntyre
April 13, 1964. Greensboro, North Carolina

The United States ought to make the Panama Canal an International Body under the United Nations. The same should be done for all major canals. (English 2 pgs.)

Mc4618. S-1964
Msgr. Joseph Sharpe to J. Francis Cardinal
McIntyre
April 24, 1964. Los Angeles, California

The two Singer brothers have a film that they have shown to some Catholic elementary schools. They do not have the Education Office approval for this.

Mc4619. S-1964
Rev. Forrest C. Weir to J. Francis Cardinal
McIntyre
May 7, 1964. Los Angeles, California

The Metropolitan Water Department will meet in the new Department Building on June 9 and requests a Chaplain to open the meeting at 10:30. (English 1 pg.) On May 11, 1964, Msgr. asks Fr. Sheridan or Fr. Healy to give the invocation. (English 1 pg.)

Mc4620. S-1964
Francis Cardinal Spellman to J. Francis Cardinal McIntyre
May 8, 1964. New York City, New York

The Decree on the Liturgy from James Cardinal Lercaro confirming the recommendations made by the Hierarchy of the United States is enclosed. (English 1 pg.)

Mc4621. S-1964
Mr. Gerald Sheppard to Mr. Ed Verhilig
May 12, 1964. Los Angeles, California

Is it possible to obtain a copy of the talk given by Cardinal McIntyre, Ebbtide in Education, so it can be reprinted in the *Freedom Club Bulletin*? (English 1 pg.)

Mc4622. S-1964
Pope Paul VI to Francis Cardinal Spellman
May 12, 1964. Vatican City

Fulfilling the promise of Pope John XXIII, the *Pieta* of Michelangelo will be placed in the Vatican Pavilion and placed in the hands of Cardinal Marella and Cardinal Spellman. (Latin 3 pgs.)

Mc4623. S-1964
Miss Madeline Sophie to J. Francis Cardinal
McIntyre
May 15, 1964 Los Angeles, California

An appeal for food until some one is physically able to work. There are job opportunities when physical strength returns. (English 2 pgs.) On May 19, 1964, the Cardinal asks the parish priest to obtain the necessary funds from the Archbishop's Fund for Charity. (English 1 pg.)

Mc4624. S-1964
Mr. John Servatius to J. Francis Cardinal
McIntyre
May 26, 1964. Utica, New York

Permission is requested to use the prayer for peace which you wrote to be sent with the license plates to pray for peace. (English 1 pg.) On June 1, 1964, the Cardinal states that he does not know which prayer is the one referred to and perhaps the Pastor can be helpful. (English 1 pg.)

Mc4625. S-1964
Mrs. Sarah Steadman to J. Francis Cardinal
McIntyre
June 25, 1964. Co. Tyrone, Ireland

A plea is made for assistance for the re-establishment of the parish and repairs for the school. (English 2 pgs.) On July 1, 1964, Bishop Manning sends a small donation. (English 1 pg.)

Mc4626. S-1964
Rev. Eugene Gilb to Mr. John R. Slater
July 1, 1964. Los Angeles, California

Catholic Welfare and Catholic Lawyers Guild would be the best sources for legal aid and advice in your area. (English 1 pg.)

Mc4627. S-1964
J. Francis Cardinal McIntyre to Mr. Walter
Smith
July 10, 1964. Los Angeles, California

Having known Mr. Al Smith so well is often related to the people in Los Angeles. This area, however, has developed a special collection method so that no outside agency is used. (English 1 pg.)

Mc4628. V-1964
J. Francis Cardinal McIntyre to Elizabeth
Bannenman
July 15, 1964. Los Angeles, California

The Church and all of Los Angeles mourns the death of your father, Dr. Von Kleinsmid, and assures the family of prayers. (English 1 pg.)

Mc4629. S-1964
Mrs. Regina Smith to Mr. Patrick Scanlon
August 4, 1964. Fullerton, California

A letter of complaint for the half truths in the article in *The Tablet* concerning Cardinal McIntyre. The placement of the article is also a matter of concern. (English 2 pgs.) On August 7, 1964, Mr. Scanlon states that no offense was intended. (English 1 pg.)

Mc4630. S-1964
J. Francis Cardinal McIntyre to Mrs. Regina
Smith
August 10, 1964. Los Angeles, California

Your defense of your Archdiocese is most gratifying and appreciated. It is good for the Eastern part of the Church to know that the Californians will fight back. (English 1 pg.)

Mc4631. S-1964
Mr. Thomas Soumas to J. Francis Cardinal
McIntyre
August 10, 1964. Costa Mesa, California

To receive a ten year old boy and to talk to him was the greatest way his wish could be fulfilled. It made a deep and surely a lasting impression on him and me. (English 1 pg.)

Mc4632. S-1964
J. Francis Cardinal McIntyre to Francis Cardinal Spellman
October 29, 1964. Los Angeles, California

Is there any comment about the visit to the North American College of Rev. Hans Kung? It is a departure from the policy of the predecessors. (English 1 pg.)

Mc4633. S-1964
Dr. Mary Stanton to J. Francis Cardinal
McIntyre
November 4, 1964. Rome, Italy

The canonization of the Ugandian martyers was a beautiful event and has provided material beyond all expectations. (English 1 pg.)

Mc4634. S-1964
Francis Cardinal Spellman to J. Francis Cardinal McIntyre
November 4, 1964. Vatican City

A friendly letter commenting on the slow pace of the discussions, the need for a fourth session of the council, and the inability of the author to face tranquilly all of the problems. (English 2 pgs.)

Mc4635. S-1964
Mr. Gilbert Shea to J. Francis Cardinal
McIntyre
December 28, 1964. Brentwood, California

The enclosed donation is for the Youth Education Fund, one of the most necessary works of the Church. (English 1 pg.) On December 29, 1964, the Cardinal states that the letterhead of the stationery brought back many memories of my boyhood. (English 1 pg.)

Mc4636. S-1964
Mr. Phillip Chandler to J. Francis Cardinal
McIntyre
N.D. Los Angeles, California

Could the Share With Others be organized? Put an undecorated tree in a prominent place and allow each person to place a donation on the tree. The donations will buy food and clothing for others. (English 1 pg.)

Mc4637. S-1964
J. Francis Cardinal McIntyre to Arbp. Pericle
Felici
N.D. Los Angeles, California

A statement that the Cardinal is in complete agreement with the remarks made by Archbishop Dino Staffa and wishes to be recorded as such. (English 1 pg.)

Mc4638. S-1964
Mr. John Slater to J. Francis Cardinal
McIntyre
N.D. Folsom, California

A plea for justice in the prison system since there is no way that a hearing can be scheduled without a lawyer. Every appeal has been unheard and sickness and discouragement are taking over. (English 4 pgs.)

Mc4639. T-1964
Mr. Leo Oliver to Msgr. Benjamin Hawkes
January 13, 1964. San Antonio, Texas

Is the Sunshine Mission still in existence in Los Angeles. Mrs. Olga Thrane has mentioned the organization in the Will and it cannot be located. (English 1 pg.) On January 16, 1964, Msgr. states that the Sunshine Mission for Women is at 2600 S. Hoover St. (English 1 pg.)

Mc4640. T-1964
Bp. John Treacy to Msgr. and Pastors
February 5, 1964. La Crosse, Wisconsin

The Lenten Pastoral should be received by each family and not read in the Churches. Do not use the word dispensation as the Lenten fast may be thought to be optional. (English 5 pgs.)

Mc4641. T-1964
J. Francis Cardinal McIntyre to Msgr. Paul
Tanner
March 25, 1964. Los Angeles, California

The Diocesan Consultors will meet with the Liturgical Commission for a discussion on the Bishops' Committee on the Liturgical Apostolate. (English 3 pgs.)

Mc4642. T-1964
Mr. Harry McKnight to J. Francis Cardinal
McIntyre
April 1, 1964. Los Angeles, California

A telephone religion survey is being considered and a request for Catholic participation is necessary. (English 2 pgs.) On April 3, 1964, Msgr. states that the information is provided in the parishes by other means. (English 1 pg.)

Mc4643. T-1964
Ms. Charlotte Balje to Msgr. Benjamin Hawkes
April 9, 1964. Hollywood, California

The Redwood trees in Jedediah Smith Redwood State Park will be destroyed for another highway. Could the Church help to protect God's gift of creation for all? (English 1 pg.)

Mc4644. T-1964
Rev. William Tobin, SP to Bp. Timothy
Manning
June 6, 1964. Tanganyika, East Africa

The retreat house for priests has a monthly labor payroll of $500 while the building is in progress. This is a hardship for us at the present time. (English 1 pg.) On June 30, 1964, the Bishop sends a donation which will help with the building program. (English 1 pg.)

Mc4645. T-1964
Ms. Agatha Torresani to J. Francis Cardinal
McIntyre
August 25, 1964. Hohenzollern, Germany

A request to investigate the sale of property so a fair return can be realized. (English 1 pg.) On September 4, 1964, the lawyer states that the transaction is in the courts and there is little the Chancery Office can do. (English 5 pgs.)

Mc4646. T-1964
Mrs. Gracia Tessier to J. Francis Cardinal
McIntyre
November 6, 1964. Glendale, California

Prayers for the success of the Vatican Council and the health of the Pope Paul and our Cardinal are offered daily. Doing God's Will is most important. (English 1 pg.)

Mc4647. T-1964
Mr. Gary Tharp to J. Francis Cardinal
McIntyre
November 27, 1964. Sherman Oaks, California

Could an interview be arranged for information on the Ecumenical Council so an article can be written for the Methodist Youth *Fellowship Odyssey.* (English 1 pg.)

Mc4648. U-1964
Dr. Robert Aragon, MD to J. Francis Cardinal
McIntyre
April 9, 1964. Los Angeles, California

An invitation is extended to a reception honoring Dr. Mario Polar U, Vice President of Peru. Pan American Week is honoring Peru this year. (English 1 pg.) On April 14, 1964, the Cardinal states that unfortunately a previous engagement will prevent attendance. (English 1 pg.)

Mc4649. U-1964
Mr. Walter Edwards to J. Francis Cardinal
McIntyre
April 14, 1964. Long Beach, California

An invitation from the Lakewood Lions Club to give the invocation for the Pan American banquet honoring Mr. Mario Polar U on April 25 is enclosed. (English 1 pg.)

Mc4650. U-1964
J. Francis Cardinal McIntyre to Miss Agnes
Underwood
June 8, 1964. Los Angeles, California

The splendid treatment of my talk given at Mt. St. Mary's College is appreciated. (English 1 pg.)

Mc4651. V-1964
Mrs. Rosemary Kuleto to Pope Paul VI
March 16, 1964. Los Angeles, California

A request for a dispensation to allow Mrs. Beatrice Valrance to be buried next to her husband in a nonsectarian cemetery is enclosed. (English 4 pgs.) On May 4, 1964, Bishop Timothy Manning states that the burial can be arranged from the parish. (English 1 pg.)

Mc4652. V-1964
Mr. Angel Varela to J. Francis Cardinal
McIntyre
June 26, 1964. Miami Beach, Florida

An appeal in Christian charity to end the ignominy and sufferings of so many Cuban citizens. (English 1 pg.)

Mc4653. V-1964
Msgr. Patrick Dignan to Msgr. Benjamin
Hawkes
August 13, 1964. Los Angeles, California

The University of Southern California has invited Rev. Adrian van Kaam, CSSP to lecture at the University. He has accepted for November 4 and will abide by all of the Diocesan regulations. (English 1 pg.)

Mc4654. W-1964
Mrs. Kathleen Williams to Rev. John Thom
January 17, 1964. Covina, California

In what way is a Catholic justified to deny others the rights guaranteed by the Constitution? (English 2 pgs.) On January 22, 1964, Fr. states that the Housing Act is a political issue and amoral issue but not a religious issue. It must be settled by the legislative process. (English 2 pgs.)

Mc4655. W-1964
Rev. Forrest Weir to J. Francis Cardinal
McIntyre
January 31, 1964. Los Angeles, California

A formal invitation is extended to participate in the discussion of the theological, moral, and practical issues that divide Christian witness. (English 1 pg.) On February 10, 1964, the Cardinal sends special blessings on the discussion. (English 1 pg.)

Mc4656. W-1964
J. Francis Cardinal McIntyre to Mr. John
Waters
March 30, 1964. Los Angeles, California

The Easter Story is told magnificently and will be shared with many others. (English 1 pg.)

Mc4657. W-1964
J. Francis Cardinal McIntyre to Mrs. Saenz
Waynes
April 4, 1964. Los Angeles, California

The Papal Nuptial Blessing and the Cardinal's blessings are extended to all members of the wedding party and to the family. (English 1 pg.)

Mc4658. W-1964
Mr. Ralph Wright to J. Francis Cardinal
McIntyre
April 9, 1964. Pasadena, California

A request for two priests to appear on a panel at the Fuller Seminary, the topic being Catholic-Protestant Ecumenicity. Fr. Charles Casassa S.J. is being invited. (English 2 pgs.) On April 13, 1964, the Cardinal asks Msgr. Patrick Dignan to appear on the panel. (English 1 pg.)

Mc4659. W-1964
Dr. Frank Waltz, MD to J. Francis Cardinal
McIntyre
May 7, 1964. Pomona, California

A request for a copy of the talk given at
Pomona College, *The Flight From Natural Law.*
The copies of the resolutions of the Republican
Party are enclosed. It seems some progress is be-
ing made. (English 2 pgs.)

Mc4660. W-1964
Bp. John Walsh to J. Francis Cardinal McIn-
tyre
July 6, 1964. Tuam, Ireland

A letter of support from the priests and people of Ireland during this difficult time in Los
Angeles. (English 1 pg.) On July 28, 1964, the
Cardinal states that the whole unaccountable
happening seems to be in the plan of God. (English 1 pg.)

Mc4661. W-1964
Mr. Anton Wilson to J. Francis Cardinal
McIntyre
July 24, 1964. Kern City, California

A new calendar which does not affect religious can be introduced and the Council seems
to be ready for a change. (English 1 pg.) On
July 28, 1964, the Cardinal states that much interest seems to be aroused but it will not be discussed in this session. (English 1 pg.)

Mc4662. W-1964
Mr. John Wagner to Msgr. Benjamin Hawkes
August 18, 1964. New York City, New York

A survey of all construction is being made
and will be published in the next *Building and
Maintenance Magazine.* (English 1 pg.) On September 18, 1964, Msgr. states that the Diocese
will write up one project. (English 1 pg.)

Mc4663. W-1964
Mr. Lionel Wiedey to Msgr. Benjamin Hawkes
December 14, 1964. San Marino, California

The 100 shares of Goodyear stock should be
used for foreign missionaries and a seminarian
who is having a difficult time with expenses.
(English 1 pg.) On December 15, 1964, Msgr.
states that Mr. Robert Bland's expenses are satisfied and Bishop Edward Lawton, OP of
Northern Nigeria will receive the donation.
(English 1 pg.)

Mc4664. W-1964
Mrs. Armin Wolf to Bp. Timothy Manning
December 14, 1964. Burbank, California

A request is made for something that the
Pope has blessed that could be given to a Sister
at the Burbank Hospital. (English 1 pg.) On December 21, 1964, the Bishop sends a Rosary
blessed by the Pope. (English 1 pg.)

Mc4665. Y-1964
Mr. Evelle Younger to J. Francis Cardinal
McIntyre
January 16, 1964. Los Angeles, California

The visit to the Superior Court and the conversation was the highlight of the session. (English 1 pg.)

Mc4666. Y-1964
Mr. Thomas Yager to J. Francis Cardinal
McIntyre
January 27, 1964. Los Angeles, California

The talk given at the Holy Name Breakfast
was taped and will remain in the library of fine
speeches. (English 1 pg.)

Mc4667. Z-1964
J. Francis Cardinal McIntyre to Hon. Howard
Ziemann
February 10, 1964. Los Angeles, California

Prayerful condolences are expressed on the
death of your mother. (English 1 pg.) On February 17, 1964, Mr. Ziemann states that during
her 95 years of life prayer was most important
and the Archdiocese benefited from her prayers.
(English 1 pg.)

Mc4668. Z-1964
Rev. Richard Zimmerman to J. Francis Cardi-
nal McIntyre
April 8, 1964. Hanover, Pennsylvania

An investigation of the Beha/Taylor marital
difficulties should be made so a one-sided decision will not be made. (English 2 pgs.) On April
23, 1964, Msgr. Rawden states that the separation seems to be justified. (English 1 pg.)

Mc4669. Z-1964
Mr. Phillip Zogaib to J. Francis Cardinal
McIntyre
N.D. Los Angeles, California

A plea for all Catholics to become more mil-
itant and fight godlessness so the slurs and slan-
ders against the Catholic Church will be ended.
(English 1 pg.)

Listing for the Year
1965

Mc4670. A-1965
Mother M. Anne to Bp. Timothy Manning
February 7, 1965. Cypress, California

The Principal's Institute was a rewarding experience that should be repeated. To exchange classroom techniques and receive ideas is good for everyone. (English 1pg.)

Mc4671. A-1965
Lt. Roberta Angelica to Msgr. Benjamin Hawkes
February 7, 1965. Belleville, Illinois

A request is made to be a bridesmaid at a Methodist wedding. (English 1 pg.) On February 11, 1965, Msgr. states that if the Base Chaplain would grant the dispensation, the Archdiocese will agree. (English 1 pg.)

Mc4672. A-1965
Msgr. William Johnson to Rev. Eugene Gilb
February 10, 1965. Los Angeles, California

Mrs. Maria Albo has plans for a home for girls in conjunction with some Religious Community. The property in Palmdale would not be practical for the type of home she envisions. Some of the ideas are not too definite. (English 2 pgs.)

Mc4673. A-1965
Bp. Timothy Manning to Editors of *America*
May 4, 1965. Los Angeles, California

The 10 point program for implementing the Vatican Council decrees is given. (English 1 pg.)

Mc4674. A-1965
Mr. Steve Allen to J. Francis Cardinal McIntyre
July, 14, 1965. Los Angeles, California

What, if anything, is the Catholic Church doing to correct the awful conditions in which migrant workers live? (English 1 pg.) On July 19, 1965, Fr. Thom states that great strides have been made in the spiritual care of the migrant workers and compensations have been raised. (English 1 pg.)

Mc4675. A-1965
Sister Agnes Theresa to J. Francis Cardinal McIntyre
July 14, 1965. Grand Rapids, Michigan

A request is made to vote to retain the quiet of the contemplative life and cloister of the Carmelite Order and allow others to seek another Community who want to travel. (English 3 pgs.)

Mc4676. A-1965
Mrs. Ruth Arnold to J. Francis Cardinal McIntyre
July 17, 1965. Hollywood, California

May a girl register at Loyola University for the following semester. (English 1 pg.) On July 21, 1965, the Cardinal states that Loyola is still all male in the under graduate level. The girl should be enrolled in one of the Catholic women's colleges. (English 1 pg.)

Mc4677. A-1965
Rev. M. Acel to J. Francis Cardinal McIntyre
August 1965. Los Angeles, California

A plea to vote for an end to celibacy for clergy so that the ranks of the Diocesan clergy will continue to be full. (English 7 pgs.)

Mc4678. A-1965
Mr. Steve Allen to Rev. Eugene Gilb
August 20, 1965. Los Angeles, California

The inquiry was to the material welfare of
the migrant workers not to the spiritual welfare.
The National Catholic Rural Life Conference is
working in other localities and what is being
done in Los Angeles? (English 1 pg.)

Mc4679. A-1965
Ms. Elizabeth Achelis to J. Francis Cardinal
McIntyre
August 27, 1965. New York City, New York

Vote for a definite date for Easter Sunday on
the World Calendar Association. The second
Sunday in April should be the day. (English 1
pg.)

Mc4680. A-1965
Ms. Marion Adams to Pope Paul VI
September 2, 1965. Norwalk, California

A request is made for the Catholic Church to
participate in the Court hearing which should
restore financial support and dignity to the family. (English 1 pg.)

Mc4681. A-1965
Sister Ambrose, DC to J. Francis Cardinal
McIntyre
September 13, 1965. Baltimore, Maryland

Seton Psychiatric Institute will continue to
give discounts to clergy but the rising costs will
necessitate a higher bill. (English 1 pg.)

Mc4682. A-1965
Mr. Al Antazak to Mr. John O'Connor
September 29, 1965. Los Angeles, California

The editorial defending Cardinal McIntyre
and expressing anti Semitic sentiments gives the
impression that friends of the Cardinal are fa-
natics. (English 1 pg.)

Mc4683. A-1965
Rev. Dennis Anaujo to J. Francis Cardinal
McIntyre
December 8, 1965. Kerala, India

A Christmas letter comments on the closing
of the Vatican Council and a general review of
his district in India. (English 1 pg.)

Mc4684. B-1965
Rev. Alfred Boeddeker to J. Francis Cardinal
McIntyre
January 5, 1965. San Francisco, California

Archbishop McGucken hosted a luncheon at
which Bishop Emmanuele Clarizio publicized
the Marion Congresses and Villa Nazaret. (English 1 pg.)

Mc4685. B-1965
Mrs. Arthur Bolint to Bp. John J. Ward
January 20, 1965. Whittier, California

A long letter complaining about the sermons
at Mass expounding political issues and trying
to teach evolution. (English 3 pgs.)

Mc4686. B-1965
Mr. William Bassett III to J. Francis Cardinal
McIntyre
January 21, 1965. San Fernando, California

Is *Life* Magazine correct in stating that there
are married clergy in the Catholic Church? (English 1 pg.) On February 1, 1965, Mr. Bassett
states that he appreciates the interest taken to
give the information sought. (English 1 pg.)

Mc4687. B-1965
Mr. Frank Brophy to J. Francis Cardinal McIn-
tyre
February 12, 1965. Phoenix, Arizona

Many non-Catholics feel consternation over
the lack of leadership on the intellectual level
from the once famous *America, The Catholic
World,* and *Commonweal.* (English 2 pgs.)

Mc4688. B-1965
Rev. James Basham, CP to Msgr. Benjamin
Hawkes
February 13, 1965. Louisville, Kentucky

A request to celebrate the First Solemn Mass
in the evening to avoid the tight Sunday schedule and to allow time for the family and friends
to arrive. (English 1 pg.) On February 19, 1965,
Msgr. states that it is agreeable with the Chancery Office if it is agreeable with the Pastor.
(English 1 pg.)

Mc4689. B-1965
Msgr. Thomas O'Dwyer to Mr. John S. Gibson
February 15, 1965. Los Angeles, California

The Blue Diamond Pit matter ought to be
taken to arbitration and the good name of Los
Angeles be cleared. This is a moral issue and
must be settled. (English

Mc4690. B-1965
Rev. Virgil Blum, SJ to J. Francis Cardinal
McIntyre
February 18, 1965. Milwaukee, Wisconsin

Attention should be given to the allocation of
Title I and Title III funds for disadvantaged
children. Negotiations should be from strength
so our students will benefit. (English 2 pgs.)

Mc4691. B-1965
Rev. A. A. Lemieux, SJ to J. Francis Cardinal
McIntyre
April 6, 1965. Seattle, Washington

A request to have the honor of Knight of St.
Gregory given to Mr. Thomas J. Bannan. (English 1 pg.) On April 20, 1965, the Cardinal
states that the usual source of information, the
Pastor, knows of Mr. Bannan. (English 1 pg.)

Mc4692. B-1965
Bp. Alden J. Bell to J. Francis Cardinal
McIntyre
April 8, 1965. Sacramento, California

The agenda for the California Bishops Meeting would be the obscenity bills, Seminary education, the need for an attorney to replace
Andrew Burke, the status of the hospitals in legal matters, and the Newman Clubs. (English
1 pg.)

Mc4693. B-1965
Dott. Benito Benedini to J. Francis Cardinal
McIntyre
April 26, 1965. Mantova, Italy

The concerns of the Church seems to be religious indifference, lack of knowledge of the
Catechism and religious practices, knowledge of
the Liturgy and a growing disbelief in the existence of God. (Italian 3 pgs.)

Mc4694. B-1965
Mr. & Mrs. Burke to J. Francis Cardinal
McIntyre
April 29, 1965. Los Angeles, California

A request to arrange for Mrs. Robert and her
daughter to have a Papal audience. They will be
in Rome from July 24-28. (English 1 pg.) On
May 6, 1965, the Cardinal states that if audiences are being held, this letter should help to
obtain an audience. (English 1 pg.)

Mc4695. B-1965
Mr. William Burke to J. Francis Cardinal
McIntyre
May 15, 1965. Pasadena, California

Is the Church revising the words of Christ or
is Charity still in the vocabulary? (English 1 pg.)

Mc4696. B-1965
Mr. Frank Brophy to J. Francis Cardinal
McIntyre
June 1, 1965. Phoenix, Arizona

The Chicago Meeting should stress that the
campaign being waged is athestic communism
and not the change of the Liturgy or any other
doctrine. (English 3 pgs.)

Mc4697. B-1965
Mr. D. D. Black to Msgr. Benjamin Hawkes
June 24, 1965. Los Angeles, California

A friendly letter commenting on the successful interview, the new position acquired, the desire to be useful in the Archdiocese, and the
death of a good friend. (English 3 pgs.)

Mc4698. B-1965
Rev. George Skender to J. Francis Cardinal
McIntyre
June 24, 1965. Zahle, Lebanon

A request to encourage Mr. Eddy Basha to
donate the required land to place a statue on
the hilltop of Zahle. The statue is ready. (English 1 pg.) On July 18, 1965, Bishop Green
states that he is certain that the land can be obtained. (English 1 pg.)

Mc4699. B-1965
Mrs. John Bruein to Pope Paul VI
August 2, 1965. Tujunga, California

A request is made for a first class relic of St.
Theresa or some saint that can help a person
who is ill. (English 4 pgs.)

Mc4700. B-1965
Rev. Bernard O'Connor to Msgr. Benjamin
Hawkes
August 3, 1965. San Gabriel, California

A deed for property dated 1914 is still in the
files. It is in Cucamonga in the Lucas Ranch
area. (English 1 pg.) On August 4, 1965, Msgr.
states it will be interesting for the consultors to
find out the present status. (English 1 pg.)

Mc4701. B-1965
Msgr. Benjamin Hawkes to Msgr. James Booth
August 19, 1965. Los Angeles, California

The deed and the preliminary investigation is
being sent for further reference. (English 1 pg.)
On September 1, 1965, Msgr. states that this is
the long-lost deed that no one could find. (English 1 pg.)

Mc4702. B-1965
Bp. Alden J. Bell to J. Francis Cardinal
McIntyre
August 31, 1965. Sacramento, California

There will be six representatives of education
attending the Governor's Conference in Kansas.
Mr. William Burke will be one. (English 1 pg.)

Mc4703. B-1965
Mrs. Emmett Brady to J. Francis Cardinal
McIntyre
September 1, 1965. Long Beach, California

A plea to prevent the adoption of the statement absolving the Jews from Deicide. The Jewish Freemasonry is still a danger to the Church.
(English 2 pgs.)

Mc4704. B-1965
Mr. Paul Brindel to Msgr. Benjamin Hawkes
September 1, 1965. Novato, California

Free speech is an American tradition but if
the members of the clergy have to sound off
against the Cardinal why do they have to talk
to the secular press? (English 2 pgs.)

Mc4705. C-1965
Mr. E. D. Brotsos to J. Francis Cardinal McIn-
tyre
September 3, 1965. Los Angeles, California

An invitation is extended to the testimonial
dinner for Fr. Leonidas Contos who will soon
begin work for the Greek Archdiocese of New
York. (English 1 pg.) On September 8, 1965,
the Cardinal states that he regrets that he cannot attend the dinner but Msgr. O'Dwyer will
represent the Archdiocese. (English 1 pg.)

Mc4706. B-1965
Mr. P. O. Baumann to Msgr. Benjamin Hawkes
September 14, 1965. Los Angeles, California

Is it the policy for Catholic Chaplains to neglect patients in the hospitals except those in
Catholic hospitals? (English 1 pg.) On September 16, 1965, Msgr. states that the parish
priests should visit the hospital during a long
stay. (English 1 pg.)

Mc4707. B-1965
J. Francis Cardinal McIntyre to
Dr. & Mrs. F. Browne
September 17, 1965. Los Angeles, California

The generous donation to the Youth Education Fund and Don Bosco Technical Institute
allows both to continue to progress. (English
1 pg.)

Mc4708. B-1965
Mrs. C. M. Brannick to J. Francis Cardinal
McIntyre
October 12, 1965. Los Angeles, California

The Pope's statement concerning celibacy
agrees with the belief of many people in our
parish. Please do inform the clergy. (English
1 pg.)

Mc4709. B-1965
Mr. Charles Bridwell to J. Francis Cardinal
McIntyre
October 30, 1965. Valley Station, Kentucky

What steps must be taken to be married by a
priest but not to have the marriage legal? (English 1 pg.) On November 3, 1965, Msgr. states
that there is no such arrangement in California.
If a priest performs a wedding ceremony, it is a
religious and a legal marriage. (English 1 pg.)

Mc4710. B-1965
J. Francis Cardinal McIntyre to Bp. Alden Bell
November 5, 1965. Los Angeles, California

Rev. William Kenney, CSP wants to organize
a demonstration to establish a Department of
Theology on the UCLA campus. The department must be begun but by a legal method. (English 1 pg.)

Mc4711. B-1965
Mr. Vito Berardi to J. Francis Cardinal
McIntyre
November 17, 1965. Inglewood, California

A request to have the parishes and Catholic
hospitals prohibit the sale of religious articles so
that legitimate business men can carry on business. (English 1 pg.)

Mc4712. B-1965
Mr. Ronald Ellensohn to J. Francis Cardinal
McIntyre
December 21, 1965. Los Angeles, California

Mayor Yorty requests the help of Rev. Louis
Bossi in the restoration project of the Olvera
Street district. (English 1 pg.)

Mc4713. B-1965
Mr. Paul Brindel to Msgr. Benjamin Hawkes
December 21, 1965. Haifa, Israel

A friendly letter commenting on the Basilica
in Nazareth, the destruction of the homes in
Haifa, and the variety of newspapers from
which one can receive the news. (English 2 pgs.)

Mc4714. B-1965
Mr. Paul Brindel to Msgr. Benjamin Hawkes
December 30, 1965. Haifa, Israel

The Little Sisters of Jesus of Fr. De Foucaud
might be an answer to the Watts area and other
depressed areas. They are the epitome of Vatican II. (English 2 pgs.)

Mc4715. B-1965
Mr. Bill Bray to Bp. Timothy Manning
December 31, 1965. Chicago, Illinois

The Moody Bible Institute would appreciate knowing your opinion of major hindrance to a unified Church especially doctrinal issues that separate the Churches. (English 1 pg.)

Mc4716. B-1965
Mother M. Benigna to Bp. Timothy Manning
N.D. Trichur, South India

An appeal for a donation for the orphans who receive no financial aid except what is given in charity. (English 1 pg.) On December 17, 1965, the Bishop encloses a donation for the orphans. (English 1 pg.)

Mc4717. C-1965
Mr. & Mrs. Bernard Clougherty to J. Francis Cardinal McIntyre
January 6, 1965. Los Angeles, California

The enclosed donation is for the development of the Church in Los Angeles. (English 1 pg.) On January 14, 1965, the Cardinal states his gratitude for the generous check. (English 1 pg.)

Mc4718. C-1965
Mrs. Norma Christensen to J. Francis Cardinal McIntyre
January 18, 1965. Los Angeles, California

Prayers are being offered for perseverance in office so that no pickets or detractors could drive you away from Los Angeles. The very human actions at the St. John's Church after Confirmation made everyone aware of the greatness of our Cardinal. (English 1 pg.)

Mc4719. C-1965
Mr. Alan Cummings to J. Francis Cardinal McIntyre
January 30, 1965. Downey, California

The Internal Revenue is disputing tuition payments which is deducted for secular subjects taught and because contributions would be made whether my children attended the school or not. (English 3 pgs.)

Mc4720. C-1965
Mrs. Anna Collin to J. Francis Cardinal McIntyre
January 27, 1965. Huntington Beach, California

The people of Los Angeles need the strong voice of the Church to still the anxieties. Is there any hope of solving the problems that seem to be uppermost in the minds of the agitators. (English 1 pg.)

Mc4721. C-1965
Ms. Carol Montgomery to J. Francis Cardinal McIntyre
February 19, 1965. Long Beach, California

The Boating Show will feature a World Peace Garden with a Shrine of Our Lady of Fatima. A shrub from Fatima will be brought for the garden. After the show, a permament home for the shrub will be the decision of the Cardinal. (English 1 pg.)

Mc4722. C-1965
Rev. Eugene Gilb to Mr. Jack Spitzer
February 26, 1965. Los Angeles, California

The Cardinal regrets that he cannot attend the Testimonial Dinner honoring Mrs. Dorothy Chandler. The schedule for dedication of a new school is definite. (English 1 pg.)

Mc4723. C-1965
Mr. Marion Gillick to Mr. Paul Coates
March 24, 1965. Los Angeles, California

The *Times* cannot have an editorial policy both for and against the Church. Breaking the law is not the usual standard taught by the Church. (English 1 pg.)

Mc4724. C-1965
Arbp. Romolo Carboni to J. Francis Cardinal McIntyre
March 24, 1965. Lima, Peru

Rev. John J. Considine, MM is organizing information for priests and religious who want to serve in Latin America. The following information is for Peru. (English 11 pgs.) On April 1, 1965, the Cardinal states that he is happy to have the information. (english 1 pg.)

Mc4725. C-1965
J. Francis Cardinal McIntyre to Miss Kathleen Cahill
March 25, 1965. Los Angeles, California

The 500 Rosaries donated to the Family Theater will be given to the people at Mary's Hour which is attended by 75,000 to 100,000 people each year. (English 1 pg.)

Mc4726. C-1965
Mr. Arthur Conrad to J. Francis Cardinal McIntyre
March 26, 1965. Bensenville, Illinois

The example of being a fine Christian gentleman while people are hurling brickbats is not lost on a great many people. (English 1 pg.)

Mc4727. C-1965
Ms. Catherine Coyle to J. Francis Cardinal
McIntyre
N.D. Fort Lauderdale, Florida

A relative, Msgr. Corr, will be honored during the dedication of St. Elizabeth's Convent and School. He worked for Catholic Charities and was the main fund raiser for the Seminary. (English 3 pgs.) On March 29, 1965, the Cardinal states that it was a pleasure to meet a member of the family at the dedication. (English 1 pg.)

Mc4728. C-1965
Bp. Emmanuel Clarizio to J. Francis Cardinal
McIntyre
April 14, 1965. Santa Domingo

The donation sent to the Apostolic Nunicature for Villa Nazeret and other charities fulfilled your requests. (English 1 pg.)

Mc4729. C-1965
Richard Cardinal Cushing to J. Francis Cardinal McIntyre
April 15, 1965. Brighton, Massachusetts

A National Workshop on Unity is being planned to exchange ideas and give practical ways to implement the Council's Decree De Oecumenismo. (English 1 pg.)

Mc4730. C-1965
Rev. Laurence Clark to Bp. Timothy Manning
April 26, 1965. Los Angeles, California

Msgr. Johnson asked me to attend the Inter-Faith Seminar on urban problems. Some definite proposals are being made and will give material for an academic discussion. (English 1 pg.) On April 27, 1965, the Bishop suggests a discussion on the material. (English 1 pg.)

Mc4731. C-1965
Mr. Bill Chiasson to Msgr. Benjamin Hawkes
May 12, 1965. Thousand Oaks, California

The Gabriel Richard Institute leadership training course can be introduced into the Arch diocese with well-trained leaders. (English 1 pg.)

Mc4732. C-1965
Mr. Joseph Chladek to Msgr. Benjamin
Hawkes
June 4, 1965. Los Angeles, California

If there is a need for help in business for the Archdiocese a call will bring the help gratis. (English 1 pg.) On June 17, 1965, Msgr. suggests that an appointment should be made to discuss the areas of interest. (English 1 pg.)

Mc4733. C-1965
Mrs. Crandall to Msgr. Benjamin Hawkes
N.D. Westminster, California

Does the Catholic Church recognize Speaking in Tongues and the Indwelling of the Spirit? (English 1 pg.) On June 22, 1965, Msgr. states that the Acts of the Apostoles and St. Paul's letters speak beautifully of the speaking in tongues. (English 1 pg.)

Mc4734. C-1965
J. Francis Cardinal McIntyre to Mr. Edward
Carter
July 22, 1965. Los Angeles, California

The donation to the Los Angeles County Art Museum will be spread over a five year period with no publicity other than our name on the donor list. (English 1 pg.) On July 27, 1965, Mr. Carter states that the donation is most welcome spread over the years. UCLA is most willing to buy Marymount property. (English 1 pg.)

Mc4735. C-1965
Mr. Philip Ciaffa to J. Francis Cardinal
McIntyre
July 25, 1965. Bronx, New York

Is there some method to obtain an annulment when the partner can no longer live in the same locality and lead a married life? (English 2 pgs.) On July 30, 1965, the Cardinal suggests looking for a good confessor and to follow his advise. (English 1 pg.)

Mc4736. C-1965
Msgr. Benjamin Hawkes to Rev. Albert
Heinzer CSC
August 6, 1965. Los Angeles, California

Appreciation is expressed for delivering the 1,500 Rosaries sent by Kathleen Cahill. The Missions will be most happy to receive this gift. (English 1 pg.) On August 16, 1965, the Cardinal states that the Rosaries will be given to the children and should bring a blessing on the donor. (English 1 pg.)

Mc4737. C-1965
Msgr. John Rawden to Msgr. John K. Clarke
August 25, 1965. Los Angeles, California

Mr. Bill Chiasson will explain the Gabriel Richard Institute to determine if this will be useful for the adult training for CCD teachers. (English 1 pg.)

Mc4738. C-1965
Mrs. Grace Connors to J. Francis Cardinal
McIntyre
November 3, 1965. Los Angeles, California

It is time to examine the Catholic Welfare
policy and for the people to give their donations
to the agencies that will aid the people in need.
(English 1 pg.)

Mc4739. C-1965
J. Francis Cardinal McIntyre to Mr. Ross
Cortese
December 15, 1965. Los Angeles, California

The dedication of the site for the Church in
Leisure World will bring many blessings and
can accomplish much good. (English 1 pg.)

Mc4740. C-1965
Mr. George Owen to Msgr. Benjamin Hawkes
December 23, 1964. Omaha, Nebraska

Information is needed concerning Mrs.
Chavez and her son. An insurance policy naming her son as the beneficiary cannot be paid.
(English 1 pg.) On January 4, 1965, Msgr.
states that Ernest is attending the Belvedere Junior High School in Los Angeles and can receive
information from the school. (English 1 pg.)

Mc4741. C-1965
Mrs. Richard Chval to J. Francis Cardinal
McIntyre
December 27, 1965. Montebello, California

We would like to have our children remember
the great Churchmen of their lifetime. Is it
possible to obtain a letter with your signature?
(English 1 pg.) On December 27, 1965, the
Cardinal sends a special blessing for the family
at the Christmas Season. (English 1 pg.)

Mc4742. D-1965
Rev. Alfred Hernandez to Msgr. Benjamin
Hawkes
January 2, 1965. Hollywood, California

The message to the Apostolic Delegate can
state that Mrs. DeCicco does not object to her
husband coming to the United States but that
she cannot be financially responsible for him.
(English 1 pg.)

Mc4743. D-1965
Arbp. Nicholas Fasolino to Msgr. Benjamin
Hawkes
February 7, 1965. Santa Fe, Argentina

A request to have the Consul of the Republic
of Paraguay sign the documents and give the
necessary information. (Spanish 1 pg.)

Mc4744. D-1965
J. Francis Cardinal McIntyre to Rev. John
Danagher
March 5, 1965. Los Angeles, California

The clergy and faithful join in thanking God
for the leadership of Archbishop Urban Vehr.
The increase of population, scientific discover-
ies, his vision and wisdom have given great
leadership to education and to the advancement
of all branches of learning. (English 1 pg.)

Mc4745. D-1965
Mr. Michael Bolger to J. Francis Cardinal
McIntyre
May 10, 1965. Los Angeles, California

The physical appraisal of the Duckworth Estates would be repairs of windows, and painting. The building is sound and the roof is good.
(English 1 pg.)

Mc4746. D-1965
Mr. Laurence Duggan to Msgr. Benjamin
Hawkes
July 18, 1965. Victoria, Australia

Los Angeles is the only city in which our ship
will be in port on a Sunday. Is there a Church
near the harbor? (English 2 pgs.) On July 22,
1965, Msgr. states that Sunday Masses are on
the hour from 6:00 a.m. to 12:00 noon in San
Pedro. (English 1 pg.)

Mc4747. D-1965
Mr. Stephen Davis to J. Francis Cardinal
McIntyre
September 17, 1965. Burbank, California

Could Mr. Donald Johnson, a Jesuit Seminarian, do one of the Scripture readings at my ordination in the Bethany Presbyterian Church?
(English 1 pg.) On September 24, 1965, the
Cardinal states that more information would
have to be given before permission is granted.
(English 1 pg.)

Mc4748. E-1965
Ms. Mary Eunice to J. Francis Cardinal
McIntyre
March 29, 1965. Belford, New Jersey

A message of encouragement during the difficult period of trial is enclosed. The Legion of
Mary is trying to work for the betterment of
entertainment and will offer some prayers for
the successful outcome of the Los Angeles time
of trial. (English 1 pg.)

Mc4749. E-1965
Mrs. Dorothy Enright to Bp. Timothy
Manning
July 16, 1965. Garden Grove, California

Is it possible for the Churches to provide
some space for a proper Thanksgiving after
Holy Communion. The Mass schedules are so
tight that one Mass is not finished before the
congregation is arriving for the next Mass. (English 1 pg.)

Mc4750. F-1965
Mr. O'Neill Martin to Bp. Timothy Manning
January 12, 1965. San Diego, California

Could the San Diego Diocese use the same
contract conditions of bonding and insurance
and the procedures for obtaining bids as are
used in Los Angeles? (English 1 pg.)

Mc4751. F-1965
Bp. Francis Furey to Msgr. Benjamin Hawkes
January 13, 1965. San Diego, California

Is it possible to have copies of the standard-
ized contracts and insurance forms used in the
Archdiocese? (English 1 pg.) On January 15,
1965, Msgr. encloses the forms and comments
that Mr. Martin might like a meeting with Mr.
Thomas Kelly, the construction coordinator of
the Archdiocese. (English 1 pg.)

Mc4752. F-1965
Msgr. Paul Tanner to J. Francis Cardinal
McIntyre
February 8, 1965. Washington, D.C.

Mr. Friedlander took advantage of an audience to publicize his book and to attack the policies of Pope Pius XII. Caution should be taken
in extending invitations to speakers. (English 1
pg.)

Mc4753. F-1965
Mr. Raymond Frazler to J. Francis Cardinal
McIntyre
February 13, 1965. Los Angeles, California

Dr. Page is broadcasting that a Protestant girl
is being detained in the Good Shepherd Convent against her will. He claims that the court
hearing was rigged. (English 1 pg.)

Mc4754. F-1965
Mr. Roger Freeman to J. Francis Cardinal
McIntyre
February 16, 1965. Stanford, California

The tax credits for tuition paid to private
schools will be the only break religious schools
will receive. This is the only way that the government can help the elementary and secondary
schools. (English 2 pgs.)

Mc4755. F-1965
Bp. Francis Furey to J. Francis Cardinal
McIntyre
March 30, 1965. San Diego, California

The Seminary Rectors met March 26–28 and
this statement is the fruit of their labors. This
will be mailed to all the Ordinaries in the
United States. (English 5 pgs.) On April 1,
1965, the Cardinal states it is hopeful that the
rule of reason will prevail and some uniformity
will be followed. (English 1 pg.)

Mc4756. F-1965
Mr. Hugh Falvey to J. Francis Cardinal
McIntyre
April 1, 1965. Santa Barbara, California

A plan for a residence for retired priests is in
the embryonic stage and awaits discussion to
bring it to reality. (English 1 pg.) On April 10,
1965, the Cardinal states that most priests want
to remain in a rectory where they may continue
to function as a priest. (English 1 pg.)

Mc4757. F-1965
Bp. Albert Fletcher to J. Francis Cardinal
McIntyre
May 5, 1965. Little Rock, Arkansas

The honor of having a Cardinal present at
the Jubilee celebration and the presentation of
the Papal honor of Assistant to the Pontifical
Throne were the outstanding aspects of the day.
(English 1 pg.)

Mc4758. F-1965
Guiseppe Cardinal Ferretto to J. Francis Cardi-
nal McIntyre
May 11, 1965. Rome, Italy

A message of gratitude for the beautiful hospitality of Los Angeles and prayers that God
will continue to bless the Archdiocese. (Italian
1 pg.)

Mc4759. F-1965
Arbp. Egidio Vagnozzi to Bp. Francis Furey
May 17, 1965. Washington, D.C.

The Cardinal Prefect of Seminaries appreciates the work of the Seminary Rectors who
wish to distribute from the treasury of experience the new and the true. (English 1 pg.) On
May 20, 1965, the Bishop states that a copy
of the letter is being sent to the Rectors. (English 1 pg.)

Mc4760. F-1965
J. Francis Cardinal McIntyre to Bp. Francis
Furey
June 9, 1965. Los Angeles, California

A Chaplain's Association will be considered
and approved, it seems. The letters to the legislature seem to have stopped the abortion bill.
(English 1 pg.)

Mc4761. F-1965
Msgr. John Fitzpatrick to Msgr. Benjamin
Hawkes
June 25, 1965. Miami, Florida

Information is needed for wage scale for
priests; ownership of cars; the scale of stole fees
for Baptism, weddings, and funerals; and the
stipends for Mass. (English 1 pg.) On July 6,
1965, Msgr. sends all of the requested information. (English 1 pg.)

Mc4762. F-1965
Bp. Albert Fletcher to J. Francis Cardinal
McIntyre
August 27, 1965. Little Rock, Arkansas

The editorial in *The Tidings* makes clear the
danger of the theory that one's conscience su-
persedes the law. Many are asking the Council
to write against the enemy, atheistic communism. (English 1 pg.)

Mc4763. G-1965
Mr. Patrick Garman to J. Francis Cardinal
McIntyre
January 15, 1965. Chicago, Illinois

An editorial appeared in Chicago *News* stating that Dr. Jude Dougherty feels that President
Kennedy could be canonized if two miracles
were performed through his intercession. (English 1 pg.)

Mc4764. G-1965
Bp. elect Rafael Grovas to J. Francis Cardinal
McIntyre
February 26, 1965. San Juan, Puerto Rico

An invitation to the consecration of the
Bishop of the new Diocese of Caguas. The semi
tropics will offer a relief from winter and work.
(English 1 pg.) On March 10, 1965, the Cardinal states that too many pressing obligations are
in the immediate future to take time off. (English 1 pg.)

Mc4765. G-1965
Mrs. Marilyn Gonzalez to Rev. Eugene Gilb
March 15, 1965. Los Angeles, California

Why are priests and sisters marching in the
protests when the Archdiocese emphasizes the
separation of the Church and State? (English
3 pgs.)

Mc4766. G-1965
Bp. Thomas Garman to J. Francis Cardinal
McIntyre
April 9, 1965. Dallas, Texas

A Bureau of Information should be established in each Diocese. The importance of such
an office was enforced in the decree of Social
Communication. (English 1 pg.)

Mc4767. G-1965
Mrs. Lolita Savage to J. Francis Cardinal
McIntyre
April 10, 1965. Beverly Hills, California

Ulysses S. Grant IV is being baptized at St.
Paul the Apostle Church. A letter to him would
be most appreciated. (English 1 pg.) On April
12, 1965, the Cardinal states that a personal
greeting will be possible at another time but
special blessing will be asked for on the Baptismal Day. (English 1 pg.)

Mc4768. G-1965
Msgr. Alfred Harrigan to J. Francis Cardinal
McIntyre
April 20, 1965. Louisville, Kentucky

Irene Dunne will be given the Bellarmine
Medal as a person who exemplifies the virtues
of charity, justice and temperateness in dealing
with difficult problems. A letter to be presented
to her on the evening of the banquet would be
appreciated. (English 1 pg.) On May 4, 1965,
the Cardinal states the honor is well deserved.

Mc4769. G-1965
Mr. E. S. Godlewski to J. Francis Cardinal
McIntyre
June 1, 1965. Los Angeles, California

An invitation is extended to give the invocation at the American Association of Cost Engineers on June 28. If it is not possible for the
Cardinal, could another member of the clergy
give the invocation. (English 1 pg.) On June 2,
1965, the Cardinal states that his schedule is
crowded but Msgr. John Rawden will be
present. (English 1 pg.)

Mc4770. G-1965
Mr. Leon Gutterman to J. Francis Cardinal
McIntyre
June 15, 1965. Beverly HIlls, California

The *Wisdom* Board of Editors announced the
Cardinal as the recipient of the award for contributions to the field of education. (English 1
pg.) On July 21, 1965, the Cardinal expressed
his appreciation to the Board of Editors. (English 1 pg.)

Mc4771. G-1965
Dr. Thomas Greenburg to J. Francis Cardinal
 McIntyre
August 23, 1965. San Antonio, Texas

Catholic colleges are doing a poor job teaching a Christian philosophy of education. Person must be understood in all aspects before rights can be received. If the colleges were not so busy making money, they could educate. (English 2 pgs.)

Mc4772. G-1965
Mr. Alastair Guinan to J. Francis Cardinal
 McIntyre
September 9, 1965. New York City, New York

A new edition of Henry Daniel-Rop's, *This Is The Mass* will adhere a closely as possible to the Latin text. A copy will be sent when it is released. (English 2 pgs.) On September 15, 1965, the Cardinal states that he will be happy to receive a copy when it is released and it is possible that he will be in New York at the time. (English 1 pg.)

Mc4773. G-1965
Mr. Wesley Grapp to Msgr. Benjamin Hawkes
September 17, 1965. Los Angeles, California

The beautiful invocation at Loyola's graduation was well received by the gathering. (English 1 pg.) On September 21, 1965, the Cardinal states that he does appreciate the comment and enclosed a copy of the invocation. (English 1 pg.)

Mc4774. G-1965
Mr. Chestor Gillis to Msgr. Benjamin Hawkes
September 25, 1965. Santa Monica, California

A long discourse on the necessity of retaining the Latin Mass and a request to do a better job in teaching the responses. (English 6 pgs.) On September 27, 1965, Msgr. states that the article will be examined as the author requests. (English 1 pg.)

Mc4775. G-1965
Mrs. Marie Greenwell to J. Francis Cardinal
 McIntyre
N.D. Glendale, California

A request for some assistance in securing a room at Santa Teresita in Duarte. Can some of the mission money be kept in Los Angeles to help the elderly? (English 2 pgs.) On October 22, 1965, Mother Margarita states that the application must be made in person. (English 1 pg.)

Mc4776. G-1965
Mr. Peter Gartlan to J. Francis Cardinal McIntyre
November 15, 1965. Los Angeles, California

Rev. Richard Garcia reflects the spirit of Pope Paul VI before the United Nations. Just as the Pope spoke so all could understand, so does Fr. use illustrations and examples for us. (English 1 pg.)

Mc4777. G-1965
Bp. Timothy Manning to Br. Gilbert, MM
November 29, 1965. Los Angeles, California

I will be present for the closing of the Council and I hope to stay at the Victoria again. I will arrive at 2:00 a.m. but I will see everyone during the course of the day. (English 1 pg.)

Mc4778. G-1965
Mrs. Teresa Gaietto to J. Francis Cardinal
 McIntyre
December 5, 1965. Chicago, Illinois

An apology for the misguided Catholics who protested the administration offices of the Archdiocese. May the Christmas season be one of peace and joy. (English 1 pg.) On December 22, 1965, the Cardinal states that he appreciated the sentiment and prays that justice will prevail. (English 1 pg.)

Mc4779. H-1965
Mrs. Marylin Hudson to J. Francis Cardinal
 McIntyre
January 12, 1965. Fullerton, California

Is it permissible to eat meat on Friday if it is required for employment. When testing recipies may a Catholic taste a meat dish? (English 1 pg.) On January 14, 1965, Fr. Gilb states that this is an individual matter and each should follow the course of counsel. (English 1 pg.)

Mc4780. H-1965
Mr. Oliver Green to J. Francis Cardinal
 McIntyre
January 12, 1965. Los Angeles, California

An invitation is extended to address the Harvard Club on April 12 at the monthly meeting. The topic would be your personal choice. If April is not possible any month will be a pleasure for us. (English 1 pg.)

Mc4781. H-1965
Mr. Thomas Hair to J. Francis Cardinal
McIntyre
January 20, 1965. Hollywood, California

The exile of Fr. Aloysius from Los Angeles
was a grave injustice to those who were receiving help and to Father himself. Surely you know
about distortion. (English 3 pgs.) On January
28, 1965, The Cardinal states that the Archdiocese appreciates the work done by Fr. His supe-
riors make his assignments. (English 1 pg.)

Mc4782. H-1965
Mrs. J. E. Hewson to Bp. Timothy Manning
February 5, 1965. Montrose, California

During these upset times, can a suggestion be
given for all priests to offer one Mass weekly
for the guidance of the Holy Spirit. Could the
Archbishop make this mandatory? (English 1
pg.)

Mc4783. H-1965
Mr. Robert Hoyt to J. Francis Cardinal
McIntyre
February 25, 1965. Santa Barbara, California

An invitation is extended to dedicate the
Campanile Crespi on March 30. The structure
is 50 ft tall and a bell of historical significance
will complete the project. (English 1 pg.) On
February 27, 1965, Bishop Manning requests
more information before any reply can be given.
(English 1 pg.)

Mc4784. H-1965
Mr. Haydn Hilling to Bp. Timothy Manning
February 28, 1965. Los Angeles, California

The Schema on *The Church in the Modern
World* seems to relinquish discipline and remove
the firm foundation of the Church. (English 2
pgs.) On March 19, 1965, the Bishop states
that the Schema as issued will be discussed
again and then rewritten. (English 1 pg.)

Mc4785. H-1965
Rev. Stanislaus Altman to Bp. Timothy
Manning
March 2, 1965. Santa Barbara, California

Mr. Hoyt's private project is a commercial development but he is interested in the religious
foundation of Santa Barbara. (English 1 pg.)

Mc4786. H-1965
Msgr. F. G. Hochwalt to J. Francis Cardinal
McIntyre
March 30, 1965. Washington, D.C.

The Citizens for Educational Freedom favor
parental rights for education and fair share of
public support for the schools of the parents'
choice. It is thought best for them not to be associated with NCWC. (English 2 pgs.)

Mc4787. H-1965
Arbp. Joseph Hurley to J. Francis Cardinal
McIntyre
April 5, 1965. St. Augustine, Florida

The quadricentennial of St. Augustine on September 8 should enlighten the nation to the religious foundation of the United States. (English
1 pg.)

Mc4788. H-1965
Mrs. Luella Heller to J. Francis Cardinal
McIntyre
April 25, 1965. Studio City, California

Your prayers should have been offered for
Mr. Heller who died suddenly. There must be
work for me to do so I remain. (English 1 pg.)
On May 5, 1965, the Cardinal states that the
prayers will continue for both members of the
family. (English 1 pg.)

Mc4789. H-1965
Mr. Henry Hess to J. Francis Cardinal
McIntyre
June 11, 1965. Los Angeles, California

If an Institutional Interior Planning Department is being considered, my education background could relieve Pastors and the Chancery
Office of some of the responsibility. (English 1
pg.) On July 1, 1965, the Cardinal states that
such plans have not been made. (English 1 pg.)

Mc4790. H-1965
Mrs. G. Allen Hancock to J. Francis Cardinal
McIntyre
June 14, 1965. Santa Maria, California

Allen's funeral under your special care was a
great consolation. Having Mass in the home
during the last illness was a real joy. (English 1
pg.) On June 29, 1965, the Cardinal promised
prayers to continue during this trying period.
(English 1 pg.)

Mc4791. H-1965
Mr. Anthony Harcar to J. Francis Cardinal
McIntyre
August 17, 1965. Pasadena, California

To recognize the people of Slovak descent, could one of the new parishes be named for St. Cyril and Methodius? Many names are probably suggested and that is understood. (English 1 pg.)

Mc4792. H-1965
Mrs. Helen Harrold to Msgr. James Clyne
August 29, 1965. Canoga Park, California

The new text book, *Come Lord Jesus* seems to be changing Scripture to assure that the Jews do not carry the exclusive responsibility for the Crucifixion. (English 1 pg.)

Mc4793. H-1965
Mr. Eugene Halm to J. Francis Cardinal
McIntyre
October 15, 1965. Goleta, California

The Peace On Earth Committee to prevent all wars in the future could use the material begun in 1917. Some material should be in the Vatican Library. There is one copy in Goleta. (English 1 pg.)

Mc4794. H-1965
Msgr. Benjamin Hawkes to J. Francis Cardinal
McIntyre
October 18, 1965. Los Angeles, California

A friendly letter commenting on events in Los Angeles: the 50th anniversary of Immaculate Heart College, the funeral of Dr. Griffin, the opening of the job bureau and the assignment of Fr. Dominic Daly. (English 2 pgs.)

Mc4795. H-1965
Mr. John Henning to J. Francis Cardinal
McIntyre
November 22, 1965. Washington, D.C.

The employment program in connection with the Urban League is most commendable. If any assistance is needed, just call. (English 1 pg.)

Mc4796. H-1965
Ms. Marion Hardy to J. Francis Cardinal
McIntyre
December 30, 1964. Dorchester, Massachusetts

The Faith will be carried on and preserved in the best manner by adhering to the main doctrines and not by giving in to every new idea that is present. (English 1 pg.)

Mc4797 H-1965
Mr. Harry Hasse to J. Francis Cardinal
McIntyre
N.D. Somerset, Kentucky

A long letter comments on the new liturgy, the racial problems, and summer responsibilities. (English 6 pgs.)

Mc4798. H-1965
Mr. Robert Hoffman to J. Francis Cardinal
McIntyre
N.D. Los Angeles, California

Point of disagreement with the Catholic Faith, the position of Mary in the Church, the teaching of Purgatory, and the Seven Sacraments must be corrected before unity is possible. (English 3 pgs.)

Mc4799. I-1965
Mr. John J. Irwin to J. Francis Cardinal
McIntyre
August 15, 1965. La Jolla, California

Could an ordination be arranged after December 18 when the academic year ends in Chile? An interview could arrange everything. (English 1 pg.)

Mc4800. J-1965
Mr. John Jerkovich to J. Francis Cardinal
McIntyre
January 18, 1965. San Pedro, California

A request to have all priests explain the Gospel at Sunday Mass in terms that the people of the parish can understand. (English 2 pgs.)

Mc4801. J-1965
Mr. William Morteon to J. Francis Cardinal
McIntyre
January 24, 1965. La Cresenta, California

An appeal is made to have people understand epilepsy and allow individuals with the condition to work and be normal. (English 3 pgs.) On February 4, 1965, Msgr. Johnson states treatment of each person is a matter of education. (English 1 pg.)

Mc4802. J-1965
Mr. George Jagels to J. Francis Cardinal
McIntyre
February 9, 1965. San Marino, California

The gift of *Your American Yardstick* is interesting reading and is appreciated. (English 1 pg.)

Mc4803. K-1965
Mr. A. D. Klein to J. Francis Cardinal
McIntyre
April 2, 1965. Fort Wayne, Indiana

The Knights of Columbus of Indiana are honoring Mr. Edward Dahm for his outstanding
work to rid newstands of indecent literature. A
message to be included in the program would
be appreciated. (English 1 pg.)

Mc4804. K-1965
Ms. Catherine Kreppein to Msgr. Benjamin
Hawkes
April 4, 1965. Los Angeles, California

A *Catholic Travel Book* is being published to
include all Shrines in the United States. Is there
a special Shrine in California that should be
mentioned. (English 1 pg.) On May 4, 1965,
Msgr. includes Our Lady of Lourdes of the
West in Altadena. (English 1 pg.)

Mc4805. K-1965
Rev. James Donnellon to J. Francis Cardinal
McIntyre
April 22, 1965. Villanova, Pennsylvania

An invitation is extended to the Golden Jubilee of the class of 1915 honoring Mr. John C.
Kelly with a dinner at the New York Hilton.
(English 1 pg.) On May 10, 1965, the Cardinal
states that the calendar is too crowded to take
time out to travel. (English 1 pg.)

Mc4806. K-1965
Mr. Frank Klock to J. Francis Cardinal
McIntyre
July 18, 1965. Corona Del Mar, California

Did the early Church Fathers condemn divorce for any reason other than the theological
grounds. Did they give any psychological reasons? (English 1 pg.) On July 20, 1965, Fr.
states that the explanation can be given more
easily in a conversation so contact the parish
priest. (English 1 pg.)

Mc4807. K-1965
Rev. Joseph Kim to Bp. Timothy Manning
October 15, 1965. Seoul, Korea

Kindly accept this gift *Catholic Korea Yesterday and Today*. It will be sold in the United
States for $25.00. (English 1 pg.) On December
16, 1965, the Bishop encloses a check to help
with the cost of production. (English 1 pg.)

Mc4808. K-1965
Rev. Eugene Gilb to Rev. Michael Kaltusky
November 8, 1965. Los Angeles, California

Cardinal McIntyre will be an honorary sponsor for the Jubilee of Dr. Andrew Sheptytskj.
Father Francis Weber will represent the Archdiocese. (English 1 pg.)

Mc4809. K-1965
Bp. Timothy Manning to Bp. John J. Krol
November 29, 1965. Los Angeles, California

The Cardinal has requested me to be present
for the closing of the Council. Please accept this
as an official notification. (English 1 pg.)

Mc4810. L-1965
Mr. John Lacy to J. Francis Cardinal McIntyre
January 6, 1965. Los Angeles, California

Many Protestant ministers are yearning to
serve the Church after they are properly in-
structed. Could some way be given to them.
Married Deacons could be the answer. (English
5 pgs.)

Mc4811. L-1965
Mr. Lawrence LaMar to J. Francis Cardinal
McIntyre
March 3, 1965. Los Angeles, California

A movement to make President Kennedy considered a martyr for the country as one who
demonstrated the highest purpose of a dedicated man. (English 1 pg.)

Mc4812. L-1965
Mr. Carl Lippold to Bp. Timothy Manning
April 21, 1965. Edwards, California

Some advice is needed before beginning a
Doctoral program in Religion at USC. My intention was to study at the Institute of Lay Theology before the moratorium. (English 2 pgs.)

Mc4813. L-1965
J. Francis Cardinal McIntyre to Msgr. Harold
Laubacher
July 7, 1965. Los Angeles, California

Chief and Mrs. Udoji of Nigeria made an ear-
nest appeal for their parish presided by Rev. W.
Ozubulu. Their native costumes were most at-
tractive. (English 1 pg.)

Mc4814. L-1965
Bp. Timothy Manning to Sister M. William,
IHM
July 13, 1965. Los Angeles, California

Dr. Eugenio Lanzuolo requests some tutoring
in languages to supplement his income to help
educate his children. (English 1 pg.)
The same letter was sent to Sister Rebecca
CSJ and to Sister Raymund RSHM

Mc4815. L-1965
J. Francis Cardinal McIntyre to
Mr. Shane Leslie
August 25, 1965. Los Angeles, California

My memory serves to recall William T. Jerome as related to the Churchill family. The law
firm of Foster-Thomson did some work for the
family and Mrs. Pauline Weber of New Jersey
may have some information. (English 1 pg.)

Mc4816. L-1965
Mrs. Stephanie Lombardi to J. Francis Cardi-
nal McIntyre
September 6, 1965. Santa Monica, California

A request for information how to raise
$25,000 for a convent in Germany. The Sisters
will not attract more vocations unless the buildings are modernized. (English 7 pgs.) On September 30, 1965, the Cardinal states that fund
raising will have to be from among friends. (English 1 pg.)

Mc4817. L-1965
Mr. Jacque Dumas to Msgr. Benjamin Hawkes
September 13, 1965. New York City, New
York

The insurance payments to the heirs of Mr.
Valentine Leim cannot be paid until the address
of the Little Sisters of the Poor is located. (English 1 pg.) On September 21, 1965, Msgr.
states that the information concerning Mr. Leim
could be given. (English 1 pg.)

Mc4818. L-1965
Mrs. Elizabeth Lenz to J. Francis Cardinal
McIntyre
November 26, 1965. Glenwood, New York

The Inter Group Relations does not seem to
be helping the cause of Religion in any way.
Our educators do not belong at these meetings.
(English 4 pgs.)

Mc4819. L-1965
Mr. Charles Luckman to J. Francis Cardinal
McIntyre
December 13, 1965. Los Angeles, California

Charity will receive a donation in place of
the usual Christmas gifts and cards. (English 1
pg.) On December 22, 1965, the Cardinal acknowledges the donation to the Child Guidance
Clinic in place of the usual Christmas gift. (English 1 pg.)

Mc4820. Mc-1965
Mr. Michael McDermott to J. Francis Cardinal
McIntyre
March 19, 1965. Los Angeles, California

Hospital workers want to form a union and
enter into collective bargaining. Proposed legislation AB 865 should be given enthusiastic support. (English 1 pg.)

Mc4821. Mc-1965
J. Francis Cardinal McIntyre to All Los Ange-
les Catholics
January 7, 1965. Los Angeles, California

A pastoral letter stressing that a stronger belief in the Divinity of Christ is needed to off set
the tendency to make Jesus just a good man.
(English 1 pg.)

Mc4822. Mc-1965
Msgr. John Rawden to J. Francis Cardinal
McIntyre
July 23, 1965. Los Angeles, California

Mr. James Ludlum is the legal counsel for the
California Hospital Association. He reviews all
insurance policies since the Association is the
policy holder for liability. (English 1 pg.)

Mc4823. Mc-1965
Mr. Henry McLaughlin to J. Francis Cardinal
McIntyre
December 22, 1965. New York City, New
York

A copy of the book of ceremonies of Episcopal consecration used on January 1941 is enclosed as a Silver Jubilee reminder. (English 1
pg.) On December 30, 1965, the Cardinal expresses his gratitude for the thoughtfulness
as the original one has been misplaced. (English
1 pg.)

Mc4824. M-1965
Mr. Alphonse Matt to J. Francis Cardinal
McIntyre
January 8, 1965. St. Paul, Minnesota

A tribute to the manner in which the work of
the Church is continued regardless of criticism.
(English 1 pg.) On January 12, 1965, the Cardinal appreciates the tribute and the donation
to the Archbishop's Fund for Charity. (English
1 pg.)

Mc4825. M-1965
Bp. Sidney Metzger to J. Francis Cardinal
McIntyre
January 30, 1965. El Paso, Texas

An invitation to the dual celebration of the
Silver Jubilee of the Bishop and the Golden Jubilee of the Diocese on May 19. (English 1 pg.)
On February 10, 1965, the Cardinal regrets
that the calendar in May does not allow traveling to El Paso but promises prayers for the continuation of the work of the Church. (English
1 pg.)

Mc4826. M-1965
Arbp. Patrick O'Boyle to J. Francis Cardinal
McIntyre
February 8, 1965. Washington, D.C.

A plea for contributions to the Marian Congresses and Village Nazaret to be built for the
destitute is requested. (English 1 pg.)

Mc4827. M-1965
Mr. Michael Woods to Paolo Cardinal Marella
February 12, 1965. Long Beach, California

A request to meet and discuss the Sacred Art
of Italy while in Rome from September 18 to
October 4. (English 1 pg.) On February 27,
1965, the Cardinal requests some background
information on Mr. Woods. (English 1 pg.)

Mc4828. M-1965
Mr. Harold Rozenberg to J. Francis Cardinal
McIntyre
February 18, 1965. Los Angeles, California

An invitation to give the invocation at the
Myasthenia Gravis Foundation dinner on May
16. (English 1 pg.) On March 10, 1965, the
Cardinal regrets that he cannot attend the dinner but Msgr. O'Dwyer will be happy to represent the Archdiocese. (English 1 pg.)

Mc4829. M-1965
Paolo Cardinal Marella to J. Francis Cardinal
McIntyre
February 24, 1965. Vatican City

A friendly letter commenting on the survey of
the Diocese pointing to the crisis of authority in
the Church, and the difficulties in Los Angeles.
A request for prayers for the trip to Nagasaki.
(English 2 pgs.)

Mc4830. M-1965
J. Francis Cardinal McIntyre to Paul Cardinal
Marella
February 27, 1965. Los Angeles, California

The invitation to the dedication of the Vatican Pavilion cannot be accepted as a dedication
of a school is scheduled for the same day. An
invitation to a visit in Los Angeles is extended.
(English 1 pg.)

Mc4831. M-1965
J. Francis Cardinal McIntyre to Paul Cardinal
Marella
March 3, 1965. Los Angeles, California

The Vincentian Fathers are introducing a new
program in the Seminaries in which it seems the
Ordinary will follow the community instead of
the community following the Ordinary. (English
1 pg.)

Mc4832. M-1965
Mr. W. H. Mosbergen to J. Francis Cardinal
McIntyre
March 9, 1965. Singapore, Malaysia

A plea to have a priest visit a daughter who is
planning to be married in a non-Catholic
Church. She has always been a good Catholic.
(English 5 pgs.) On March 16, 1965, Rev.
Euguene Gilb states that the address given is
not correct as the daughter is not known at that
house. (English 1 pg.)

Mc4833. M-1965
Mrs. Cherie Mallo to J. Francis Cardinal
McIntyre
March 15, 1965. Hollywood, California

Permission is requested to use birth control
medicine as there are three children 3, 2, and 9
months and there is no money. (English 1 pg.)
On March 20, 1965, Fr. suggests a conference
with a priest rather than an answer in the letter.
(English 1 pg.)

Mc4834. M-1965
Rev. Donald Montrose to
  Mr. & Mrs. L. Murphy
April 20, 1965. Los Angeles, California

Because the race issue is current and the
book, *Black Like Me,* is popular, the faculty
thinks it best to face the issue and talk about it.
(English 1 pg.)

Mc4835. M-1965
J. Francis Cardinal McIntyre to Paul Cardinal
Marella
May 1, 1965. Los Angeles, California

The voice of America is not heard as clearly
as it should be in the discussions on the Council
floor. I am sending a *Catholic Directory* to
show how the United States has interpreted the
provisions of the code. (English 1 pg.)

Mc4836. M-1965
Mr. Joseph Mortz to J. Francis Cardinal
McIntyre
May 4, 1965. Los Angeles, California

Could a prayer be added to daily Mass for
justice under law so the welfare of everyone will
be guaranteed? (English 1 pg.)

Mc4837. M-1965
Mrs. Robert Merrick to Msgr. Benjamin
Hawkes
July 15, 1965. Whittier, California

Will a parish and school be built soon in the
area of Rowland Heights? St. Martha's School
is five and a half miles from the house. (English
1 pg.) On July 19, 1965, Msgr. states that there
is no immediate plans for a church and school
in that area. (English 1 pg.)

Mc4838. M-1965
Mr. Robert Magdlen to Mrs. Gladys Root
July 23, 1965. Los Angeles, California

The Catholic Church is not legally responsible for the acts of any party and will refuse to
pay any so-called damages. (English 5 pgs.) On
August 3, 1965, the Cardinal states that he
hopes this will close the case. (English 1 pg.)

Mc4839. M-1965
Mother Mary of Jesus to J. Francis Cardinal
McIntyre
August 23, 1965. Detroit, Michigan

The members of the Solemn Papal Enclosure
want to remain cloistered and desire that the
contemplative life continue. (English 2 pgs.)

Mc4840. M-1965
Mr. Karl Mundt to J. Francis Cardinal McIn-
tyre
September 9, 1965. Washington, D.C.

The Senate Bill S 309 for decent literature
seems ready to pass. The House Bill seems very
close to the Senate Bill. The Inter-faith groups
can fight for passage and fight indecent literature in the cities. (English 1 pg.)

Mc4841. M-1965
Mrs. Rita Melrose to J. Francis Cardinal
McIntyre
September 10, 1965. Santa Monica, California

An ecclesial annulment must be granted so
Michael can lead a normal, healthy life and
marry and rear a family. (English 1 pg.) On
September 16, 1965, Msgr. O'Flaherty states
there is no basis for an annulment of the marriage. (English 1 pg.)

Mc4842. M-1965
Mr. Zsolt Torak to Bp. Timothy Manning
September 22, 1965. Los Angeles, California

The history of Laszlo Makay is very sad and
he needs help. He is alone, ill, and handicapped.
Where does a Catholic receive help in these circumstances? (English 3 pgs.) On October 27,
1965, the Bishop expresses his admiration for
one who would write a letter for another. (English 1 pg.)

Mc4843. M-1965
Dr. Wilhelm Michaelis to J. Francis Cardinal
McIntyre
November 16, 1965. Hamburg, Germany

A proposal is presented to study the lifting of
the ban of ex-communication against Luther as
a means of ecumenism. (English 1 pg.)

Mc4844. M-1965
Mr. Myron Fox to Msgr. Benjamin Hawkes
December 2, 1965. Beverly Hills, California

Mrs. Suzanne Mayer would like this donation
to be given to a poor parish in the Archdiocese.
(English 1 pg.) On December 3, 1965, Msgr.
expresses the gratitude of the Archdiocese and
the people of St. Leo's in Watts for the donation. (English 1 pg.)

Mc4845. M-1965
Paul Cardinal Marella to J. Francis Cardinal
McIntyre
December 9, 1965. Vatican City

The schema *De Episcopis* is approved with
almost unanimous consent. The final session
ended with very beautiful ceremonies. (English
2 pgs.) On December 16, 1965, the Cardinal
states that the effects of the Council will be
long-lasting and profitable. (English 1 pg.)

Mc4846. M-1965
Msgr. Francis O'Connor to Msgr. Benjamin
Hawkes
December 22, 1964. Buffalo, New York

The Magnificat is publishing a series of articles on the five American Cardinals. An accurate biography, pictures formal and casual, and
clippings are needed. (English 1 pg.)

Mc4847. M-1965
Arbp. Egidio Vagnozzi to J. Francis Cardinal
McIntyre
December 24, 1964. Washington, D.C.

The themes for the Marian Congresses are
Mary and the New Testament and The Spiritual
Motherhood of Mary. A village for the poor
will be constructed near the site of the Congresses. (English 2 pgs.)

Mc4848. N-1965
Rev. Michael Nolan to Msgr. Benjamin
Hawkes
March 1, 1965. Palm Springs, California

Is the Los Angeles Orphanage still in existence? If not, where are the records kept? A
marriage must be validated. (English 1 pg.) On
March 3, 1965, Msgr. states that Sister Frances
D.C. is the superior of Maryvale. (English 1 pg.)

Mc4849. N-1965
Mr. James Joseph to Rev. Frank Norris
May 27, 1965. Claremont, California

An invitation is extended to present a paper
on Ecumenical Council and lead a discussion
later. Please suggest a book to be read in preparation for the meeting. (English 1 pg.) On July
6, 1965, the Cardinal states that either Msgr.
Dignan or Msgr. O'Callaghan could take over
the conference. (English 1 pg.)

Mc4850. N-1965
Ms. Ella Nugent to J. Francis Cardinal
McIntyre
August 16, 1965. Somerville, Massachusetts

In order to honor a woman for the enrich-
ment of life of human beings, all Bishops are
asked to submit names of candidates worthy of
the Siena Medal. (English 2 pgs.) On August
25, 1965, the Cardinal submits the names of
Irene Dunne and Sister Winifred of St. Anne's
Maternity Home. (English 1 pg.)

Mc4851. O-1965
Mr. Edward O'Hare to Msgr. Benjamin
Hawkes
N.D. Long Beach, California

A request to have a grandson transferred out
of the Juvenile Home in Saugus and into a
Catholic home. (English 1 pg.) On April 15,
1965, Msgr. Languille states that a discussion
will be held and every effort will be made to
transfer the boy to Rancho San Antonio. (English 1 pg.)

Mc4852. O-1965
Bp. Timothy Manning to Mr. Anthony Owens
January 7, 1965. Los Angeles, California

The soliciting of funds by lottery is illegal and
a violation of the Lottery Statue and against the
City Ordinance. (English 1 pg.) On January 14,
1965, Mr. Owens states that he did not know it
was illegal but all of the mailings are out. (English 1 pg.)

Mc4853. O-1965
Mr. Paul Pagel to Pope Paul VI
January 27, 1965. Inglewood, California

A long discussion on the author's book, *The
Cross or the Star,* in which the elimination of
Existentialism is advocated and the correct emphasis be placed on Judaism and the Jew. (English 3 pgs.)

Mc4854. O-1965
Arbp. Patrick O'Boyle to J. Francis Cardinal
McIntyre
February 8, 1965. Washington, D.C.

A contribution to alleviate the poverty of the
destitute at Santo Domingo by building Villa
Nazareth is being requested. (English 1 pg.) On
February 15, 1965, the Cardinal states that the
finesse of the touch of the appeal deserves a token. What should the token be? (English 1 pg.)

Mc4855. O-1965
Mr. Jack Odom to J. Francis Cardinal
McIntyre
February 20, 1965. Fort Bragg, California

To better relations among the Catholic and
the Protestants Churches, order the Protestant
girl released from the Good Sheperd Convent.
This is no way to increase membership in your
church. (English 1 pg.)

Mc4856. O-1965
Judge James Scoppottone to J. Francis Cardi-
nal McIntyre
March 2, 1965. Santa Cruz, California

An endorsement of *Our Land is Broad* by
Glen Oliver should be given. Immoral books are
condemned so good books should be praised.
(English 3 pgs.)

Mc4857. O-1965
J. Francis Cardinal McIntyre to Arbp. Patrick
O'Boyle
July 22, 1965. Los Angeles, California

The bankers' judgement is an unasked question. Does the Board want to use the incre-
ment? Is it lawful to use it? (English 3 pgs.)

Mc4858. O-1965
Miss Helen Ormond to J. Francis Cardinal
McIntyre
September 12, 1965. New York City, New
York

A long condemnation of the use of religion
and religious for public relations work. The influence of history on religious is most interesting. (English 9 pgs.)

Mc4859. O-1965
Ms. Helen O'Rourke to J. Francis Cardinal
McIntyre
October 6, 1965. Staten Island, New York

A friendly letter comments on the visit of
Pope Paul to the United Nations and New
York, and the desire that some of the friends
have for a visit to Lourdes and Rome. (English
6 pgs.)

Mc4860. O-1965
J. Francis Cardinal McIntyre to Arbp. Patrick
O'Boyle
November 30, 1965. Los Angeles, California

Some of the lawyers and clergy have been
joined with physicians on the birth control issue. Archbishop McGucken could have a good
panel if this is desired. (English 1 pg.)

Mc4861. O-1965
Miss Agnes O'Reilly to J. Francis Cardinal
McIntyre
December 9, 1965. New York City, New York

The donation is for the education of a student for the priesthood who is attending All
Hallows College and will be ordained for Los
Angeles. (English 1 pg.) On December 15,
1965, the Cardinal states that surely the student
will pray for special intentions. (English 1 pg.)

Mc4862. P-1965
Mr. Paul Pagel to J. Francis Cardinal McIntyre
January 28, 1965. Inglewood, California

A copy of *The Cross or The Star* is being
sent. Although ideas will differ, the purpose is
moral order. (English 1 pg.)

Mc4863. P-1965
Mr. Frank Perkins to J. Francis Cardinal
McIntyre
March 16, 1965. Van Nuys, California

Is it possible to have both a Catholic wedding
and a Protestant wedding? Parents are being
impossible and life will be difficult without two
ceremonies. (English 1 pg.) On March 25,
1965, the Cardinal asks the Pastor to meet with
the couple. (English 1 pg.)

Mc4864. P-1965
Rev. Feliciano Paoli, OFM to J. Francis Cardi-
nal McIntyre
April 21, 1965. Perugia, Italy

An invitation to Pontificate at the beginning
of the solemn novena to St. Francis on September 26. It is the feast of Our Lady of the Angels.
(Italian 1 pg.) On May 12, 1965, the Cardinal
states that he cannot be in Italy on September
26. It would be an occasion of great joy, if it
were possible. (English 1 pg.)

Mc4865. P-1965
Mrs. Francis Pomeroy to Mayor Samuel Yorty
May 15, 1965. Hollywood, California

A plea is made to revive the Mission Play at
Hollywood High School. It would one way to
assist the youth to know more about California
history. (English 1 pg.)

Mc4866. P-1965
Mr. Carl Pearlson to J. Francis Cardinal
 McIntyre
July 28, 1965. Torrance, California

An invitation to have a member of the clergy
present the Catholic viewpoint on shared time,
money for parochial schools, anti poverty programs, and tax exemptions on church property.
(English 1 pg.) On August 6, 1965, Fr. Montrose states that the law is favorable at the
present time and we should be cautious. (English 1 pg.)

Mc4867. P-1965
Dr. Thomas Peyton to J. Francis Cardinal
 McIntyre
August 14, 1965. Los Angeles, California

The message on the radio should be enforced
by my book, *Quest for Dignity.* Everyone can
benefit from the quotations. (English 1 pg.)

Mc4868. P-1965
Mr. Wilford Penny to Msgr. Benjamin Hawkes
August 30, 1965. Los Angeles, California

An invitation is extended to give the invocation at the luncheon opening the 34th International Conference of Financial Executives on
November 1. (English 1 pg.) On September 2,
1965, the Cardinal states that he will be happy
to be present. (English 1 pg.)

Mc4869. P-1965
Dr. Mykola Plaksij to J. Francis Cardinal
 McIntyre
September 23, 1965. Sherman Oaks, California

The Jubilee Committee is arranging a concert
on December 12 for the anniversary of Andrew
Sheptysky. (English 1 pg.) On September 25,
1965, the Cardinal states that preparation for
the Council is consuming all of the time available. Preceding this event, a time can be arranged. (English 1 pg.)

Mc4870. P-1965
Mr. Dennis Pettibone to J. Francis Cardinal
 McIntyre
November 9, 1965. Newbury Park, California

Does the Church have an official position on
diplomatic relations between the United States
and the Vatican? Does there seem to be an
American attitude? (English 1 pg.) On November 15, 1965, the Cardinal states that the ad-
vantages are with the government not the
Vatican. (English 1 pg.)

Mc4871. P-1965
J. Francis Cardinal McIntyre to Sheriff Peter
 Pitchess
December 14, 1965. Los Angeles, California

The portable T.V. was a diversion during the
period of recuperation. Your visit to Rome was
an opportunity to enjoy the unusual. (English 1
pg.)

Mc4872. P-1965
Rev. Raymond Pelly to J. Francis Cardinal
 McIntyre
December 15, 1965. Co. Kildare, Ireland

A friendly letter comments on the Pope's visit
to the United Nations and sending Christmas
wishes. (English 1 pg.) On December 30, 1965,
the Cardinal sends Christmas blessings to the
family. (English 1 pg.)

Mc4873. P-1965
J. Francis Cardinal McIntyre to Judge Joseph
 Proskauer
December 30, 1965. Los Angeles, California

Your autobiography gave pleasure during a
period of forced rest and the many incidents
and people you mentioned recall a pleasant period of time. (English 1 pg.)

Mc4874. P-1965
Sister Mary Paul OLC to Bp. Timothy
 Manning
N.D. Taiwan, Free China

An appeal is made to build a convent for the
Sisters who escaped from China and are doing
missionary work in Taiwan. (English 2 pgs.)

Mc4875. Q-1965
Rev. John R. Quinn to Bp. Timothy Manning
August 13, 1965. San Diego, California

An invitation is extended to give the annual
retreat to the Seminarians from January 21–28.
This is the only period that a retreat can be
given. (English 1 pg.) On October 27, 1965, the
Bishop states that the Confirmation schedule is
definite and he regrets that he cannot give the
retreat. (English 1 pg.)

Mc4876. Q-1965
Mr. John R. Quirk to J. Francis Cardinal
 McIntyre
November 19, 1965. Santa Monica, California

The material on the Q Security Clearance, *Its
Scientific Basis* which was promised during the
election can now be sent. (English 3 pgs.)

Mc4877. R-1965
Mrs. Ann Raymond to J. Francis Cardinal
McIntyre
January 7, 1965. Chino, California

Two young people ages 16 and 17 were married by the Justice of the Peace and now want a Catholic wedding. The priest does not seem to encourage them. What should be done? (English 3 pgs.) On January 14, 1965, the Cardinal asks Fr. Michael O'Day to investigate the family. (English 1 pg.)

Mc4878. R-1965
J. Francis Cardinal McIntyre to Bp. Bryan
McEntegart
January 26, 1965. Los Angeles, California

Mr. John Reilly would be interested in being the broker for securing bonds for the Pension Fund if that is the method that is being used. (English 1 pg.)

Mc4879. R-1965
Mrs. Robert Robinson to J. Francis Cardinal
McIntyre
February 17, 1965. Santa Monica, California

More emphasis and publicity should be given on the good being done by the Archbishop's Fund for Charity for the various parishes. It will diminish some of the criticism. (English 2 pgs.)

Mc4880. R-1965
Bp. Timothy Manning to Rev. Redmond
Roche, SJ
March 22, 1965. Los Angeles, California

A draft of 100 pounds is enclosed to be used for the school in whatever manner is thought best. (English 1 pg.) On March 27, 1965, Fr. states that the money will be used for a new refectory or perhaps a development of the science department. (English 1 pg.)

Mc4881. R-1965
Mr. Fred Redmond to J. Francis Cardinal
McIntyre
May 7, 1965. Albuquerque, New Mexico

Instead of mandatory busing of the school children, a guaranteed annual wage would eliminate ghettos and allow people to live where they desire. (English 2 pgs.)

Mc4882. R-1965
J. Francis Cardinal McIntyre to Mrs. John
Rauen
May 11, 1965. Los Angeles, California

A crucifix from Germany was a gift from you several years ago. Is there a special history connected with that crucifix? A Sister won the crucifix at a drawing at the Seminary. (English 1 pg.)

Mc4883. R-1965
Mr. John Rhatigan to J. Francis Cardinal
McIntyre
June 11, 1965. San Marino, California

By giving God his rightful place in the graduation address, the most important aspect of scholastic life was locked into place. (English 1 pg.)

Mc4884. R-1965
Rev. Richard Rolf, SJ to J. Francis Cardinal
McIntyre
June 27, 1965. Los Angeles, California

Permission is requested to celebrate Mass at home as my father is confined to the house. It has been years since he has been able to assist at Mass. (English 1 pg.) On July 1, 1965, the Cardinal grants permission for Mass at home once or twice a month according to the schedule. (English 1 pg.)

Mc4885. R-1965
J. Francis Cardinal McIntyre to Rev. Edward
Ryan, CMF
July 28, 1965. Los Angeles, California

The lay organizations national, diocesan, and parochial are an application in practice of what the Council has been promoting. (English 1 pg.)

Mc4886. R-1965
Bp. John Ward to J. Francis Cardinal McIntyre
September 8, 1965. Los Angeles, California

Mrs. Marie Reissig's prayer for exorcism against Satan would confuse rather than help the faithful. It is not in keeping with Canon Law. (English 1 pg.)

Mc4887. R-1965
Mr. John Rauen to J. Francis Cardinal
McIntyre
October 6, 1965. Los Angeles, California

The United States, Catholics and Protestants, received Pope Paul VI well. The talk given at the United Nations was well received and should bear fruit. (English 1 pg.)

Mc4888. R-1965
Bp. Timothy Manning to Rev. Redmond Roche, SJ
October 27, 1965. Los Angeles, California

A copy of *The Seminary Rule* and the survey of *Seminary Training in Time of Change* are enclosed. (English 1 pg.)

Mc4889. R-1965
Mr. F. J. Romadka to J. Francis Cardinal McIntyre
October 31, 1965. Milwaukee, Wisconsin

These leaflets can be used for convert activity and for assistance at Mass. *Share Your Treasure* will create interest and answer many questions. (English 3 pgs.)

Mc4890. R-1965
Bp. Timothy Manning to Rev. Justin Rigali
November 30, 1965. Los Angeles, California

I will represent the Cardinal at the closing session of the Council. The signatures will be as Procurator of the Cardinal. Is a meeting with Cardinal Cicognani necessary or advisable? (English 1 pg.)

Mc4891. R-1965
Rev. Luis Ricciarelli to Bp. Timothy Manning
December 1, 1965. Cebu City, Philippines

An appeal for the homeless boys in Cebu is made. They can be educated and have a better life than the streets if funds are available. (English 1 pg.) On December 17, 1965, the Bishop encloses a donation for the homeless children. (English 1 pg.)

Mc4892. R-1965
Mr. Robert Ramirez to J. Francis Cardinal McIntyre
N.D. Riverside, California

A Mexican American knows about prejudice but the civil rights movement does not help us. You work for us quietly and that does more good. (English 2 pgs.)

Mc4893. S-1965
Msgr. Benjamin Hawkes to Mr. William Starrs
January 3, 1965. Los Angeles, California

A list of priests that will assist parole officers is enclosed. It is understood that the priests will help with spiritual problems. (English 1 pg.)

Mc4894. S-1965
Miss Mary Smith to J. Francis Cardinal McIntyre
January 17, 1965. Long Beach, California

Everyone seems ready for change. The Catholics are speaking English and the Christian Science Monitor says, "The Master would not deprive anyone that which is right and useful". Is that medicine? (English 2 pgs.)

Mc4895. S-1965
Dr. Charles Strebig to J. Francis Cardinal McIntyre
February 3, 1965. San Bernardino, California

California needs more medical and dental schools and more than one should be Catholic. Financial contributions will be made if this is done. (English 1 pg.) On February 10, 1965, the Cardinal states that it cannot be realized in the immediate future. (English 1 pg.)

Mc4896. S-1965
Ms. Jo T. Smith to Bp. Timothy Manning
February 15, 1965. Falls Church, Virginia

Every Bishop and Cardinal should have the courage of Cardinal Camara who has the courage to speak out against Communism and rescue the area of Rio de Janeiro from the Communists. (English 1 pg.)

Mc4897. S-1965
J. Francis Cardinal McIntyre to Francis Cardinal Spellman
February 18, 1965. Los Angeles, California

Senator George Murphy inquired about our viewpoint of Federal Aid to education. California voted against it the last time it was discussed. (English 1 pg.)

Mc4898. S-1965
J. Francis Cardinal McIntyre to Joseph Cardinal Siri
February 18, 1965. Los Angeles, California

The annual meeting would be of parliamentary procedure rather than collegiality. Parliamentary procedure presumes a decision by the majority and invokes a power that is not present in collegiality. (English 1 pg.)

Mc4899. S-1965
Francis Cardinal Spellman to Eugene Cardinal Tisserant
March 3, 1965. New York City, New York

Cardinals have the duty to speak on civil matters and this must be at the discretion of the Cardinal. The Pope can call anyone or all of the Cardinals at any time he wishes. (English 1 pg.)

Mc4900. S-1965
Arbp. Egidio Vagnozzi to Francis Cardinal
Spellman
March 6, 1965. Washington, D.C.

Encourage a large number of clergy to attend
the Marian Congresses, the first such Congress
since the proclamation of Mary as Mother of
the Church. (English 1 pg.)

Mc4901. S-1965
Mrs. Thomas Stanley to J. Francis Cardinal
McIntyre
March 15, 1965. Panorama City, California

Confusion reigns over the changes in the
Mass. Nothing will be done unless the Cardi-
nals and Bishops know how the people feel.
(English 3 pgs.)

Mc4902. S-1965
Mrs. John Mooney to J. Francis Cardinal
McIntyre
March 18, 1965. North Bergen, New Jersey

An explanation is needed to understand why
a wonderful Catholic mother cannot have a
Mass and Catholic burial because a plot was
bought in a non-Catholic cemetery. (English
6 pgs.)

Mc4903. S-1965
Joseph Cardinal Siri to J. Francis Cardinal
McIntyre
March 22, 1965. Genoa, Italy

The College of Cardinals has a very special
function and is different from the meetings of
Bishops. The danger of parliamentarism should
not be considered. (Latin 2 pgs.)

Mc4904. S-1965
Joseph Cardinal Siri to J. Francis Cardinal
McIntyre
March 22, 1965. Genoa, Italy

The changes suggested in *Lumen Gentium*
were not favorable to the Bishops. Letters were
circulated among the Cardinals and Bishops to
know the thoughts of each including the Pope.
(Latin 2 pgs.)

Mc4905. S-1965
Mr. David Scott to J. Francis Cardinal
McIntyre
April 9, 1965. New York City, New York

A copy of the Deluxe Edition of *Journal Of A
Soul* one of 500 is enclosed. Number one was
delivered to the Pope Paul VI. (English 1 pg.)
On April 12, 1965, the Cardinal states that this
is a treasure to be kept. (English 1 pg.)

Mc4906. S-1965
Mr. A. A. Scott to J. Francis Cardinal
McIntyre
May 27, 1965. Los Angeles, California

An invitation to give the invocation at the International Convention of the Loyal Order of
Moose on July 22 at 9:30 a.m. is extended. (English 1 pg.) On June 8, 1965, Msgr. states that
due to the heavy schedule of the Cardinal,
Msgr. John Languille will give the invocation.
(English 1 pg.)

Mc4907. S-1965
Msgr. Benjamin Hawkes to Rev. Anthony Kelly
June 9, 1965. Los Angeles, California

Student priests will be available for the month
of August to help in parishes. Would a visiting
priest be helpful in the parish? (English 1 pg.)

Mc4908. S-1965
Rev. Edward Bunn, SJ to J. Francis Cardinal
McIntyre
June 14, 1965. Washington, D.C.

Dr. and Mrs. Edward Semansky's donation to
Georgetown University through your good
hands is most gratefully received. (English 1 pg.)

Mc4909. S-1965
Mr. Akos Szalas to J. Francis Cardinal
McIntyre
June 21, 1965. La Canada, California

Is there a possibility of an annulment if the
wife just walks out of the house and marriage.
Advice is needed. (English 1 pg.) On June 24,
1965, Fr. Thom asks the pastor to contact the
party and investigate the case. (English 1 pg.)

Mc4910. S-1965
Mr. E. B. Shaw to Pope Paul VI
June 21, 1965. Los Angeles, California

Are there any plans to change the law of abstinence from meat regulations for Catholics?
The seafood industry needs to know. (English
1 pg.)

Mc4911. S-1965
J. Francis Cardinal McIntyre to Francis Cardi-
nal Spellman
June 30, 1965. Los Angeles, California

The deluxe edition of "*Michelangelo: The Pieta and Other Masterpieces*" will have a prominent place in the library at St. John's Seminary.
(English 1 pg.)

Mc4912. S-1965
J. Francis Cardinal McIntyre to Rev. Thomas
  Stransky
July 13, 1965. Los Angeles, California

The statement concerning the Baptism of the
President's daughter is made without knowledge. It is difficult to obtain from the minister
the form used and ritual. The very sweeping
statement was unjust and unnecessary. (English
2 pgs.)

Mc4913. S-1965
Mr. Gerald Smith to J. Francis Cardinal
  McIntyre
July 15, 1965. Los Angeles, California

Before any vote is taken on the position of the
Jews and the death of Jesus, a careful reading of
the document should be made and tradition and
Scripture studied. (English 4 pgs.)

Mc4914. S-1965
Rev. Joseph Scannell, CSSR to Bp. Timothy
  Manning
July 19, 1965. Pittsburgh, Pennsylvania

The cable from the *Rota* gave a happy affirmative answer. It is due to the kindness and understanding of the Bishop that the case was
given a favorable answer. (English 1 pg.)

Mc4915. S-1965
Rev. Evaristus Sala to Msgr. Benjamin Hawkes
July 27, 1965. Barcelona, Spain

If the Cardinal and Bishops are coming to the
Council early, a visit to Montserrat and some of
the schools could be arranged. (English 1 pg.)
On August 5, 1965, Msgr. states that the Cardinal will go directly to Rome and forgo the
visit unfortunately. (English 1 pg.)

Mc4916. S-1965
Bp. John J. Scanlan to Bp. Timothy Manning
August 6, 1965. Honolulu, Hawaii

On May 21, 1966, the twenty-fifth anniversary of the creation of the Diocese of Hawaii
and the Silver Jubilee of the consecration of the
first Bishop will be celebrated. Please mark the
date on your calendar. (English 1 pg.)

Mc4917. S-1965
Mrs. Blanca Sulsons to J. Francis Cardinal
  McIntyre
August 29, 1965. Wilmington, California

Please build a residential home for special
children. It is a matter of justice to give special
children the training that is necessary. (English
2 pgs.)

Mc4918. S-1965
Mr. Frank Schmidt to J. Francis Cardinal
  McIntyre
August 31, 1965. Los Angeles, California

A copy of the article, *A Roman Holy Day* is
enclosed to give you a Protestant's reaction to
the Holy Father, St. Peter's, and the Vatican
Council. (English 1 pg.)

Mc4919. S-1965
Francis Cardinal Spellman to J. Francis Cardi-
  nal McIntyre
September 3, 1965. New York City, New York

An invitation to Bishop Manning to give the
retreat to the clergy in New York in June 1966
is extended. (English 1 pg.) On September 16,
1965, the Cardinal states that the Bishop is giving the retreat in Santa Fe but definite dates are
not available. (English 1 pg.)

Mc4920. S-1965
J. Francis Cardinal McIntyre Statement
September 3, 1965. Los Angeles, California

The rehabilitation program of the federal,
state, and city should be given the moral support of all Churches and the relations of the
NCCJ should continue. (English 1 pg.)

Mc4921. S-1965
Lawrence Cardinal Shehan to American
  Hierarchy
October 21, 1965. Vatican City

The American hierarchy will meet October
25 at 4:00 p.m. at the North American College
to discuss *"Positio"* of the Sacred Apostolic
Penitentiary. The conclusion from the *Vota* will
be given. (English 1 pg.)

Mc4922. S-1965
Msgr. Benjamin Hawkes to Rev. John
  Stafford, CSV
December 2, 1965. Los Angeles, California

Los Angeles has no set stipend for a Mass but
usually in handling a bequest, an offering of
$2.00 is suggested. (English 1 pg.)

Mc4923. S-1965
Rev. Joseph Stieger to Msgr. Benjamin Hawkes
December 4, 1965. San Luis, Obispo,
  California

Should there be an active endorsement of the
legislation being introduced by Mr. Warren
Dorn? (English 1 pg.) On December 6, 1965,
Msgr. states that the subject is decency and we
are in favor. Petitions can be signed outside the
Church. (English 1 pg.)

Mc4924. S-1965
J. Francis Cardinal McIntyre to Francis Cardinal Spellman
December 10, 1965. Los Angeles, California

A report on the riots of last August is being submitted to the Governor. The result is a historical document and well prepared. (English 1 pg.)

Mc4925. S-1965
Rev. Robert Serrano to J. Francis Cardinal McIntyre
December 18, 1964. Villanueva, Mexico

A special message of gratitude for the period of time spent in Los Angeles and the great charity shown. (English 1 pg.) On January 7, 1965, the Cardinal states to be remembered at Christmas was a special blessing. (English 1 pg.)

Mc4926. S-1965
J. Francis Cardinal McIntyre to Miss Judy Serbaroli
December 30, 1965. Los Angeles, California

The magnificent crucifix will be a challenge to find a fitting place for it to be displayed. (English 1 pg.)

Mc4927. T-1965
Mr. Oscar Trippet to Sister Anastasia
January 22, 1965. Los Angeles, California

To assure the continued care of the injured child, a second trust will be established by Mr. Kelly. This should insure her care and education. (English 2 pgs.) On January 29, 1965, the Cardinal assures Sister that Mr. Trippet will do as he says. (English 1 pg.)

Mc4928. T-1965
Eugenio Cardinal Tisserant to J. Francis Cardinal McIntyre
January 25, 1965. Vatican City

Some ideas are expressed on collegiality and the possible use of the concept in the Sacred College of Cardinals. An annual meeting of the College of Cardinals is given some consideration. (Italian 1 pg.)

Mc4929. T-1965
J. Francis Cardinal McIntyre to Eugenio Cardinal Tisserant
February 18, 1965. Los Angeles, California

All matter in public discussion should be in accord with the Pope's stated opinion. If another opinion exists it should be given in private. A yearly convocation of the College of Cardinals seems to be unnecessary. (English 2 pgs.)

Mc4930. T-1965
J. Francis Cardinal McIntyre to Bp. Thomas Toolen
March 31, 1965. Los Angeles, California

The situation is Selma parallels the conditions in Los Angeles. Demonstrations will be the way of life for some time and the cause of Religion may not be furthered. (English 2 pgs.) On April 20, 1965, the Bishop states that the participation by priests and sisters did not put the Church in a high position. (English 1 pg.)

Mc4931. T-1965
J. Francis Cardinal McIntyre to Msgr. Paul Tanner
June 8, 1965. Los Angeles, California

The whole structure of NCWC must be revised with limited juridical power. The Bishops themselves should be on the Administrative Board. (English 3 pgs.)

Mc4932. T-1965
Mr. William Taylor to J. Francis Cardinal McIntyre
June 9, 1965. Miami, Florida

Mrs. Rose Toombs of Los Angeles made a generous contribution to the Variety Children's Hospital on June 3 in memory of Pope John XXIII. She promises to repeat this each year. (English 1 pg.) On June 14, 1965, the Cardinal expresses his appreciation for the generous donation. (English 1 pg.)

Mc4933. T-1965
Mrs. William Tyler to Gov. Richard Hughes
June 16, 1965. Santa Barbara, California

A protest is made over the closing of Shelton College. Government monopoly of education is not good. Will Catholic and other private colleges be the next to go? (English 1 pg.)

Mc4934. T-1965
Msgr. Paul Tanner to J. Francis Cardinal McIntyre
June 17, 1965. Washington, D.C.

The present method of electing Bishops to the Board is unsatisfactory. Some of them are elected to various positions because of the importance of the See and not the general interest of the Department. Any ideas for better organization should be given. (English 3 pgs.)

Mc4935. T-1965
J. Francis Cardinal McIntyre to Msgr. Paul Tanner
July 15, 1965. Los Angeles, California

The present questions may give the necessary information concerning the corporation and the legal scope of the Board. (English 2 pgs.) On July 29, 1965, Msgr. answers the questions and offered prayers for Fr. Thom and the Cardinal. (English 3 pgs.)

Mc4936. T-1965
J. Francis Cardinal McIntyre to Msgr. Paul Tanner
August 6, 1965. Los Angeles, California

The confusion over separate corporations and reporting responsibilities must be cleared. The National Council of Bishops has no part of NCWC. (English 2 pgs.)

Mc4937. T-1965
Rev. Sylvester Taggart to J. Francis Cardinal McIntyre
December 21, 1965. Philadelphia, Pennsylvania

The main controversy at St. John's University is academic freedom and control of the University. There must be a difference between a Catholic and a secular University. Some members of the faculty are insisting on final control of the University. (English 2 pgs.)

Mc4938. T-1965
Mr. Tom Tedesco to Msgr. Benjamin Hawkes
December 28, 1965. Los Angeles, California

An offer to donate a 16 unit apartment complex to the Archdiocese for tax purposes. Msgr. states that after an appraisal the Archdiocese will accept if a quick sale can be realized. On December 30, 1965, the offer was withdrawn until the following year. (English 3 pgs.)

Mc4939. V-1965
Rev. Werenfried van Straaten to J. Francis Cardinal McIntyre
March 2, 1965. Houston, Texas

An appeal is made for Iron Curtain Church Relief Society which is under the Sacred Congregation and under Bishop John Morkovsky in Houston. (English 5 pgs.)

Mc4940. V-1965
Arbp. Egidio Vagnozzi to J. Francis Cardinal McIntyre
March 15, 1965. Washington, D.C.

The planning commission for the fourth session of the Vatican Council needs to know the present plan for attendance and accommodations. (English 1 pg.) On March 22, 1965, the Cardinal states that the Auxiliary Bishops will be present for the opening of the Council and on October 8, the Cardinal will come.

Mc4941. V-1965
Mrs. Van Inwagen to J. Francis Cardinal McIntyre
March 19, 1965. Branchport, New York

A request to discuss World Wide Family Unity With God program. Whenever an interview is possible, the time can be arranged. (English 2 pgs.)

Mc4942. V-1965
Arbp. Egidio Vagnozzi to J. Francis Cardinal McIntyre
June 8, 1965. Los Angeles, California

The Secretariate of State is not responsible for the many pamphlets and circulars being sent to the members of the Council. Everyone is free to judge what consideration should be given to the material. (English 1 pg.)

Mc4943. V-1965
Rev. Boyce Vardiman to J. Francis Cardinal McIntyre
July 5, 1965. Ferris, Texas

Are the newspaper accounts of the dismissal of Rev. William Dubay and Rev. Phillip Berryman accurate? This Methodist minister would like to know. (English 1 pg.) On July 22, 1965, the Cardinal states that racial distinctions, religious sympathies, and political persuasions are carefully cared for in Los Angeles.

Mc4944. V-1965
Rev. Harvey McIntyre to Msgr. Benjamin Hawkes
August 2, 1965. Seattle, Washington

A man operating as a priest is practicing psychiatry. He claims he is from Los Angeles a Rev. Andre Vaucher. (English 1 pg.) On August 6, 1965, Msgr. states there is no record of his ever having ministered in this area. Long Beach does not even have a chapel by that name. (English 1 pg.)

Mc4945. V-1965
Dr. Oliver Vreeland, MD to J. Francis Cardinal McIntyre
November 11, 1965. Monroe, Louisiana

Using the CCD text book, *God's Plan For Us,* is somewhat dangerous for the student who does not know the difference between Socialism and social justice. (English 2 pgs.) On December 14, 1965, the Cardinal states that the analysis will be considered. (English 1 pg.)

Mc4946. W-1965
Mr. Victor Weaver to J. Francis Cardinal McIntyre
January 6, 1965. Shawnee, Oklahoma

The *Look* Magazine article was a distortion of the truth colored by the liberal philosophy of the time. The defense of the Church can never be challenged. (English 1 pg.)

Mc4947. W-1965
Mrs. Dolores Walsh to J. Francis Cardinal McIntyre
January 7, 1965. Garden Grove, California

A request is made to establish a chapter of Stella Maris, an organization for divorcees, in the Archdiocese. (English 1 pg.) On January 19, 1965, Fr. Murphy states for the present, the needs could be met in the Legion of Mary or the Council of Catholic Women. (English 1 pg.)

Mc4948. W-1965
Mrs. Zelda Woeber to Bp. Timothy Manning
March 4, 1965. Oildale, California

May Catholics attend non-Catholic worship if one does not participate in the service? (English 1 pg.) On March 6, 1965, the Bishop states that the laws of the Church have not changed. If there is a specific reason, then one should consult the pastor. (English 1 pg.)

Mc4949. W-1965
Mr. Robert Wagner to Bp. Timothy Manning
March 26, 1965. Santa Barbara, California

The Catholic Human Rights Council staged a Memorial Demonstration in which priests, brothers, and sisters participated. These demonstrations cause confusion. (English 3 pgs.)

Mc4950. W-1965
Dr. Frank Waltz MD to J. Francis Cardinal McIntyre
March 28, 1965. Pomona, California

An appeal is made to help revoke the law No 64-1164 PH. Children need natural parents not those assigned by the courts. (English 3 pgs.)

Mc4951. W-1965
Mrs. Joyce Webster to J. Francis Cardinal McIntyre
May 17, 1965. Los Angeles, California

Why is a priest not permitted to join AA and have the support needed to remain sober? A group could be arranged just for priests and religious. (English 1 pg.)

Mc4952. W-1965
Mr. George Wunderlick to J. Francis Cardinal McIntyre
June 13, 1965. Dallas, Texas

The Catholic Church should consider a Foundation in Los Angeles similar to the Baptist Foundation in Texas. The basic plan is enclosed. (English 4 pgs.)

Mc4953. W-1965
Msgr. James Wilders to J. Francis Cardinal McIntyre
August 8, 1965. New York City, New York

Could some special consideration be given to the two sons of the Winans family. A Catholic education is a stipulation of the Court. (English 1 pg.) On September 15, 1965, the Pastor states that the only possibility is St. John's Military Academy. (English 1 pg.)

Mc4954. W-1965
Rev. Eugene Gilb to Mr. Michael Wood
September 17, 1965. Los Angeles, California

Cardinal Marella's connection with Sacred Art is remote and others would be more beneficial to your work. (English 1 pg.) On September 25, 1965, Mr. Woods states that a letter of introduction to the person most knowledgeable would be appreciated. (English 1 pg.)

Mc4955. W-1965
Mrs. William Wolf to J. Francis Cardinal McIntyre
September 23, 1965. Hermosa Beach, California

The Biltmore Hotel in the area of Hermosa is for sale. It would make an ideal home for Catholic senior citizens. Getting to Mass is becoming more of a problem for so many. (English 1 pg.)

Mc4956. W-1965
Bp. Aloysius Willinger to J. Francis Cardinal McIntyre
September 28, 1965. Fresno, California

Prayerful support is promised. The reply to the San Francisco article made many proud of you. (English 1 pg.)

Mc4957. W-1965
Rev. Gerald Ryan, OFM to Msgr. Benjamin
  Hawkes
November 14, 1965. Santa Barbara, California

The Wolf family wants to buy a double grave
in the non-sectarian section of the cemetery.
Only Mrs. Wolf is a Catholic. May she be buried there? (English 1 pg.) On November 16,
1965, Msgr. states that she may be buried there
and the priest can bless the grave at another
time. (English 1 pg.)

Mc4958. W-1965
Mrs. Christine Weikum to Bp. Timothy
  Manning
November 23, 1965. Palos Verdes, California

Some instruction ought to be given to the
priests so that they would be more considerate
at the time of death. (English 2 pgs.)

Mc4959. W-1965
Mr. Ronald Weekes to J. Francis Cardinal
  McIntyre
November 23, 1965. Seattle, Washington

The greatest test of the success of the Council
will be the proper respect for law and order.
(English 1 pg.)

Mc4960. W-1965
Arbp. Joseph Walsh to J. Francis Cardinal
  McIntyre
December 12, 1965. Tuam, Ireland

A Christmas message asks continued blessings upon the Cardinal and his Archdiocese.
(English 1 pg.) On December 27, 1965, the
Cardinal states that the Church in Ireland
should share in the blessings of the Divine
Child is the prayer of the Cardinal. (English 1
pg.)

Mc4961. W-1965
J. Francis Cardinal McIntyre to Rev. Forrest
  Weir
December 21, 1965. Los Angeles, California

At Christmas time the blessings of God is
asked for you and your congregation. (English
1 pg.)

Listing for the Year
1966

Mc4962. A-1966
Mr. Lucilo Alza to J. Francis Cardinal
    McIntyre
February 22, 1966. Culion, Philippines

An appeal is made for a donation to allow
the oldest member of the family to complete his
degree in education. In this way he can contribute to the other members of the family. (English
2 pgs.)

Mc4963. A-1966
Sister Anthony Marie to Bp. Timothy Manning
May 25, 1966. Los Angeles, California

The Sacrament of confirmation administered
at the County Hospital seems to have done the
child the good that was prayed for. She has
added strength and courage. (English 1 pg.)

Mc4964. A-1966
Sister M. Aurora, SAC to Bp. Timothy
    Manning
June 3, 1966. Madrid, Spain

A Sister from the Community will be moved
to Osaka, Japan, to work in evangelization of
the people. She has the permission of both bishops. (Spanish 2 pgs.)

Mc4965. A-1966
Anonymous to J. Francis Cardinal McIntyre
September 6, 1966. Los Angeles, California

Retirement would be disastrous for Los Angeles. Much good still must be done and leaders
are needed to do the work. (English 2 pgs.)

Mc4966 A-1966
Mr. Gabriel Aceves to J. Francis Cardinal
    McIntyre
September 15, 1966. Los Angeles, California

Some assistance is needed to understand the
divorce proceedings. (English 4 pgs.) On November 17, 1966, the Cardinal requests Catholic Welfare to offer legal advice. (English 1 pg.)

Mc4967. A-1966
Mr. John Altenburg to Msgr. Eugene Gilb
September 20, 1966. Los Angeles, California

If a non-Catholic minister can assist at a
Catholic wedding, may a priest be present for a
Baptism in the Episcopal Church? (English 1
pg.) On October 18, 1966, Msgr. states that the
Vatican Council did not permit a priest to act in
these circumstances. (English 1 pg.)

Mc4968. A-1966
Mr. Floyd Anderson to Msgr. Benjamin
    Hawkes
September 22, 1966. Washington, D.C.

Questions are being asked for a nation-wide
survey to know the work being done to implement the Vatican Council. (English 2 pgs.) On
October 11, 1966, Msgr. states there are active
experiments and others will be added after the
Bishops' Conference. (English 2 pgs.)

Mc4969. A-1966
Mr. J. Hugh Anwyl to J. Francis Cardinal
    McIntyre
September 29, 1966. Los Angeles, California

Rev. James Pike spoke on the Contemporary
Pulpit Series and gave his views on abortion.
Both sides of this issue ought to be heard. An
invitation is being extended for this purpose.
(English 1 pg.) On October 6, 1966, the Cardinal states that his calender is too crowded at
this time. (English 1 pg.)

Mc4970. A-1966
Mr. Robert Garrick to Msgr. Benjamin
Hawkes
October 7, 1966. Los Angeles, California

What is an acceptable method to invite a
priest to give the invocation at the Anheuser-
Busch national sales convention banquet? (English 1 pg.) On October 14, 1966 Msgr. states
that Msgr. Laubacher would be happy to give
the invocation. (English 1 pg.)

Mc4971. A-1966
Mr. John Altenburg to Msgr. Eugene Gilb
October 30, 1966. Los Angeles, California

The child will be Baptized in the Episcopal
Church. A special legal document allowed me
to rear the children of this marriage in the
Christian faith. (English 1 pg.)

Mc4972. A-1966
Rev. Denis J. Aroujo to J. Francis Cardinal
McIntyre
December 1966. Kerala, India

An appeal for donations for a co-educational
college to provide educated leaders for a true
democracy. The younger children are being educated and cooperatives are being introduced
for the workers. (English 1 pg.)

Mc4973. A-1966 Mr. J. J. Brandlin to Bp.
William Adrian
December 2, 1966. Los Angeles, California

The Bill recently introduced will curb traffic
of salacious literature and avoid the unconstitutional aspects of other legislation. (English
1 pg.)

Mc4974. A-1966
Miss Theresa Anderson to J. Francis Cardinal
McIntyre
N.D. Long Beach, California

The beautiful Mass honoring Our Lady of
Czestochowa will be remembered for many
years. Special prayers are offered for our Cardinal. (English 3 pgs.)

Mc4975. B-1966
Mr. Frank Brophy to Rev. F. X. Connelly, SJ
January 10, 1966. Los Angeles, California

Since Brophy Prep has my name, something
must be done about the leftist liberal teachers.
The student should be ready to meet the test of
faith when it comes. (English 1 pg.)

Mc4976. B-1966
J. Francis Cardinal McIntyre to Bp. Charles
Buddy
January 12, 1966. Los Angeles, California

A pamphlet on the constitutionality of religion and theology in public higher education
is enclosed. It may be of some interest. (English
1 pg.)

Mc4977. B-1966
Bp. Alden Bell to J. Francis Cardinal McIntyre
January 14, 1966. Sacramento, California

The California Bishops' meeting should be after Easter on April 13. Points for the agenda
could be the birth control/abortion issue, and
reapportionment for openers. (English 1 pg.)
On January 21, 1966, the Cardinal agrees with
the date and adds pornography to the agenda.
(English 1 pg.)

Mc4978. B-1966
Bp. Leo Maher to Bp. Alden Bell
February 11, 1966. Santa Rosa, California

An indepth educational program should be
begun to acquaint all levels with the Church's
stand on abortion but stressing positive family
issues. Stress good and evil, truth and false-
hood, sacred and secular. (English 2 pgs.)

Mc4979. B-1966
Mr. William Ball to J. Francis Cardinal
McIntyre
February 24, 1966. Harrisburg, Pennsylvania

America is accustomed to allow public offi-
cials to act on their own. An example is the use
of public money for birth control programs.
(English 1 pg.) On March 1, 1966, the Cardinal
elaborates on the ideas of Thomas Jefferson.
(English 2 pgs.)

Mc4980. B-1966
Mr. Robert Brown to J. Francis Cardinal
McIntyre
March 4, 1966. Prairie Creek, Indiana

Leadership from such as the Cardinal can assure the Church of a sane way out of the chaos
and give the world some law and order. (English
1 pg.)

Mc4981. B-1966
Mr. Joseph Bower to J. Francis Cardinal
McIntyre
March 11, 1966. Palm Beach, Florida

A friendly letter commenting on the assistance given to a stricken friend and the wonderful work being furthered by Bishop Carroll.
(English 1 pg.)

Mc4982. B-1966
Mr. J. J. Brandlin to J. Francis Cardinal
McIntyre
March 22, 1966. Los Angeles, California

The meeting of the Diocesan attorneys in
Washington D.C. was worthwhile giving a
broader picture of potential problems. An infor-
mal meeting of the California attorneys will be
useful. (English 3 pgs.)

Mc4983. B-1966
J. Francis Cardinal McIntyre to Mrs. Thomas
Boyle
March 22, 1966. Los Angeles, California

Prayerful condolences are sent asking God's
blessings on Thomas for his apostolate for the
poor and special blessings for those members of
the family remaining. (English 1 pg.)

Mc4984. B-1966
Bp. Giuseppe Nicolini to J. Francis Cardinal
McIntyre
April 2, 1966. Assisi, Italy

An appeal for funds to complete the arrangements for the Ecumenical meeting between the
Catholics and Episcopalians at Assisi. (English
2 pgs.)

Mc4985. B-1966
Agostino Cardinal Bea to Francis Cardinal
Spellman
April 6, 1966. Vatican City

A memorandum on the differences between
the Catholic and Protestant concepts of basic religious fundamentals is sent for review. (English
2 pgs.)

Mc4986. B-1966
Mr. Joshua Berger to J. Francis Cardinal
McIntyre
April 17, 1966. New York City, New York

Comments on the similarity between the
worker-priest movement in France and the assistance being given by the clergy to unionize
workers in California would be appreciated.
(English 2 pgs.)

Mc4987. B-1966
Rev. Cornelius Burns to Bp. Timothy Manning
May 6, 1966. San Francisco, California

The testimony of Larry Duggan has been
taken and the letter from the Archdiocese of Los
Angeles and the Archbishop's formal *Votum
Ordinarii* are the only items remaining before
sending the material to Rome. (English 1 pg.)

Mc4988. B-1966
Bp. Vincent Brizgys to J. Francis Cardinal
McIntyre
May 12, 1966. Chicago, Illinois

An invitation is extended to attend the Solemn Mass and dedication of the Chapel of Our
Lady of Siluva in the National Shrine on September 4. (English 1 pg.) On June 1, 1966, the
Cardinal sends his regrets that he cannot attend. (English 1 pg.)

Mc4989. B-1966
Sister Benedict Joseph to Bp. Timothy
Manning
June 12, 1966. Alhambra, California

A friendly letter recalls former teaching assignments and former pupils in Los Angeles. I
am anticipating a new assignment for the next
scholastic year. (English 6 pgs.) On June 18,
1966, the Bishop states that the new assignment
will allow your talents to be used. (English
1 pg.)

Mc4990. B-1966
Mrs. J. Barthelemy to Msgr. Benjamin Hawkes
N.D. Troyes, France

A plea to help prevent a marriage that would
ruin a strong national and family relationship.
(French 3 pgs.) On June 15, 1966, Mrs. Bar-
thelemy states that her husband will come to
Los Angeles before the marriage can be held.
(French 1 pg.)

Mc4991. B-1966
Mr. Ted Birnberg to J. Francis Cardinal
McIntyre
June 16, 1966. Los Angeles, California

The *Tre Ore* booklets used in the Cathedral
must be updated to correspond to the Vatican II
pronouncement on the statement on the Jews.
(English 1 pg.) On July 5, 1966, the Cardinal
states that more recent texts rectify the statements. (English 1 pg.)

Mc4992. B-1966
J. Francis Cardinal McIntyre to Mrs. Francis
Browne
July 8, 1966. Los Angeles, California

Msgr. has sent the donation to *Future* magazine which will promote education. The donation to the Archdiocese will be used for the
Archbishop's Fund for Charity (English 1 pg.)

Mc4993. B-1966
Mr. William Bailog to J. Francis Cardinal
McIntyre
N.D. Hollywood, California

An appeal for help to take a child suffering
from Brights Disease to Lourdes. The doctors
have no known cure. (English 3 pgs.) On July
25, 1966, Rev. Vincent McGinty states that he
knows the family but feels that they should return to the area where they are known. (English
1 pg.)

Mc4994. B-1966
Rev. James Becherer to Msgr. Benjamin
Hawkes
September 30, 1966. Washington, D.C.

The American Institute of Family Relations
can be suggested to Catholics since the counselors respect the person's beliefs and the fees are
reasonable. (English 1 pg.)

Mc4995. B-1966
Mother M. Benigna to Msgr. Benjamin
Hawkes
October 3, 1966. Trichur, South India

Money for food for the orphans is needed. As
soon as the crops can be harvested there will be
food for the school. (English 1 pg.)

Mc4996. B-1966
Bp. Hugh Boyle to Bp. Timothy Manning
October 15, 1966. Transvaal, South Africa

A message of gratitude for the money received from the Mission Society is enclosed. The
Society can be assured of the prayers of the Missionaries and the people in Africa. (English
1 pg.)

Mc4997. B-1966
Mrs. Frances Brockman to J. Francis Cardinal
McIntyre
November 4, 1966. Louisville, Kentucky

A request for a discussion on the Catholic
press at the Bishops' Meeting so the average
Catholic and all interested people can be better
informed. (English 1 pg.)

Mc4998. B-1966
Mr. George Becwar to Msgr. Benjamin
Hawkes
November 6, 1966. Los Angeles, California

At the Salvation Army rehabilitation center
can a Catholic read the Scripture, sing hymns,
and preach a sermon in exchange for room and
board? (English 1 pg.) On November 16, 1966,
Mr. Campion states that Mr. Becwar can do the
same thing in a Catholic center if he wishes.
(English 1 pg.)

Mc4999. B-1966
Mr. Robert Looker to Msgr. Eugene Gilb
November 29, 1966. Redondo Beach,
California

The Brownline Corporation would like to donate lumber for book shelves and interior construction if any Catholic organization is in need
of lumber. (English 1 pg.)

Mc5000. B-1966
Mrs. Marion Barnwell to Bp. Timothy
Manning
December 9. 1966. El Segundo, California

Could the story of Fatima, Lourdes, and
Guadalupe be animated as It's a Small World at
Disneyland is? It could be an educational experience. (English 1 pg.) On December 12, 1966,
the Bishop states that the endless complications
would make the project impossible. (English
1 pg.)

Mc5001. C-1966
Amleto Cardinal Cicognani to J. Francis Cardi-
nal McIntyre
January 4, 1966. Vatican City

A Papal appointment is made as the Vice
president of the Post Conciliary commission De
Episcopis et Diocesium Regimine. (Latin 1 pg.)

Mc5002. C-1966
Mr. Jack Tyrell to J. Francis Cardinal
McIntyre
February 12, 1966. Lakewood, California

An invitation to address the California Contract Cities annual seminar in Palm Springs
May 27–29. (English 1 pg.) On February 18,
1966, the Cardinal sends regrets that the graduation schedule makes it impossible. Either
Msgr. Languille or Johnson is available. (English 1 pg.)

Mc5003. C-1966
Mrs. B. Clavet to J. Francis Cardinal McIntyre
February 25, 1966. Hawthorne, California

A request that the new parish to be formed
would be dedicated to Our Lady with the title
of Our Lady of Knock. (English 2 pgs.) On
March 4, 1966, Msgr. Gilb states that the
Shrine has not been given official canonical recognition. It will be investigated. (English 1 pg.)

Mc5004. C-1966
Bp. William Condon to Bp. Timothy Manning
March 14, 1966. Great Falls, Montana

A community of Sisters will come to the Diocese from Ireland. Are special concessions made in Los Angeles for vacations and the length of commitment. (English 1 pg.) On March 22, 1966, the Bishop states that no special concessions are made. The contract is enclosed. (English 1 pg.)

Mc5005. C-1966
Mr. Lawrence Cusack to Msgr. Benjamin Hawkes
March 24, 1966. New York City, New York

Is a copy of the synodal statutes of the priest's Will available so a comparison can be made. (English 1 pg.) On March 31, 1966, Msgr. gives detailed obligations of the Will and the personal property inventory. (English 1 pg.)

Mc5006. C-1966
Mrs. B. J. Cashman to J. Francis Cardinal McIntyre
March 25, 1966. San Diego, California

A summer program is being proposed in which a Catholic priest, a Rabbi, and a Minister will speak to the youth. Please give your opinion. (English 1 pg.) On April 1, 1966, the Cardinal suggests that the question be addressed to Rev. F. F. Hurd of San Diego. (English 1 pg.)

Mc5007. C-1966
Rev. Richard Coyne SJ to Bp. Timothy Manning
April 15, 1966. Limerick, Ireland

A request to reprint an article from *The Tidings*, "Bishop Manning Tells Meaning of the Missions". We will get permission from *The Tidings* likewise. (English 1 pg.) On April 18, 1966, the Bishop's permission to use the article is given and a picture is enclosed that can be used. (English 1 pg.)

Mc5008. C-1966
Carlo Cardinal Confalonieri to Arbp. Robert Lucey
April 18, 1966. Vatican City

The request to change the Marriage Tribunal second instance from Los Angeles to Dallas, Texas, is granted. (Latin 1 pg.)

Mc5009. C-1966
Mr. John Cohn to J. Francis Cardinal McIntyre
April 20, 1966. Los Angeles, California

The foundation check for $500 is enclosed which is designated for a poor parish. The next check will be delivered to the parish personally. A letter of recommendation is needed for the School of Business at University of Southern California. (English 1 pg.)

Mc5010. C-1966
J. Francis Cardinal McIntyre to Mrs. Norman Chandler
May 27, 1966. Los Angeles, California

Bestowing a special degree upon you at Mt. St. Mary's will be an honor and a privilege. It will be good to hear the feminine influence on society given a special recognition. (English 1 pg.)

Mc5011. C-1966
Los Angeles City Council Resolution
June 1966. Los Angeles, California

A tribute to Cardinal McIntyre on the Silver Jubilee of Episcopal Consecration and the 45th anniversary of ordination to the Priesthood.

Mc5012. C-1966
Mr. Porter Chandler to J. Francis Cardinal McIntyre
June 3, 1966. New York City, New York

The copy of the Supreme Court of California decision on Proposition 14 is most interesting. The New York case concerning text books is being prepared for court now. (English 2 pgs.)

Mc5013. C-1966
J. Francis Cardinal McIntyre to Hon. John Cassidy
July 7, 1966. Los Angeles, California

A message of gratitude for the Resolution passed by the City Council honoring the Archbishop for his years of service to the city. The Cardinal asks for special blessings for the city and the Council. (English 1 pg.)

Mc5014. C-1966
J. Francis Cardinal McIntyre to Mr. & Mrs. Thomas Cotton
August 20, 1966. Los Angeles, California

Pope Paul VI extends special nuptial blessings on your bridal party and on you. The same nuptial blessings are imparted by the Cardinal. (English 1 pg.)

Mc5015. C-1966
J. Francis Cardinal McIntyre to Amleto Cardinal Cicognani
September 10, 1966. Los Angeles, California

A letter of protest is sent for the latest Carnegie report on education in the United States. It labels Catholic education as un-American and the conclusions drawn are questionable. (English 2 pgs.)

Mc5016. C-1966
Msgr. Nicholas Wegner to Msgr. Benjamin Hawkes
September 23, 1966. Boys Town, Nebraska

Mr. Thomas Crelly sent a substantial donation to Boys Town with a confused note. If the gentleman needs the money, the donation will be returned. (English 1 pg.) On September 29, 1966, Msgr. states that after investigation, Mr. Crelly is not in need. Keep the donation. (English 1 pg.)

Mc5017. C-1966
Rev. Cephos, S P to J. Francis Cardinal McIntyre
October 1, 1966. Jemez Springs, New Mexico

An interview with Rev. Henry Angelino is requested before his return to *Via Coeli*. (English 1 pg.) On October 7, 1966, the Cardinal asks for more information before the interview. (English 1 pg.)

Mc5018. C-1966
Mr. James Copley to J. Francis Cardinal McIntyre
October 3, 1966. La Jolla, California

A message of appreciation for the opportunity to visit the Pope during the recent visit in Rome. A copy of the letter sent to the Pope pointing out the great work of the Cardinal is enclosed. (English 2 pgs.)

Mc5019. C-1966
Bp. John Ward to J. Francis Cardinal McIntyre
December 12, 1966. Los Angeles, California

Dr. Alphonse Clemens denies ever recommending American Institute of Family Relations. He knows that some priests attend the Institute but not on his recommendation. (English 1 pg.)

Mc5020. C-1966
Mr. Herbert Clish to J. Francis Cardinal McIntyre
December 28, 1965. Brooklyn, New York

A friendly letter commenting on the problems faced by St. John's University and the professors wishing to take over the University. (English 2 pgs.) On January 6, 1966, the Cardinal promises prayers for the improvement of the situation. (English 1 pg.)

Mc5021. C-1966
Mr. Joseph Corcoran to J. Francis Cardinal McIntyre
N.D. Philadelphia, Pennsylvania

The various forms of discrimination that are practiced in the United States are emphasized and in particular discrimination that is shown in education. (English 23 pgs.)

Mc5022. D-1966
Mr. L. M. Brings to J. Francis Cardinal McIntyre
January 19, 1966. Minneapolis, Minnesota

A request to have a qualified writer begin a biography that will be published by Denison Company. (English 1 pg.) On February 2, 1966, the Cardinal states that any biography of him will done by the Archdiocese. (English 1 pg.)

Mc5023. D-1966
Ms. Dorothy Day to J. Francis Cardinal McIntyre
March 1966. New York City, New York

An appeal is sent to keep the houses of hospitality open and to provide for those who come seeking help. (English 1 pg.)

Mc5024. D-1966
Mrs. Patricia Davis to J. Francis Cardinal McIntyre
March 6, 1966. Sherman Oaks, California

Is there a blood donor program available in the Archdiocese? Two pints of blood must be donated to the American Red Cross in my name. (English 1 pg.) On March 21, 1966, Msgr. states that many donations of blood are being offered to the Red Cross. (English 1 pg.)

Mc5025. D-1966
Mr. James Delaney to Msgr. Benjamin Hawkes
March 10, 1966. St. Louis, Missouri

A request for a retirement facility in the Pasadena area is made and to help locate an elderly priest for spiritual direction. (English 1 pg.) On April 2, 1966, Mr. Delaney asks to recommend a hotel where elderly people live. (English 1 pg.)

Mc5026. D-1966
Bp. John Donovan to J. Francis Cardinal
  McIntyre
March 14, 1966. Detroit, Michigan

An invitation is sent to the installation as
Bishop of Toledo on April 18 at 11:00 a.m.
(English 1 pg.) On March 18, the Cardinal
states he realizes the tradition of not inviting
Cardinals but business keeps this Cardinal at
home not tradition. (English 1 pg.)

Mc5027. D-1966
Mr. Ralph Dighton to J. Francis Cardinal
  McIntyre
March 29, 1966. Los Angeles, California

A stated position on the newly discovered
ability to control heredity by genetic surgery
and genetic alchemy is needed. (English 1 pg.)
On April 9, 1966, the Cardinal states that he is
content to wait for more developments. (English
1 pg.)

Mc5028. D-1966
Mr. Red Eisen to Mr. Eugene Debs
April 1966. Los Angeles, California

The real issue is not pornography but an anti-
Christ campaign disguised as art or situations
presented as social comment. (English 2 pgs.)

Mc5029. D-1966
J. Francis Cardinal McIntyre to Bp. William
  McDonald
April 1, 1966. Los Angeles, California

The matter of accreditation for smaller seminaries might become a problem with the new
G.I. Bill of Rights. Ask Rev. John Schmidt to
speak to Mr. Terrance Duffy at the NCEA. (English 1 pg.) On April 5, 1966, the Bishop states
that Fr. will not be at the NCEA but will be
happy to discuss the material. (English 1 pg.)

Mc5030. D-1966
J. Francis Cardinal McIntyre to Rev. John P.
  Schmidt
April 1, 1966. Los Angeles, California

A letter of introduction for Mr. Terrance A.
Duffy who would be interested in discussing the
article in the Catholic University bulletin. (English 1 pg.)

Mc5031. D-1966
Mr. George Doderlein to J. Francis Cardinal
  McIntyre
April 13, 1966. Chatsworth, California

Instead of building elementary schools in
each parish why isn't an all purpose recre-
ational and social center built? It will provide a
place for religious instruction and help control
juvenile delinquency. (English 2 pgs.)

Mc5032. D-1966
Mr. Michael Bolger to Msgr. Benjamin Hawkes
April 15, 1966. Los Angeles, California

Mr. Earl J. Dealy ought to receive a special
commendation for his conscientious viligance
for any violation of school property. (English 1
pg.) On April 25, 1966, Msgr. expresses his appreciation for all of the help given. (English
1 pg.)

Mc5033. D-1966
Msgr. Eugene Gilb to Mr. George Doderlein
April 15, 1966. Los Angeles, California

Every Catholic elementary student cannot be
educated in a parish school but the CCD does
function to give a religious education. We are
hopeful for the continued support of the people.
(English 1 pg.)

Mc5034. D-1966
Mrs. Marie Daly to J. Francis Cardinal
  McIntyre
May 4, 1966. Los Angeles, California

Is there anything being done on the local level
for greater unity between Greek Orthodox and
Catholics? (English 1 pg.) On May 7, 1966, the
Cardinal states that great strides were made at
the Council and unity will come from the top
not from the local level. (English 1 pg.)

Mc5035. D-1966
Arbp. Egidio Vagnozzi to Msgr. Benjamin
  Hawkes
May 9, 1966. Washington, D.C.

Please visit Horacio L. Dicono in detention.
He came into the United States under his brother's passport. An appeal may be possible. (English 1 pg.) On June 18, 1966, Msgr. states that
apparently Horacio is not as innocent as stated.
(English 1 pg.)

Mc5036. D-1966
J. Francis Cardinal McIntyre to Mr. and Mrs.
  Daniel Donohue
June 27, 1966. Los Angeles, California

The celebration of my Silver Jubilee of Episcopal consecration was most thoughtful, generous, and will provide a lasting memory. (Eng
lish 2 pgs.)

Mc5037. D-1966
Mr. Louis Drew to J. Francis Cardinal
  McIntyre
July 29, 1966. Los Angeles, California

A long letter asking why something is not being done in the Church to warn people about
conditions in the country and especially about
Communistic activity. (English 4 pgs.)

Mc5038. D-1966
Ms. Dorothy Day to J. Francis Cardinal
McIntyre
October 4, 1966. New York City, New York

An appeal for assistance for the houses of hospitality which accept the poor, homeless, and the abandoned of society is made. (English 1 pg.)

Mc5039. D-1966
Arbp. Victor Foley to J. Francis Cardinal
McIntyre
October 28, 1966. Suva, Fiji

The kind reception of Fr. Dutton and the promise to allow priests to come to Fiji for two or three years is a real bonus. (English 2 pgs.)

Mc5040. D-1966
Mr. Joseph Delahanty to Msgr. Benjamin
Hawkes
October 29, 1966. Los Angeles, California

A visit to the Chancery Office before beginning the study of the parish as a political concept is necessary. (English 1 pg.)

Mc5041. D-1966
Mrs. Ethel Daely to Msgr. Eugene Gilb
December 2, 1966. Long Beach, California

A request for some guidance for a mother whose daughter is married out of the Church. Can she still be a mother to her? (English 2 pgs.) On December 15, 1966, Msgr. states to be a mother as Mary is a mother to everyone of us. (English 1 pg.)

Mc5042. E-1966
Jose Cardinal Rivera to Bp. Timothy Manning
August 1, 1966. Guadalajara, Mexico

An invitation is sent to the Fifth National Missionary Congress of Mexico from November 9 to 13. (Spanish 1 pg.) On August 12, 1966, the Bishop asks Bishop Escalante for more definite information about the Congress. (English 1 pg.)

Mc5043. E-1966
Bp. Nicholos Elko to J. Francis Cardinal
McIntyre
September 26, 1966. Pittsburgh, Pennsylvania

The newspaper account of the naming of the Auxiliary Bishop in the American Carpatho-Russian Orthodox Church is not good for the ecumenical movement. (English 1 pgs.)

Mc5044. E-1966
J. Francis Cardinal McIntyre to the
Seminarians
December 16, 1966. Camarillo, California

A talk given at St. John's Seminary entitled Nova et Vetera is being sent to the library. (English 3 pgs.)

Mc5045. F-1966.
Bp. John Fearns to J. Francis Cardinal
McIntyre
January 9. 1966. New York City, New York

A prayerful message that medical science can help in the recovery of sight. (English 1 pg.) On January 15, 1966, the Cardinal states that his vision is almost completely restored. (English 1 pg.)

Mc5046. F-1966
Bp. Francis Furey to J. Francis Cardinal
McIntyre
January 14, 1966. San Diego, California

The brochure, Religion, Theology and Public Higher Education, will be helpful with the opening of the University of California San Diego, (English 1 pg.)

Mc5047. F-1966
Bp. Francis Furey to J. Francis Cardinal
McIntyre
March 12, 1966. San Diego, California

By presiding at Bishop Buddy's funeral a fitting tribute was paid to a remarkable man. (English 1 pg.)

Mc5048. F-1966
Mrs. Rebecca Farley to Rev. Eugene Gilb
April 7, 1966. Burbank, California

A long detailed request for permission to be absolved from Friday abstinence and from attending Mass while traveling in Europe during the year is made. (English 5 pgs.)

Mc5049. F-1966
Ms. Anne Ferraris to J. Francis Cardinal
McIntyre
April 26, 1966. San Francisco, California

A request is made for an interview so that a feature article can be written with accuracy about Los Angeles. (English 1 pg.) On May 10, 1966, the Cardinal referred the matter to Msgr. William Johnson for the information on social welfare. (English 1 pg.)

Mc5050. F-1966
Bp. Joseph Federal to Bp. Timothy Manning
May 12, 1966. Salt Lake City, Utah

Some information about the City of Hope is needed before a campaign for funds can begin. (English 1 pf.) On May 23, 1966, the Bishop states that the hospital is free and does cooperate with all of the parishes. It is worthy of consideration. (English 1 pg.)

Mc5051. F-1966
Msgr. Lawrence O'Leary to J. Francis Cardinal McIntyre
August 18, 1966. Los Angeles, California

Mr. Ferguson is interested in providing air service for the missions. The aviation industry is willing to cooperate. (English 1 pg.) On August 30, 1966, Dr. Ulric Bray invites the Cardinal to a luncheon to hear Mr. Ferguson speak about his experiences. (English 1 pg.)

Mc5052. F-1966
Rev. Martha Claiborne to J. Francis Cardinal McIntyre
September 1, 1966. Apple Valley, California

A plea for some help in organizing a drive for the Apple Valley Church of God School is requested. (English 1 pg.) On September 7, 1966, the Cardinal states that Apple Valley is in the San Diego Diocese and the request should be sent there. (English 1 pg.)

Mc5053. F-1966
Dr. James Fifield to J. Francis Cardinal McIntyre
September 19, 1966. Los Angeles, California

Legislation was introduced to tax all business property owned by the Church. Would a copy of the Bill be useful? (English 1 pg.) On September 21, 1966, the Cardinal states that the legal department in Washington is studying the Bill. (English 1 pg.)

Mc5054. F-1966
Rev. Edward Fitton, SP to Bp. Timothy Manning
October 5, 1966. Grenada, West Indies

A request to visit the Archdiocese and solicit funds from the people to whom I can be directed. The people here are very poor. (English 1 pg.) On October 13, 1966, the Bishop states that the donation is not large but all of the available money must be given to many charities. (English 1 pg.)

Mc5055. F-1966
Bp. Joseph Federal to Bp. Timothy Manning
October 27, 1966. Salt Lake City, Utah

A recommendation is needed for a construction company that is advertising a building process that will cut the cost of construction. (English 1 pg.) On November 4, 1966, the Bishop states that the company is unknown in this area. (English 1 pg.)

Mc5056. F-1966
J. Francis Cardinal McIntyre to Bp. Francis Furey
October 28, 1966. Los Angeles, California

Msgr. Donald Montrose will give a report at the Superintendent of Education Meeting. If your paper is ready for the Bishops' meeting, it will be a fertile field for discussion. (English 1 pg.)

Mc5057. F-1966
Bp. Francis Furey to J. Francis Cardinal McIntyre
November 6, 1966. San Diego, California

To open the Bishops' Meeting to the press is ridiculous. All important decisions are given to the press as well as other courtesies. (English 1 pg.)

Mc5058. F-1966
Judge F. George Fiedler to J. Francis Cardinal McIntyre
December 1, 1966. Chicago, Illinois

The Chicago Bar Association is studying the possibility of broadening the legal grounds for abortion. Is a copy of the Catholic Bishops of California statement available? (English 1 pg.) On December 7, 1966, the Cardinal states that the statement will open the campaign against further legislation. (English 1 pg.)

Mc5059. F-1966
Mr. Edward Kussman to J. Francis Cardinal McIntyre
December 2, 1966. Los Angeles, California

The participation of the Cardinal in the statement calling for fair housing and education opportunities and the end of discrimination is encouraging. (English 1 pg.)

Mc5060. G-1966
Rabbi Juda Glasner to Los Angeles *Times*
February 12, 1966. Los Angeles, California

To impress on the minds of the students that there is a Master Plan in the world and a Personal God, daily prayer ought to be encouraged in schools. (English 1 pg.) On February 23, 1966, the Rabbi requests a discussion with the Cardinal on prayer. (English 1 pg.)

Mc5061. G-1966
Mr. Victor Zanoni to J. Francis Cardinal
McIntyre
February 12, 1966. Los Angeles, California

An appeal for assistance is made for the Children's hospital in the Tijuana area. Almost everything is needed. There is no discrimination in the hospital. (English 5 pgs.) On March 23, 1966, Msgr. Roman Garcia states that he is hopeful that a hospital will be built. (English 1 pg.)

Mc5062. G-1966
Miss Mary Galvanauskas to J. Francis Cardinal McIntyre
May 17, 1966. Chicago, Illinois

A request to begin a community of Contemplative Religious within the Archdiocese. (English 2 pgs.) On May 24, 1966, the Cardinal states that the eremitical life would probably not attract many women today. (English 1 pg.)

Mc5063. G-1966
Msgr. Henry Gross to Bp. Timothy Manning
July 12, 1966. Los Angeles, California

A suggestion that the Bishop move to St. Brendan's Parish and continue the work that Msgr. Fogarty began. (English 1 pg.)

Mc5064. G-1966
Mr. William Govan to J. Francis Cardinal
McIntyre
August 14, 1966. Los Angeles, California

The achievement program of St. Tiburius' Parish is another of the many programs that the people of Los Angeles Archdiocese ought to be proud. (English 2 pgs.) On August 18, 1966, the Cardinal states that the program is consoling in many respects. (English 1 pg.)

Mc5065. G-1966
Mr. Richard Gilman to J. Francis Cardinal
McIntyre
October 11, 1966. Los Angeles, California

An invitation to join the presidents of the local colleges at a dinner to welcome Bishop James Shannon to Occidental College as guest lecturer. (English 1 pg.) On October 19, 1966, the Cardinal regrets that he cannot attend the dinner as other commitments are scheduled. (English 1 pg.)

Mc5066. G-1966
J. Francis Cardinal McIntyre to Bp. Francis
Green
December 15, 1966. Los Angeles, California

During this period of experimentation, the Christmas season is one source of stability, joy, and happiness. (English 1 pg.)

Mc5067. H-1966
Mr. Thomas A. Kelly to Mr. Ralph Hill
February 10, 1966. Los Angeles, California

The number of liens filed is increasing. Payment is being withheld until the work is satisfactory and this policy will continue. (English 1 pg.)

Mc5068. H-1966
Mrs. Mary Downs to Mr. Robert Hutchins
March 28, 1966. Los Angeles, California

A visitation to the Watts area or the reading of the McCone Report are suggestions that should be done before another article is written. (English 1 pg.)

Mc5069. H-1966
Br. R. T. Unsworth to Msgr. Benjamin Hawkes
April 11. 1966. Montebello, California

Mr. John Howard will end his affiliation with Cantwell High School in June. There was no deception intended. (English 1 pg.) On April 20, 1966, Msgr. states that Bishop Manning would be happy to be of assistance if that is needed. (English 1 pg.)

Mc5070. H-1966
Dr. Frederick Hacker, MD to J. Francis Cardinal McIntyre
April 26, 1966. Beverly Hills, California

As new ideas in the field of psychiatry develop, it would be an honor to call these to your attention at the Chancery. (English 1 pg.) On April 29, 1966, the Cardinal states that it would be a pleasure to hear about the new developments. (English 1 pg.)

Mc5071. H-1966
Ms. Rose Hawkins to J. Francis Cardinal
McIntyre
May 10, 1966. Los Angeles, California

The wording in the new St. Joseph Missal and the Maryknoll Missal are different. The theology is different, Christ was raised and Christ rose. (English 1 pg.) On May 12, 1966, the Cardinal states that many people have voiced the need for correction. (English 1 pg.)

Mc5072. H-1966
Mrs. Edith Hoffman to J. Francis Cardinal
McIntyre
July 7, 1966. Ventura, California

A check for $1,000 is enclosed to assist in the foundation of the magazine Fortune. (English 1 pg.) On July 8, 1966, the Cardinal states that he is sure that the promoters will justify your confidence and generous support. (English 1 pg.)

Mc5073. H-1966
Dr. George Hummer to J. Francis Cardinal
McIntyre
August 15, 1966. Santa Monica, California

An invitation to give the invocation opening
the American Red Cross convention of Blood
Banks on October 26 is extended. (English 1
pg.) On August 19, 1966, the Cardinal states
that it will be a pleasure to give the invocation.
(English 1 pg.)

Mc5074. H-1966
Arbp. Edward Hunkeler to J. Francis Cardinal
McIntyre
September 18, 1966. Kansas City, Kansas

The copy of Father Clark Butterfield's incar-
dination into the Archdiocese of Kansas City
is enclosed. It is regrettable that opportunities
do not occur for discussions and visits. (English
1 pg.)

Mc5075. H-1966
Mr. L. T. Moldenhauer to Msgr. Benjamin
Hawkes
October 12, 1966. Terra Haute, Indiana

The Sunday Visitor tithing envelope system
can be used in any Diocese and still allows for
drives and special collections. (English 1 pg.)

Mc5076. H-1966
Mr. Gabriel Huck to Bp. Timothy Manning
October 17, 1966. New York City, New York

At the annual Bishops' Meeting consider commenting on the Vietnam War and the respect
for all human life. (English 1 pg.)

Mc5077. H-1966
Mr. Charles Hartman to J. Francis Cardinal
McIntyre
November 4, 1966. Pasadena, California

A visit to Washington, D.C. and to the Jefferson Memorial would be an educational experience to imbibe the philosophy of Thomas
Jefferson. (English 2 pgs.) On November 9,
1966, the Cardinal states that Thomas Jefferson's quotations are often used in my talks.
(English 1 pg.)

Mc5078. H-1966
J. Francis Cardinal McIntyre to Arbp. Edward
Hunkeler
December 7, 1977. Los Angeles, California

Rev. James Richardson, CM is in charge of
the agenda for the Conference of Religious Men
and Women being held in Sierra Madre Retreat
House. He understands that all decisions will
be referred to the Conference of Bishops. (English 2 pgs.)

Mc5079. I-1966
Mr. Theodore Infalt to J. Francis Cardinal
McIntyre
June 9, 1966. San Francisco, California

In order to return God to our jungle, could
radio and television be used to teach basic
truths? This could be an ecumenical project but
under the sponsorship of the Catholics. (English
2 pgs.) On June 15, 1966, the Cardinal states
that he has carefully noted the suggestion. (English 1 pg.)

Mc5080. J-1966
Mrs. Claudia Johnson to J. Francis Cardinal
McIntyre
February 18, 1966. Los Angeles, California

The Friday abstinence law is a definite hardship when half of the world is allowed to eat
meat and the other half is not. (English 2 pgs.)

Mc5081. J-1966
Mr. Earl Joseph to Msgr. Benjamin Hawkes
February 20, 1966. Camarillo, California

The California Historical Society is working
to restore the homesite of Don Adolpho Camarillo. Is the land to be used for some purpose by
the nuns? (English 1 pg.) On March 2, 1966,
Msgr. states that no one, to our knowledge, is
contemplating purchasing the land. (English
1 pg.)

Mc5082. J-1966
Mr. Ernest Jakel to J. Francis Cardinal
McIntyre
December 16, 1965. Orange, California

Federal Aid to education means Federal control and soon the government will take over everything. (English 1 pg.)

Mc5083. K-1966
Msgr. Bernard Koenig to Msgr. Benjamin
Hawkes
March 30, 1966. Kansas City, Missouri

There are plans for a chapel to be in the new
Mid-Continent International Airport. What is
the size of the chapel in the Los Angeles Airport
and what services does it provide? (English 1
pg.) On April 4, 1966, Msgr. states that there is
no chapel in the airport but there are two
nearby parishes. (English 1 pg.)

Mc5084. K-1966
Bp. Gerald Kennedy to J. Francis Cardinal
McIntyre
June 3, 1966. Los Angeles, California

The gift to the Agricultural Aids Foundation
is appreciated. Msgr. John Languille will be
most welcome at the annual conference in Red-
lands. The gift, a tractor, will be given to the
Missionaries of the Sacred Heart in New
Guinea for the use of the students. (English
1 pg.)

Mc5085. K-1966
Mr. Bernard Kamins to Msgr. Benjamin
Hawkes
June 10, 1966. Los Angeles, California

Before entering the race for the Board of Education, what services should a member of the
Board provide for all schools? (English 1 pg.)
On June 20, 1966, Msgr. states that a Board
member should be able to withstand pressure
groups and do the very best for all citizens.

Mc5086. K-1966
Rev. Emmett Kelly to Msgr. Benjamin Hawkes
September 3, 1966. Helena, Montana

Please send the scale for salary for pastor, assistants, and other office assignments so a comparison can be made. (English 1 pg.) On
September 7, 1966, Msgr. sends the compensations scale. (English 1 pg.)

Mc5087. K-1966
Rev. Joseph Kearney to Bp. Timothy Manning
October 26, 1966. Cochabamba, Bolivia

A friendly letter relates life in Bolivia, learning a new language and a new culture before
beginning to teach. (English 4 pgs.) On November 7, 1966, the Bishop comments on events in
St. Gregory's Parish and in Los Angeles. (English 1 pg.)

Mc5088. K-1966
Mr. Thomas Keating to J. Francis Cardinal
McIntyre
December 2, 1966. Detroit, Michigan

The annual contribution to Don Bosco Technical Institute is enclosed with a very special
80th birthday wish. (English 1 pg.) On December 10, 1966, the Cardinal expresses his gratitude that the work can continue. (English 1 pg.)

Mc5089. L-1966
J. Francis Cardinal McIntyre to Mr. John
Lecrivain
January 13, 1966. Los Angeles, California

The generous gift of the site for St. Simon
and Jude Parish in Huntington Beach is deeply
appreciated. This brings the promise of prayers
from the Chancery Office. (English 1 pg.)

Mc5090. L-1966
Mr. Paul Larsen to J. Francis Cardinal
McIntyre
January 19, 1966. Beaver, Utah

An appeal for assistance as the Sheriff has
posted a sale sign on the ranch. A promise for
some help was given years ago. (English 1 pg.)
On February 9, 1966, Msgr. Hedderman states
that he did not know about the financial difficulty. (English 1 pg.)

Mc5091. L-1966
Arbp. Robert Lucey to J. Francis Cardinal
McIntyre
March 14, 1966. San Antonio, Texas

To lighten the burden of the Matrimonal Bureau, we request the transfer of the cases of Second Instance to the Tribunal in Dallas, Texas.
(English 1 pg.) On March 21, 1966, the Cardinal states that the Tribunal will be happy to be
given fewer cases. (English 1 pg.)

Mc5092. L-1966
James Cardinal Lercaro to J. Francis Cardinal
McIntyre
April 10, 1966. Bologna, Italy

The clergy in the smaller towns and villages
are in need of Mass stipends to keep the
churches open. (English 1 pg.) On May 2, 1966,
the Cardinal encloses an immediate donation
and states that the Propagation of the Faith will
send other assistance. (English 1 pg.)

Mc5093. L-1966
Miss Loretta Young Lewis to J. Francis Cardi-
nal McIntyre
May 13, 1966. Los Angeles, California

A request for a position in one of the many
Chancery Office departments for her brother,
Jack Y. Lindley is made. (English 1 pg.)

Mc5094. L-1966
Mr. John Lombardi to Rev. George Cranham
May 16, 1966. Los Angeles, California

The importance of the Newman Centers and
the Philosophy Clubs will be stressed in the new
role as Assistant Superintendent of Education.
The students should have the opportunity to
seek the truth. (English 1 pg.)

Mc5095. L-1966
Mr. Charles Luckman to J. Francis Cardinal
McIntyre
August 15, 1966. Los Angeles, California

Is the property owned by the Archdiocese on
Wilshire Blvd. available for sale? (English 1 pg.)
On August 16, 1966, the Cardinal states that
the property is under conditional option. A discussion can be arranged. (English 1 pg.)

Mc5096. L-1966
Mrs. Arabelle Hurlbut to J. Francis Cardinal
McIntyre
August 30, 1966. Los Angeles, California

A portrait to be used in the program of the
Las Damas Pan Americanas Presentation Ball is
needed. All proceeds are to be used for the Holy
Family Adoption Center. (English 1 pg.) On
September 1, 1966, the Cardinal states that the
work of the Adoption Center is most deserving
of assistance. (English 1 pg.)

Mc5097. L-1966
Mr. Joseph Laraneta to J. Francis Cardinal
McIntyre
November 18, 1966. San Pedro, California

A request for an interview toward becoming
a broker to liquidate the stocks and bonds donated to the Archdiocese. (English 1 pg.) On
November 22, 1966, Rev. William Barry sends
a letter of introduction for Mr. Laraneta. (English 1 pg.)

Mc5098. Mc-1966
Mr. Harold Joyce to J. Francis Cardinal
McIntyre
January 30, 1966. Los Angeles, California

The First Degree of the Knights of Columbus
is bestowed upon Cardinal McIntyre at the Hollywood Palladium. (English 1 pg.)

Mc5099. Mc-1966
Mrs. Larry McGovern to J. Francis Cardinal
McIntyre
March 16, 1966. West Covina, California

A letter of protest that parishes are encouraging people to go to Las Vegas by selling chances
with this as a prize and offering special trips to
Las Vegas. (English 1 pg.) On April 1, 1966,
Msgr. Gilb states that the Cardinal protests
such advertising for the shows. (English 1 pg.)

Mc5100. Mc-1966
Mrs. Mary McElwee to J. Francis Cardinal
McIntyre
November 6, 1966. Coral Gables, Florida

A letter of protest that the Catholic Press is
not serving the Catholic people but doing the
work of the anti Catholic element. (English
2 pgs.)

Mc5101. M-1966
Arbp. John Maguire to J. Francis Cardinal
McIntyre
February 4, 1966. New York City, New York

An invitation to the celebration of Cardinal
Spellman's Golden Jubilee of ordination on
May 4 is extended. (English 1 pg.) On February
4, 1966, the Cardinal states that he will try to
rearrange meetings and commitments so he can
be present. (English 1 pg.)

Mc5102. M-1966
Mr. Joseph Mammoser to J. Francis Cardinal
McIntyre
February 8, 1966 Chicago, Illinois

A favorable comment in made on the talk
given to the Hollywood Holy Name Society
asking for a national day of reparation and
penance. (English 1 pg.)

Mc5103. M-1966
Miss Charlene Minetti to J. Francis Cardinal
McIntyre
N.D. Cayucos, California

A request for a comment on education that
can be read for the eighth grade graduation ceremony is made. (English 1 pg.) On February 11,
1966, the Cardinal states that all gifts come
from God and each has an obligation to know
and respect the Divine commands and desires.
(English 1 pg.)

Mc5104. M-1966
Mr. Richard Moore to J. Francis Cardinal
McIntyre
February 22, 1966. Los Angeles, California

The Executive Committee has chosen Chief of
Police William Parker to receive the Medallion
of Merit. Ambassador Cremin will present it.
He requests an interview with the Cardinal.
(English 1 pg.) On February 24, 1966, the Cardinal asks for a definite time that will be convenient. (English 1 pg.)

Mc5105. M-1966
Mr. William Morgan to J. Francis Cardinal
McIntyre
February 28, 1966. Salisburg, North Carolina

A congratulatory message on the definite
stand taken against the blatant liberalism in the
Church and a desire to be a Catholic and a
priest. (English 2 pgs.) On March 8, 1966, the
Cardinal requests some background information on Rev. Morris from Msgr. James Mc-
Sweeney in Raleigh, North Carolina. (English
1 pg.)

Mc5106. M-1966
Bp. Timothy Manning to J. Francis Cardinal
McIntyre
March 22, 1966. Los Angeles, California

The promulgation of the Jubilee should an-
nounce that the Cardinal will celebrate Mass at
the 4 corners of the Archdiocese to show the
bond between the Shepherd and the flock. (English 1 pg.)

Mc5107. M-1966
Mrs. Anna Mercer to Msgr. Benjamin Hawkes
June 22, 1966. Redondo Beach, California

Is the St. Labre Indian School an authentic
charity under the auspices of the Church? (English 1 pg.) On June 25, 1966, the information
is given that the Indian School is under the direction of the Franciscan Capuchin Fathers.
(English 1 pg.)

5108. M-1966
Mr. William Mooring to J. Francis Cardinal
McIntyre
September 24, 1966. Hollywood, California

A letter of resignation states that the liberals
are using motion pictures and T V for propaganda. The new order makes reviewing difficult. (English 1 pg.) On September 26, 1966,
the Cardinal asks to keep the pen active in the
cause of better standards. (English 1 pg.)

Mc5109. M-1966
Paul Cardinal Marella to J. Francis Cardinal
McIntyre
September 25, 1966. New York City, New
York

A friendly letter recalls former visits to New
York and the people that made the visits pleasant. (English 1 pg.) On October 3, 1966, the
Cardinal states that he often remembers with
pleasure the early years in New York. (English
1 pg.)

Mc5110. M-1966
Bp. John Morkovsky to J. Francis Cardinal
McIntyre
October 21, 1966. Houston, Texas

The blessing of the library auditorium of St.
Mary's Diocesan Seminary was a special blessing for the entire Diocese. (English 1 pg.) On
October 27, 1966, the Cardinal asks the Bishop
to designate the charity for the stipend enclosed. (English 1 pg.)

Mc5111. M-1966
Arbp. Miguel Miranda to J. Francis Cardinal
McIntyre
October 29, 1966. Mexico City, Mexico

A letter of introduction for Mother Maria Joseph a missionary working in Japan is enclosed.
Her community has houses in Bolivia and Japan. (English 1 pg.)

Mc5112. M-1966
Msgr. James Madden to Msgr. Benjamin
Hawkes
November 16, 1966. Houston, Texas

The details of the retirement benefit for
priests of the Archdiocese are needed. (English 1
pg.) On November 30, 1966, Msgr. states that
Medicare, Blue Cross supplement, Priests' Relief
Society, and their full salary is the usual pack-
age. (English 1 pg.)

Mc5113. N-1966
Mrs. Pauline Newcomer to J. Francis Cardinal
McIntyre
January 29, 1966. Atherton, California

An offer of two glass doors with the coat-of-
arms of four Popes can be bought for $800
each. (English 1 pg.) On February 2, 1966, the
Cardinal states that he does recognize the value
of the doors but cannot use them at the present
time. (English 1 pg.)

Mc5114. N-1966
Rev. Festus Ngige to Msgr. Benjamin Hawkes
April 7, 1966. New York City, New York

Is there a parish or institution that needs a
priest for the month of June? (English 1 pg.) On
April 25, 1966, Msgr. states that St. Paul's Parish would welcome a priest for the month of
June. (English 1 pg.)

Mc5115. O-1966
Mr. Patrick O'Mara to J. Francis Cardinal
McIntyre
March 16, 1966. Glendale, California

An appeal encourages the Cardinal to end
segregation and injustices in housing and employment by an active campaign of sermons and
talks. (English 2 pgs.)

Mc5116. O-1966
Rev. Charles O'Hern to Msgr. Benjamin
Hawkes
April 2, 1966. San Francisco, California

Hospitality in a parish near the airport on
April 17 is needed. (English 1 pg.) On April 4,
1966, Msgr. states that Msgr. McNicholas at St.
Jerome's Parish will be happy to offer hospitality. (English 1 pg.)

Mc5117. O-1966
J. Francis Cardinal McIntyre to Arbp. Egidio
Vagnozzi
April 5, 1966. Los Angeles, California

Mrs. Helene O'Rourke who is blind has an
active apostolate for shut ins. She uses the mail
and radio for contacts. Could the Pope give a
special blessing to shut ins during a Wednesday
blessing or audience? (English 1 pg.)

Mc5118. O-1966
Bp. Quentin Olwell to Bp. Timothy Manning
August 9, 1966. Cotabato, Philippines

The Diocese has no house for the Bishop and
no Chancery Office. All other necessities were
built first. If a donation is possible it will be
gratefully received. (English 1 pg.) On August
16, 1966, the Bishop encloses a donation that
shows interest in the Diocese. (English 1 pg.)

Mc5119. O-1966
Msgr. Raymond O'Flaherty to J. Francis Car-
dinal McIntyre
September 11, 1966. Santa Monica, California

One adverse condition in the Archdiocese is
lack of communication. Many priests do not
feel that they know the Archbishop. Could the
clergy conferences be divided into smaller
groups where discussions could be more infor-
mal? (English 2 pgs.)

Mc5120. O-1966
Dr. Gilbert Oddo to J. Francis Cardinal
McIntyre
December 16, 1966. Guadalupe, Mexico

A request for an opportunity to explain the
ten year development program for higher education in Mexico. (English 1 pg.) On January 6,
1966, the Cardinal states that an appointment
can be made upon arrival in Los Angeles. (English 1 pg.)

Mc5121. P-1966
J. Francis Cardinal McIntyre to Princess Con-
chita Pignatelli
January 6, 1966. Los Angeles, California

Mr. David Brant donated shares of stock of
Title Insurance Company for the Archbishop's
Fund for Charity. He commented that the sug-
gestion came from you. (English 1 pg.)

Mc5122. P-1966
Arbp. Thomas Connolly to J. Francis Cardinal
McIntyre
March 23, 1966. Seattle, Washington

The money from the Pious Fund ought to be
distributed to the Dioceses as mentioned and
then they can donate the money to Montezuma
Seminary. (English 1 pg.)

Mc5123. P-1966
Bp. Timothy Manning to Mr. John McInerny
March 28, 1966. Los Angeles, California

Could the extradition of Mr. William Peters
be postponed until further study can be made
of his case. (English 1 pg.) On April 5, 1966,
the Governor will withhold the order of extradition for a plan to solve the problem. (English
1 pg.)

Mc5124. P-1966
Mr. Donald Perkins to J. Francis Cardinal
McIntyre
April 13, 1966. Inglewood, California

Do all Catholics believe that Mary was con-
ceived and born without original sin? Many
Catholics have never heard of that teaching.
(English 1 pg.) On April 14, 1966 the Cardinal
states that all Catholics do believe in the Immaculate Conception. (English 1 pg.)

Mc5125. P-1966
Arbp. Joseph McGucken to J. Francis Cardinal
McIntyre
May 3, 1966. San Francisco, California

Would it be agreeable for the NCWC to be
given the power of attorney to accept the yearly
payments of the Pious Fund? (English 1 pg.)
On May 5, 1966, the Cardinal asks if the legal
department has all of the facts at hand. (English
1 pg.)

Mc5126. P-1966
Arbp. Joseph McGucken to J. Francis Cardinal
McIntyre
May 6, 1966. San Francisco, California

The State Department is dealing with the
Mexican Government and the NCWC. All of
the Bishops agree that the NCWC should have
the power-of-attorney. The Mexican Government will pay as little as possible. (English
1 pg.)

Mc5127. P-1966
J. Francis Cardinal McIntyre to Arbp. Joseph
McGucken
May 12, 1966. Los Angeles, California

The Bishops' plan is agreeable. Who will rep-
resent the Bishops of California? (English 1 pg.)
On May 16, 1966, the Archbishop states the
Bishops of the Territory include Salt Lake City,
Portland, as well as the Jesuits and the Fran-
ciscians. The Cardinal should represent the
Bishops. (English 1 pg.)

Mc5128. P-1966
Mrs. Clovis Peres to J. Francis Cardinal
McIntyre
May 26, 1966. Camarillo, California

A message of gratitude for the wonderful pastor and parish school at St. Mary Magdalen
Parish is sent to the Chancery Office. (English 1
pg.) On June 1, 1966, the Cardinal states his
happiness at hearing the good things abut the
parish. (English 1 pg.)

Mc5129. P-1966
Mr. Albert Martin to Msgr. Benjamin Hawkes
June 16, 1966. Whittier, California

Rev. Lawrence Purcell will return from Rome
on July 16. An evening Mass is being planned
for some of the relatives in the parish church.
(English 1 pg.)

Mc5130. P-1966
Arbp. Joseph McGucken to J. Francis Cardinal
McIntyre
June 20, 1966. San Francisco, California

The form of the power of attorney given to
the NCWC allows them to collect the payments
from the Mexican Government but does not
allow them to dispose of the money. (English
3 pgs.)

Mc5131. P-1966
Mrs. Morrison Pixley to J. Francis Cardinal
McIntyre
July 9, 1966. Porterville, California

Is the Catholic Church joining the National
Council of the World Council of Churches?
Does the Pope align himself with subversive
groups? (English 1 pg.)

Mc5132. P-1966
Mr. William Price to Arbp. Patrick O'Boyle
August 2, 1966. Harrisburg, Pennsylvania

A resume of the legislature's defeat of the
Planned Parenthood initiative is sent for review.
(English 4 pgs.)

Mc5133. P-1966
Mr. John Duff to Arbp. Joseph McGucken
October 18, 1966. San Francisco, California

The Mexican Government is prepared to settle the Pious Fund in United States dollars
$719,546. They refuse to pay any interest. It
seems that there is no alternative than to accept
the offer. (English 7 pgs.) On October 21, 1966,
the Cardinal states that the offer should be accepted. (English 1 pg.)

Mc5134. P-1966
Bp. Paul Tanner to Arbp. Joseph McGucken
October 28, 1966. Washington, D.C.

The Mexican Government agrees to pay
$719,546 thereby closing the agreement made
in 1902 by the Permanent Court of Arbitration
at the Hague. (English 1 pg.)

Mc5135. Q-1966
Arbp. Egidio Vagnozzi to J. Francis Cardinal
McIntyre
February 5, 1966. Washington, D.C.

The Chinese Ambassador desires the Pontifical Honor of Knight Commander with the Star
of St. Sylvester for Dr. Frank Lee. (English 1
pg.) On February 18, 1966, the Cardinal asks
Rev. Matthew Quinn for an evaluation of the
family. (English 1 pg.)

Mc5136. R-1966
Mrs. Marge Robinson to Bp. Timothy
Manning
January 1, 1966. Costa Mesa, California

A room in our house has an altar and all necessary vessels for Mass. May a Mass be celebrated as a dedication ceremony? (English 1
pg.) On January 12, 1966, Mass may be celebrated on special occasions but the Blessed Sacrament may not be reserved. (English 1 pg.)

Mc5137. R-1966
J. Francis Cardinal McIntyre to Sister Renee,
DC
January 17, 1966. Los Angeles, California

The Blue Cross will not pay the assisting sur-
geon. Could his name be sent to the office as
well as the bill for the hospital services. (English
1 pg.)

Mc5138. R-1966
Msgr. John A. Rawden to All Priests
February 21, 1966. Los Angeles, California

All priests and religious should register at the
Social Security Office for Part A and Part B. On
July 1 the Blue Cross Plan will terminate for
those over 65. (English 1 pg.)

Mc5139. R-1966
J. Francis Cardinal McIntyre to Mrs. E. R.
Rodgers
March 31, 1966. Manhattan Beach, California

Prayerful condolences are sent on the death of
Mr. Edward Rodgers. The generous Mass stipend will be sent to the Missions and Masses
will be offered for him. (English 1 pg.)

Mc5140. R-1966
Bp. Timothy Manning to Rev. Redmond
Roche, SJ
April 11, 1966. Los Angeles, California

Becoming unsettled in the Seminary is one
way that a definite decision can be made. A
check for the seminary is enclosed. (English 1
pg.) On June 9, 1966, Fr. states that decisions
are hard and must be made independently. (English 1 pg.)

Mc5141. R-1966
J. Francis Cardinal McIntyre to Mr. John
Rouen
May 27, 1966. Los Angeles, California

The money market is very confusing at the
present time and New York does not seem to
see any settling factors. (English 1 pg.)

Mc5142. R-1966
Rev. David Rea to J. Francis Cardinal
McIntyre
June 2, 1966. New York City, New York

A request is made for summer employment
for two Seminarians who would like to spend
July and August in Los Angeles. (English 1 pg.)
On June 13, 1966, Msgr. Languille states that
the Seminarians can be employed at a camp or
a settlement house. (English 1 pg.)

Mc5143. R-1966
J. Francis Cardinal McIntyre to Msgr. Daniel
Ryan
June 3, 1966. Los Angeles, California

Mr. Frank Modic will not continue into the
Theology Department at St. John's Seminary.
Perhaps a conference could be arranged. (En-
glish 1 pg.)

Mc5144. R-1966
Rabbi Stuart Rosenberg to J. Francis Cardinal
McIntyre
June 9, 1966. Toronto, Canada

A copy of *Judaism* is enclosed. The Paulist
Press wants a book that can be used in Religion
classes in the high schools. (English 1 pg.)

Mc5145. R-1966
J. Francis Cardinal McIntyre to Mr. John
Rauen
June 29, 1966. Los Angeles, California

The generous donation will be used for a Diocesan project for which there is no revenue.
The check for Don Bosco Technical Institute is
most generous and greatly appreciated. (English
1 pg.)

Mc5146. R-1966
Mr. Joseph Crosby to J. Francis Cardinal
McIntyre
July 9, 1966. Los Angeles, California

An invitation is extended to give the invocation at the United Republican Convention on
August 13. (English 1 pg.) On July 18, 1966,
the Cardinal states that prior commitments will
necessitate Msgr. Osborne giving the invocation. (English 1 pg.)

Mc5147. R-1966
Sister M. Rebecca to Bp. Timothy Manning
July 26, 1966. Los Angeles, California

The excellence of the content and the beautiful dramatic presentation of Job the Man deserves the appreciation of all of the Sisters.
(English 1 pg.)

Mc5148. R-1966
Bp. Victor Reed to J. Francis Cardinal
McIntyre
July 28, 1966. Oklahoma City, Oklahoma

The National Association of Diocesan Support Program will have a convention in Oklahoma City in October. Some priests and laity
would be most welcome. (English 1 pg.)

Mc5149. R-1966
Rev. Francis Richard, MS to Msgr. Benjamin
  Hawkes
September 5, 1966. Colorado Springs,
  Colorado

A request is made for a small country parish
where people are without a priest but not a parish that a young priest would want. (English 1
pg.) On September 27, 1966, Fr. states that
Santa Catalina seems to be too much. There is
another offer of Sunday Mass and that seems to
be more to my ability. (English 1 pg.)

Mc5150. R-1966
Mr. Frank Rivera to J. Francis Cardinal
  McIntyre
October 23, 1966. Los Angeles, California

A friendly letter comments on the great respect in which the Cardinal is held and the need
for voluntary abstinence on Fridays. (English 2
pgs.) On October 27, 1966, the Cardinal states
that the comments are most encouraging. (English 1 pg.)

Mc5151. R-1966
Rev. John Reedy, CSC to J. Francis Cardinal
  McIntyre
October 28, 1966. Notre Dame, Indiana

Ave Maria requests as complete coverage of
the annual Bishops' meeting as the Bishops will
allow. (English 1 pg.) On November 2, 1966,
the Cardinal states that he opposes participation by the press. (English 1 pg.)

Mc5152. R-1966
Rev. John Reedy, CSC to J. Francis Cardinal
  McIntyre
November 8, 1966. Notre Dame, Indiana

When there is disagreement on an issue, it is
hoped that both believe that the other operates
on a philosophical principle. (English 1 pg.)

Mc5153. R-1966
Rev. Victor Roden, CM to Msgr. Benjamin
  Hawkes
November 18, 1966. Tucson, Arizona

Is there an extra medal of the Pope's visit to
the United Nations? A lady with a very short
life span would be most grateful. (English 1 pg.)
On November 25, 1966, Msgr. states that a Papal medal and a picture of the Cardinal are being sent under separate cover. (English 1 pg.)

Mc5154. R-1966
Mr. Thomas T. Rogers to Msgr. Eugene Gilb
November 21, 1966. Newport Beach,
  California

The Los Angeles *Times* and the Pastors of the
Archdiocese are the most important lobbying
potential in the fight against abortion. (English
2 pgs.)

Mc5155. S-1966
Mr. John K. Smith to J. Francis Cardinal
  McIntyre
March 6, 1966. Anaheim, California

As an educated layman, there are many problem areas in the Church's teachings that should
be discussed. (English 2 pgs.) On March 11,
1966, the Cardinal states that he hears the concern. (English 1 pg.)

Mc5156. S-1966
J. Francis Cardinal McIntyre to Francis Cardi-
  nal Spellman
March 30, 1966. Los Angeles, California

The school superintendents will soon be organized as advisors to the Bishops in educational matters. They will then have more
influence than formerly. (English 1 pg.)

Mc5157. S-1966
Bp. Timothy Manning to Rev. Vincent Sheahy
April 20, 1966. Los Angeles, California

Los Angeles does not give the information
that is requested by the Bureau of Census concerning building. It is really voluntary information: (English 1 pg.)

Mc5158. S-1966
J. Francis Cardinal McIntyre to Francis Cardi-
  nal Spellman
May 5, 1966. Los Angeles, California

A friendly letter of congratulations on the
birthday celebration and the anxiety of the possible visitation of the Seminaries by Rome is
discussed. (English 1 pg.)

Mc5159. S-1966
Mr. Walter Bailey to J. Francis Cardinal
  McIntyre
June 17, 1966. New York City, New York

E. R. Squibb Company is a fully integrated
company employing minorities on all levels of
employment of the corporation. The company
has its Affirmative Action Committee. (English
2 pgs.)

Mc5160. S-1966
Mrs. Naomi Sparling to J. Francis Cardinal
McIntyre
June 24, 1966. Sherman Oaks, California

Could a priest be summoned when the police
are called to a homicide? Many people die without a priest because the person cannot request a
priest and no one thinks to call one. (English 1
pg.) On July 5, 1966, the Cardinal states that
the hospitals do receive prompt attention from
the priests. (English 1 pg.)

Mc5161. S-1966
J. Francis Cardinal McIntyre to Mr. Eugene
St. John
August 16, 1966. Los Angeles, California

Prayerful condolences are expressed on the
death of Mrs. St. John and appreciation for the
donation in her name to the Archbishop's Fund
for Charity. (English 1 pg.)

Mc5162. S-1966
J. Francis Cardinal McIntyre to Francis Cardi-
nal Spellman
September 2, 1966. Los Angeles, California

The Knightly Order of St. Brigitte does not
receive any encouragement from the Chancery
Office. Dr. Butkovich is the salesman for the
Order enrolling both Catholics and non-
Catholics. (English 1 pg.)

Mc5163. S-1966
Msgr. Benjamin Hawkes to Msgr. Fred
Schwertz
October 11, 1966. Los Angeles, California

The elderly priests remain in the parishes as
Pastor Emeritus and retain a pastor's salary.
Blue Cross coverage takes care of medical bills
and when they need to be hospitalized the
Brothers of St. John of God are in Los Angeles.
(English 1 pg.)

Mc5164. S-1966
Rev. Concordio Sarte to Bp. Timothy Manning
October 12, 1966. Bula Camarines, Philippines

The church built in 1576 is in complete ruins
and a new building must be erected. Every donation will be used for this purpose. Even ten
dollars would be a most worthy donation for
us. (English 1 pg.) On October 24, 1966, the
bishop sends a donation for the construction of
a new church. (English 1 pg.)

Mc5165. S-1966
Rev. Leonard Scannell to Msgr. Benjamin
Hawkes
October 20, 1966. Hamilton Air Force Base,
California

A request to investigate the possibility of retreat work for high school and college level
groups is made. (English 1 pg.) On November
15, 1966, Msgr. states that he could feel free to
investigate all possibilities, but come to the
Chancery Office soon. (English 1 pg.)

Mc5166. S-1966
Mrs. Mary Shippey to J. Francis Cardinal
McIntyre
November 14, 1966. Los Angeles, California

A request is made to join a novena for the
men and women dying in Viet Nam. If a novena
could be suggested to all parishes, a Christmas
present worthy of their sacrifice could be given
to the military. (English 1 pg.)

Mc5167. S-1966
Bp. William Adrian to Msgr. Benjamin
Hawkes
November 26, 1966. Nashville, Tennessee

Is the printed information about the campaign to overcome obscenity available? (English
1 pg.) On November 29, 1966, Msgr. states
that the initiative was defeated but a strong
mandate was given to the State legislature. A
copy of The Tiding's article and the Cardinal's
letter are enclosed. (English 1 pg.)

Mc5168. S-1966
Bp. Maurice Schexnayder to J. Francis Cardi-
nal McIntyre
November 30, 1966. Lafayette, Louisiana

A letter to the Los Angeles County Bureau of
Adoption would remove a restriction and allow
a family to adopt a child. (English 1 pg.) On
December 10, 1966, Msgr. Johnson states that
if the family can afford it, the woman should
remain at home for a period of time to be acquainted with the child. (English 1 pg.)

Mc5169. S-1966
Miss Terry Sherf to Msgr. Benjamin Hawkes
December 26, 1966. Los Angeles, California

A study of the Mission in Santa Barbara in
color by Mr. James Bettio is a gift to the Vatican. Are there any suggestions for a way that it
can be presented? (English 1 pg.)

Mc5170. S-1966
Msgr. Benjamin Hawkes to Mr. Gilbert Shea
December 30, 1966. Los Angeles, California

The generous donation for a school in East
Los Angeles is most gratefully received. A luncheon can be arranged easily if a definite day
can be determined. (English 1 pg.)

Mc5171. T-1966
Rev. Sylvester Taggart, CM to J. Francis Cardi-
nal McIntyre
January 10, 1966. Jamaica, New York

A complete report concerning St. John's University is being mailed. The faculty appreciates
the concern and prayers. (English 1 pg.)

Mc5172. T-1966
Mrs. Eva Thomas to Msgr. Eugene Gilb
April 20, 1966. Alhambra, California

Advice is needed so the present position will
not be lost and race relations will not ruin everything. (English 1 pg.) On April 25, 1966,
Msgr. states that as the matter is so personal, a
dialogue with the parish priest should be arranged. (English 1 pg.)

Mc5173. T-1966
Mr. Heronims Tichovskis to J. Francis Cardi-
nal McIntyre
August 25, 1966. Storrs, Connecticut

An appeal is made for a scholarship for a
year's study and research. (English 2 pgs.) On
August 30, 1966, the Cardinal states that the
Archdiocesan scholarships are used for high
school students. (English 1 pg.)

Mc5174. T-1966
Rev. Aloysius Trifari to J. Francis Cardinal
McIntyre
September 2, 1966. Birmingham, Alabama

A friendly letter comments on the Cardinal's
80th birthday and the many problems facing the
Church and the work being done in Alabama.
(English 2 pgs.) On September 7, 1966, the
Cardinal expresses his appreciation for the
birthday prayers. (English 1 pg.)

Mc5175. T-1966
Mr. Frank Trager to J. Francis Cardinal
McIntyre
September 22, 1966. New York City,
New York

A copy of the statement concerning American
policy toward Communist China is enclosed.
(English 3 pgs.)

Mc5176. T-1966
Mr. Lawrence Twedell to J. Francis Cardinal
McIntyre
October 25, 1966. Sierra Madre, California

A request to send a young priest to San Sebastian de Garabandal in Spain to become acquainted with some of the difficulties and
dangers facing the world. (English 2 pgs.) On
October 28, 1966, the Cardinal states that the
suggestion will be carefully considered. (English
1 pg.)

Mc5177. T-1966
Mr. Ed. Ainsworth to Los Angeles *Times*
December 4, 1966. Anaheim, California

Mr. Thomas Workman Temple has located
the Baptismal records of the Yorba family in
Barcelona, Spain. His research is preparation
for the 200th anniversary of the founding of
California. Antonio Yorba came to California
two months before Junipero Serra. (English 1
pg.)

Mc5178. T-1966
Bp. Paul Tanner to J. Francis Cardinal
McIntyre
December 7, 1966. Washington, D.C.

A profile of areas of expertise should be sent
to Archbishop Krol so a stronger Episcopal
Committee can be organized. (English 1 pg.) On
December 13, 1966, the Cardinal states that
Chancery Administration seems to be my area
of expertise. (English 1 pg.)

Mc5179. T-1966
Mrs. Margaret Ustick to Msgr. Benjamin
Hawkes
December 13, 1965. Sacramento, California

Information is needed concerning Frances
Tracey so that unclaimed property can be settled. (English 1 pg.) On February 4, 1966,
Msgr. states that a check has been made in the
area that was her former home and no one has
any information. (English 1 pg.)

Mc5180. U-1966
Msgr. Michael Fedorowich to J. Francis Cardi-
nal McIntyre
N.D. Philadelphia, Pennsylvania

An appeal for world support for the Church
of Silence in the Ukraine is made. The Ukrainian Archbishop has been arrested by the KGB
and the history of the Soviet treatment is reviewed. (English 11 pgs.)

Mc5181. V-1966
Arbp. Egidio Vagnozzi to J. Francis Cardinal
    McIntyre
July 2, 1966. Washington, D.C.

A congratulatory message for the dedication
ceremony of the Seminary College in Camarillo
is enclosed. (English 1 pg.)

Mc5182. V-1966
Sr. Cecile van Goetz to Rev. Francoeur, SJ
October 15, 1966. Washington, D.C.

A long discourse on the differences in the
thinking and interpretation of Teilhard de
Chardin's writings is being prepared. (English
4 pgs.)

Mc5183. W-1966
Amleto Cardinal Cicognani to Mr. Roger
    Wagner
March 23, 1966. Vatican City

The Holy Father acknowledges the recordings
of the Roger Wagner Chorale and extends the
Apostolic Blessing upon the members of the
Chorale. (English 1 pg.)

Mc5184. W-1966
Mrs. William Wagner to J. Francis Cardinal
    McIntyre
April 20, 1966. Canoga Park, California

Is it possible to have a televised Mass on Sundays for those who cannot attend Mass on a
regular basis? (English 1 pg.) On April 25,
1966, the Cardinal states that a High mass is
broadcast weekly from Immaculate Conception
on the radio. (English 1 pg.)

Mc5185. W-1966
Miss Fran Williams to J. Francis Cardinal
    McIntyre
June 25, 1966. Queensland, Australia

Please have a member of a young people's
group contact me before departing from Australia. (English 1 pg.) On July 11, 1966, the
Cardinal states that some one from the Stella
Maris House will give all of the necessary information. (English 1 pg.)

Mc5186. W-1966
Rev. Donald Montrose to Mr. Robert Wolf
September 2, 1966. Los Angeles, California

Marriage and sex education belong in the
home with a strong religious foundation. Attend the parent orientation meeting and then
make a prudent decision about the voluntary
student participation. (English 1 pg.)

Mc5187. W-1966
Mr. William Webster to J. Francis Cardinal
    McIntyre
October 3, 1966. San Francisco, California

A request to be directed to some locality
where, as a dedicated layman, the Gospel can
be spread. (English 3 pgs.)

Mc5188. Y-1966
J. Francis Cardinal McIntyre to Bp. Vincent
    Montiz
October 3, 1966. Los Angeles, California

Mrs. Thomas Young Lewis is writing an article about the reported apparitions in Garanban-
dal, Spain. She will abide by any regulations
suggested. (English 1 pg.) On October 13,
1966, the Cardinal states that he has current
news on the apparitions at San Sebastian. (English 1 pg.)

Listing for the Year
1967

Mc5189. A-1967
J. Francis Cardinal McIntyre to Dr. Clarence
Albaugh
January 12, 1967. Los Angeles, California

Your willingness to accept what the insurance
company will pay is most generous. Please accept this supplementary token. (English 1 pg.)

Mc5190. A-1967
Mr. Jack Adams to Msgr. Benjamin Hawkes
January 25, 1967. Santa Barbara, California

A project to assist in communication among
the various groups within the area is being developed. It could be beneficial to the parishes
composed of a large number of Mexican Americans. (English 2 pgs.)

Mc5191. A-1967
J. Francis Cardinal McIntyre to Bp. Sergio
Arceo
April 4, 1967. Los Angeles, California

The plan for the church in Cuernavaca has
$1,000 deposited but still needs $4,000. The
Archdiocese will donate $2,500 to the project
that we assume has the Bishop's approval. (English 1 pg.)

Mc5192. A-1967
Ms. Nellie Ahart to Msgr. Benjamin Hawkes
July 11, 1967. Maywood, California

A section of the Bible needs explanation before the meaning is clear. It is James' Epistle
Chapter 5, verses 15–16. (English 1 pg.) On
August 2, 1967, Rev. Lawrence Shelburne explains the passage and offers to explain any
other passage that gives trouble. (English 1 pg.)

Mc5193. A-1967
Mr. John Aldes, MD to J. Francis Cardinal
McIntyre
July 18, 1967. Los Angeles, California

Receiving the John E. Davis Award is not as
rewarding as being introduced to the Cardinal
and talking with him. It would be an honor to
show you the Rehabilitation Center. (English
1 pg.)

Mc5194. A-1967
Mr. David Rowe to J. Francis Cardinal
McIntyre
September 1, 1967. New York City, New York

On September 25, 170 representatives will
meet in Taipei to form the World Anti Communist League. Your name would add prestige to
the organization. (English 2 pgs.)

Mc5195. B-1967
Bp. Timothy Manning to Hon. Richard Barnes
March 13, 1967. Los Angeles, California

The tribute to Bishop Buddy from the California legislature was a fitting testimonial to a
great man. (English 1 pg.)

Mc5196. B-1967
Mr. John Bender to J. Francis Cardinal
McIntyre
March 26, 1967. Richland, Washington

The saddness of Dad's death was lessened by
the presence of the Cardinal at the funeral
Mass. Our prayers will increase for your intentions. (English 1 pg.) On April 4, 1967, the
Cardinal states that Our Lady will help to heal
the loss of a great man. (English 1 pg.)

Mc5197. B-1967
Mr. William Munnell to J. Francis Cardinal
McIntyre
May 24, 1967. Pasadena, California

A request is made for a letter to be a part of a testimonial book to be presented to Mr. Arthur J. Baum at his Testimonial dinner on June 21. He has done such outstanding work in the Monterey Park area. (English 1 pg.)

Mc5198. B-1967
Mr. J. G. Bell to J. Francis Cardinal McIntyre
June 7, 1967. Cleveland, Ohio

Youth needs advice. A letter of advice contributed to the book, *Here's How by Who's Who*, could give the guidance necessary to some young person. The sale of the book will help the Boys' Club of America. (English 1 pg.)

Mc5199. B-1967
J. Francis Cardinal McIntyre to Mr. J. G. Bell
July 15, 1967. Los Angeles, California

Youth must have respect for authority, have a strong self discipline and be guided by religion to be a whole person. (English 1 pg.)

Mc5200. B-1967
Mr. Bruce Brant to J. Francis Cardinal
McIntyre
July 21, 1967. Los Angeles, California

As a politician who is neither right nor left but a man for the people, the abortion law must be repealed. The force of the Cardinal and Bishops of California can be most useful. (English 4 pgs.)

Mc5201. B-1967
Msgr. James Booth to J. Francis Cardinal
McIntyre
July 31, 1967. San Diego, California

Msgr. Franklin Hurd was killed in an automobile accident in New Jersey. A requiem Mass will be celebrated August 4, at 11:00 a.m. in St. Joseph Cathedral. (English 1 pg.) On August 1, 1967, Bishop Manning states that prayers are being offered for Msgr. and a member of the Archdiocese will attend the Mass.

Mc5202. B-1967
Mr. Joseph Strohsahl to J. Francis Cardinal
McIntyre
August 22, 1967. Upland, California

A request to investigate the circumstances of the first marriage, so a religious ceremony can be performed and receive the blessings of the Church. (English 2 pgs.) On August 29, 1967, the Cardinal sends the letter to Msgr. Booth as Upland is in the San Diego Diocese. (English 1 pg.)

Mc5203. B-1967
Ms. Muriel Bird to J. Francis Cardinal
McIntyre
August 26, 1967. Los Angeles, California

A request to serve on the Founder Fund Committee for the Metropolitan Ballet Company of Los Angeles is made. Both a Spring and Fall season is being planned and it is the goal of the company to be a part of the Music Center. (English 2 pgs.)

Mc5204. B-1967
J. Francis Cardinal McIntyre to Mr. J. J.
Brandlin
September 1, 1967. Los Angeles, California

A property transaction is being offered to the Archdiocese so our charities will benefit and the real estate agents would receive tax benefits. (English 2 pgs.) On September 8, 1967, Mr. Brandlin states that there will be a meeting with the real estate agents. (English 1 pg.)

Mc5205. B-1967
Rev. Louis Bossi to J. Francis Cardinal
McIntyre
September 14, 1967. Los Angeles, California

Archbishop Romolo Carboni will be in Los Angeles from October 5 to 9. An appointment will be arranged with the Chancery Office for a visit. (English 1 pg.) On September 15, 1967, the Cardinal offers hospitality for the Archbishop and an invitation to dinner if the hospitality is not accepted. (English 1 pg.)

Mc5206. B-1967
Rev. Derek Lang, OSM to Bendix Corporation
September 17, 1967. Los Angeles, California

The property owned by Bendix could be donated for a Youth Center and a $900,000 tax certificate be recorded. Public opinion would be favorable and juvenile problems would be lessened. (English 2 pgs.)

Mc5207. B-1967
Mr. Carl Burness to J. Francis Cardinal
McIntyre
September 25, 1967. New York City,
New York

The work of the United States Catholic Conference is more easily understood after the conversation in the Chancery Office. The discussion clarified many issues in the Church. (English 1 pg.)

Mc5208. B-1967
Mr. J. J. Brandlin to J. Francis Cardinal
McIntyre
September 28, 1967. Los Angeles, California

The real estate proposition offered to the Archdiocese is not the type of program that should be entered into. The tax problems that might develop could be a hardship in the long run. (English 3 pgs.)

Mc5209. B-1967
Mr. Joel Bennett to Hon. Ronald Reagan
October 18, 1967. Los Angeles, California

An application is submitted for an appointment to the Superior Court in Los Angeles. (English 3 pgs.) On October 31, 1967, Bishop Manning states that he will be happy to write a recommendation if one is wanted. (English 1 pg.)

Mc5210. B-1967
Mr. James Balduc to Msgr. Benjamin Hawkes
December 2, 1967. Granada Hills, California

A request for the position vacated by Mr. Paul Riley as auditor for Catholic Welfare Bureau is being filed. (English 1 pg.) On December 4, 1967, Msgr. requests Msgr. Johnson to talk to Mr. Riley about the appointment. (English 1 pg.)

Mc5211. B-1967
Hon. E. Richard Barnes to J. Francis Cardinal
McIntyre
December 18, 1967. San Diego, California

The work of Msgr. Achille Lupi who arranged the 260 Popes in chronological order is being sent with the blessing of the Season. (English 1 pg.) On December 26, 1967, the Cardinal states that it is an unusual collection and a real treasure. (English 1 pg.)

Mc5212. B-1967
Miss Susan Butchko to J. Francis Cardinal
McIntyre
N.D. Glendale, California

A request to have Rev. Liam Burn give lectures on leprosy so that more people can be knowledgeable about the disease. A check for $100 is enclosed for the poor. (English 5 pgs.)

Mc5213. C-1967
Mr. Chester Mann to J. Francis Cardinal
McIntyre
January, 1967. Seattle, Washington

A copy of Catholic Concern Over the Council of Churches is enclosed. (English 10 pgs.)

Mc5214. C-1967
Mr. Charles Chapel to J. Francis Cardinal
McIntyre
January 20, 1967. Sacramento, California

A copy of the Assembly Weekly, Legislature Digest, and Legislative Index will be sent weekly while the Legislature is in session. (English 1 pg.) On January 24, 1967, the Cardinal states that he is most happy to receive this material. (English 1 pg.)

Mc5215. C-1967
Mr. Joseph Connelly to J. Francis Cardinal
McIntyre
February 7, 1967. Los Angeles, California

The lecture brought back memories of former friends. This copy of the Rotogravure will refresh memories of your earlier days. (English 1 pg.) On February 16, 1967, the Cardinal states that he cannot keep this issue of the New York Times. It is a treasure. (English 1 pg.)

Mc5216. C-1967
Mr. Daniel Ciernick to J. Francis Cardinal
McIntyre
March 8, 1967. Colma, California

Could Catholic schools abolish tuition and pledge donations to the parish that would be tax free. This would be a saving for the parents. (English 1 pg.) On March 10, 1967, the Cardinal states that he is advocating a bill comparable to the G.I. Bill of Rights for all parents. (English 1 pg.)

Mc5217. C-1967
Miss Donna Courtney to Bp. Timothy
Manning
April 4, 1967. Julian, California

A number of mosaics are available for a Chapel in one of the missions being refurbished. The mosaics are similar to the Chapel of the Roses in Pueblo, Mexico. (English 1 pg.)

Mc5218. C-1967
Ms. Donna Courtney to Bp. Timothy Manning
May 21, 1967. Julian, California

The Elemental Mosaicistry and heirloom embroidery would add beauty to the Churches and teach Bible lessons. Some work with the underprivileged could then be begun. (English 1 pg.)

Mc5219. C-1967
Mrs. James Campilio to J. Francis Cardinal
McIntyre
May 27, 1967. Santa Barbara, California

Could a second collection be taken once a
month for the poor so that begging letters
would stop. No one can give to everything. (English 2 pgs.) On June 5, 1967, Msgr. states that
to a degree this is being done but Los Angeles is
known for charity so the begging letters will
continue. (English 1 pg.)

Mc5220. C-1967
Mr. Robert Chambers to J. Francis Cardinal
McIntyre
July 6, 1967. Pacoima, California

All parochial assistance by the Congress
would stop immediately if the people had their
desires. All church holdings including Yankee
Stadium should be taxed. (English 1 pg.)

Mc5221. C-1967
J. Francis Cardinal McIntyre to Amleto Cardi-
nal Cicognani
July 6, 1967. Los Angeles, California

The mail brings concern over the National
Council of Churches and the proposal that the
laity be consulted in the selection of Cardinal
Ritter's successor. (English 1 pg.)

Mc5222. C-1967
Bp. John A. Choi to Bp. Timothy Manning
N.D. Pusan, Korea

Please accept this table scarf which our
women made as a part of Operation Bootstrap.
This project gives employment to 2,000 otherwise destitute women. (English 1 pg.) On July
26, 1967, the Bishop states that the generous
donation gives added security to the women.
(English 1 pg.)

Mc5223. C-1967
Msgr. Franco Brambilla to Msgr. Benjamin
Hawkes
September 12, 1967. Washington, D.C.

An investigation is requested to determine the
care of Carmela and Serafina Cuzzuch. This
might be an adoption case so care should be
used. (English 1 pg.) On September 19, 1967,
Msgr. states that no one can locate the address
in Santa Barbara, Lompoc, or Solvang parishes.
(English 1 pg.)

Mc5224. C-1967
Dr. Joaquin Saenz Arriaga to Pope Paul VI
October 4, 1967. Mexico City, Mexico

An open letter relating the difficulties being
experienced in the Church in Cuernavaca, Mexico, and requesting some help and solutions.
(English 3 pgs.)

Mc5225. C-1967
Arbp. Romaldo Carboni to J. Francis Cardinal
McIntyre
October 17, 1967. Kansas City, Missouri

A message of gratitude for the hospitality
given during the recent visit in Los Angeles, and
an appreciation for the work being done in the
city. (English 1 pg.)

Mc5226. C-1967
Mr. Charles Collins to J. Francis Cardinal
McIntyre
November 3, 1967. Los Angeles, California

A letter requesting the endorsement of Andrew Collins as a member of the Knights of
Malta. (English 1 pg.) On November 9, 1967,
the Cardinal gives the background of Mr. Andrew Collins. (English 1 pg.)

Mc5227. C-1967
Bp. Giovanni Benelli to Mr. Albert V. Casey
November 7, 1967. Vatican City

Pope Paul appreciated the Masterpiece Edition of the Bible but cannot send a special message for this edition. Many similar requests are
made. (English 1 pg.)

Mc5228. C-1967
Rev. Austin Green, OP to J. Francis Cardinal
McIntyre
November 16, 1967. River Forest, Illinois

A pamphlet explaining *Caritas Christi* is enclosed. Anyone wishing more information can
write. Your prayers are requested for this Institute of religious women. (English 1 pg.)

Mc5229. C-1967
Arbp. William Cousins to J. Francis Cardinal
McIntyre
December 21, 1967. Milwaukee, Wisconsin

An invitation to send priests to the Albert
Cardinal Meyer Institute for continuing pastoral education is extended. (English 1 pg.)

Mc5230. D-1967
Mr. James Delahanty to Msgr. Benjamin
  Hawkes
January 20, 1967. Los Angeles, California

A cover letter is requested before the questionnaire is sent to the Pastors. Later a questionnaire will be sent to the leaders of the
parish organizations. (English 14 pgs.) On January 31, 1967, Msgr. states that not too many
Pastors will answer anything that is too long.
(English 1 pg.)

Mc5231. D-1967
Mr. Joseph Doran to J. Francis Cardinal
  McIntyre
January 25, 1967. New York City, New York

During the past week many files were destroyed. Is there a copy of the letter approving
the purchase of land for St. Elizabeth's Hospital? (English 1 pg.) On January 30, 1967, the
Cardinal states that those files are not in Los
Angeles but the incident is fresh in my memory.
(English 1 pg.)

Mc5232. D-1967
Rev. James O'Reilly to Msgr. Benjamin
  Hawkes
February 5, 1967. Los Angeles, California

The questionable items will be omitted from
Mr. Delahanty's questionnaire. The material is
being gathered for a doctoral thesis. (English
1 pg.)

Mc5233. D-1967
J. Francis Cardinal McIntyre to Arbp. John
  Dearden
March 16, 1967. Los Angeles, California

A study should be undertaken by the Bishops
to show the effects that the newspaper articles
on the Diocesan indebtedness have on the banks
and the people. The large numbers given to the
press fan the flames of tax exempt critics. (English 3 pgs.)

Mc5234. D-1967
Msgr. Charles Diviney to J. Francis Cardinal
  McIntyre
May 25, 1967. Brooklyn, New York

An invitation is extended to the Golden Jubilee of ordination of Archbishop Bryan J. McEntegart on December 8 and the dedication of the
college seminary library in Queens. (English
1 pg.) On June 5, 1967, the Cardinal states that
he will rearrange appointments to attend the Jubilee. (English 1 pg.)

Mc5235. D-1967
J. Francis Cardinal McIntyre to Dr. John
  Doyle, MD
June 19, 1967. Los Angeles, California

We thank Almighty God for fifty years of
your service in the medical profession giving
health and help to many people in Los Angeles.
(English 1 pg.)

Mc5236. D-1967
Mr. John Dunn to Msgr. Benjamin Hawkes
July 29, 1967. Ventura, California

A parish accounting ought to be given to the
congregation yearly. Many suggestions could be
made to reduce costs by supplying other items.
(English 1 pg.) On August 2, 1967, Msgr. states
that each parish submits a report to the Chancery Office and this report can be given to the
parish. (English 1 pg.)

Mc5237. D-1967
J. Francis Cardinal McIntyre to Dr. James
  Doyle
August 22, 1967. Los Angeles, California

There are doctors, lawyers, and public citizens working on the Right to Life issues. Many
will attend the convention. (English 1 pg.)

Mc5238. D-1967
Msgr. Donald Doxie to Msgr. Benjamin
  Hawkes
October 30, 1967. San Diego, California

The pictures of Cardinal Spellman's visit to
San Diego are enclosed. (English 1 pg.) On November 3, 1967, Msgr. states that he appreciated the excellent pictures. (English 1 pg.)

Mc5239. E-1967
Mother M. Eucharia to Bp. Timothy Manning
February 7, 1967. Burlingame, California

Your talk to the Sisters should have been published so everyone could benefit from your message. We are praying that the upset over St.
John's Military School's closing will soon pass.
(English 1 pg.)

Mc5240. E-1967
Ms. Nancy Enloe to J. Francis Cardinal
  McIntyre
February 21, 1967. Pasadena, California

The sacramental requirements for a marriage
must be explained to the family. As Christian
Scientists, we do not understand the Catholic
Church's teaching. (English 1 pg.) On February
24, 1967, the Cardinal states it would be easier
to talk to the family than to write an explanation. (English 1 pg.)

Mc5241. E-1967
J. Francis Cardinal McIntyre to Msgr. Thomas
English
October 3, 1967. Los Angeles, California

The transaction by the Firestone Group is not
suitable for participation by the Archdiocese.
We do not want to be involved in tax transactions. (English 1 pg.)

Mc5242. F-1967
Mr. Max Osslo to Bp. Francis Furey
January 20, 1967. San Diego, California

The committee working on abortion legislation feels each diocese should work independently and contact members of the legislature.
California could be the testing ground for the
nation. (English 3 pgs.)

Mc5243. F-1967
Mr. Donald Baker to J. Francis Cardinal
McIntyre
February 16, 1967. Los Angeles, California

Rev. James Fifield will retire from the Congregational Church. A testimony booklet is being developed and a letter from the Archbishop
of Los Angeles would be appreciated. (English 1
pg.) On February 21, 1967, the Cardinal sends
prayers for a peaceful retirement. (English 1 pg.)

Mc5244. F-1967
Mr. Vincent Flaherty to J. Francis Cardinal
McIntyre
April 8, 1967. Los Angeles, California

An appeal is made to lend the influence of
the Catholic Church to sports leagues and programs to get the youth interested in wholesome
activities. (English 2 pgs.)

Mc5245. F-1967
Mr. H. B. Fitzpatrick to Msgr. Benjamin
Hawkes
June 15, 1967. Los Angeles, California

The generation gap will not exist if the lines
of communication are kept open between parents and children and between pastors, assistants and people. (English 1 pg.)

Mc5246. F-1967
Rev. Charles Findlay, OSB to Bp. Timothy
Manning
July 2, 1967. Elizabeth, New Jersey

Psychological aid is needed for a man in jail
before any type of rehabilitation can begin. Can
the Church help since the State does not provide
this care? (English 2 pgs.) On July 10, 1967, the
Bishop states that every effort will be made to
get the care needed for the man. (English 1 pg.)

Mc5247. F-1967
Mrs. C. M. Fredrickson to Rev. Daniel Lyons,
SJ
July 13, 1967. Gardena, California

Moral Rearmament with the training film,
Mr. Brown, is a devastating piece of brain
washing and not to be recommended. (English
1 pg.) On July 21, 1967, Fr. states that at no
time did he ever recommend or endorse Moral
Rearmament. (English 1 pg.)

Mc5248. F-1967
Mr. Frank Modugno to J. Francis Cardinal
McIntyre
August 14, 1967. San Fernando, California

An invitation to attend the annual Fernando
Award dinner honoring Mr. Joe Flynn on September 21 in North Hollywood is enclosed.
(English 1 pg.) On August 18, 1967, the Cardinal states that a previous commitment will prevent his attendence but Bishop John Ward will
be able to attend. (English 1 pg.)

Mc5249. F-1967
Mr. Leo Fecht to J. Francis Cardinal McIntyre
August 15, 1967. Arleta, California

An appeal for employment as an art teacher
who is knowledgeable about religious art as
well as regular class room art is made. (English
3 pgs.) On August 30, 1967 Fr. Montrose states
that the high schools could not afford to pay a
salary sufficient for Mr. Fecht to rear his family. (English 1 pg.)

5250. F-1967
Msgr. William Johnson to J. Francis Cardinal
McIntyre
September 6, 1967. Los Angeles, California

Mr. Fecht refuses to try commercial art so he
will try other references. There are no openings
for art professors with us. (English 1 pg.)

Mc5251. F-1967
Mr. John Friedrich to J. Francis Cardinal
McIntyre
September 30, 1967. Oxnard, California

Unionize farm workers and then all small
farms will be out of business. Farmers worry
about wet or dry weather, insects, and do not
need labor problems too. (English 2 pgs.)

Mc5252. F-1967
Rev. Aldo Nesi to J. Francis Cardinal McIntyre
November 6, 1967. Florence, Italy

The Church in Florence, Italy, will be ready
to be re-dedicated after the floods. The generosity of the Archdiocese is appreciated. (Italian
1 pg.)

Mc5253. G-1967
Msgr. Eugene Gilb to Msgr. Thomas Grady
January 12, 1967. Los Angeles, California

The enrollment in the League of the National
Shrine of the Immaculate Conception is most
pleasing to the Cardinal. It is a remembrance
for his episcopal anniversary. (English 1 pg.)

Mc5254. G-1967
Mr. Ernest George to J. Francis Cardinal
McIntyre
February 5, 1967. Los Angeles, California

If the doctor will permit, Dr. and Mrs. Kor-
cek will take their daughter to Rome. Everyone
is most grateful for the arrangement of the Papal audience. (English 1 pg.)

Mc5255. G-1967
Msgr. Gerald Hughes to J. Francis Cardinal
McIntyre
February 16, 1967. Dallas, Texas

An invitation to the celebration of Bishop
Thomas Gorman's Golden Jubilee of ordination
and the dedication of Holy Trinity Seminary on
June 13–14 is extended. (English 1 pg.)

Mc5256. G-1967
Dr. R. Schnackenburg to J. Francis Cardinal
McIntyre
February 27, 1967. Warzburg, Germany

Mr. Richard Gardner, a non-Catholic, has
applied to study for a PhD in Catholic Theology with a special interest in New Testament.
He is a student at the Fuller Theological Seminary in Pasadena. He will need a letter of recommendation. (English 2 pgs.)

Mc5257. G-1967
J. Francis Cardinal McIntyre to Mr. Peter
Grace
March 7, 1967. Los Angeles, California

A congratulatory message on being given the
Laetare Medal is enclosed. Both your father and
Cardinal O'Hara are proud. (English 1 pg.) On
March 10, 1967, Mr. Grace states that his first
thoughts were of the same two people men-
tioned by the Cardinal. (English 1 pg.)

Mc5258. G-1967
Mr. Robert Gilmore to J. Francis Cardinal
McIntyre
March 8, 1967. Los Angeles, California

As a registered pharmacist for thirty years, I
would like to apply for the vacant seat on the
State Board of Pharmacy. A letter of recommendation would be appreciated. (English 1 pg.)

Mc5259. G-1967
Bp. Jaroslav Gabro to J. Francis Cardinal
McIntyre
April 12, 1967. Chicago, Illinois

A newly created division of Ukrainian Catho-
lic Press Association will bring news of the
Eastern Church to the people living in the
United States. (English 1 pg.)

Mc5260. G-1967
Mr. Guido Gabrielli to Msgr. Benjamin
Hawkes
April 17, 1967. Hollywood, California

An appeal to open a religious art gallery
where the best art could be displayed and sold
with the profits going to the Archdiocese. (English 1 pg.) On April 19, 1967, Msgr. states
that at the present time this project is not possible. (English 1 pg.)

Mc5261. G-1967
Dr. Padraig Carney to Msgr. Benjamin Hawkes
May 9, 1967. Long Beach, California

The funeral for Dr. Lyle Gray from St. Matthew's Church was an education to the many
non Catholics and a consolation to the Gray
family. (English 1 pg.)

Mc5262. G-1967
Dr. Hiram Gallagher to Mr. Cecil Brown
July 7, 1967. Los Angeles, California

To name Pope Paul VI and the United States
as adversaries to the new State of Israel is
wrong. The United States has sent millions of
dollars and Pope Paul wants the places of pilgrimage of the three great religions held sacred.
(English 2 pgs.)

Mc5263. G-1967
Mr. Andree M. Gonzalez to Msgr. Benjamin
Hawkes
August 22, 1967. Madrid, Spain

Constant prayers are being offered for the
Bishops' Synod so that the modernists will not
prevail. 500 excellent posters will be brought to
Los Angeles. (English 2 pgs.)

Mc5264. G-1967
Mr. Robert Grant to J. Francis Cardinal
McIntyre
December 22, 1967. Los Angeles, California

The medallion designed for the 75th anniversary of the Portland Cement Company is being
presented to those held in high esteem by the
company. (English 1 pg.) On January 16, 1967,
the Cardinal states that the medallion is on the
desk being used as a paper weight. (English
1 pg.)

Mc5265. H-1967
Msgr. Benjamin Hawkes to Mrs. Allan
Hancock
January 9, 1967. Los Angeles, California

The beautiful red roses added to the celebration of the anniversary of the Cardinal's consecration. He is recuperating at home. (English
1 pg.)

Mc5266. H-1967
Mr. Emilio Aldao to J. Francis Cardinal
McIntyre
January 10, 1967. Buenos Aires, Argentina

A request is made to send information on the
building of helicopters. (Spanish 1 pg.) On January 18, 1967, Msgr. Gilb states that since the
Chancery Office does not build helicopters, he
redirected the letter to a company that does this
work. (English 1 pg.)

Mc5267. H-1967
Msgr. Edward Herrmann to Msgr. Benjamin
Hawkes
January 11, 1967. Washington, D.C.

Is the tithing program of the *Sunday Visitor*
successful in Los Angeles? Does the cost match
the overall success? (English 1 pg.) On January
18, 1967, Msgr. states to his best knowledge,
no parish uses the program. (English 2 pgs.)

Mc5268. H-1967
Mrs. Rosario Hall to Msgr. Benjamin Hawkes
February 3, 1967. Walnut Creek, California

The Archdiocese of Los Angeles is the Executor of my Will. This must be changed since I
moved to the San Francisco area. Please send
the copy of the Will to the bank. (English 1 pg.)
On February 8, 1967, Msgr. states that the
Chancery Office has no copy of the Will. (English 1 pg.)

Mc5269. H-1967
Mr. Walter Hoffman to J. Francis Cardinal
McIntyre
February 22, 1967. Ventura, California

The newsletter of the Council of California
Growers gives some interesting points. The
Church must work for those who cannot be
heard but must get the facts straight. (English
2 pgs.) On March 2, 1967, the Cardinal states
that the facts as printed cannot be accurate.
(English 1 pg.)

Mc5270. H-1967
Mr. Robert Harriss to J. Francis Cardinal
McIntyre
March 2, 1967. Forest Hills, New York

The foreign policy of the United States is the
cause of our major problems. Forty years of
mistakes will take time to correct but get
started. (English 4 pgs.)

Mc5271. H-1967
Mr. James Healy to J. Francis Cardinal
McIntyre
March 9, 1967. New York City, New York

A friendly letter comments on the days on
Wall Street and the work with Mr. Herbert
Hoover. A request is made to introduce a
daughter of an old friend to Irene Dunne. (English 2 pgs.)

Mc5272. H-1967
J. Francis Cardinal McIntyre to Msgr. Martin
Guiste
April 6, 1967. Los Angeles, California

A request for a Papal audience for Mr. and
Mrs. Holladay and the special privilege to do
some research work in the Vatican Library.
This is the grandson of Mr. Colis Huntington.
(English 2 pgs.)

Mc5273. H-1967
Rev. L. Hannan to Msgr. Benjamin Hawkes
April 15, 1967. Suva, Fiji

The letter sent by Archbishop Faley apparently did not get delivered. A copy is being sent
for the Cardinal's reply. (English 1 pg.) On
April 21, 1967, the Cardinal states that priests
are being sent to Latin American and the Military, so no priests can be spared for Fiji at this
time. (English 1 pg.)

Mc5274. H-1967
Mr. Arthur Coons to J. Francis Cardinal
McIntyre
June 17, 1967. Newport Beach, California

A letter of protest that a Catholic service can-
not be performed at the Little Church of the
Flowers in Forest Lawn Cemetery. Christians
ought to show some regard for one another.
(English 2 pgs.) On June 21, 1967, Msgr. states
that the usual Catholic procedure of Rosary and
Mass in the parish church was not agreeable.
(English)

Mc5275. H-1967
Ms. Mary Hoedge to Senators of the United
    States
August 21, 1967. San Francisco, California

Care must be taken to support the smaller
nations that look to the United States for support and protection. Each time a small nation
falls, the other countries become more fearful.
(English 2 pgs.)

Mc5276. H-1967
Mr. Walter Hoffman to J. Francis Cardinal
    McIntyre
December 19, 1967. Ventura, California

The death of Cardinal Spellman must bring
great sorrow. Prayers and sympathy are extended but pleasant memories remain. (English
1 pg.) On December 28, 1967, the Cardinal
states that he appreciated the prayers and the
contribution to the seminary. (English 1 pg.)

Mc5277. G-1967
Mrs. Dolores Hope to J. Francis Cardinal
    McIntyre
N.D. Hollywood, California

A message of gratitude for the blessed medals
that were distributed to Bob's troupe. Two men
were certain that the medals brought them
through the Viet Cong territory alive. (English
2 pgs.)

Mc5278. I-1967
J. Francis Cardinal McIntyre to Dr. Rodman
    Irvine
January 12, 1967. Los Angeles, California

The skill and surveillance of the professional
team have made my recovery very swift. Please
accept this token of my appreciation. (English
1 pg.) On January 21, 1967, Dr. states that the
check will be used for surgery for a child that
might otherwise not be able to have surgery.
(English 1 pg.)

Mc5279. I-1967
Mr. Eugene Fontinelli to J. Francis Cardinal
    McIntyre
June 2, 1967. New Rochelle, New York

An invitation to the program on Communica-
tion and Community sponsored by Institute for
Freedom in the Church. A dialogue with other
Bishops will try to discover what is wrong with
communications in the Church and the nation.
(English 1 pg.)

Mc5280. I-1967
Mr. Leo Cherne to J. Francis Cardinal
    McIntyre
June 22, 1967. New York City, New York

An invitation is extended to a dinner sponsored by the Freedom Award honoring General
Sarnoff. President Johnson will be the honorary
chairman. (English 1 pg.) On June 27, 1967,
Msgr. states that the Cardinal is in Rome but
will have the letter on his return. (English 1 pg.)

Mc5281. J-1967
Mr. E. J. Jamison to Columbia Editor
May 4, 1967. Playa del Rey, California

If the Knights of Columbus continue to recommend liberal causes, the parishes should curtail
the use of facilities and special considerations
for membership drives (English 1 pg.)

Mc5282. J-1967
Mr. Frank Rivera to Msgr. Eugene Gilb
July 14, 1967. Los Angeles, California

If the Churches and Shrines in Jerusalem are
protected and treated with respect, then which
ever of God's children that desire can rule the
land. Internationally administered areas are
usually not well administered. (English 1 pg.)

Mc5283. J-1967
Mrs. May Jones to J. Francis Cardinal
    McIntyre
August 3, 1967. Los Angeles, California

Many things can be done to provide wholesome recreation for the young people. The
greatest need is a place that is large enough for
dancing, games, and movies. (English 1 pg.) On
August 7, 1967, the Cardinal asks Mrs. Jones
to contact the CYO and offer assistance. (English 1 pg.)

Mc5284. J-1967
J. Francis Cardinal McIntyre to Miss Eva
    Jennings
September 5, 1967. Los Angeles, California

The beautiful plaque of my coat-of-arms will
find a place in the Archives. (English 1 pg.)

Mc5285. K-1967
Rev. Michael Hanlon to Msgr. Eugene Gilb
January 12, 1967. Los Angeles, California

The speech of Mr. Baldo Kristovich for the
Holy Name Rally is enclosed. The speech will
be repeated on the radio and a 10 minute section is reserved for the Cardinal's remarks. (English 1 pg.)

Mc5286. K-1967
Rev. Joseph Kearney, MM to Bp. Timothy
Manning
January 17, 1967. Cochabamba, Bolivia

A friendly letter commenting on the beginnings of a labor management institute in Ariguipa, Peru, and the priests from Los Angeles studying in the area who supply news of the Archdiocese. (English 2 pgs.) On January 31, 1967, the Bishop states that there is a possibility of a trip to South America for a vacation. (English 1 pg.)

Mc5287. K-1967
Rev. Joseph Kearney, MM to Bp. Timothy
Manning
March 1, 1967. Cochabamba, Bolivia

The move into Peru will be a change of pace into the real work of teaching in Spanish. The position of Illich is one of shock attack. He tries to shock a person into a thinking position. (English 4 pgs.) On March 13, 1967, the Bishop states that the trip is interesting but will have to wait for another year. (English 1 pg.)

Mc5288. K-1967
Bp. Gerald Kennedy to J. Francis Cardinal
McIntyre
April 20, 1967. Los Angeles, California

Is there some method that can be used to assure visitors to Rome that the Pope will have an audience? (English 1 pg.) On April 28, 1967, the Cardinals suggest that a phone call from Paris or another area to Msgr. Zryd would be the best method. (English 1 pg.)

Mc5289. K-1967
J. Francis Cardinal McIntyre to Mr. Ryozo
Kado
June 10, 1967. Los Angeles, California

The twenty years of service in helping to beautify the cemeteries and the other Diocesan areas is very much appreciated. (English 1 pg.)

Mc5290. K-1967
Mr. Kenneth Hahn to J. Francis Cardinal
McIntyre
August 24, 1967. Los Angeles, California

A testimonial letter is being requested that can be bound into the book being prepared for Mr. Hal Kennedy. The letter should be in the office by September 5. (English 1 pg.)

Mc5291. K-1967
Mr. John Kelly to Msgr. Benjamin Hawkes
September 3, 1967. Philadelphia, Pennsylvania

A description of St. Joseph's Train is given. It is a regular train with twelve cars available to go anywhere on tracks to teach Catholic doctrine. Each car is dedicated to a particular aspect of Church doctrine. (English 5 pgs.)

Mc5292. K-1967
Msgr. Benjamin Hawkes to Mr. L. J. Kolitsch
September 11, 1967. Los Angeles, California

Anyone applying for a teaching position on the high school level should apply directly to the school where he wishes to teach. Please contact the Pastor about the CCD teaching position. (English 1 pg.)

Mc5293. K-1967
Mr. Lewis Kribs to J. Francis Cardinal
McIntyre
September 16, 1967. Los Angeles, California

If the clergy changes among the assistant priests were listed in *The Tidings*, the lay people could keep the Diocesan Directory up to date. (English 1 pg.) On September 26, 1967, Msgr. states that it is the policy not to list the changes of the assistants. (English 1 pg.)

Mc5294. L-1967
Mr. Joseph Lichten to J. Francis Cardinal
McIntyre
January 20, 1967. New York City, New York

The copies of the booklet published by the John XXIII Center for instruction of the spirit of Christian-Jewish relations should reach the office soon. They are for parish and school use. (English 1 pg.)

Mc5295. L-1967
Sister M. LaLande to Bp. Timothy Manning
January 27, 1967. Los Angeles, California

The talk given at the Sister Formation meeting was a work of genius. Not to be able to tape the talk, at your request, was a disappointment to the Sisters who could not attend. (English 1 pg.)

Mc5296. L-1967
Mr. Melvin Loventhal to Msgr. Benjamin
Hawkes
February 11, 1967. Studio City, California

How does a parishioner know if his donation goes to the Bishop's Fund or to the parish? All cancelled checks are stamped the same. (English 1 pg.) On February 15, 1967, Msgr. states that the pastor usually deposits the individual checks and mails one check to the Chancery Office. (English 1 pg.)

Mc5297. L-1967
J. Francis Cardinal
  McIntyre to Mrs. Clara Booth Luce
March 1, 1967. Los Angeles, California

Prayerful condolences are extended on the death of Henry Luce. A friendship over many years is not easily forgotten. (English 1 pg.)

Mc5298. L-1967
J. Francis Cardinal McIntyre to Mr. Joseph
  Lespron
March 3, 1967. Los Angeles, California

The forty years of dedicated service to the Archdiocese is appreciated and a special blessing is sent to you. (English 1 pg.)

Mc5299. L-1967
Mr. Robert Leckie to J. Francis Cardinal
  McIntyre
March 8, 1967. Mountain Lake, New Jersey

The *Religion in America Series* next publication will center emphasis from 1941–1966. The most significant movements during these years will be stressed. What do you consider the most important movements? (English 1 pg.) On April 11, 1967, Msgr. states that *The Tidings* would give important movements. (English 1 pg.)

Mc5300. L-1967
J. Francis Cardinal McIntyre to Mr. & Mrs.
  J. Litchfield
April 1, 1967. Los Angeles, California

Pope Paul VI extends his Apostolic Benediction on this special occasion of your wedding. The blessing extends to all members of the family and wedding party. The Cardinal offers heartfelt prayers that a happy life will be yours. (English 1 pg.)

Mc5301. L-1967
Msgr. Benjamin Hawkes to J. Francis Cardinal
  McIntyre
April 10, 1967. Los Angeles, California

The Ambassador to the Vatican from Nationalist China came for a visit. Dr. Frank Lee wants the Office to know that he is now a Commander of St. Sylvester. (English 1 pg.)

Mc5302. L-1967
Mrs. James Logar to J. Francis Cardinal
  McIntyre
April 18, 1967. Granada Hills, California

Is there a Diocesan program that would educate people to spread the Catholic faith in Mexico? (English 1 pg.) On April 28, 1967, the Cardinal states that it would be best to confer with the Pastor or with Msgr. Gerken at the Seminary. (English 1 pg.)

Mc5303. L-1967
Arbp. Egidio Vagnozzi to Msgr. Benjamin
  Hawkes
April 28, 1967. Washington, D.C.

Francesco Lopez is a Cuban refugee attending Cathedral High School and needs financial help in school and a job. (English 1 pg.) On May 12, 1967, a scholarship is arranged and a job will be provided. (English 1 pg.)

Mc5304. L-1967
James Cardinal Lercaro to J. Francis Cardinal
  McIntyre
May 15, 1967. Bologna, Italy

An appeal is made to help the priests living in the small villages and towns. Mass stipends would be most helpful. (English 1 pg.) On June 17, 1967, the Cardinal states that a small token is enclosed and a visit will be made later. (English 1 pg.)

Mc5305. L-1967
Miss Sophie Lofebvre to J. Francis Cardinal
  McIntyre
June 24, 1967. New York City, New York

Some boys from Lafayette, New York, will be in Long Beach on June 30 and would appreciate a visit to the Chancery Office. (English 1 pg.) On July 7, 1967, the Cardinal states that unfortunately he was in Rome while the boys were in California. (English 1 pg.)

Mc5306. L-1967
Msgr. Nicholas Lester to Bp. Timothy
  Manning
July 6, 1967. Ambato, Ecuador

In order to save the younger generation from hunger and misery, a Boys' Town will be opened under the guidance of St. Patrick. Would a speaking engagement be allowed in the Archdiocese? (English 1 pg.)

Mc5307. L-1967
Rev. Willis Egan, SJ to J. Francis Cardinal
  McIntyre
September 1, 1967. Los Angeles, California

The University of Munich requires a letter attesting to the good character and faith of a man before a doctorate in Sacred Theology can be granted. Mr. Gary Lease, a graduate of Loyola University, is ready for this degree. (English 1 pg.)

Mc5308. L-1967
James Cardinal Lercaro to J. Francis Cardinal McIntyre
November 4, 1967. Bologna, Italy

A request to remember Bologna and the poor priests living in small villages and small towns. (English 1 pg.) On November 25, 1967, the Cardinal sends Mass stipends and states that the Propagation of the Faith does the remaining charity. (English 1 pg.)

Mc5309. Mc-1967
J. Francis Cardinal McIntyre to Bp. William McDonald
January 16, 1967. Los Angeles, California

For the many years working in the affairs of The Catholic University and as a member of the Board of Trustees, the reason for my resignation should be read. Some embarrassment to the Board will occur. (English 1 pg.)

Mc5310. Mc-1967
Rev. Martin McManus to J. Francis Cardinal McIntyre
January 31, 1967. San Diego, California

Dean Robert Kingley asked me to give the invocation at his induction as a member of Appeals Board in Los Angeles, Bishop Buddy approves. (English 1 pg.) On February 9, 1967, the Cardinal welcomes Fr. to Los Angeles. (English 1 pg.)

Mc5311. Mc-1967
Bp. William McDonald to J. Francis Cardinal McIntyre
February 6, 1967. Washington, D.C.

The minutes were typed and your letter was omitted. It can be recorded in the minutes of the next meeting. (English 1 pg.) On February 16, 1967, the Cardinal states that the omission is a grave injustice which must be corrected. (English 1 pg.)

Mc5312. Mc-1967
Mr. Joe McCoy to Msgr. Eugene Gilb
March 21, 1967. La Mesa, California

Can a Roman Catholic fulfill Sunday obligation by assisting in a Mass celebrated by a Maronite priest? What about confession? (English 1 pg.) On March 28, 1967, Msgr. states that the Maronite priest has the power to absolve sin and celebrate Mass. (English 1 pg.)

Mc5313. Mc-1967
Msgr. Benjamin Hawkes to Mr. George McDonald
July 13, 1967. Los Angeles, California

The very generous donation will be used for Bishop Mora High School. Matching funds will be given by Textram. (English 1 pg.)

Mc5314. M-1967
Mr. Nick Magallanes to J. Francis Cardinal McIntyre
N.D. Lynwood, California

St. Emydius Parish is growing so large that another parish is needed and maybe even two parishes. (English 1 pg.) On January 4, 1967 the Cardinal states that the suggestion is being referred to the Committee of Diocesan Consultors. (English 1 pg.)

Mc5315. M-1967
J. Francis Cardinal McIntyre to Mrs. Walter Muller
January 17, 1967. Los Angeles, California

The beautiful colored T.V. will allow the household to keep up with the times. My recent eye surgery makes me appreciate your patience. (English 1 pg.)

Mc5316. M-1967
Mr. Ralph Miller to J. Francis Cardinal McIntyre
February 5, 1967. San Diego, California

The land near a Girls' High School, owned by the Diocese, is being sold to Synanon for the treatment of drug addicts. Law enforcement agencies oppose the sale of the land. (English 2 pgs.) On February 7, 1967, the Cardinal states that the jurisdiction is Bishop Furey's but a discussion can be held at any time. (English 1 pg.)

Mc5317. M-1967
Mr. Cy Martinez to Msgr. Benjamin Hawkes
February 15, 1967. Los Angeles, California

A request to work in the Chancery Office and to be close to the people who are important in life. (English 2 pgs.) On February 21, 1967, Msgr. states an appointment can be arranged, if a phone call can be made. (English 1 pg.)

Mc5318. M-1967
Rev. Peter Mullen to Msgr. Benjamin Hawkes
May 22, 1967. Fall River, Massachusetts

Could the expression and experience of preparation in the Diocesan Synod be shared by the study group. (English 1 pg.) On May 31, 1967, Msgr. states that the notes and legislation of the last Diocesan Synod are enclosed. (English 1 pg.)

Mc5319. M-1967
Mr. Sheldon Mills to J. Francis Cardinal
McIntyre
July 11, 1967. Santa Barbara, California

The internationalization of Jerusalem is the
Pope's great ambition. The Bishops should en-
force the Pope's desire and give backbone to the
government. (English 2 pgs.) On July 17, 1967,
the Cardinal states that the complicated Israeli
status has to be studied carefully. (English 1 pg.)

Mc5320. M-1967
Bp. Timothy Manning to Rev. Donald
Montrose
July 15, 1967. Los Angeles, California

A young ordained minister wants to complete
high school in a Catholic school. He is 18 and
wears a Roman collar. (English 1 pg.) On July
18, 1967, Fr. states it would be better for him
to complete high school in an adult evening
school. Usually Catholic schools require two
years in attendence before graduation. (English
1 pg.)

Mc5321. M-1967
J. Francis Cardinal McIntyre to Paul Cardinal
Marella
August 3, 1967. Los Angeles, California

An invitation is extended to visit in Los Angeles after the celebration of the Golden anniversary of Father Flanagan's Boys' Town.
(English 1 pg.) On August 9, 1967, The Cardinal states that time will not permit but a visit to
Los Angeles is something that I would like to
do. (English 1 pg.)

Mc5322. M-1967
Msgr. Benjamin Hawkes to Mr. J. J. Brandlin
August 29, 1967. Los Angeles, California

Mrs. Malaby wishes to have the Archdiocese
sponsor her publication of text books. There
are many loopholes that need to be considered.
(English 1 pg.) On September 8, 1967, Mr.
Brandlin states that the Welfare Exemption
must be considered. There is a difference between the right to publish and the duty. (English
2 pgs.)

Mc5323. M-1967
Rev. Donald Montrose to Mrs. Selma Malaby
October 18, 1967. Los Angeles, California

Some of the data in the books is questioned
by the evaluators and the Archdiocese cannot
sponsor your publications. We are grateful for
your consideration. (English 1 pg.)

Mc5324. M-1967
Mr. Walter Matt to J. Francis Cardinal
McIntyre
October 27, 1967. St. Paul, Minnesota

The *Wanderer* is now in the control of Al. He
bought my shares of the paper and his son will
be the editor. At present, there are no definite
plans. (English 1 pg.) On November 2, 1967,
the Cardinal states that it is good to get the real
story because the newspapers reports were confusing. (English 1 pg.)

Mc5325. M-1967
Mrs. Mary Morrison to J. Francis Cardinal
McIntyre
December 6, 1967. South Gate, California

Is there a reason why no Churches have floats
in the Santa Claus Parade? Could something religious be added. (English 1 pg.) On November
28, 1967, Msgr. states that the parade is pri-
marily commercial and apparently no Church
wants to support it. (English 1 pg.)

Mc5326. M-1967
Bp. John Maguire to J. Francis Cardinal
McIntyre
December 6, 1967. New York City, New York

The entire Archdiocese is grateful for your
presence at Cardinal Spellman's funeral. New
York is happy that for 28 years the Cardinal
was in the city and pray that he will have his
eternal rewards. (English 1 pg.)

Mc5327. M-1967
Paul Cardinal Marella to J. Francis Cardinal
McIntyre
December 1967. Vatican City

Yesterday a Requiem Mass was celebrated in
the Titular Church of St. John and Paul for
Cardinal Spellman. The suddenness of his death
was a shock to everyone. (English 1 pg.) On December 21, 1967, the Cardinal states that
prayers for the Cardinal are continuing. (English 1 pg.)

Mc5328. N-1967
Mr. Don Newcombe to Msgr. Benjamin
Hawkes
June 9, 1967. Los Angeles, California

The contribution to Opportunities Industrial-
ization Center is appreciated since we realize
the needs of the Archdiocese. (English 1 pg.)

Mc5329. N-1967
Msgr. Joachim Nabuco to J. Francis Cardinal
McIntyre
November 6, 1966. Vatican City

A copy of the *Papal Ceremonials* is being sent
as a contribution to renewal of Papal ceremonials. (English 1 pg.) On January 19, 1967, the
Cardinal states that the booklet constitutes an
addition to the reference library in liturgy. (English 1 pg.)

Mc5330. N-1967
Msgr. Benjamin Hawkes to Mr. & Mrs.
Michael Nidorf
December 6, 1967. Los Angeles, California

The Cardinal celebrated Mass for Càrdinal
Spellman. He is most grateful for the generous
contribution to the Archbishop's Fund for
Charity. (English 1 pg.)

Mc5331. O-1967
Mrs. Michael Ortiz to J. Francis Cardinal
McIntyre
January 13, 1967. Pacoima, California

Will the land, owned by the Church on Pierce
and Fenton Streets, be used for a Church in the
reasonable future? (English 1 pg.) On January
24, 1967, Msgr. states that the location is not a
priority since the population is not moving in
that direction. (English 1 pg.)

Mc5332. O-1967
Mrs. Richard Olerich to J. Francis Cardinal
McIntyre
March 14, 1967. Los Angeles, California

Some untrue statements are being circulated
about the work being done on Regis House.
Mr. Olerich wants his name cleared. (English
3 pgs.) On March 21, 1967 Mrs. Olerich states
that the contracts are signed and rumors ended
with the return of Sister Frederica. (English
3 pgs.)

Mc5333. O-1967
Rev. T. Joseph O'Donoghue to Msgr. Benjamin
Hawkes
N.D. Hyattsville, Maryland

Are the seminary facilities and the instructors
used for post ordination programs? (English
1 pg.) On March 22, 1967, Msgr. states that
the facilities are used for Clergy conferences
and vocation meetings. The instructors are
guides for the studies and examination of the
Junior clergy and give professional papers. (English 1 pg.)

Mc5334. O-1967
J. Francis Cardinal McIntyre to Msgr. William
O'Connor
October 3, 1967. Los Angeles, California

An invitation to speak at the Vocation Rally
on November 5 is extended. Experience and
knowledge can be shared with the group. (English 1 pg.) On November 11, 1967, Msgr.
states that the experience in Los Angeles was
most pleasant and will have a place in future
prayers. (English 1 pg.)

Mc5335. O-1967
J. Francis Cardinal McIntyre to Patrick Cardi-
nal O'Boyle
December 26, 1967. Los Angeles, California

The Albert Cardinal Meyer Institute is causing some alarm as it seems to be in competition
to The Catholic University. Is Archbishop Dearden familiar with the project? (English 1 pg.)

Mc5336. P-1967
Ms. Dorothy Parker to J. Francis Cardinal
McIntyre
January 2, 1967. Los Angeles, California

The gospel story of giving to the last employed worker the full day's pay is lived in the
Archdiocese. The beautiful Christmas greeting
and gift was unexpected as I am the last person
hired in the office. (English 1 pg.)

Mc5337. P-1967
Msgr. Benjamin Hawkes to Arbp. Jean Rupp
January 16, 1967. Los Angeles, California

Mr. and Mrs. Gregory Peck are making an
organ available if the Diocese in Monaco has
need of one. If you wish to see it, contact the
attorney of Mr. Peck and then inform us. (English 1 pg.)

Mc5338. P-1967
Rev. John Perusina to Msgr. Benjamin Hawkes
N.D. Houston, Texas

Has a study been made for the best techniques for teaching Religion to the children in
the Catholic schools and the public schools?
(English 1 pg.) On January 25, 1967, Msgr.
states that more definite information is needed
to answer the question. There are 195, 163 children enrolled in CCD and definite methods are
used. (English 1 pg.)

Mc5339. P-1967
J. Francis Cardinal McIntyre to Mrs. Louella
Parsons
February 17, 1967. Los Angeles, California.

The news of your illness has increased our
prayers and be assured of remembrance at the
Altar. (English 1 pg.) On February 27, 1967,
Mr. Neil Rau states that the letter to Louella
was an example of great comfort. (English
1 pg.)

Mc5340. P-1967
Mrs. Anselmo Pozzo to J. Francis Cardinal
McIntyre
March 2, 1967. Los Angeles, California

An invitation is extended to join a small
party honoring Msgr. Henry Gross at 1:00 p.m.
on April 2. (English 1 pg.) On March 7, 1967,
the Cardinal states that the occasion will give
great joy. (English 1 pg.)

Mc5341. P-1967
Rev. Raymond Pelly to J. Francis Cardinal
McIntyre
July 7, 1967. Co. Kildare, Ireland

Could a student from the University of Dublin serve his last year in medical school at one
of the Catholic hospitals in Los Angeles? (English 1 pg.) On July 27, 1967, the Cardinal
asks the young man to write directly to Msgr. Francis Keane, the Director of Health and Hospitals.
(English 1 pg.)

Mc5342. P-1967
J. Francis Cardinal McIntyre to Principe Giulio
Pacelli
September 7, 1967. Los Angeles, California

The magnificent volume, *Il Romanico,* will
be placed in the Doheny Library at St. John's
Seminary in Camarillo. (English 1 pg.)

Mc5343. P-1967
Msgr. Benjamin Hawkes to Mr. Thomas Pike
December 12, 1967. Los Angeles, California

Bishop Manning will be installed in Fresno
on December 15. Mrs. Hoffman can call for an
appointment during the following week. (English 1 pg.)

Mc5344. P-1967
Msgr. Lorenzo Antonetti to Msgr. Benjamin
Hawkes
December 13, 1967. Washington, D.C.

The picture of Pope Paul and the rosary can
be forwarded to Mrs. Amelia Parra unless the
Cardinal has some reason why it should not be
sent. (English 1 pg.)

Mc5345. Q-1967
Mr. D'Arcy Quinn to Bp. Timothy Manning
September 11, 1967. Brawley, California

A request to have the Silver Wedding anniversary Mass in the Cardinal's Chapel as this was
the Chapel used by Archbishop Cantwell for the
wedding. (English 1 pg.) On September 14,
1967, Msgr. states that the Bishop is on vacation and will respond on his return. (English
1 pg.)

Mc5346. Q-1967
Bp. Timothy Manning to Mr. D'Arcy Quinn
October 26, 1967. Los Angeles, California

Until the news of the appointment was released, I could not answer your letter. December
15 is the date of my installation in Fresno. (English 1 pg.)

Mc5347. R-1967
Bp. Timothy Manning to Rev. Redmond
Roche, SJ
February 20, 1967. Los Angeles, California

Enclosed is a donation for the Apostolic
School and a request for prayers. (English 1 pg.)
On March 30, 1967, Fr. states that the Irish
Bishops are studying changes in the seminaries.
The Apostolic College will have to integrate
philosophy and theology and possibly dissolve
the Junior Seminary. (English 3 pgs.)

Mc5348. R-1967
Rev. Gerald Rosecrants to Msgr. Benjamin
Hawkes
March 11, 1967. Tulsa, Oklahoma

A request for faculties for the Archdiocese for
Holy Week and Easter Week with a special request for permission for an evening Mass that
would permit some fishing. (English 1 pg.)

Mc5349. R-1967
Mrs. Celeste Rush to J. Francis Cardinal
McIntyre
May 26, 1967. Los Angeles, California

A lengthy comment is made on the changes in
the Mass and the respect for authority. Comments were unfavorable about the Sisters. (English 3 pgs.)

Mc5350. R-1967
J. Francis Cardinal McIntyre to Mr. & Mrs.
John Rouen
June 12, 1967. Los Angeles, California

The traditional birthday gathering will be
forfeit this year as I will be in Rome for the
Consistory. (English 1 pg.)

Mc5351. R-1967
Rev. John Renehan, CSSR to J. Francis Cardinal McIntyre
July 3, 1967. Suffield, Connecticut

The opportunity to give the priests' retreat was a great experience. The priests were wonderful in their hospitality. The visit to Rome, I trust, was most enjoyable. (English 1 pg.)

Mc5352. R-1967
Mr. Thomas Rogers to Msgr. Benjamin Hawkes
July 5, 1967. Newport Beach, California

The constitution of the National Association of Laymen is enclosed. The Catholic faith is not a requirement for membership. It will be an ultra liberal organization. (English 2 pgs.)

Mc5353. R-1967
Mr. Leonard Ross to J. Francis Cardinal McIntyre
July 6, 1967. Santa Ana, California

Is the Mass valid if the priest says that he is not a Roman Catholic but a Las Vegas Catholic? (English 1 pg.) On July 18, 1967, Msgr. states that the letter was sent to the Chancery office in Reno, Nevada. (English 1 pg.)

Mc5354. R-1967
Ms. Helen Regan to J. Francis Cardinal McIntyre
October 31, 1967. Los Angeles, California

A request to have the Baltimore Catechism returned to all of the classrooms and to have less attention to sex education in the junior high schools and high schools. (English 1 pg.)

Mc5355. R-1967
Mrs. Katherine Ritchey to J. Francis Cardinal McIntyre
November 20, 1967. Los Angeles, California

A friendly letter requesting an interview to recall old times and to talk to someone interested in the "sidewalks of New York". (English 3 pgs.) On November 24, 1967, the Cardinal would like a visit, so please call for an appointment. (English 1 pg.)

Mc5356. S-1967
J. Francis Cardinal McIntyre to Francis Cardinal Spellman
January 5, 1967. Los Angeles, California

Chief Justice Phil Gibson is being considered as a member of the Rosensteel Foundation. He is a man whom I can recommend although he is not a Catholic. (English 1 pg.)

Mc5357. S-1967
Ms. Mary Scott to J. Francis Cardinal McIntyre
January 23, 1967. Los Angeles, California

The prayers of the Mass offered by the laity should give comfort to the young men fighting in Viet Nam. Could some mention be made for this intention during the prayers of the faithful. (English 1 pg.)

Mc5358. S-1967
Msgr. Benjamin Hawkes to Miss Terry Sherf
January 26, 1967. Los Angeles, California

The beautiful picture of the Santa Barbara Mission can be presented to the Pope by the Franciscans in Santa Barbara or from St. Joseph's Parish. (English 1 pg.)

Mc5359. S-1967
Arbp. Egidio Vagnozzi to Msgr. Benjamin Hawkes
February 23, 1967. Washington, D.C.

The Vatican would be happy to receive the colored picture of the Santa Barbara Mission. If it can be sent to the Delegation, it will be shipped to Rome. (English 1 pg.)

Mc5360. S-1967
Mrs. Raymond Strickland to J. Francis Cardinal McIntyre
February 28, 1967. Atlanta, Texas

A request to meet the ship coming from Australia and arrange a hotel for the couple who will go by train to Texas the following day. (English 2 pgs.) On March 4, 1967, Msgr. states that the letter was late and therefore no one could meet the ship. (English 1 pg.)

Mc5361. S-1967
Mrs. Mary Scott to Msgr. Eugene Gilb
March 4, 1967. Los Angeles, California

The intentions of Mass overlooked the men fighting in Viet Nam. Where is the Church leadership in winning the world for Christ? (English 1 pg.)

Mc5362. S-1967
Mr. Stokoe to Bp. Timothy Manning
April 3, 1967. Los Angeles, California

A proposal to receive Holy Communion in back of the altar to give the symbolism of leaving the world for heaven. (English 3 pgs.) On April 5, 1967, the Bishop states that the proposal would not be in harmony with the relationship between the Sacrament and the altar. (English 1 pg.)

Mc5363. S-1967
Mr. John Schmitz to Pope Paul VI
April 22, 1967. San Gabriel, California

There is a need for an Encyclical letter on the
Science of Making a Living for a Family. This
should stress fair taxation and the return of
freedom to the people. (English 1 pg.)

Mc5364. S-1967
Dr. John Stehly, MD to J. Francis Cardinal
McIntyre
May 22, 1967. Fullerton, California

The vigilance of academic freedom in the
Catholic school is appreciated by many. (English
1 pg.) On May 31, 1967, the Cardinal states
that the sentiment is appreciated as is your contribution to the abortion problem. (English
1 pg.)

Mc5365. S-1967
Rev. Patrick Sheridan, CR to Msgr. Benjamin
Hawkes
June 12, 1967. St. Mary's, Kentucky

A request to work for a month during the
summer in a Los Angeles Parish as a change
from seminary work. (English 1 pg.) On June
22, 1967, Msgr. states that if any priest asks for
help, a call will be made. (English 1 pg.)

Mc5366. S-1967
Mr. Richard Moore to J. Francis Cardinal
McIntyre
July 20, 1967. Los Angeles, California

An invitation to meet Justice Potter Stewart
and a few friends at the California Club on July
26 at 4:30. (English 1 pg.) On July 22, 1967,
the Cardinal states that it will be a pleasure to
meet Justice Stewart. (English 1 pg.)

Mc5367. S-1967
Mr. Gordon Smedley to Msgr. Eugene Gilb
August 25, 1967. Dallas, Texas

A request for an appointment with the Cardinal to inform him of the retirement facility that
is being planned for San Diego and to ask his
blessing on the project. (English 1 pg.) On September 1, 1967, the Cardinal asks the gentle-
men to contact Bishop Furey of San Diego for
the project. (English 1 pg.)

Mc5368. S-1967
Francis Cardinal Spellman to Bp. Francis Furey
August 31, 1967. New York City, New York

The invitation to be a guest at the home of
Sir Daniel Donohue and the Countess is very
kind. The Military and the Chancery can work
out details. (English 1 pg.)

Mc5369. S-1967
Mr. Preston Hotchkis to J. Francis Cardinal
McIntyre
September 7, 1967. Los Angeles, California

An invitation is extended to the dinner honoring His Excellency Giuseppe Saragat, president of the Republic of Italy on September 20 at
7:30 p.m. (English 1 pg.) On September 8,
1967, the Cardinal states that it will be a privilege to be present. (English 1 pg.)

Mc5370. S-1967
Sir Daniel Donohue to J. Francis Cardinal
McIntyre
September 30, 1967. Los Angeles, California

It would be easy for the Cardinal to go from
La Jolla to San Diego to the meeting. If time
permits for the Cardinal to remain in LaJolla,
please plan to join him. (English 2 pgs.)

Mc5371. S-1967
Msgr. Patrick Skehan to J. Francis Cardinal
McIntyre
October 3, 1967. Washington, D.C.

A lecture will be given at Occidental College
on the manner of transmission of the Old Testament books from 200 B.C. to 100 A.D. in He-
brew and Greek. (English 1 pg.) On October 9,
1967, the Cardinal states that it is a pleasure to
welcome a Scripture scholar to Occidental. (English 1 pg.)

Mc5372. S-1967
Bp. Francis Furey to Msgr. James F. Rigney
October 4, 1967. San Diego, California

Cardinal Spellman will be met and taken to
the Hotel where the ceremonies of the Military
Order is being held. Captain Robert Anderson
is aware of the plans. (English 1 pg.)

Mc5373. S-1967
Miss Bula Swartz to J. Francis Cardinal
McIntyre
November 6, 1967. Tulsa, Oklahoma

Who is responsible for the breakdown of the
Catholic press? Is it still Catholic when the
Diocesan newspaper distorts encyclicals and encourages active and passive disobedience? (English 2 pgs.)

Mc5374. S-1967
Miss Catherine Sullivan to J. Francis Cardinal
McIntyre
November 22, 1967. Los Angeles, California

Why is the traditional wedding march not allowed in Los Angeles? Generations of Catholics
walked down the aisle to this march. (English
1 pg.)

Mc5375. S-1967
J. Francis Cardinal McIntyre to Mr. & Mrs.
W. L. Scully
November 27, 1967. Los Angeles, California

The ordination of a son is a great moment in
any family and one that will be long held in
memory. (English 1 pg.)

Mc5376. S-1967
Msgr. Kenneth Stack to Bp. Timothy Manning
December 19, 1967. San Diego, California

The classic beauty of the installation talk was
a masterpiece worthy of the Newman of the
American clergy. Would a copy of the talk be
available? (English 1 pg.)

Mc5377. S-1967
Mrs. Thomas Sartor to J. Francis Cardinal
McIntyre
N.D. Norwalk, Connecticut

The new Parish Advisory Board is being
formed and I am the Ecumenical Chairman.
Please send any articles that will help this committee. (English 2 pgs.)

Mc5378. S-1967
Miss Barbara Silva to Rev. Douglas Saunders
N.D. La Puente, California

The Catholics preach concern for the underprivileged but do very little to supply teachers
for the handicapped. This material can be distributed where it will do the greatest good. (English 2 pgs.)

Mc5379. S-1967
Mr. Robert Stokoe to J. Francis Cardinal
McIntyre
N.D. Los Angeles, California

Suggestions that could improve participation
in the church are enclosed. One would be an
8:00 p.m. Mass so more people could assist at
Mass and provide the opportunity for people to
practice on an organ so that there could be an
ample supply of organists for congregational
singing. (English 1 pg.)

Mc5380. T-1967
Ms. Mary Toman to J. Francis Cardinal
McIntyre
January 3, 1967. Ontario, California

A request for an interview so that a priest can
be assigned as executor of the Will. (English
1 pg.) On January 9, 1967, Msgr. states that a
telephone call after February, will arrange an
interview. (English 1 pg.)

Mc5381. T-1967
Mrs. Michael Tobin to J. Francis Cardinal
McIntyre
N.D. Pittsburgh, Pennsylvania

There will be a new Rev. Edward Tobin in
the Fall of 1967. Please pray for him. (English
1 pg.) On February 6, 1967, the Cardinal states
there are many happy memories of Fr. Edward
and prayers will be offered for the young Fr.
Edward. (English 1 pg.)

Mc5382. T-1967
Rev. Michael Torsy to Bp. Timothy Manning
N.D. Tehuacan, Mexico

An appeal to correct the manuscript and then
present it to Fox Studio. The money that will
come will be used to complete the Seminary.
(English 3 pgs.) On April 14, 1967, the Bishop
states that this material would not be used in
any studio. (English 1 pg.)

Mc5383. T-1967
Mrs. Ray Terwilliger to J. Francis Cardinal
McIntyre
April 22, 1967. New York City, New York

Is there some means to check on Captain
Walter Perkins in Oxnard? He wants to work on
some activities against the new breed liberals.
(English 5 pgs.) On April 29, 1967, Msgr. states
that the Captain is active in church organizations and a Knight of Columbus. (English 1 pg.)

Mc5384. T-1967
Arbp. T. J. Toolen to J. Francis Cardinal
McIntyre
August 28, 1967. Mobile, Alabama

An invitation is extended to the anniversary
celebration on October 25. Distances are no
longer great by plane. (English 1 pg.) On September 1, 1967, the Cardinal states that October 25 is on the calendar for a special
celebration. (English 1 pg.)

Mc5385. U-1967
Mr. Edward Roberts to J. Francis Cardinal
McIntyre
May 8, 1967. Akron, Ohio

The National Investigating Committee of
Aerial Phenomenon lists your name. Would you
comment on the UFO phenomenon? (English
2 pgs.)

Mc5386. U-1967
Msgr. Benjamin Hawkes to Mr. Herbert Harry
June 7, 1967. Los Angeles, California

The latest edition of the 76 *Bonanza* allows
us to learn more about Union Oil. It will be
helpful to solve the problems at the Murphy
drillsite. (English 1 pg.)

Mc5387. V-1967
Mr. William Fitzpatrick to Msgr. Benjamin
Hawkes
January 4, 1967. New Brunswick, New Jersey

Dietrich von Hildebrand will be in Los Angeles from January 28 to February 2. If a lecture
would be possible, the biographical and advertising material will be sent. (English 1 pg.)

Mc5388. V-1967
J. Francis Cardinal McIntyre to Mr. & Mrs.
C. Von der Ahe
January 21, 1967. Los Angeles, California

Pope Paul VI bestows his Apostolic Benedica-
tion on your 60th Anniversary. His blessing is
extended to the members of the family. Personal
congratulations and blessings are added. (English 1 pg.)

Mc5389. V-1967
Arbp. Egidio Vagnozzi to Bp. Timothy
Manning
February 8, 1967. Washington, D.C.

Pope Paul VI is sending four volumes: *Im-
magini del Concil io Vaticano II* and *La Teolo-
gia delle Indulgenza SS Oecumenicum
Concilium Vaticanum II* (English 1 pg.) On
February 27, 1967, the Bishop states that it
will be an honor to receive the books. (English
1 pg.)

Mc5390. V-1967
Mr. & Mrs. C. Von der Ahe to J. Francis Car-
dinal McIntyre
February 28, 1967 Los Angeles, California

The Mass of Thanksgiving was beautiful and
the enclosed donation is for one of the Archdiocesan charities. (English 1 pg.) On March 2,
1967, the Cardinal states that the donation will
be used for the Archbishop's Fund for Charity.
(English 1 pg.)

Mc5391. V-1967
Msgr. Benjamin Hawkes to Mr. John Van de
Kamp
March 1, 1967. Los Angeles, California

The article, *Thoughts on Lent*, was excellent
and deserves congratulations. (English 1 pg.)

Mc5392. V-1967
Rev. Terence VanOrshoven to Msgr. Benjamin
Hawkes
March 3, 1967. San Diego, California

Three priests request permission to be in the
procession and be present for the ordinations by
Bishop Bloy on March 11. (English 1 pg.) On
March 5, 1967, Msgr. states if the Bishop of
San Diego grants the permission, Los Angeles
will agree. (English 1 pg.)

Mc5393. V-1967
Mr. Paul Vaughter to J. Francis Cardinal
McIntyre
April 4, 1967. Westminster, California

The changes in the Church since Vatican II
do not have to drive the faithful into one camp
or another. There is a way to meet change and
accept them. (English 1 pg.)

Mc5394. V-1967
Mrs. Carol Veith to J. Francis Cardinal
McIntyre
May 10, 1967. Hamilton, Illinois

The problems faced in the Archdiocese evoke
prayers from one to whom you administered the
Sacrament of Confirmation years ago. (English
2 pgs.) On May 18, 1967, the Cardinal states
that it is gratifying that the Holy Spirit continues to strengthen and encourage prayer. (English
1 pg.)

Mc5395. V-1967
Mr. Edward Valentine to J. Francis Cardinal
McIntyre
June 12, 1967. Santa Barbara, California

The Valentine Foundation encloses a check
for the Propagation of the Faith. (English 1 pg.)
On June 20, 1967, the Cardinal states that the
generous donation is greatly appreciated and
prayers are being offered for Mr. Valentine's return to health. (English 1 pg.)

Mc5396. V-1967
Hon. Peter Velez de Silva to J. Francis Cardi-
nal McIntyre
June 21, 1967. Hollywood, California

An invitation is extended to visit Guatemala
and other Central American countries. (English
1 pg.) On June 26, 1967, Msgr. states that the
invitation will be given to the Cardinal when he
returns from Rome. (English 1 pg.)

Mc5397. V-1967
Dr. Rafael Villareal to J. Francis Cardinal
McIntyre
July 17, 1967. Los Angeles, California

The *Academia Santa Maria de Guadalupe* of
Our Lady of Lourdes Parish requests enrollment
in the Basilica of Guadalupe to receive the blessings and considerations given to the members.
(English 1 pg.)

Mc5398. V-1967
Msgr. Benjamin Hawkes to J. Francis Cardinal
McIntyre
July 19, 1967. Los Angeles, California

A letter of recommendation is requested for
Anthony Valle to join the Western Association
of the United States Knights of Malta. Patrick
Frawley would like to be associated with the
Eastern branch. (English 1 pg.)

Mc5399. V-1967
Mrs. Hope Schechter to J. Francis Cardinal
McIntyre
N.D. Los Angeles, California

An invitation to a party honoring Mr. Jack
H. Vaughn, the director of the Peace Corps on
September 9 from 4:00–7:00 p.m. is enclosed.
(English 1 pg.) On August 23, 1967. Msgr.
states that the Cardinal will be departing for
Europe on that date. (English 1 pg.)

Mc5400. V-1967.
Egidio Cardinal Vagnozzi to J. Francis Cardi-
nal McIntyre
December 8, 1967. Rome, Italy

The Christmas season in Rome will be different from the happy Christmas seasons in the
United States. My prayer is for a stronger
Church in the United States. (English 1 pg.) On
December 21, 1967, the Cardinal states the
present Delegate has created two new Dioceses
and consecrated a Bishop. (English 1 pg.)

Mc5401. W-1967
Rev. Richard Cotter to Msgr. Benjamin
Hawkes
March 12, 1967. Pacific Palisades, California

The Pacific Palisades Community Forum
wants to invite Bishop Sheen to speak but before the invitation is sent, Mr. Waddington
would like to speak to you. (English 1 pg.)

Mc5402. W-1967
Mr. Raymond Whalley to J. Francis Cardinal
McIntyre
April 11, 1967. Los Angeles, California

A consideration of our firm to build the
church in Mission Viejo would be appreciated.
(English 1 pg.) On April 11 and 12, 1967, letters of recommendation are sent by Msgr. John
K. Clarke and Msgr. Thomas McNicholas. (English 2 pgs.)

Mc5403. W-1967
Mr. Ronald Weekes to J. Francis Cardinal
McIntyre
N.D. Seattle, Washington

What would be the best method to obtain the
signature of Pope Paul VI for the collection of
ecclesiastic memorabilia? (English 1 pg.) On
May 3, 1967, the Cardinal states to send a card
with an appropriate symbol with room for a
signature to Cardinal Secretariate and it will be
signed. (English 1 pg.)

Mc5404. W-1967
Mr. Jim Woeber to Msgr. Benjamin Hawkes
June 12, 1967. Irving, Texas

A sample picture of the Sacred Heart is enclosed which can be used for Enthronement of
the Sacred Heart. If it meets with approval,
copies can be made. (English 1 pg.) On June 22,
1967, Msgr. states that all necessary approvals
are given and a special blessing for the Enthronement work is given. (English 1 pg.)

Mc5405. W-1967
Mr. Hiley Ward to J. Francis Cardinal
McIntyre
June 15, 1967. Royal Oaks, Michigan

Please contribute an example of ecumenical
humor that can be published in a new book and
can give some new stories to tell. (English 1 pg.)
On June 30, 1967, Msgr. states that the request
will be brought to the attention of the Cardinal
on his return from Rome. (English 1 pg.)

Mc5406. W-1967
Mr. Kenneth Wells to J. Francis Cardinal
McIntyre
August 11, 1967. Valley Forge, Pennsylvania

A request to write your definition of freedom
which will be included with the fifty top citizens of the United States in a new book that
will be published. (English 1 pg.)

Mc5407. W-1967
J. Francis Cardinal McIntyre to Mr. Martin
Work
August 23, 1967. Los Angeles, California

To pressure laymen to join the National Association of Pastoral Renewal should have the
Chancery Office knowledge and approval. (English 1 pg.) On September 1, 1967, Mr. Work
states he has no connection with the National
Association nor does the NCCM. (English 1
pg.)

Mc5408. W-1967
Msgr. Benjamin Hawkes to Bp. Francis Furey
September 18, 1967. Los Angeles, California

Rev. Donald Weber can live at St. Mark's Parish while he attends Loyola. Fr. Hynes knows that Fr. will not be available for Masses on Sunday. (English 1 pg.)

Mc5409. W-1967
J. Francis Cardinal McIntyre to Mrs. Vera
  Wardell
December 5, 1967. Los Angeles, California

Prayers were offered during your son's illness and now prayers for his happiness in heaven will be said. (English 1 pg.)

Mc5410. Z-1967
Mr. & Mrs. D. Zingleman to J. Francis Cardinal McIntyre
February 18, 1967. San Gabriel, California

Loyalty and admiration are expressed for the Cardinal and his position on respect for authority. (English 2 pgs.) On February 21, 1967, the Cardinal states that he is most grateful for the sentiments of respect. (English 1 pg.)

Mc5411. Z-1967 Msgr. Robert Brennan to
  Msgr. Benjamin Hawkes
September 6, 1967. Altadena, California

Rev. Silvio Zanoni will be in the Archdiocese for the remainder of the year doing missionary work. His faculties will have to be extended. (English 1 pg.)

Mc5412. Z-1967
Mr. Isidor Zwirn to Msgr. Benjamin Hawkes
N.D. Los Angeles, California

Bishop Pike is getting the limelight on his God is Dead campaign. Does Father Curran hold the same ideas? Where are the members of the opposition? (English 2 pgs.)

Listing for the Year
1968

Mc5413. A-1968
Msgr. Benjamin Hawkes to Mr. Edward Allen
June 12, 1968. Los Angeles, California

This strange card was received by the Cardinal. In an official position, it might be good to check it out. (English 1 pg.) On June 13, 1968, Mr. Allen states that the card denotes mental illness and will be investigated. (English 1 pg.)

Mc5414. A-1968
J. Francis Cardinal McIntyre to Mrs. Edward
 Anspach
July 1, 1968. Los Angeles, California

Finding another person born on the same day and in the same year is an interesting experience. Send greetings and my blessing to your husband. (English 1 pg.)

Mc5415. A-1968
Mr. Donald Avery to Msgr. Benjamin Hawkes
September 7, 1968. Santa Monica, California

Before visiting an Arab country, one must have a Church document to prove non Jewish background. A letter would suffice. (English 1 pg.) On September 17, 1968, Msgr. asks Msgr. O'Flaherty to write the letter. (English 1 pg.)

Mc5416. B-1968
Msgr. William Johnson to J. Francis Cardinal
 McIntyre
February 8, 1968. Los Angeles, California

Mr. Wesley Brazier is retiring and the dinner being given for him is given by the Urban League. He is an excellent person doing good for others. (English 1 pg.) On February 9, 1968, the Cardinal asks Msgr. to represent the Archdiocese. (English 1 pg.)

Mc5417. B-1968
Mr. Benedict Bieschke to Msgr. Lawrence
 Gibson
February 14, 1968. Lawndale, California

Is there anything that the Catholic Church can do to be represented on the Deity Board with the other Churches? (English 1 pg.) On February 19, 1968, Msgr. suggests contacting the pastor at St. Catherine's Laboure Parish. (English 1 pg.)

Mc5418. B-1968
Mr. John Boser to J. Francis Cardinal
 McIntyre
March 11, 1968. Bismarck, North Dakota

A request to know the laws of the Church on divorce and membership in the Church. (English 1 pg.) On March 15, 1968, Msgr. states that it would be better to talk to a priest than to try to answer the letter. (English 1 pg).

Mc5419. B-1968
Mrs. Ruth Burson to J. Francis Cardinal
 McIntyre
March 14, 1968. Alhambra, California

A friendly letter relates admiration and respect for the work of the Cardinal. (English 1 pg.) On March 21, 1968, the Cardinal states that he sends special blessings to the family. (English 1 pg).

Mc5420. B-1968
Mr. J. J. Brandlin to KFWB Studios
April 10, 1968. Los Angeles, California

As the attorney for the Archdiocese of Los Angeles, please supply the office with all references made to the Cardinal in your news broadcast on Monday. (English 1 pg.)

Mc5421. B-1968
Msgr. Lawrence Gibson to Mr. Jerry Bellamy
April 15, 1968. Los Angeles, California

It is necessary for you to realize that Cardinal
Antoniutti was created Cardinal by Pope John
XXIII and Pope Paul made him Cardinal Pre-
fect of Religious. (English 1 pg.)

Mc5422. B-1968
Mr. Jack Bean to J. Francis Cardinal McIntyre
April 16, 1968. Beverly Hills, California

Catholics everywhere should be proud of the
statement made from the Chancery Office on
the death of Martin Luther King Jr. (English
1 pg.)

Mc5423. B-1968
Mrs. Ed. Bruner to J. Francis Cardinal
McIntyre
May 6, 1968. Whitewater, California

A friendly letter comments on the confusion
in the world and submitting a poem that can be
used in whatever manner needed. (English 3
pgs.) On May 13, 1968, The Cardinal states
that peace will come again and calm will be restored. (English 1 pg.)

Mc5424. B-1968
Mr. J. J. Brandlin to J. Francis Cardinal
McIntyre
July 16, 1968. Los Angeles, California

A request is made for a letter of recommendation for Mr. Richard Buckley who is applying
for the appointment of Judge of the Superior
Court in Los Angeles County. (English 4 pgs.)

Mc5425. B-1968
Dr. Leo Bauer to J. Francis Cardinal McIntyre
August 19, 1968. New York City, New York

The materials made by the refugees from areas behind the Iron Curtain can be shown and
orders taken. Letters of recommendation are enclosed. (English 9 pgs.) On August 23, 1968,
Fr. states that the parishes are well supplied
from other religious groups. (English 1 pg.)

Mc5426. B-1968
Miss Hazel Bremm to J. Francis Cardinal
McIntyre
N.D. Los Angeles, California

An author's copy of the latest book should
bring some relaxation and pleasure. (English
1 pg.) On August 21, 1968, Msgr. states that
the Cardinal will enjoy the book when he returns. (English 1 pg.)

Mc5427. B-1968
Bp. Joseph Bernardin to J. Francis Cardinal
McIntyre
September 10, 1968. Washington, D.C.

The annual meeting of the Bishops will be
held November 11–15 with the Administrative
Committee meeting on November 9. The Extension Society Meeting will be in Houston, Texas,
in April 1969. (English 1 pg.)

Mc5428. B-1968
Dr. Jur. Bastian to J. Francis Cardinal
McIntyre
September 17, 1968. Munich, Germany

An invitation to subscribe to the Memorial
suggested at the Vatican Council which should
reduce prejudice against any nation or race.
(English 2 pgs.) On September 27, 1968, the
Cardinal states the project will be in progress
for some time and Los Angeles should be consulted later. (English 1 pg.)

Mc5429. B-1968
Mrs. Marion Barnwell to J. Francis Cardinal
McIntyre
September 17, 1968. El Segundo, California

A request is made for the Cardinal to celebrate Mass for the LOTS members. Special considerations should be given to vocations.
(English 2 pgs.) On September 23, 1968, the
Cardinal states that the Mass will be celebrated
and the generous donation will be sent to the
Propagation of the Faith. (English 1 pg.)

Mc5430. B-1968
Mrs. Thelma Byrd to J. Francis Cardinal
McIntyre
October 16, 1968. Burbank, California

A request to write a statement for publication
about President John Kennedy and Robert
Kennedy is made. A collection of items concerning their lives is growing. An autographed
picture would add to the collection. (English
2 pgs.)

Mc5431. B-1968
Mrs. Lee Bolman to J. Francis Cardinal
McIntyre
October 26, 1968. Long Beach, California

The revision of the California Constitution
could sound the end of power in the hands of
the people, increased taxation, and anathema to
all Christians. (English 1 pg.) On October 28,
1968, Rev. James Lynch states that Mrs. Bolman wants a stand to be taken against Prop. I.
(English 1 pg.)

Mc5432. B-1968
Mr. David Brant to J. Francis Cardinal
McIntyre
November 23, 1968. Beverly Hills, California

The yearly contribution will continue to be
sent to the Children's Christmas Party as sug
gested by Princess Pignatelli. If there are any
questions contact Freeman Brant. (English
1 pg.)

Mc5433. B-1968
Rev. A. Bugnini CM to J. Francis Cardinal
McIntyre
November 26, 1968. Vatican City

It is necessary to select a Pontifical Master of
Ceremonies for any function. Select from the
list by December 15. (Italian 1 pg.) On December 10, 1968, the Cardinal states it will be better for the office to select a Master of
Ceremonies. (English 1 pg.)

Mc5434. B-1968
Mr. David Berman to J. Francis Cardinal
McIntyre
November 29, 1968. Hollywood, California

The kind reception of the members of the
company merits a donation to St. Anne's Maternity Hospital and the City of Hope in the
Cardinal's name. (English 1 pg.)

Mc5435. B-1968
J. Francis Cardinal McIntyre to Mrs. Thomas
Bannon
December 16, 1968. Los Angeles, California

The meeting with the President elect and the
others was an opportunity for a delightful exchange of opinions. (English 1 pg.)

Mc5436. B-1968
Miss Marjorie Baker to Msgr. Benjamin
Hawkes
N.D. Garden Grove, California

The Inter Faith Crisis Seminar developed into
an action committee for painting houses and
cutting down weeds. Love speaks louder than
words. (English 2 pgs.)

Mc5437. C-1968
Mr. Hernando Courtright to J. Francis Cardi-
nal McIntyre
January 15, 1968. Los Angeles, California

An invitation to be one of the founding fathers of Los Amigos del Pueblo to encourage
knowledge of the Spanish Mexican heritage of
California. (English 1 pg.) On January 18,
1968, the Cardinal states that he is happy to
unite with such distinguished citizens. (English
1 pg.)

Mc5438 C-1968
J. Francis Cardinal McIntyre to Mrs. C. E.
Connors
January 23, 1968. Los Angeles, California

There are several speakers bureaus depending
on the subject matter requested. The Holy
Name Society and the Archdiocesan Council of
Catholic Women can be contacted. (English
1 pg.)

Mc5439. C-1968
Mr. Arthur Conrad to J. Francis Cardinal
McIntyre
February 8, 1968. Bensenville, Illinois

The graciousness shown during the visit to
the Chancery Office is appreciated. Msgr. Russell discussed the Two Worlds Program with us
at length. (English 1 pg.)

Mc5440. C-1968
Mrs. Peter Caropino to J. Francis Cardinal
McIntyre
March 11, 1968. Alhambra, California

A nine year old girl wanted a special gift for
the Cardinal when he visited the parish but Father forgot to give the gift. (English 1 pg.) On
April 2, 1968, the Cardinal states that the "loving cup" is a lovely gift from a little girl who
must be a very loving person. (English 1 pg.)

Mc5441. C-1968
Miss Mary Collins to J. Francis Cardinal
McIntyre
April 20, 1968. Bristol, Connecticut

The performance of the dancing nun in San
Francisco is not the method of prayer used by
most Catholics. Hollywood performances are
not in the best taste in Church. (English 1 pg.)

Mc5442. C-1968
Msgr. Matthew Cox to J. Francis Cardinal
McIntyre
April 23, 1968. Poughkeepsie, New York

An invitation is extended to the celebration of
the 25th anniversary of my ordination with a
Mass on May 3. (English 1 pg.) On May 3,
1968, the Cardinal states it would be a pleasure
to be present as I officiated at your ordination
but prayers will be offered. (English 1 pg.)

Mc5443. C-1968
Mr. James Collins to J. Francis Cardinal
McIntyre
June 20, 1968. Inglewood, California

The Archbishop Cantwell Award is most
gratefully received. The money will be used for
further education. A copy of the essay is available. (English 1 pg.) On June 25, 1968, the Cardinal states that it would be good to have a
copy of the essay on file. (English 1 pg.)

Mc5444. C-1968
Mrs. Winifred Clinnin to J. Francis Cardinal
McIntyre
June 23, 1968. Los Angeles, California

Most of the faithful of the Archdiocese are in praise of your leadership in guiding the Church through difficult times. (English 3 pgs.) On June 28, 1968, the Cardinal states that difficult situations will mend and anxiety will be removed. (English 1 pg.)

Mc5445. C-1968
J. Francis Cardinal McIntyre to Mr. & Mrs.
G. Cranham
July 8, 1968. Los Angeles, California

Pope Paul VI bestows his Apostolic Blessing on the occasion of your Golden Wedding Anniversary. The blessing extends to the members of the family. Personal congratulations and prayers are offered on this very special occasion. (English 1 pg.)

Mc5446. C-1968
Dr. Clifford Cherry to J. Francis Cardinal
McIntyre
July 10, 1968. Los Angeles, California

Could special permission be given to Lt. Lawrence Stuppy to be married at an evening Mass? He will arrive home on September 20 and be married on the 21st and then leave for final training for over-seas assignment on the 22nd. (English 1 pg.) On July 16, 1968, the Cardinal states it is the pastor's decision. (English 1 pg).

Mc5447. C-1968
Rev. Charles Carroll to J. Francis Cardinal
McIntyre
July 19, 1968. San Francisco, California

The quality of life is important and while fighting against abortion, the plight of the poor and the persecuted should be considered. (English 2 pgs.)

Mc5448. C-1968
Msgr. Patrick Dignan to J. Francis Cardinal
McIntyre
July 30, 1968. Los Angeles, California

The essay of Mr. James Collins is timely, well written and should be submitted to one of the National Reviews. (English 1 pg.)

Mc5449. C-1968
J. Francis Cardinal McIntyre to Mr. John A.
Coleman
August 5, 1968. Los Angeles, California

The *Credo of the People of God* is a wonderful presentation of a magnificent document. (English 1 pg.)

Mc5450. C-1968
Bp. James Pike to J. Francis Cardinal McIntyre
September 18, 1968. New York City, New York

The Catonsville Nine put their careers and future on the line, now are there others who will put money on the line for their defense. It will take $50,000. (English 1 pg.)

Mc5451. C-1968
Mr. Louis Conte to J. Francis Cardinal
McIntyre
N.D. Granada Hills, California

If more Catholics were teaching in the public schools, the children would not be faced with godless education. Catholic teachers could turn the school system around. (English 3 pgs.) On October 17, 1968, the Cardinal asks Rev. Laurence O'Brien to talk to Mr. Conte. (English 1 pg.)

Mc5452. C-1968
Mr. Charles Cochrane to J. Francis Cardinal
McIntyre
December 2, 1968. Philadelphia, Pennsylvania

The Bishops who are trying to excuse the marriage of Jacqueline Kennedy are doing a disservice to all Catholics who have lived a single life after a failed marriage. (English 1 pg.)

Mc5453. C-1968
Mr. Leo Cherne to J. Francis Cardinal
McIntyre
December 12, 1968. New York City,
New York

An invitation is sent to be a sponsor of the International Rescue Committee honoring General Lucius Clay. (English 1 pg.) On December 18, 1968, the Cardinal states that local activities will preclude the acceptance of the honor. (English 1 pg.)

Mc5454. C-1968
Mr. Julian DaLuna to J. Francis Cardinal
McIntyre
N.D. Los Angeles, California

Mr. Lorenzo Castro is being denied his legal rights because he should never have been put in prison. The crime was a juvenile act and an appeal for parole should be made. (English 3 pgs.)

Mc5455. C-1968
Mr. Thomas Neill to J. Francis Cardinal
McIntyre
N.D. St. Louis, Missouri

The National Committee on Catholic Concerns will meet April 25–27 discussing the concerns of the Church and the world. Any advice or suggestions would be appreciated. (English 3 pgs.)

Mc5456. D-1968
Msgr. Benjamin Hawkes to Dr. William
Dignam
January 19, 1968. Los Angeles, California

The third and fourth year theologians request
an evening discussion during March. The faculty and the Chancery would most grateful if
this can be arranged. (English 1 pg.) On March
2, 1968, Msgr. states that the Seminary will be
ready on March 20. (English 1 pg.)

Mc5457. D-1968
Miss Consuelo B. Dolly to J. Francis Cardinal
McIntyre
February 18, 1968. Rochester, New York

In Cuernavaca, Ivan Illich and Bishop Men-
dez Arceo are causing revolt in the Church in
Mexico. The Center for Intercultural Formation
is the center of unrest. (English 1 pg.)

Mc5458. D-1968
Mrs. Dolores Davoren to J. Francis Cardinal
McIntyre
February 21, 1968. Covina, California

When is the Church going to take a stand
against indecent ads, pictures, and situation
comedies lowering respect for authority of the
Church and clergy? (English 3 pgs.) On February 27, 1968, the Cardinal states that when reaction such as this is registered, results will
happen. (English 1 pg.)

Mc5459. D-1968
Mr. John Dart to J. Francis Cardinal McIntyre
March 28, 1968. Los Angeles, California

A request to do a feature article on the activities of the Archbishop and by spending five or
six hours of a day with the Archbishop, the
public could have an appreciation of the schedule and pressures of the Office. (English 1 pg.)
On March 29, the Cardinal states that Holy
Week would make this request impossible. (English 1 pg.)

Mc5460. D-1968
Mr. Robert Sherlock to J. Francis Cardinal
McIntyre
May 12, 1968. Los Angeles, California

Miss Agnes Mary Dalton died and her estate
gives to the Cardinal ten percent for Masses for
the family. (English 1 pg.). On May 17, 1968,
the Cardinal request Msgr. Laubacher to send
the money to the Missions. (English 1 pg.)

Mc5461. D-1968
Mr. Patrick Dowd to J. Francis Cardinal
McIntyre
July 2, 1968. Hollywood, California

Conjugal love is for procreation and any de-
vices or methods to prevent life is wrong. But
much of the dialogue is so confused that no one
knows what to believe. (English 2 pgs.)

Mc5462. D-1968
Mr. John Dart to Msgr. Benjamin Hawkes
August 12, 1968. Los Angeles, California

A feature article will be written for the *Times*
and an interview is necessary before talking
with the various groups of people. (English 1
pg.) On August 19, 1968, Msgr. states that the
position of the Archdiocese is positive not de-
fensive. (English 1 pg.)

Mc5463. D-1968
Mr. Patrick Dowd to Msgr. Lawrence Gibson
August 16, 1968. Hollywood, California

Frustrations are expressed because there is no
role for the laymen to have in the Church. The
encyclicals are outdated, opinions of one are
not the opinions of many, but the Church must
be functional. (English 1 pg.)

Mc5464. D-1968
Mrs. Frank Droesch III to Msgr. Benjamin
Hawkes
August 19, 1968. Mission Viejo, California

Is there a date for the establishment of a
church and school in Mission Viejo? (English
1 pg.) On August 21, 1968, Msgr. states that
probably within a two year period a church and
rectory will be built. (English 1 pg.)

Mc5465. D-1968
Rev. William DuBay to Mr. Robert Dease
August, 25, 1968. Los Angeles, California

The service and help rendered to clergymen
seeking jobs simplifies the process and the skills
and self confidence given are a tremendous
help. (English 1 pg.)

Mc5466. D-1968
Mr. Robert Dease to Bp. Timothy Manning
September 23, 1968. Los Angeles, California

Several projects are in use to help during
transitional periods from one profession to another. If help is needed, it can be provided in
the Next Step Program or something similar.
(English 1 pg.)

Mc5467. D-1968
Mr. Patrick Daley to Msgr. Benjamin Hawkes
October 20, 1968. Littlerock, California

In what area of science has the Catholic
school system the greatest need? Obtaining the
training will not be a problem but the use of
education must be realistic. (English 1 pg). On
October 23, 1968, Msgr. Montrose states that
because of a nervous condition, the man might
not be good in high schools. (English 1 pg.)

Mc5468. D-1968
Mr. George Dunlap to J. Francis Cardinal
McIntyre
November 15, 1968. Canoga Park, California

The birth control pill controversy could be
ended by stating that the pill is a drug that pro-
duces temporary or permanent sterility. Women
should go to Catholic doctors who are guided
by the Church's teaching. (English 1 pg.)

Mc5469. D-1968
Msgr. Denis Doherty to Bp. Timothy Manning
December 13, 1968. Fresno, California

December 15 will always be a special day for
the people of Fresno. The first anniversary
makes everyone aware of the goodness and
thoughtfulness of the Bishop. (English 1 pg.)

Mc5470. E-1968
Mr. Larry Evers to J. Francis Cardinal
McIntyre
January 20, 1968. Los Angeles, California

A request for a donation so Pathetique the
Clown can perform in hospitals and homes for
the aged and then continue to the next location.
(English 1 pg.)

Mc5471. E-1968
Mrs. Joseph Emzweiler to J. Francis Cardinal
McIntyre
March 25, 1968. Doheny Park, California

The people of St. Edward's Parish are most
grateful for our priest. Great strides are being
made to gather people from all points of the
area for Mass. (English 1 pg.)

Mc5472. E-1968
Mr. Ainsworth Eyre to J. Francis Cardinal
McIntyre
June 18, 1968. New York City, New York

Please forward this check to Father Mannoon
in Kerala, India. (English 1 pg.) On June 25,
1968, the Cardinal states that the check is forwarded and a long ago friendship is revived
from New York days. (English 1 pg.)

Mc5473. F-1968
Miss Ida Feuerstein to Bp. Joseph McGucken
March 22, 1968. Los Angeles, California

A plea to be assured that my burial will take
place as promised. My vault is paid and ready.
(English 2 pgs.) On March 28, 1968, the Archbishop states that all of the papers are in the
Los Angeles Chancery Office and the bonds are
there too. (English 1 pg.)

Mc5474. F-1968
Dr. Walter Flaherty to Rev. Donald Strange
April 8, 1968. Orange, California

A plea is made not to make people feel guilty
for the death of Martin Luther King. Many
people and organizations are working for the
good of all races. (English 3 pgs.) On April 9,
1968, the Cardinal asks Fr. to interview Dr. and
to stress the necessity of prayer for peace. (English 1 pg.)

Mc5475. F-1968
Dr. Walter Flaherty to J. Francis Cardinal
McIntyre
April 22, 1968. Tustin, California

Could a musical group be sponsored and
trained by the Archdiocese for the Watts Festival giving some young people healthy activity
during the summer? (English 2 pgs.)

Mc5476. F-1968
Mr. Paul Foran to Msgr. Benjamin Hawkes
May 7, 1968. Beverly Hills, California

Could a society be established to locate families that could move into the poverty areas and
establish themselves in that area. These families
would try to combat poverty. (English 1 pg.)

Mc5477. F-1968
Dr. Eddie Feliu to Msgr. John Rawden
May 22, 1968. Piso, Mexico

A request for *El Pedregal* to help in the organization of parochial services and finances
where help is needed. (English 1 pg.) On May
28, Msgr. states that the enclosed *Parochial Finance Book* and the Parish Annual Report
forms may be helpful. (English 1 pg.)

Mc5478. F-1968
Msgr. Francis Keane to Msgr. Lawrence
O'Leary
July 9, 1968. Los Angeles, California

Mr. Foran's plan could arouse hostility in
some parishes. Scholarships for education
would be one method to give incentive to the
youth. At no time was the program given endorsement. (English 1 pg.)

Mc5479. F-1968
Mr. John Friedrich to J. Francis Cardinal
McIntyre
August 1, 1968. Oxnard, California

The boycott of California grapes by the
Bishop of Detroit signals a change in the attitude of the Church. The Bishop ought to know
that many people do not agree with him. (English 1 pg.)

Mc5480. F-1968
Msgr. Benjamin Hawkes to Miss Claire Falken-
stein
October 14, 1968. Los Angeles, California

The massive project of the windows is almost
finished and installation can now begin. They
will add beauty to the finished project. (English
1 pg.)

Mc5481. F-1968
Dr. James Ford, MD to J. Francis Cardinal
McIntyre
October 28, 1968. Lynwood, California

It is frustrating for doctors to be told that a
priest is advising women to use contraceptives.
A medical journal is sent for your information.
(English 1 pg.) On November 4, 1968, the Cardinal states that the encyclical is causing alarm
and concern. The priests will have a talk at the
Theological Conference. (English 1 pg.)

Mc5482. F-1968
Msgr. William Farricker to J. Francis Cardinal
McIntyre
October 31, 1968. New York City, New York

The class reunion will be held on November
17 with dinner at 6:00 p.m. There is extra
room in the rectory if that is convenient. (English 1 pg.) On November 6, 1968, the Cardinal states it will be good to be with the
members of the class on Sunday. (English 1 pg.)

Mc5483. F-1968
Mr. Brad Fletcher to J. Francis Cardinal
McIntyre
N.D. Camarillo, California

Permission is requested for the Bible Study
group of the parish to join with the Presbyterian
Church for a Bible Camp in August. (English
1 pg.)

Mc5484. G-1968
J. Francis Cardinal McIntyre to Mr. and Mrs.
R. Grant
February 9, 1968. Los Angeles, California

The beautiful volume of art will find a place
in the Doheny Library. The magnificent photog-
raphy and the introduction by Cardinal Spellman hold special interest to me. (English 1 pg.)

Mc5485. G-1968
Mr. E. A. Russell to J. Francis Cardinal
McIntyre
March 12, 1968. Los Angeles, California

An invitation to tour the Southern California
Gas lines as background for a study of the city's
growth. (English 1 pg.) On March 21, 1968,
the Cardinal states that Mr. Thomas Kelly, the
Construction Coordinator, will take the tour.
(English 1 pg.)

Mc5486. G-1968
Bp. Thomas Gorman to Arbp. John F. Dearden
March 27, 1968. Dallas, Texas

The Bishops of the United States must take a
stand with the Catholic Press and with the
members of the committee for the revision of
religion text books. (English 2 pgs.)

Mc5487. G-1968
Mr. Richard Grant to J. Francis Cardinal
McIntyre
March 27, 1968. Los Angeles, California

The death of Countess Bernardine Murphy
will bring more work into the office. Mr. Edward House could replace me on the Board of
Don Bosco Technical and could work on the
committee. (English 1 pg.)

Mc5488. G-1968
Msgr. Lawrence Gibson to Miss Kathy Gon-
salves
June 18, 1968. Los Angeles, California

The Cardinal is free to officiate at the wedding ceremony on September 28. All necessary
permissions must be made with your pastor.
(English 1 pg.)

Mc5489. G-1968
Msgr. Benjamin Hawkes to Mrs. Hortense
Gribbell
July 3, 1968. Los Angeles, California

The generous donation was sent to Nazareth
House for Boys where the Sisters will put it to
good use. (English 1 pg.)

Mc5490. G-1968
Judge Joseph Grillo to J. Francis Cardinal
McIntyre
July 8, 1968. Los Angeles, California

The greatest hope is that having served as a
Municipal Judge, the city will be a better place.
A copy of an often given speech is enclosed.
(English 9 pgs.)

Mc5491. G-1968
Mrs. A. J. Steigerwald to J. Francis Cardinal
McIntyre
August 21, 1968. Los Angeles, California

An invitation is extended to join The Generation Mix, a group involving all ages and ethnic groups on December 2 and 3. Others can be recommended. (English 1 pg.)

Mc5492. G-1968
J. Francis Cardinal McIntyre to Mr. & Mrs.
Larry Gordon
September 28, 1968. Los Angeles, California

Pope Paul VI extends his Apostolic Blessing for health and happiness throughout your married life. May Our Lady watch over and protect you. (English 1 pg.)

Mc5493. G-1968
Bp. Francis Green to J. Francis Cardinal
McIntyre
October 31, 1968. Tucson, Arizona

Bishop Shannan is distressed over the leaks to the press and he is no way responsible for them. (English 1 pg.)

Mc5494. G-1968
Mrs. Aline Gallegas to J. Francis Cardinal
McIntyre
November 2, 1968. Sylmar, California

The *McCall* article in the November issue has disregarded the truth. It is difficult enough to rear a family without this type of article. (English 1 pg.) On November 26, 1968, Msgr. states that surely the world should soon show a better picture. (English 1 pg.)

Mc5495. G-1968
Mr. R. W. James to J. Francis Cardinal
McIntyre
December 2, 1968. Long Beach, California

There are 300,000 ounces of gold available if the Vatican or Archdiocese wishes to buy it. The gold could be stored. (English 2 pgs.) On December 4, 1968, the Cardinal states that the newspaper article is misleading. Neither the Vatican nor the Archdiocese is in the gold market. (English 1 pg.)

Mc5496. G-1968
Rev. Carl Garner to J. Francis Cardinal
McIntyre
December 4, 1968. Needville, Texas

A request to bless the ichthus which will be used as a gift. This is the symbol of the Methodist Church. (English 1 pg.) On December 15, 1968, Rev. Garner states that the ichthus came with a beautiful medal. Would a ring from a deceased Bishop be available? (English 1 pg.)

Mc5497. G-1968
Mr. Arthur Baker to J. Francis Cardinal
McIntyre
December 20. 1968. Lake Orion, Michigan

Would an evaluation of the therapeutic results of Guest House be possible. Each graduate is being asked to answer a questionnaire but a more objective view is needed. (English 2 pgs.)

Mc5498. G-1968
J. Francis Cardinal McIntyre to Rev. Carl
Garner
December 20, 1968. Los Angeles, California

The Bishop's ring is usually handed down from one to another and does not circulate in another orbit. (English 1 pg.)

Mc5499. H-1968
Mr. James A. Hayes to J. Francis Cardinal
McIntyre
January 12, 1968. Sacramento, California

The loyalty oath will be re-established in California preventing anyone from holding public office who would try to overthrow the government. (English 1 pg.)

Mc5500. H-1968
J. Francis Cardinal McIntyre to Mr. Don
Hutchinson
January 24, 1968. Los Angeles, California

The meeting at the Knights of Columbus was most enjoyable. The claim for the refund in Orange County has been filed. (English 1 pg.)

Mc5501. H-1968
Mr. Gene Handsaker to J. Francis Cardinal
McIntyre
March 4, 1968. Los Angeles, California

As a member of the Associated Press, a request is being made for an opportunity to talk and tape an interview and take pictures of your home and office. (English 1 pg.) On March 7, 1968, the Cardinal asks who would receive and be interested in such an intimate profile. (English 1 pg.)

Mc5502. H-1968
Mr. C. W. Haugh to St. Michael's Church
March 14, 1968. Vermillion, South Dakota

The Baptismal records of Douglas Paul Patterson were found on the road and will be returned to your Church. (English 1 pg.) On March 26, 1968, Msgr. states it would be better to send the records to the Chancery Office in Sioux Falls. (English 1 pg.)

Mc5503. H-1968
Rev. Florence Hoste, OFM to J. Francis Cardinal McIntyre
March 30, 1968. Mishawaka, Indiana

The Bishops' Pastoral is a document which should produce the desired results. The need to teach mental prayer to children can spread this into a nation wide movement. (English 14 pgs.)

Mc5504. H-1968
Mr. Arthur Hughes to J. Francis Cardinal McIntyre
April 26, 1968. Brooklyn, New York

Can you recall a discussion with Cardinal Spellman and Carlton Hayes on the National Conference of Christian and Jews. (English 1 pg.) On May 3, 1968, the Cardinal states that he doesn't remember a discussion on the NCCJ but on many other topics. (English 1 pg.)

Mc5505. H-1968
Mr. Francis Hidvegi to Msgr. Benjamin Hawkes
May 4, 1968. Los Angeles, California

Are the workers of the Chancery Office covered by Social Security? Expenses are mounting due to my wife's illness and bills cannot be paid. (English 1 pg.) On May 7, 1968, Msgr. states that the salary will be paid until Mrs. Hidvegi formally ends her employment and then Social Security can begin. (English 1 pg.)

Mc5506. H-1968
Mrs. Catherine Harrington to J. Francis Cardinal McIntyre
June 10, 1968. Los Angeles, California

The Mass in every parish for Robert Kennedy was great but why not a Mass in every parish for the men who have given their lives for the country? (English 1 pg.) On June 20, 1968, Msgr. states that the Mass in Calvary Cemetery was an inspiring and fitting tribute. (English 1 pg.)

Mc5507. H-1968
Mr. Theodore Humes to J. Francis Cardinal McIntyre
June 24, 1968. Towson, Maryland

The broadcast by NBC in its News Special on the Church was a sham. Continue to speak for a traditional Church and dignity. (English 1 pg.)

Mc5508. H-1968
Mrs. Grace Higgins to J. Francis Cardinal McIntyre
July 8, 1968. Oroville, California

A request to give some guidelines before Mass and instructions before a child can receive Communion. (English 2 pgs.) On July 16, 1968, Msgr. states that the request will be given consideration. (English 1 pg.)

Mc5509. H-1968
Rev. Michael Hoban to J. Francis Cardinal McIntyre
July 17, 1968. Centereach, New York

Since Bishops are surfacing again to make the highways safe for those on the road to heaven, is there a copy of the talk given to the clergy available? (English 1 pg.)

Mc5510 H-1968
J. Francis Cardinal McIntyre to Mr. Joaquin Hidalgo
July 24, 1968. Los Angeles, California

The proposal would be excellent if in the reorganization of the United States Catholic Conference new committees were not set up. The same discussions are taking place now. (English 1 pg.)

Mc5511. H-1968
Msgr. Benjamin Hawkes to Sister Patricia Clare, CSJ
September 23, 1968. Los Angeles, California

The scholarship promised by the Cardinal is enclosed. He understands that Miss Ingrid Honore will benefit by it. (English 1 pg.) On September 28, 1968, Miss Honore states that her goal is to be a teacher and the scholarship will help her to attain that goal. (English 1 pg.)

Mc5512. H-1968
Mrs. Majaienta Hills to J. Francis Cardinal McIntyre
November 11, 1968. Pampa, Texas

At the Bishop's Meeting urge leadership. The laity need guidelines that are clear and definite. (English 1 pg.)

Mc5513. H-1968
Mr. John Kemble to Msgr. Benjamin Hawkes
December 5, 1968. Los Angeles, California

An invitation to join the Historical Society of Southern California is extended. The Society encourages the preservation of historical artifacts, buildings, and memorabilia. (English 1 pg.)

Mc5514. H-1968
Mr. Richard Harbison to Msgr. Benjamin Hawkes
December 10, 1968. Los Angeles, California

A meeting should be arranged so the bookkeeping techniques of the Archdiocese can be explained. (English 1 pg.) On December 11, 1968, Msgr. states that a luncheon meeting can be arranged at your convenience. (English 1 pg.)

Mc5515. H-1968
J. Francis Cardinal McIntyre to Mrs. Grace Hart
December 20, 1968. Los Angeles, California

A generous donation to the St. Vincent de Paul Society comes at an opportune time. The beneficiaries will surely pray for you. (English 1 pg.)

Mc5516. H-1968
J. Francis Cardinal McIntyre to Mrs. Walter Hoffman
December 27, 1968. Los Angeles, California

The generous donation at Christmas will find a place in areas that are prayerfully productive. It will be a pleasure to see you when a meeting is held in Camarillo. (English 1 pg.)

Mc5517. I-1968
Msgr. Benjamin Hawkes to Mr. James Irvine Jr.
February 15, 1968. Los Angeles, California

The fallout shelter can be arranged in the schools outlined by Mr. Thomas Kelly, our construction coordinator. (English 1 pg.)

Mc5518. I-1968
Mrs. Adele Icaza to J. Francis Cardinal McIntyre
September 9, 1968. Manhattan Beach, California

A request to hear, study, and consider the position of many people on the birth control issues. (English 3 pgs.) On September 13, 1968, the Cardinal request Msgr. Johnson to talk to Mrs. Icaza. (English 1 pg.)

Mc5519. J-1968
Mr. James Jones to J. Francis Cardinal McIntyre
January 22, 1968. Bridgeville, Pennsylvania

A request for prayers for peace in the world and in the Church and suggests novenas for a better social condition in the world. (English 3 pgs.)

Mc5520. J-1968
Mr. Wilbur Johnson to J. Francis Cardinal McIntyre
July 24, 1968. Phoenix, Arizona

Archbishop Dearden is pledging one million dollars to stamp out racism. What is Los Angeles doing to relieve the sufferings of the Blacks and the Browns? (English 1 pg.) On July 26, 1968, Msgr. states that for years Los Angeles has been working for complete integration of all institutions. (English 1 pg.)

Mc5521. J-1968
Mr. Thomas Jardine to J. Francis Cardinal McIntyre
October 7, 1968. Los Angeles, California

The Los Angeles *Times* assumes the role of being omnipotent and all knowing on all subjects without erring. (English 1 pg.)

Mc5522. J-1968
Mr. William Johnson to J. Francis Cardinal McIntyre
December 11, 1968. Bellevue, Kentucky

On a visit to Edward Air Force Base in 1954, you are noted as seeing an UFO. Could a confirmation of this event be made? (English 1 pg.) On December 18, 1968, the Cardinal states that if the visit took place it was an ecclesiastical visit not a scientific mission. (English 1 pg.)

Mc5523. K-1968
Mr. Jacobus L. Kiat to J. Francis Cardinal McIntyre
January 12, 1968. Belitung, Indonesia

A request is made for a grant to bring the family to the United States from Djakarta and for livelihood until a permanent position can be secured. (English 9 pgs.) On February 9, 1968, Msgr. states that the Propagation of the Faith does not have sufficient money to fund this request. (English 1 pg.)

Mc5524. K-1968
Msgr. George Kelly to J. Francis Cardinal McIntyre
February 15, 1968. New York City, New York

A request recommends Mr. Patrick Kelly to the educational department in the areas of purchasing and supplies. (English 1 pg.) On February 23, 1968, the Cardinal asks Mr. Kelly to come for a visit and a discussion of the present set up. (English 1 pg.)

Mc5525. K-1968
Mr. Preston Hotchkis to J. Francis Cardinal McIntyre
March 18, 1968. Los Angeles, California

An invitation to the World Affairs Council dinner honoring His Excellency Josef Klaus of Austria on April 16 is extended. (English 1 pg.) On March 26, 1968, the Cardinal states that it is unfortunate that he cannot attend. (English 1 pg.)

Mc5526. K-1968
Ms. Dorothy Krae to Msgr. Benjamin Hawkes
August 2, 1968. Fullerton, California

The Crisis Seminar pointed to non-violence as a method of correcting abuses. Phase II and Phase III will follow. (English 5 pgs.)

Mc5527. K-1968
Mr. Roger Kelly to J. Francis Cardinal
    McIntyre
August 13, 1968. Boston, Massachusetts

A strong statement on marriage and family are needed and support will be given for any undertaking to establish a strong religious educational system. (English 2 pgs.)

Mc5528. K-1968
Mr. J. M. Kendra to J. Francis Cardinal
    McIntyre
N.D. Denver, Colorado

A request is made for a relic of St. Vibiana. After several strokes, only prayer can prevent another stroke. (English 1 pg.) On September 13, 1968, Msgr. states that a relic of St. Vibiana is not available but another relic is enclosed. (English 1 pg.)

Mc5529. K-1968
Miss King to J. Francis Cardinal McIntyre
October 17, 1968. Superior, Wisconsin

Every statement made against another Bishop gives him more support. There is enough positive work to be done in the Church that negative work has no place in the ranks. (English 1 pg.)

Mc5530. L-1968
Mr. John Lacy to J. Francis Cardinal McIntyre
March 7, 1968. Garrison, New York

Enclosed is an Open Letter to all America to come together in prayer for peace and justice in the world. (English 2 pgs.) On March 12, 1968, the Cardinal prays that the recommendations may be fruitful. (English 1 pg.)

Mc5531. L-1968
Mr. David Levenkron to President Lyndon
    Johnson
April 12, 1968. Los Angeles, California

The only suitable place for peace negotiations is Vatican City. There is no turmoil or hostility present there. In such a peaceful place, peace negotiations could be successful. (English 3 pgs.)

Mc5532. L-1968
Mr. James Lockwood to J. Francis Cardinal
    McIntyre
May 5, 1968. Menlo Park, California

The Humanitarians among the new breed are following the tactics of the Communists and the name calling and disrespect that follows is natural. (English 2 pgs.)

Mc5533. L-1968
Mr. Leonard Greenburg to J. Francis Cardinal
    McIntyre
August 12, 1968. Los Angeles, California

An invitation is sent to join the Lions International which is the largest service organization in the world. (English 1 pg.)

Mc5534. L-1968
Mrs. Joseph Portillo to J. Francis Cardinal
    McIntyre
September 1, 1968. Los Angeles, California

A request is made for a photo that can be used for the Presentation Ball for the *Las Damas Pan Americanas*. The proceeds for the Ball will be sent to the Holy Family Adoption Center. (English 1 pg.) On September 7, 1968, a letter of appreciation and picture are sent. (English 1 pg.)

Mc5535. L-1968
Mrs. Evelyn Lanza to J. Francis Cardinal
    McIntyre
September 25, 1968. Fullerton, California

Since there seems to be some question about the Canon of the Mass being said in English, why doesn't the priest use the Latin Canon? (English 1 pg.)

Mc5536. L-1968
Rev. Donald Montrose to Mr. A. E. Lopez
September 26, 1968. Los Angeles, California

The N.E.A. continues to provide services that are beneficial to the teachers. They seem to favor government control of education. (English 1 pg.)

Mc5537. L-1968
J. Francis Cardinal McIntyre to Mr. & Mrs.
    M. LeRoy
December 2, 1968. Los Angeles, California

The kind invitation to dine with the Governor and attend Up With People must be declined due to previous commitments. (English 1 pg.)

Mc5538. Mc-1968
Bp. Bryan McEntegart to J. Francis Cardinal
McIntyre
July 25, 1968. Brooklyn, New York

The prayers and message sent for my retirement was a friendly gesture and one that is deeply appreciated. The invitation to visit California is a wish that might be fulfilled. (English 1 pg.)

Mc5539. Mc-1968
Mr. John McConville to J. Francis Cardinal
McIntyre
August 21, 1968. Los Angeles, California

A request is made for a job in whatever field that the Archdiocese needs a worker. Self respect must be restored. (English 1 pg.)

Mc5540. Mc-1968
Mrs. Agnes McDonald to J. Francis Cardinal
McIntyre
September 18, 1968. Coos Bay, Oregon

If a candle can light an area, the candle of the Church could start a forest fire and light the path for many. Leadership is all that is needed. (English 4 pgs.)

Mc5541. Mc-1968
J. Francis Cardinal McIntyre to President-elect
R. Nixon
December 7, 1968. Los Angeles, California

It was a momentous occasion to be in the gathering of so many accomplished people so well known to you. Your comments were encouraging for our State and Nation. (English 2 pgs.)

Mc5542. Mc-1968
Mr. Patrick McCormick to J. Francis Cardinal
McIntyre
December 14, 1968. Los Angeles, California

A request is made to write a letter of recommendation to Senator George Murphy for the position of United States Attorney for the Southern District of California. (English 1 pg.) On December 20, 1968, the Cardinal states that he hopes that the community might share from this benefit. (English 1 pg.)

Mc5543. Mc-1968
Mr. Charles McFarland to J. Francis Cardinal
McIntyre
December 31, 1968. Oklahoma City, Oklahoma

The inroads that sex education is making in our schools is frightening. Support for the fight to stop this type of education is growing in every denomination. (English 1 pg.)

Mc5544. Mc-1968
Mr. George McDonald to J. Francis Cardinal
McIntyre
N.D. Los Angeles, California

A tribute to the steady pace that the Church in Los Angeles is taking in following Vatican II and a true appreciation for the leadership of the Cardinal. (English 2 pgs.)

Mc5545. M-1968
Msgr. John Languille to Mr. Richard Mishler
January 12, 1968. Los Angeles, California

The self-help program for the farm laborers in the San Joaquin Valley should be made known to Bishop Timothy Manning in Fresno. (English 2 pgs.)

Mc5546. M-1968
Rev. James Moynihan to Msgr. Benjamin
Hawkes
January 30, 1968. Rochester, New York

Is there a plan in Los Angeles whereby surplus funds from one parish can be made available to another parish? (English 1 pg.) On February 6, 1968, Msgr. states that all surplus funds are deposited in the Chancery Office and the parish receives 2½% interest. All borrowing is done through the Chancery Office. (English 1 pg.)

Mc5547. M-1968
J. Francis Cardinal McIntyre to Mr. & Mrs.
Owen Miller
February 24, 1968. Los Angeles, California

The very generous donation is being credited to the Youth Education Fund and both St. Brendan and St. Thomas Aquinas parishes are given credit. (English 1 pg.)

Mc5548. M-1968
Rev. George Niederauer to Rev. Francis Weber
February 28, 1968. Camarillo, California

Mr. Leo Moore's poems are theologically correct but the literary merit is not great. They can be printed with Ecclesiastical Approval. (English 1 pg.)

Mc5549. M-1968
Miss Barbara Mercer to J. Francis Cardinal
McIntyre
April 17, 1968. San Leandro, California

The encouraging letter for a National Presidential Prayer Day will help to bring this event to reality. A letter to the Pope is enclosed. (English 4 pgs.)

Mc5550. M-1968
Mr. George Montgomery to *The Loyolan*
April 26, 1968. Los Angeles, California

Satire and ridicule of the Cardinal and his policies in *The Loyolan* are out of line. School newspapers have a standard to uphold the respect that is due to the ecclesial head of the Archdiocese. (English 3 pgs.)

Mc5551. M-1968
Mr. Thomas Melady to J. Francis Cardinal McIntyre
June 17, 1968. New York City, New York

A copy of the address given at the commencement exercises for the University of Scranton stressing the justice of federal and state scholarships to Church-related schools and universities is enclosed. (English 5 pgs.)

Mc5552. M-1968
Msgr. Lawrence Gilb to Miss Barbara Mercer
June 20, 1968. Los Angeles, California

Since the resolution for the Presidential Prayer Day will begin in Oakland, it would be a courtesy to have the Bishop give the *Imprimatur* for the prayer. (English 1 pg.)

Mc5553. M-1968
Paul Cardinal Marella to J. Francis Cardinal McIntyre
July 8, 1968. Vatican City

A friendly letter comments on the events in the world that result from the Vatican Council and the Pope's profession of Faith in the Square. (English 2 pgs.)

Mc5554. M-1968
Paul Cardinal Marella to J. Francis Cardinal McIntyre
September 2, 1968. Vatican City

A friendly letter explains the work of the Secretariate and the forth coming publications. (English 3 pgs.) On September 11, 1968, the Cardinal states that the distinctions made are most beneficial as is the material that was sent. (English 1 pg.)

Mc5555. M-1968
Msgr. Benjamin Hawkes to Bp. Luigi Raimondi
September 26, 1968. Los Angeles, California

Mr. Patrick Mahony is interested in the mystical manifestations reported by the missionaries from Africa. These testimonies are in the Vatican Archives. We can advise him to write directly to the Vatican Library. (English 1 pg.)

Mc5556. M-1968
Mr. Edward Maxwell to J. Francis Cardinal McIntyre
September 30, 1968. Oxnard, California

A more thorough study of the Tulare County situation should have been made before signing the document. The National Labor Relations Act will put the small rancher out of business. (English 4 pgs.)

Mc5557. M-1968
J. Francis Cardinal McIntyre to Mr. Edward Maxwell
October 7, 1968. Los Angeles, California

The Church must favor those less fortunate and less qualified and competent to assist themselves. The Bishops of the State did study the situation in Tulare County.

Mc5558. M-1968
Paul Cardinal Marella to J. Francis Cardinal McIntyre
October 14, 1968. Vatican City

A friendly letter comments on the arrival of Mother Margarita and the opportunity of granting tickets to the beatification. The reports of the Cardinal in Los Angeles were good. (English 2 pgs.)

Mc5559. M-1968
Mr. Edward Meck to J. Francis Cardinal McIntyre
November 8, 1968. Anaheim, California

The visit of Juan Cardinal Landazari Rickett to Disneyland was an honor and a privilege. These pictures can be sent to him and his companions. (English 1 pg.) On November 12, 1968, the Cardinal expresses his appreciation for the thoughtfulness. (English 1 pg.)

Mc5560. N-1968
Mrs. Alex Navarro to Msgr. Benjamin Hawkes
April 30, 1968. Los Angeles, California

The kindness shown to Alex during his lifetime and for being present at his Rosary are deeply appreciated. (English 1 pg.) On May 6, 1968, the Cardinal states that if the funeral and ordination were not at the same time, I would have been present at the funeral. (English 1 pg.)

Mc5561. N-1968
Mrs. J. W. Nelson to J. Francis Cardinal McIntyre
June 30, 1968. Altadena, California

A request is made for special permission to have her daughter's wedding in the Mayfield High School Chapel. The Sisters were most kind during the tragedy. (English 1 pg.) On July 3, 1968, the Cardinal asks Father Cahill to explain why this practice cannot be permitted. (English 1 pg.)

Mc5562. N-1968
Bp. Edward Swanstrom to J. Francis Cardinal
McIntyre
July 12, 1968. New York City, New York

Catholic Relief Services is sending food and
other assistance to both Nigeria and Biafra. (English 2 pgs.)

Mc5563. N-1968
J. Francis Cardinal McIntyre to Mrs. Louis
Nash
July 17, 1968. Los Angeles, California

Sincere sympathy is extended on the death of
Louis, a staunch supporter and defender of the
people in the State Hospital. (English 1 pg.)

Mc5564. N-1968
Miss Rosalie Nolan to J. Francis Cardinal
McIntyre
August 4, 1968. Los Angeles, California

A request to celebrate Mass for Gertrude
Walsh's birthday on August 11. She was born
in Galway and came to Denver in 1914. (English 1 pg.) On August 5, 1968, the Cardinal
states that Miss Walsh should know that the
Mass will be celebrated by one whose mother
also came from Galway in 1880. (English 1 pg.)

Mc5565. N-1968
Rev. Robert Demeny to J. Francis Cardinal
McIntyre
September 6, 1968. Kansas City, Missouri

Please send the name of the priest or layman
who will be able to utilize the modern techniques of fund raising developed by the National Council for Diocesan Support Program.
(English 7 pgs.)

Mc5566. N-1968
Rev. Anthony Nack to J. Francis Cardinal
McIntyre
October 29, 1968. Chicago, Illinois

A request to offer one of the three Masses on
Christmas Day that all people will grow in
greater love of Jesus in the Blessed Sacrament.
(English 1 pg.) On November 6, 1968, the Cardinal assures Father one Mass will be celebrated
for that intention. (English 1 pg.)

Mc5567. N-1968
J. Francis Cardinal McIntyre to Sister Cecile
Louise, CSJ
December 12, 1968. Los Angeles, California

Mr. Guiseppi de Nobili, a nephew of Cardinal Bossi, is a professor of Gregorian Chant. He
would like to visit the Mount. He can be contacted at the Beverly Hills Hotel. (English 1 pg.)
On the same day a similar letter was sent to Sister M. Raymond McCay. (English 1 pg.)

Mc5568. N-1968
J. Francis Cardinal McIntyre to Amleto Cardinal Cicognani
December 16, 1968. Los Angeles, California

Dr. Doyce Nunis, a professor of history at
USC, requests permission to do research in the
Vatican Archives and the Vatican Library. (English 1 pg.) On the same date a letter of introduction of Dr. Nunis to Gregory Cardinal
Agagianian is sent. (English 1 pg.)

Mc5569. O-1968
Msgr. Raymond O'Flaherty to J. Francis Cardinal McIntyre
February 3, 1968. Santa Monica, California

A suggestion is made to form a Personnel
Board that could assist with the changes of
priests and solve some of the problems. The
Consultors could then approve the suggestions.
(English 1 pg.)

Mc5570. O-1968
Msgr. Marijan Oblak to J. Francis Cardinal
McIntyre
April 1, 1968. Zader, Yugoslavia

The Croatian people have invited me to come
to the United States and to celebrate Mass in
their language and wherever possible a second
collection will be taken for the seminarians under our care. (English 1 pg.)

Mc5571. O-1968
Mr. Francis O'Neill to J. Francis Cardinal
McIntyre
April 14, 1968. Los Angeles, California

An appeal is made to have the area around
all Churches free from individuals passing out
propaganda for some political causes. (English 3
pgs.)

Mc5572. O-1968
Mr. Frank O'Brien to Msgr. Benjamin Hawkes
April 22, 1968. Los Angeles, California

The same importance should be given to the
message of Fatima as has been given to the nine
First Fridays. Peace can be restored. (English 4
pgs.)

Mc5573. O-1968
Mrs. Genevieve O'Brien to J. Francis Cardinal
McIntyre
April 28, 1968. Poughkeepsie, New York

A friendly letter comments on Msgr. Cox's
silver jubilee of ordination and looking forward
to the month of May. (English 2 pgs.) On May
3, 1968, the Cardinal comments on events of
the former days. (English 1 pg.)

Mc5574. O-1968
Mr. H. H. Oppenheimer to J. Francis Cardinal
McIntyre
June 19, 1968. Flushing, New York

Our first line of defense must be a loud voice which should condemn hatred and proclaim to all of the world that wealth is given to some for the good of all. (English 2 pgs.) On July 3, 1968, the Cardinal states that the comments are timely and appreciated. (English 1 pg.)

Mc5575. O-1968
Rev. Gregory O'Brien to J. Francis Cardinal
McIntyre
July 16, 1968. Los Angeles, California

Dr. Wesley Robb is president of the American Academy of Religion which is open to all teachers of religion. He publishes a *Journal of American Academy of Religion*. (English 2 pgs.)

Mc5576. O-1968
Mr. Harold O'Leary to J. Francis Cardinal
McIntyre
August 21, 1968. East Meadow, New York

The Government does not want the Korean Government to capitalize on the capture of the USS Pueblo. Can we pray for the safe and speedy return of the men being held prisoners. (English 1 pg.)

Mc5577. O-1968
J. Francis Cardinal McIntyre to Patrick Cardinal O'Boyle
October 17, 1968. Los Angeles, California

The class reunion on November 17 will necessitate that I double up on Father Time as there is a clergy conference here on Monday afternoon. (English 1 pg.)

Mc5578. O-1968
Mrs. A. O'Leary to J. Francis Cardinal
McIntyre
October 23, 1968. Santa Paula, California

The Concerned Parents of Ventura County request an interview with the Cardinal concerning the magazines in the Catholic grade and high schools. (English 1 pg.) On October 28, 1968, Msgr. states that the Cardinal is scheduled for another appointment on October 30, but the Department of Education is available. (English 1 pg.)

Mc5579. O-1968
Rev. Thomas O'Mahoney to J. Francis Cardinal McIntyre
November 19, 1968. El Paso, Texas

Please ask the Pope to make firm statements so the Bishops will have the courage to fight grave violations of Liturgical laws and Papal authority. (English 1 pg.) On November 25, 1968, the Cardinal states that the statement of the Bishops should meet the requirement. (English 1 pg.)

Mc5580. O-1968
J. Francis Cardinal McIntyre to Mr. & Mrs.
J. E. O'Rourke
December 14, 1968. Los Angeles, California

Pope Paul VI extends his Papal Benediction on the day of your wedding to you and the members of your wedding party. Personal congratulations and prayers are added. (English 1 pg.)

Mc5581. P-1968
Msgr. Eugene Gilb to Miss Enrica Polese
January 12, 1968. Los Angeles, California

The priest that gave the sermon at Holy Trinity Church on Christmas is not from this Diocese and the Pastor is trying to obtain a copy of the sermon for you. (English 1 pg.)

Mc5582. P-1968
Mr. Alberto Pasquini to J. Francis Cardinal
McIntyre
July 14, 1968. Viterbo, Italy

A plea is made to give financial assistance to a family in great need. (Italian 1 pg.) On August 1, 1968, the Cardinal sends $100.00 to the priest in the parish for the family, if the financial need is real. (English 1 pg.)

Mc5583. P-1968
Mr. Harry Popkin to J. Francis Cardinal
McIntyre
August 1, 1968. Los Angeles, California

The members of the Hollywood Temple *Beth El* appreciates the leadership and inspiration given to Los Angeles. (English 1 pg.) On August 5, 1968, the Cardinal states that we stand united for peace in Los Angeles. (English 1 pg.)

Mc5584. P-1968
Rev. Clement Connolly to Mrs. Priscilla Cruz
October 9, 1968. Los Angeles, California

The Cardinal regrets that previous commitments prevents him from attending the Puerto Rican Festival. To your committee and to the Puerto Rico people the Cardinal sends his special blessing. (English 1 pg.)

Mc5585. P-1968
Mr. Alberto Pasquini to J. Francis Cardinal
McIntyre
October 18, 1968. Viterbo, Italy

Alberto has received the generous gift and his
faith in the goodness of man has been strengthened. If this caused any inconvenience, the family is sorry but most grateful. (English 1 pg.)

Mc5586. P-1968
Rev. Joseph Powers to Msgr. Benjamin Hawkes
November 6, 1968. Huntington Beach, Cali-
fornia

With permission from Rome, may I have the
faculties from the Archdiocese while I live with
my sister and support her and her son. (English
1 pg.)

Mc5587. Q-1968
Bp. Jose Querexeta to J. Francis Cardinal
McIntyre
December 8, 1968. Philippine Islands

A plea to be put on the Missionary Cooperation Plan for 1969 so some money could come
to a very neglected area of the Philippine Islands. (English 1 pg.)

Mc5588. R-1968
J. Francis Cardinal McIntyre to Chief Thomas
Reddin
January 31, 1968. Los Angeles, California

The talk given at St. John's Seminary was en-
lightening and helpful. Experience will permit
the seminarians to employ the wisdom they received. (English 1 pg.)

Mc5589. R-1968
Mr. William Reilly to J. Francis Cardinal
McIntyre
April 4, 1968. New York City, New York

A friendly letter comments on the successor
to Cardinal Spellman, the former friendship
with Cardinal O'Hara, and the success of
Reilly's two sons. The Fransican Daily Missal is
being sent for comments. (English 2 pgs.)

Mc5590. R-1968
Rev. Leo Remington to Msgr. Benjamin
Hawkes
May 15, 1968. Portland, Oregon

A request is made to live in a parish close to
USC during the months of summer school. A
daily Mass and help on Sundays could be given.
(English 1 pg.) On May 31, 1968, Msgr. states
as soon as a letter from the Bishop is received, a
parish will be assigned. (English 1 pg.)

Mc5591. R-1968
J. Francis Cardinal McIntyre to Mrs. John
Rauen
May 24, 1968. Los Angles, California

An invitation it extended to a tea on June 6
at 3:00 p.m. at which time the first annual Cardinal's Dinner will be planned. Santa Marta
Hospital will be the recipient of the funds realized. (English 1 pg.)

Mc5592. R-1968
Mr. John Gardner to J. Francis Cardinal
McIntyre
July 29, 1968. New York City, New York

The Society for the Family of Man will honor
Mr. John D. Rockefeller III on October 21.
May your name be used as a member of the
Sponsoring Committee? (English 1 pg.) On Au-
gust 6, 1968, the Cardinal states he would be
happy to add his name. (English 1 pg.)

Mc5593. R-1968
Mr. Lester Recktenwald to J. Francis Cardinal
McIntyre
July 31, 1968. Wayne, Pennsylvania

California allows college professors to teach
in Junior Colleges after the age of 65. There is a
possibility that teaching could be insured in a
Catholic college or university. (English 1 pg.)
On August 5, 1968, the Cardinal states that experience should be capitalized but the State is
the best source of information. (English 1 pg.)

Mc5594. R-1968
Msgr. Benjamin Hawkes to Rev. Alban Boult-
wood, OSB
September 24, 1968. Los Angeles, California

Rev. Stephen Rein, OSB could be assigned to
a high school or a parish if he is given the
proper letters. (English 1 pg.)

Mc5595. R-1968
Mr. J. Maloy Roach to J. Francis Cardinal
McIntyre
December 6, 1968. Hollywood, California

My new song, Bring Us Together, could be
used to raise money for the hospital if it were
sung by Bing Crosby or Perry Como. (English 1
pg.) On December 10, 1968, the Cardinal states
that the suggestion was most interesting.

Mc5596. S-1968
Mr. Paul Schafer to J. Francis Cardinal
McIntyre
January 9, 1968. Chatsworth, California

A recording of a home Mass and a recorder
are enclosed so you have an opportunity to listen to the Mass. Comments will be requested in
February. (English 1 pg.)

Mc5597. S-1968
Bp. John Scanlan to Bp. Timothy Manning
January 26, 1968. Honolulu, Hawaii

A request for the information concerning the retirement plan for Bishop Willinger. It will be useful should Bishop Sweeney retire. (English 1 pg.)

Mc5598. S-1968
Dr. Wilhelm Scheich to Pope Paul VI
February 19, 1968. Los Angeles, California

A blessing is asked for a non-profit organization being formed to get food to the starving of the world. The same techniques will be used as the aero-space program used to preserve the food. (English 6 pgs.)

Mc5599. S-1968
Hon. James Delaney to the House of Representatives
February 27, 1968. Washington, D.C.

A tribute to Francis Cardinal Spellman will be printed in the Congressional Record. (English 2 pgs.)

Mc5600. S-1968
Mr. Paul Schafer to J. Francis Cardinal McIntyre
February 29, 1968. Chatsworth, California

There is deep respect for the opinions and the authority of the Archbishop but in turn a discussion of differences of opinion should be available to one who wants to learn. (English 2 pgs.)

Mc5601. S-1968
Bp. Charles Buswell to Rev. John Sutton
April 4, 1968. Pueblo, California

Permission is given to return to the Chaplains' Corps or California whichever can be made available for you. (English 1 pg.) On May 28, 1968, the Cardinal asks Father Sutton to come to the Chancery Office. (English 1 pg.)

Mc5602. S-1968
J. Francis Cardinal McIntyre to Msgr. George Scott
April 30, 1968. Los Angeles, California

Msgr. Marijan Oblak will meet with the Croatian people. Perhaps a Saturday Mass could be arranged with a dinner following to give him time to visit. (English 1 pg.)

Mc5603. S-1968
Msgr. George Scott to J. Francis Cardinal McIntyre
May 28, 1968. San Pedro, California

The Croatian people were most generous to the Bishop. His departure was sudden because of the illness of his Archbishop. (English 1 pg.)

Mc5604. S-1968
Mrs. Mary Siddall to J. Francis Cardinal McIntyre
June 26, 1968. Appleton, Wisconsin

A birthday is the time to tell a person how special he is and how the world is a better place because of him. (English 3 pgs.) On July 3, 1968 the Cardinal states that many memories come to mind when certain names are recalled. (English 1 pg.)

Mc5605. S-1968
Mrs. Ruth Stokes to Editors of *Newsweek*
July 1, 1968. Santa Monica, California

The highly slanted, inaccurate, and most unfair article on Cardinal McIntyre does not resemble the person known in Los Angeles. The Churches are full and religion is alive and well. (English 1 pg.)

Mc5606. S-1968
Mrs. Ruth Sollet to Msgr. Benjamin Hawkes
July 29, 1968. Los Angeles, California

The decision to ask for and to receive an interview was the greatest decision I could make. The vacancies are filled and working smoothly. (English 1 pg.)

Mc5607. S-1968
Bp. John J. Ward to J. Francis Cardinal McIntyre
August 5, 1968. Los Angeles, California

Sixteen years ago you baptized Princess Sherezade the granddaughter of the Shah of Iran. She desires to receive the Sacrament of Confirmation in your Chapel on September 3 at 4:00 p.m. (English 1 pg.)

Mc5608. S-1968
Rev. Edward J. Sullivan to Msgr. Benjamin Hawkes
September 16, 1968. Niagara, New York

Master of Arts in Philosophy will be granted to me in June. The classes in Scholastic and Contemporary Philosophy are good. (English 1 pg.)

Mc5609. S-1968
Mr. Raoul Silva to Msgr. Benjamin Hawkes
September 17, 1968. Garden Grove, California

The Silver Anniversary Mass is set for 12:00 noon on October 5. What arrangements should be made for being in the Sanctuary? (English 1 pg.) On September 24, 1968, Msgr. states that whatever is the custom in the parish will be followed. (English 1 pg.)

Mc5610. S-1968
Mrs. Edmund Schlegel to J. Francis Cardinal McIntyre
September 24, 1968. Whittier, California

A request for a special school and home for mentally retarded children that would have a Catholic atmosphere love, and security should be considered for Los Angeles. (English 1 pg.)

Mc5611. S-1968
J. Francis Cardinal McIntyre to Mrs. Edmund Schlegel
October 3, 1968. Los Angeles, California

Before the conference on special children, it would be good to contact the Kennedy Clinic at St. John's Hospital and the Doheny Campus of Mt. St. Mary's College. (English 1 pg.)

Mc5612. S-1968
Msgr. William Johnson to J. Francis Cardinal McIntyre
October 18, 1968. Los Angeles, California

Miss Mae Sargent will retire after working for forty years for Catholic Welfare. Would an appropriate Papal Honor be possible? (English 1 pg). On October 23, 1968, the Cardinal requests the *Benemerenti* Medal for this outstanding lady. (English 1 pg.)

Mc5613. S-1968
J. Francis Cardinal McIntyre to Mrs. Frank Seaver
December 24, 1968. Los Angeles, California

The generous donation to the Don Bosco Technical Institute will aid in the transition of the Institute to the Junior College status. (English 1 pg.)

Mc5614. T-1968
Rev. John Scola to Msgr. Benjamin Hawkes
January 2, 1968. Union City, Tennessee

A request to investigate to determine if Mr. Harold Thomason works in the Printers' Union Office. His son wants to contact him. (English 1 pg.) On January 5, 1968, Msgr. states that the family moved more than five years ago. (English 1 pg.)

Mc5615. T-1968
Bp. Paul Tanner to J. Francis Cardinal McIntyre
March 8, 1968. Washington, D.C.

An invitation is extended to the installation as Bishop of St. Augustine, Florida on March 26–27. A paragraph about the history of St. Augustine is enclosed. (English 2 pgs.) On April 30, 1968, the Bishop states that the Cardinal's gift was an outstanding gift and deeply appreciated. (English 1 pg.)

Mc5616. T-1968
Mr. C. E. Tygart to Msgr. Benjamin Hawkes
March 26, 1968. Bellflower, California

A sociological study of the clergy is being attempted to show what factors influence the thinking of the clergy. It will not produce sensationalism. (English 1 pg.)

Mc5617. T-1968
Rev. Albert Thakadiyil to Msgr. Benjamin Hawkes
April 18, 1968. Chicago, Illinois

Is there a possible summer assignment for a priest from India to work in Los Angeles? (English 1 pg.) On April 29, 1968, Msgr. states that the parish of St. Pius V would be happy to bring you to Los Angeles and have the opportunity to become acquainted. (English 1 pg.)

Mc5618. T-1968
Rev. Salvatoro Trozzo to Msgr. Donald Montrose
May 8, 1968. Gardena, California

The first three Encounter weekends were so successful that a fourth weekend was added. The movement will be held again and adult Encounters will be given. (English 3 pgs.)

Mc5619. T-1968
Msgr. Donald Montrose to Dr. Joseph Takamine
July 17, 1968. Los Angeles, California

It would be an advantage to have a medical doctor on the Encounter team. The movement of the Encounter is not under the Sodality auspices. (English 1 pg.)

5620. T-1968
Mr. Peter Thuong to J. Francis Cardinal McIntyre
September 20, 1968. Rome, Italy

A request is made for funds to complete the seminary at *Propaganda Fide* and then be adopted by the Archdiocese. (English 2 pgs.)

Mc5621. T-1968
J. Francis Cardinal McIntyre to Mr. Al Thom
October 14, 1968. Los Angeles, California

The beautiful executive desk, swivel chair, arm chairs and credenza are the objects of everyone's admiration. I am most grateful.

Mc5622. T-1968
J. Francis Cardinal McIntyre to Mr. and Mrs. A. C. Thom
October 19, 1968. Los Angeles, California

Prayerful remembrances are often sent heavenward as we see the memorial cross on the sacred spot. We visited Father's grave recently. (English 1 pg.)

Mc5623. T-1968
Miss Carlotta Taber to J. Francis Cardinal McIntyre
November 7, 1968. New York City, New York

Could the national holidays and the local holidays be incorporated into the Liturgical calendar so the laity could be united with God and country? (English 1 pg.)

Mc5624. U-1968
Mr. James Twomey to J. Francis Cardinal McIntyre
April 25, 1968. Washington, D.C.

A seminar will be held at the Ambassador Hotel given by the United States Department of Housing and Urban Development on May 23–24. If any of the parishes are interested in the meeting, this advanced notice will give them an opportunity to attend. (English 2 pgs.)

Mc5625. U-1968
Msgr. Benjamin Hawkes to Msgr. John Languille
June 28, 1968. Los Angeles, California

Could a tour of the Watts Community Center, St. Leo's Parish, and Verbum Dei High School be arranged for Mr. Peter Dwan of the Urban Systems who suggests that we get involved in the community? (English 1 pg.)

Mc5626. U-1968
Msgr. Vincent Yzermans to J. Francis Cardinal McIntyre
July 19, 1968. Huntington, Indiana

The magazine *Unity Trends* is a joint venture of the National Council of Churches and *Our Sunday Visitor*. Additional copies can be sent at a discount. (English 1 pg.)

Mc5627. U-1968
Mr. John McManemin to Arbp. Leo Byrne
August 13, 1968. New York City, New York

Una Voce strongly recommends the return to the Latin Mass as a curb to all of the grotesque liturgical experiments carried on in the church. When the law allows freedom, then freedom must be given to the Latin or English spoken at Mass. (English 2 pgs.)

Mc5628. U-1968
Mr. Raymond Kelly to Msgr. Benjamin Hawkes
September 4, 1968. Los Angeles, California

A request to have a priest give the invocation at the United States Constitution Day celebration is enclosed. The program is dedicated to youth so a young priest would be most desirable. (English 1 pg.)

Mc5629. U-1968
Pope Paul VI to Association of St. Ceclia
September 26, 1968. Vatican City

The purposes of the renewal of sacred music must be kept uppermost in our minds. The task of judging, encouraging, and checking the music can be difficult. (English 2 pgs.)

Mc5630. U-1968
Pope Paul VI to the *Liturgical Consilium*
October 24, 1968. Vatican City

Exhortations are sent to return to the basics and to retain the Sacred Liturgy as the main prayer of the Universal Church. Experiments in some localities have gone too far from the proscribed boundary. (English 2 pgs.)

Mc5631. V-1968
Bp. Luigi Accogli to J. Francis Cardinal McIntyre
January 12, 1968. Taipei, Taiwan

A letter of introduction for Msgr. Van Buggenhout who is soliciting funds for the Chinese Bishops' Conference is enclosed. (English 1 pg.). On March 21, 1968, the Cardinal questions the wisdom of the solicitation. (English 1 pg.)

Mc5632. V-1968
Rev. Francis Larkin to J. Francis Cardinal McIntyre
November 20, 1968. San Diego, California

Dietrich von Hildebrand will be in Southern California for ten days beginning in January. Perhaps a group would sponsor a lecture. (English 1 pg.)

Mc5633. W-1968
Rev. Clement Connolly to Rabbi S. Weisberg
January 3, 1968. Los Angeles, California

There are no records of any specific dialogue between Catholics and Jews. Msgr. O'Callaghan would welcome any suggestions. (English 1 pg.)

Mc5634. W-1968
Rev. Fred Wilken to J. Francis Cardinal
McIntyre
January 20, 1968. Hanford, California

Gabriel Loire's window, City of the Angels, has been shown to Rev. Gerald Kennedy of the Methodist Church and if he cannot buy it, the Catholic Church would have the next opportunity. (English 1 pg.) On February 1, 1968, the Cardinal states that he finds no suitable place for the window. (English 1 pg.)

Mc5635. W-1968
Mr. Alfred Wahrman to J. Francis Cardinal
McIntyre
January 30, 1968. Los Angeles, California

A request to search each of the California missions grounds for buried treasures. Each area would be documented. There are gold bars buried. (English 1 pg.) On February 6, 1968, the Cardinal states that the Historical Association would be the best place to start. (English 1 pg.)

Mc5636. W-1968
Mr. John Woodward to J. Francis Cardinal
McIntyre
May 10, 1968. Los Angeles, California

The program of low cost housing being sponsored by the Archdiocese in Central City is a beautiful example for all. (English 1 pg.) On May 14, 1968, the Cardinal states that the project can receive only moral support since we are so heavily in debt. (English 1 pg.)

Mc5637. W-1968
Miss Helen Wells to J. Francis Cardinal
McIntyre
August 17, 1968. Brocklyn, New York

A friendly letter comments on the divisions between the various people in the Church and the book by Stefan Zweig, *The Queen of Scots*. (English 1 pg.)

Mc5638. W-1968
Ms. Mary Walp to J. Francis Cardinal
McIntyre
October 17. 1968. Van Nuys, California

The Catholic Church could make Project Equality a success in Los Angeles as it has been in Detroit and St. Louis. (English 1 pg.) On October 23, 1968, the Cardinal states that the method used seems to be boycott and that is not generally accepted on the West Coast. (English 1 pg.)

Mc5639. Y-1968
Mr. J. J. Brandlin to Mrs. Ding Pui Yin
January 24, 1968. Los Angeles, California

There is no legal method for the Catholic Archdiocese to obtain information from the Department of Justice. Their information is given only to law enforcement agencies. (English 1 pg.)

Mc5640. Y-1968
Mr. Donald Cotter to J. Francis Cardinal
McIntyre
May 21, 1968. Chicago, Illinois

Young Christian Students (YCS) is a movement in which the youth will work with youth to make the Church and the world a better place. A symbolic offering for the work would show acceptance. (English 1 pg.)

Mc5641. Y-1968
Mrs. Frances Yates to J. Francis Cardinal
McIntyre
July 13, 1968. Laramie, Wyoming

The *Credo of the People of God* should charte the course of true renewal in the Church. Some of my recent poems are included. (English 14 pgs.)

Mc5642. Y-1968
Mr. Richard Aubry to J. Francis Cardinal
McIntyre
August 29, 1968. Los Angeles, California

A request is made to hold a meeting in South Central Los Angeles honoring St. Martin de Porres. It will be for Youth Incorporated. (English 4 pgs.)

Mc5643. Y-1968
Miss Nancy Yates to J. Francis Cardinal
McIntyre
October 30, 1968. Pacific Palisades, California

A request is made for permission to be married in the Chapel of St. Catherine's Military School since my father was the architect of the Chapel. (English 3 pgs.) On November 5, 1968, the Cardinal states that it is contrary to Canon Law and the permission cannot be given. St. Boniface Church can be arranged. (English 1 pg.)

Mc5644. Z-1968
Ms. Rosa María Zaldivar to J. Francis Cardinal McIntyre
March 12, 1968. Los Angeles, California

There is more than one way to reach the goal of life. There is need to listen to others who are seeking an answer with new vision. (English 2 pgs.) On March 25, 1968, Miss Zaldivar writes to stop and listen with the mind of Christ in the 20th century. (English 1 pg.)

Mc5645. Z-1968
Mr. Mario Zamparelli to Msgr. Benjamin Hawkes
April 29, 1968. Los Angeles, California

Any graphic arts work that the Archdiocese needs can be done easily in this company. (English 1 pg.) On May 1, 1968, Msgr. states that when the need arises, a call will be made. (English 1 pg.)

Mc5646. Z-1968
Rev. Louis Masoero to J. Francis Cardinal McIntyre
August 29, 1968. San Gabriel, California

A request for a Papal recognition for Mr. Michael Zingarelli who is a faithful worker for Don Bosco Technical Institute is made. (English 1 pg.) On August 30, 1968, the Cardinal asks for the *Benemerenti* medal for Mr. Zingarelli. (English 1 pg.)

Listing for the Year
1969

Mc5647. A-1969
J. Francis Cardinal McIntyre to Mrs. Lloyd Austin
January 6, 1969. Los Angeles, California

Prayerful condolences are sent on the death of Lloyd whom I hold in reverence for his ability and admiration and loyalty for his integrity. (English 1 pg.)

Mc5648. A-1969
Mrs. Angela Ambrosic to J. Francis Cardinal McIntyre
January 29, 1969. Los Angeles, California

Some of the films produced by the Franciscans are of questionable good taste. (English 1 pg.) On February 8, 1969, Fr. Baldonado states that the Tele Spots are well received in thirty five Dioceses. (English 1 pg.)

Mc5649. A-1969
Mr. Santos Elespe to J. Francis Cardinal McIntyre
May 29, 1969. Los Angeles, California

The *Aerolineas Argentinas* requests a special blessing on the first landing in Los Angeles on June 15. The delegation will be received by the Mayor and then go to the Cathedral. (English 2 pgs.)

Mc5650. A-1969
Mr. Robert Abernethy to Bp. Timothy Manning
June 15, 1969. Fresno, California

An invitation is extended to be interviewed on KNBC as soon as possible. The actual session will last about an hour. (English 1 pg.) On July 3, 1969, the Archbishop elect asks for a time after August 2. (English 1 pg.)

Mc5651. A-1969
Arbp. Timothy Manning to the News Services
July 9, 1969. Fresno, California

The role of the Bishop is being explained and clarified in a series of articles and interviews for the people of Fresno and Los Angeles. (English 5 pgs.)

Mc5652. A-1969
Mr. Norbert Abrahams to J. Francis Cardinal McIntyre
September 22, 1969. New York City, New York

What is the best method to stop abortions? Would a letter to the doctors be better than talking to the women at the door of the doctor's office? Where do adoptions take place? (English 1 pg.)

Mc5653. A-1969
Mr. Robin Anderson to J. Francis Cardinal McIntyre
October 24, 1969. Rome, Italy

A concert of Cardinal Merry de Val works will be held in Rome. Records will be made available of the concert. Any donation to cover the expense is most welcome. (English 1 pg.)

Mc5654. B-1969
Mr. Leonard Basal to Rev. Clement Connolly
March 25, 1969. Los Angeles, California

Could the re-publication of section III of an 1880 book receive an *Imprimatur* from the Cardinal? The original *Imprimatur* was given by John Cardinal McCloskey. (English 4 pgs.) On March 29, 1969, the Cardinal gave the *Imprimatur* and Msgr. Dignan the *Nihil Obstat*. (English 1 pg.)

Mc5655. B-1969
Mr. John Burch to Rev. Clement Connolly
April 8, 1969. Lompoc, California

At the Bishops' Meeting some discussion should take place concerning the Catholic press and the text books being used in Religion classes. (English 2 pgs.) On April 10, 1969, Fr. states that the Bishops are working hard to right the wrongs. (English 1 pg.)

Mc5656. B-1969
Rev. H. H. Hayes to Msgr. Benjamin Hawkes
April 9, 1969. Naples, Italy

Miss Maria Binet will be in Los Angeles for spinal surgery. She speaks a little English but her mother speaks no English. Is there a priest that could communicate with them? (English 1 pg.) On April 16, 1969, Msgr. states that the hospital will contact Rev. Giulio Cancelli when Miss Binet registers. (English 1 pg.)

Mc5657. B-1969
Rev. Clement Connolly to Mr. M. J. Burg
April 22, 1969. Los Angeles, California

There is a definite place on the calendar for a new parish in Mission Viejo and we are hopeful that it will not be too long delayed. (English 1 pg.) On April 28, 1969, Mr. Burg states that it is useless to wait for construction costs to be reduced. At least 20,000 people without a church is a disgrace. (English 1 pg.)

Mc5658. B-1969
Msgr. Thomas McGovern to J. Francis Cardinal McIntyre
May 21, 1969. New York City, New York

The Archdiocese of New York works for the betterment of all people and while large sums of money are spent, there is a limit to what can be done through Catholic Charities and the educational system. (English 4 pgs.)

Mc5659. B-1969
Mr. Robert Bray to Msgr. James Clyne
June 24, 1969. Los Angeles, California

Are statistics of enrollment in all Catholic institutions available from 1962–1968? As a part of my dissertation, I am working on cost benefit analysis of Catholic schools. (English 1 pg.)

Mc5660. B-1969
Mr. Eddis Butler to J. Francis Cardinal McIntyre
July 7, 1969. Harlan, Iowa

A request to write a letter of recommendation to the Archbishop of Omaha relating my musical experience. I will give a concert in Rome and relate the horrible condition of Church music in the United States. (English 2 pgs.)

Mc5661. B-1969
Arbp. Timothy Manning to Big Brother Organization
August 5, 1969. Los Angeles, California

The time is demanding that the older generation stretch out hands to help, encourage and bridge the gap for those of the younger generation. The Big Brothers give this help and commitment. (English 1 pg.)

Mc5662. B-1969
Mr. William Buckley Jr. to J. Francis Cardinal McIntyre
September 5, 1969. New York City, New York

Combat has revealed the contents of the Black Panther Coloring Book and has become an indispensable source for preserving America. (English 2 pgs.)

Mc5663. B-1969
Rev. Clement Connolly to Mrs. Bollier
September 10, 1969. Los Angeles, California

Archbishop Manning will be in San Francisco on September 14 but will leave in the evening to give the first week of the priests' retreat in Sacramento. (English 1 pg.)

Mc5664. B-1969
Mrs. Mary Burkhalter to NBC Program Director
September 17, 1969. Sherman Oaks, California

The Laugh In program did a hatchet job on the Pope and the Sacrament of Baptism. All Christians should have been offended by it. This is one way to assure censorship. (English 1 pg.)

Mc5665. B-1969
Msgr. Mario Peressin to Msgr. Benjamin Hawkes
September 22, 1969. Washington, D.C.

Please tell Mrs. Bredgland that the exchange of a zucchetto during an audience is never registered so the one she has cannot be authenticated. (English 1 pg.)

Mc5666. B-1969
Mrs. Margaret Brown to J. Francis Cardinal McIntyre
September 30, 1969. Edison, New Jersey

A request is made for prayers and advice in marital relations. (English 6 pgs.) On October 9, 1969, the Cardinal states it would be best to follow the doctor's advice and pray for patience. (English 1 pg.)

Mc5667. B-1969
Mr. James Tynion to J. Francis Cardinal
McIntyre
September 30, 1969. New York City, New
York

The recommendations of Mr. Fritz Burns and
Mr. Robert Burns for membership in the
Knights of Malta are received and accepted and
formal invitations will be sent. (English 1 pg.)

Mc5668. B-1969
Mr. Robert Bray to Msgr. Benjamin Hawkes
October 3, 1969. Pomona, California

A request to know the amount of taxes paid
for all of the Church property owned from
1958–1967. This is an important part of the
dissertation. (English 1 pg.) On October 14,
1969, Msgr. states that all of the information is
a public record and can be obtained from the office of the County Tax Assessor. (English 1 pg.)

Mc5669. B-1969
Mr. J. G. Bell to J. Francis Cardinal McIntyre
October 9, 1969. Cleveland, Ohio

A copy of *Here's How by Who's Who* is being sent. Now the best method of promotion
and advertising needs to be discovered. Any
suggestions will be gratefully considered. (English 1 pg.)

Mc5670. B-1969
Mr. Maurice Arth to J. Francis Cardinal
McIntyre
October 15, 1969. New York City, New York

Booz, Allen, and Hamilton Inc. have made an
extensive study of the best method to utilize the
Diocesan resources. We are available to Los Angeles. (English 3 pgs.)

Mc5671. B-1969
Bp. Alden Bell to Arbp. Timothy Manning
October 27, 1979. Sacramento, California

A tentative agenda for the Western Bishops'
Meeting in Washington, D.C. is enclosed. No
suggestions are being submitted. (English 2 pgs.)

Mc5672. B-1969
Mr. Earl Blue to J. Francis Cardinal McIntyre
November 7, 1969. San Francisco, California

A transition from active ministry to other
types of employment is difficult. There are
many avenues available if former members of
the clergy are referred to us. (English 1 pg.)

Mc5673. B-1969
Bp. Timothy Manning to Dr. Ray Billington
November 28, 1969. Los Angeles, California

The honor of your presence at the dedication
of the library at San Fernando Mission made
the event most memorable. (English 1 pg.)

Mc5674. B-1969
Bp. Joseph Bernardin to Arbp. Timothy
Manning
December 6, 1969. Washington, D.C.

A request to meet with a group of Hispanic
priests called Padres who want a liaison committee to work directly with the Bishops concerned with Hispanic problems. (English 8 pgs.)
On December 16, 1969, the Archbishop states
that some members of the Padres should come
to Los Angeles and look at the program here.
(English 2 pgs.)

Mc5675. B-1969
Bp. Joseph Bernardin to J. Francis Cardinal
McIntyre
December 12, 1969. Washington, D.C.

Dr. Leo Bauer alias Leopold Blau is not helping refugees nor is he authorized to do so by
Caritas Augsburg. He should not collect money
for this cause. (English 3 pgs.)

Mc5676. C-1969
Mr. Joseph Corcoran to J. Francis Cardinal
McIntyre
January 10, 1969. Philadelphia, Pennsylvania

A request for the Cardinal to write to President elect Nixon and request a pledge to remove
discrimination in immigration into the United
States. (English 3 pgs.)

Mc5677. C-1969
Mr. Robert LaBonge to J. Francis Cardinal
McIntyre
February 6, 1969. Los Angeles, California

Mr. Gene Calhoun, the Catholic Press Coun-
cilor, has discovered that he must have eye surgery. He feels your prayers will be most
advantageous. (English 1 pg.)

Mc5678. C-1969
Mr. Harry Volk to J. Francis Cardinal
McIntyre
March 6, 1969. Los Angeles, California

An invitation to be a sponsor for the dinner
honoring Mr. Otis Chandler. The proceeds will
be contributed to the Child Study Center. (English 1 pg.) On March 7, 1969, the Cardinal
states that Msgr. William Johnson will be the
sponsor. (English 1 pg.)

Mc5679. C-1969
Mr. Walter Evich to J. Francis Cardinal
McIntyre
March 8, 1969. Wyandotte, Michigan

A master plan for a calendar change that
would have 28 days in all 13 months is en
closed. There would be 13 months and one additional Saturday. (English 13 pgs.)

Mc5680. C-1969
J. Francis Cardinal McIntyre to Miss Nellie
Cantwell
April 10, 1969. Los Angeles, California

Soon the beautiful Bishop's house on Fremont Place will be changed and we will move
into St. Basil's Rectory. The difficulties of hiring
adequate help make the change necessary. (English 1 pg.)

Mc5681. C-1969
Arbp. John J. Carberry to J. Francis Cardinal
McIntyre
April 18, 1969. St. Louis, Missouri

The wishes of the contemplative religious re-
garding renewal are being investigated. There is
no wish to lessen contemplative life. (English 1
pg.)

Mc5682. C-1969
Msgr. Mario Carlomagno to Arbp. Timothy
Manning
June 12, 1969. Vatican City

A congratulatory message on returning to Los
Angeles as the new Archbishop is enclosed. (English 1 pg.) On July 1, 1969, the Archbishop
states that a visit to Lourdes and Rome will
take place before going to Los Angeles. (English
1 pg.)

Mc5683. C-1969
Rev. Daniel Young, SJ to J. Francis Cardinal
McIntyre
June 12, 1969. Los Angeles, California

An appeal to use all influences possible to
change the advertisements for cigarettes on radio and T.V. (English 3 pgs.)

Mc5684. C-1969
Mr. & Mrs. Francis Callaghan to J. Francis
Cardinal McIntyre
June 21, 1969. Long Beach, California

The Angelus Shop is again under former
ownership. It will carry standard reading material and art work. (English 1 pg.) On June 26,
1969, the Cardinal states that it is good to have
stalwart Catholics in the field of books and art.
(English 1 pg.)

Mc5685. C-1969
Msgr. Benjamin Hawkes to Mr. Joseph Liguori
July 3, 1969. Los Angeles, California

If there is a legitimate cause, there will be another Cardinal Dinner. There is no definite date
established. (English 1 pg.)

Mc5686. C-1969
Mrs. G. Campa to Msgr. Benjamin Hawkes
July 7, 1969. Los Angeles, California

Is there some method within the Diocese to
help a priest in Arroyo Grande, California. He
cannot use his church because he has no insurance. (English 3 pgs.) On July 9, 1969, Msgr.
states that the matter will be taken to the
Fresno Chancery Office. (English 1 pg.)

Mc5687. C-1969
Mr. William Kircher to Mr. Johnny Carson
July 8, 1969. Los Angeles, California

The book mentioned by Senator George Murphy is actually a pamphlet published by *Twin
Circle,* an ultra conservative newspaper. (English 2 pgs.)

Mc5688. C-1969
Rev. James Richter to Bp. John Ward
July 16, 1969. Huntington, New York

In the revision of the Church calendar, a re-
quest to recommend November 20 as a feast of
Mary. It is the date on which the National
Shrine was dedicated in 1959. (English 1 pg.)

Mc5689. C-1969
Rev. William Consedine to J. Francis Cardinal
McIntyre
July 22, 1969. Washington, D.C.

The Archdiocese of St. Paul is entering the
antitrust lawsuit against Children's Library
Book distributors. Any Diocese may join the lit-
igation if it desire. (English 3 pgs.)

Mc5690. C-1969
Mr. Angelo Conte to Arbp. Timothy Manning
August 4, 1969. New York City, New York

At the next Bishop's Meeting, the philoso-
phies of those who are confusing the people of
God should be condemned. (English 2 pgs.)

Mc5691. C-1969
Mrs. Beatrice Challis to Arbp. Timothy
Manning
August 5, 1969. Los Angeles, California

Welcome to St. Brendan Parish! It is a great
honor for the parish and the people of the area
to have the Archbishop live there. (English 1
pg.) On August 7, 1969, the Archbishop states
that he asks for prayers that he will be worthy
of the people of the parish. (English 1 pg.)

Mc5692. C-1969
Rev. Michael Carlos to J. Francis Cardinal
McIntyre
August 5, 1969. San Clemente, California

The reduction of our indebtedness by
$100,000 relieves the tension and brings hope
and joy to the people and the priests. Your letter
will be published in our Sunday bulletin. (English 1 pg.)

Mc5693. C-1969
Bp. John J. Cassata to Knights and Ladies of
Dallas
September 12, 1969. Dallas, Texas

The Testimonial dinner for Bishop Thomas
Gorman's resignation will be held on October
13 at 7:30 p.m. (English 1 pg.) On September
23, 1969, the Cardinal states that he regrets
that he cannot be present for the testimonial
dinner. (English 1 pg.)

Mc5694. C-1969
Mr. Thomas Smith to J. Francis Cardinal
McIntyre
September 17, 1969. Los Angeles, California

An invitation is extended to give the invocation at the Central City Association luncheon
honoring Hon. John A. Volpe on October 16.
(English 1 pg.) On September 18, 1969, the
Cardinal states it will be a pleasure to be
present at the luncheon. (English 1 pg.)

Mc5695. C-1969
Mr. Stuart Cuthberton to John Cardinal
Wright
October 10, 1969. Santa Barbara, California

The arguments stated in the Los Angeles
Times concerning the abortion issue are faulty
and should be more seriously considered or else
the theological issue of the encyclical will be destroyed. (English 2 pgs.)

Mc5696. C-1969
Mr. J. Nevins McBride to Arbp. Timothy
Manning
October 14, 1969. Washington, D.C.

An invitation is extended to be present at the
Alumni Association of Georgetown University
honoring Senator George Murphy. (English 1
pg.) On October 20, 1969, the Archbishop
states that it will be a pleasure to be present.
(English 1 pg.)

Mc5697. C-1969
Mr. Stuart Cuthbertson to Rev. Clement
Connolly
October 20, 1969. Santa Barbara, California

The whole controversy over abortion should
have been solved by a Papal statement and not
by arguments. (English 1 pg.)

Mc5698. C-1969
Br. Bertram Coleman to J. Francis Cardinal
McIntyre
November 21, 1969. Rheem Valley, California

If some decision is being considered about
consolidating or closing schools, could the Provincials be notified? (English 2 pgs.) On November 26, 1969, Brother wrote stating that
there is no master plan. Cathedral High School
will continue but La Salle is a question. (English 2 pg.)

Mc5699. C-1969
Msgr. Harold Laubacher to J. Francis Cardinal
McIntyre
November 26, 1969. Los Angeles, California

Archbishop Romolo Carboni has left Peru
and is in Rome. He could use some help for his
personal needs. (English 1 pg.) On December
1969, the Archbishop sends special greetings
and requests prayers. (English 1 pg.)

Mc5700. C-1969
Rev. Christopher McDonnell to Msgr. Benjamin Hawkes
December 26, 1969. Hollywood, California

A man posing as a priest is making the
rounds of the parishes. He stayed with the
priests at Blessed Sacrament and left for San
Francisco with their financial help. (English
1 pg.)

Mc5701. D-1969
Ms. Dorothy Day to J. Francis Cardinal
McIntyre
March 1969. New York City, New York

A yearly news letter from St. Joseph House of
Hospitality is enclosed and a request to meet
the needs of the many visitors. (English 1 pg.)

Mc5702. D-1969
Mr. Alvin Downey to J. Francis Cardinal
McIntyre
April 15, 1969. Downey, California

The Life of Christ by Giovanni Papini republished by Dell Publishing Company will give
beautiful reasons for celibacy for the clergy.
(English 2 pgs.) On April 23, 1969, the Cardinal states that celibacy will continue in the
Church for many years. (English 1 pg.)

Mc5703. D-1969
Rev. Dave Zunino to J. Francis Cardinal
McIntyre
May 16, 1969. Bellflower, California

The work of Mrs. Mary Down has been an
example for the parish. The Cardinal's blessing
and the Papal blessing should be given to her.
(English 1 pg.) On May 21, 1969, the Cardinal
congratulates Mrs. Down on her years of service to the parish. (English 1 pg.)

Mc5704. D-1969
Rev. Robert Donoghue to J. Francis Cardinal
McIntyre
August 8, 1969. Isla Vista, California

The reduction of the parish debt by $100,000 is a welcome and wonderful surprise. St. Marks' Church would not be in existence if the Cardinal were not so thoughtful. (English 1 pg.)

Mc5705. D-1969
Mrs. Jean Radofsky to State Legislators
N.D. Covina, California

Taxpayers are organizing to withhold taxes if teachers like Angela Davis will be hired to teach in State schools. Every education bond will receive a NO vote unless the teaching profession is more carefully chosen. (English 1 pg.)

Mc5706. E-1969
Mr. Thomas Emerson to Arbp. Timothy
Manning
August 14, 1969. Venice, California

A request for an interview to discuss the problem of dress at Mass and Holy Communion. (English 5 pgs.) On August 19, 1969, the Archbishop request that a call be made for an appointment. (English 1 pg.)

Mc5707. E-1969
Mrs. Amy Ellis to J. Francis Cardinal McIntyre
August 30, 1969. Ventura, California

Is the devotion popular in Naples, Italy, known only in Italy? Is there some place that more information can be obtained about this devotion? (English 1 pg.) On September 25, 1969, the Cardinal states that if any information is desired a letter to Pompeii will bring all of the desired information. (English 1 pg.)

Mc5708. E-1969
Miss Helen Imbrigotto to J. Francis Cardinal
McIntyre
December 8, 1969. Los Angeles, California

A warning should be given to priests to be most cautious about what they say to Mr. John Elsbach. He quotes you and the priests in a most unfavorable manner. (English 1 pg.) On December 11, 1969, the Cardinal states that he does not know the gentleman. (English 1 pg.)

Mc5709. F-1969
Mrs. Mary Jane Ford to J. Francis Cardinal
McIntyre
March 22, 1969. Ft. Lauderdale, Florida

The November paper referred to you as the awesome Archbishop of Los Angeles. If this means that you are careful to teach the faith, then there should be more awesome Bishops. (English 2 pgs.)

Mc5710. F-1969
Msgr. John Rawden to Mr. Frank Fisher
May 27, 1969. Los Angeles, California

The generous donation to the American Catholic Overseas Fund is most deeply appreciated. (English 1 pg.)

Mc5711. F-1969
J. Francis Cardinal McIntyre to Mrs. Ralph
Fortezzo
May 28, 1969. Los Angeles, California

With the Pius X Medal of Honor comes the blessing of the Cardinal and congratulations for the dedicated service given to the parish through the CCD. (English 1 pg.).

Mc5712. F-1969
Msgr. Benjamin Hawkes to Miss Claire
Falkenstein
June 12, 1969. Los Angeles, California

The beautiful sculpture and the fabulous stained glass windows in St. Basil's Church will aid the faithful to pray and reflect. (English 1 pg.)

Mc5713. F-1969
Mr. Thomas Finneran to J. Francis Cardinal
McIntyre
June 22, 1969. Houston, Texas

A friendly letter commenting on the 83rd birthday and a proposed trip to New York to walk along the same streets once so important. A contribution to the Archbishop's Fund for Charity is enclosed. (English 1 pg.) On July 3, 1969, the Cardinal comments on the changes one should expect in New York and everywhere. (English 1 pg.)

Mc5714. F-1969
Dr. James Fifield to J. Francis Cardinal
McIntyre
July 3, 1969. Los Angeles, California

The neighborhood of Fremont Place is not the same since your departure. Would the Church be interested in the next house? (English 1 pg.) On July 8, 1969, the Cardinal states that for the present, there is no discussion except to rent the house if a suitable tenant can be found. (English 1 pg.)

Mc5715. F-1969
Mrs. Olga Fischer to Arbp. Timothy Manning
September 5, 1969. Los Angeles, California

There is a project that must be presented to you concerning the Blessed Mother that will interest and gladden you. (English 1 pg.) On September 10, 1969, the Archbishop asks for an appointment when it is convenient. (English 1 pg.) On October 14, 1969, the Archbishop asks for the recitation of the Rosary. (English 1 pg.)

Mc5716. G-1969
Count Enrico Galeazzi to J. Francis Cardinal
McIntyre
January 21, 1969. Vatican City

A friendly letter commenting on the amount
of news coverage that the Church is receiving
and the amount of work that must be done.
(English 1 pg.)

Mc5717. G-1969
J. Francis Cardinal McIntyre to Bp. Thomas
Gorman
February 28, 1969. Los Angeles, California

The forthcoming elections during the Bishops' Meeting should be carefully watched. (English 1 pg.) On March 10, 1969, the Bishop
states that it is difficult to replace the present
president without a strong candidate. (English
1 pg.)

Mc5718. G-1969
Mr. Ernest George to J. Francis Cardinal
McIntyre
April 17, 1969. Los Angeles, California

A move from Fremont Place will be a grave
mistake as is the handling of the sale of Diocesan property. Father Gardner can give great assistance in T.V. and communications to the
Diocese. (English 2 pgs.)

Mc5719. G-1969
Bp. Joseph Green to Arbp. Timothy Manning
July 9, 1969. Reno, Nevada

If the *Cursillo Symposium* can be rearranged,
I will be able to attend the installation. I have
been asked to give the major address. (English
1 pg.)

Mc5720. G-1969
Msgr. Jean Marie Gerard to Arbp. Timothy
Manning
July 12, 1969. Quebec, Canada

A request is made for a copy of the coat-of-
arms and the name of the church and city of
which you are titular archbishop. (English 1
pg.)

Mc5721. G-1969
J. Francis Cardinal McIntyre to Bp. Thomas
Gorman
July 22, 1969. Los Angeles, California

An invitation to the Pontifical Mass on August 2 welcoming Archbishop Manning as Coadjutor Archbishop of Los Angeles and Bishop
Dougherty as an Auxiliary Bishop of Los Angeles is enclosed. (English 1 pg.)

Mc5722. G-1969
Mr. Raymond Gauer to Arbp. Timothy
Manning
August 1, 1969. Los Angeles, California

The fight against obscenity continues and
some successes are being made. An update of
the work is available. (English 1 pg.)

Mc5723. G-1969
J. Francis Cardinal McIntyre to Mr. Richard
Grant
August 7, 1969. Los Angeles, California

The Ford Foundation published *The Law and
Lore of Endowment Funds*. If copies are not
available, I'll loan you mine. (English 1 pg.)

Mc5724. G-1969
Mr. Chester Gillis to Arpb. Timothy Manning
August 20, 1969. Los Angeles, California

It seems some political elements are trying to
do in the United States what the extremists are
doing in Northern Ireland. (English 1 pg.)

Mc5725. G-1969
Mr. Alastair Guinan to J. Francis Cardinal
McIntyre
August 24, 1969. New York City, New York

An invitation to celebrate the birthday of a
classmate Msgr. Stanislaus McGovern on September 10 is enclosed. (English 1 pg.) On August 29, 1969, the Cardinal states that he sees
no possibility of a trip at this time. (English 1
pg.)

Mc5726. G-1969
Mr. Chester Gillis to Arbp. Timothy Manning
August 27, 1969. Los Angeles, California

Is there any definite plan to relocate St. Vibiana's Cathedral in the new Square being
planned for the renewal project? (English 2
pgs.) On September 11, 1969, the Archbishop
states that he is following with interest the renewal project since the Church is at the heart of
it spiritually and geographically. (English 1 pg.)

Mc5727. G-1969
Bp. Thomas Gorman to J. Francis Cardinal
McIntyre
September 5, 1969. Dallas, Texas

I anticipate with pleasure the privilege of
watching from the sidelines the interesting developments of the Church. (English 1 pg.)

Mc5728. G-1969
J. Francis Cardinal McIntyre to Bp. Thomas
Gorman
October 8, 1969. Los Angeles, California

A statement of support for Cardinal O'Boyle
should have been issued by the Board. The committee quoted statements made by the Cardinal
but did not mention his name nor the Archdiocese of Washington. (English 1 pg.)

Mc5729. G-1969
Mrs. Lucille Gunn to Bp. John J. Ward
October 18, 1969. Costa Mesa, California

Is the Catholic Pentecostals an underground
movement not accepted by the Cardinal? Many
good people are in the movement. (English 3
pgs.)

Mc5730. H-1969
Mrs. Minnie Harbeck to J. Francis Cardinal
McIntyre
January 5, 1969. Moline, Illinois

The Christmas fund is being transferred to
the Archdiocese. It will be useable in November
for Queen of Angels Hospital and for the Archdiocese. (English 5 pgs.) On January 31, 1969,
the Cardinal states that the check will be
mailed to your house and then can be sent to
the ones in need. (English 1 pg.)

Mc5731. H-1969
Mr. James Harris to Arbp. Timothy Manning
June 24, 1969. Chicago, Illinois

An invitation is extended to give the invocation at the opening of the Interracial Justice
Meeting on August 21 at Loyola University.
(English 1 pg.) On July 3, 1969, the Archbishop
states that there are too many uncertain commitments for August to accept any invitation.
(English 1 pg.)

Mc5732. H-1969
Mrs. Betje Howell to Msgr. Benjamin Hawkes
June 25, 1969. Santa Monica, California

The article on the works of Claire Falkenstein
and St. Basil's Church is enclosed. Are tickets
required for the dedication of the church? (English 1 pg.) On June 26, 1969, Msgr. states that
two tickets are enclosed and he expresses gratitude for the article. (English 1 pg.)

Mc5733. H-1969
Mrs. Myrtle Houston to J. Francis Cardinal
McIntyre
July 7, 1969. Rowland Heights, California

An inquiry as to when a Church and school
will be built in Rowland Heights area since
many young couples are moving into this area.
(English 1 pg.) On July 10, 1969, the Cardinal
states that a proposal will be made soon for
better facilities. (English 1 pg.)

Mc5734. H-1969
Arbp. Timothy Manning to Bp. James A.
Hickey
August 11, 1969. Los Angeles, California

The statement on celibacy should be the
paragraphs from 17 to 20 and the statement issued at Houston should be included. (English 1
pg.)

Mc5735. H-1969
Mr. Harry C. Hagerty to J. Francis Cardinal
McIntyre
August 15, 1969. New York City, New York

The money market is very tight at the present
time. No one is interested in loaning large sums
of money except for office buildings with assured rentals. (English 2 pgs.)

Mc5736. H-1969
Bp. James A. Hickey to Arbp. Timothy
Manning
August 15, 1969. Chicago, Illinois

The Bishops wanted an updated statement
emphasizing the theological, ascetical, and positive elements of the spiritual witness given by
celibacy. (English 1 pg.)

Mc5737. H-1969
Mr. Nolan Hamilton to J. Francis Cardinal
McIntyre
August 23, 1969. Los Angeles, California

The goodness of the Archbishop to the families of sons killed in the war must be acknowledged with gratitude. These deeds are not
published and only God and those in need
know about them. (English 1 pg.)

Mc5738. H-1969
Mrs. Ceclila Haupt to Arbp. Timothy
Manning
September 4, 1969. Altadena, California

An appeal for some assistance for a Catholic
son who is a conscientious objector to the Viet
Nam War. (English 2 pgs.) On September 10,
1969, the Archbishop states that every assistance will be given when the young man states
his objection. (English 1 pg.)

Mc5739. H-1969
Mr. Walter Hoffman to J. Francis Cardinal
McIntyre
October 17, 1969. Ventura, California

The yearly donation to St. John's Seminary
and Santa Marta Hospital is enclosed. (English
1 pg.) On October 20, 1969, the Cardinal states
that it is most gratifying to receive these donations. (English 1 pg.)

Mc5740. H-1969
Mrs. Patrick Hardy to J. Francis Cardinal
McIntyre
October 22, 1969. Los Angeles, California

Could Sunday, November 9 be declared a day
of special prayer for all men missing in action
or held in prison camps in Viet Nam? (English
1 pg.) On October 28, 1969, the Cardinal states
that the announcement will be made on November 2 for the following week. (English 1
pg.)

Mc5741. H-1969
Mr. Walter Hansen to Arbp. Timothy
Manning
October 26, 1969. Los Angeles, California

Please have the courage to insist on good
Church music and not the rock and roll being
introduced into the Mass. We have Gregorian
Chant and we should keep it. (English 1 pg.)
On October 30, 1969, the Archbishop states it
is hopeful that good music will be left when all
of the ferment dies away. (English 1 pg.)

Mc5742. H-1969
Dr. Armand Hammer to J. Francis Cardinal
McIntyre
December 1968. Los Angeles, California

The St. Patrick's Well Shrine will be completely free from debt with this check for
$10,000. Please forward the check to County
Tipperary, Ireland, for the last payment. (English 1 pg.) On January 3, 1969, the Cardinal
expresses his appreciation for the most generous
donation to the project. (English 1 pg.)

Mc5743. H-1969
Mrs. Mildred Hunt to J. Francis Cardinal
McIntyre
December 3, 1969. Torrance, California

Why is heresy being allowed in the Offertory
and the Canon of the Mass? Are the Catholics
giving up to the Protestants? (English 1 pg.)

Mc5744. H-1969
Dr. Howard House to J. Francis Cardinal
McIntyre
December 8, 1969. Los Angeles, California

Having you present at the dinner given in my
honor was the best part of the evening. You
are held in high esteem in our family. (English
1 pg.)

Mc5745. H-1969
Rev. John Wehmhoefer to Arbp. Timothy
Manning
December 10, 1969. Santa Ana, California

A request for a letter of recommendation for
Mr. Robert Huestis so he can study in the Deacon Program at St. John's Collegeville, Minnesota. (English 1 pg.) On December 22, 1969,
the Archbishop states that the one who writes
the letter of recommendation is the Bishop that
will be prepared to offer him a position. (English 1 pg.)

Mc5746. I-1969
Mr. John Irwin to J. Francis Cardinal
McIntyre
January 20, 1969. La Jolla, California

The letter to President Nixon endorsing my
Federal Judgeship is appreciated. Fr. Jim Irwin
will study at UCLA in the Latin American Center this year. (English 2 pgs.)

Mc5747. K-1969
Rev. Joseph Cameron to Msgr. Benjamin
Hawkes
January 30, 1969 Montreal, Canada

Before doing business with Dave Koval Enter-
prises, could the Diocese have a recommendation from your Chancery Office. (English 1 pg.)
On February 10, 1969, states that a complete
search of banks, insurance companies, and
credit bureaus showed no such company in this
locality. (English 1 pg.)

Mc5748. K-1969
Mrs. Marge Kristy to Arbp. Timothy Manning
N.D. Hacienda Heights, California

The lack of vocations does not exist. The
seminary is making it too difficult to remain.
Not every priest has to be a genius. (English 2
pgs.) On February 6, 1969, the Archbishop
states that the remarks will be sent to the seminary. (English 1 pg.)

Mc5749. K-1969
Mr. Henry Koval to Arbp. Luigi Raimondi
February 20, 1969. Charsworth, California

A copy of *Catholic Crosswords* is enclosed
which could receive the endorsement of the Apostolic Delegate. (English 2 pgs.) On February
26, 1969, Msgr. Hawkes states that it is the policy to be impartial and not to give endorsements. (English 1 pg.)

Mc5750. K-1969
Mr. Joon Chul Chang to J. Francis Cardinal
McIntyre
March 25, 1969. Los Angeles, California

An invitation to Korean Night on April 12 at
which time the progress of the Korean people
will be made visible. (English 2 pgs.) On March
25, 1969, the Cardinal sends special blessings
for the Korean people. (English 1 pg.)

Mc5751. K-1969
Mr. Jerry Kelly to J. Francis Cardinal McIntyre
June 17, 1969. Coral Gables, Florida

Your letter of recommendation to Notre
Dame University four years ago proved to be
accurate. I did receive my degree in Sociology.
(English 1 pg.) On June 25, 1969, the Cardinal
states that he was willing to follow Uncle Tom
Kelly's recommendation. (English 1 pg.)

Mc5752. K-1969
Arbp. Timothy Manning to Rev. Paul Konoske
July 1, 1969. Fresno, California

It will be difficult to follow in your footsteps
at St. Brendan's. Please leave instructions and
recommendations for me to follow. (English 1
pg.) On July 7, 1969, Fr. states that everyone is
awaiting your arrival and is happy with the new
pastor. (English 1 pg.)

Mc5753. K-1969
Miss Jeanette Kanowsky to Arbp. Timothy
Manning
July 27, 1969. La Canada, California

If a Committee of Correspondence could be
established to print a short instruction in the
Sunday bulletin, Catholics could be better in-
structed in their faith. (English 2 pgs.) On August 5, 1969, the Archbishop states that the
plan has real merit and will be considered. (English 1 pg.)

Mc5754. K-1969
Msgr. Kevin Keane to Arbp. Timothy Manning
August 1, 1969. Culver City, California

A request for a message that can be printed in
the brochure that is being planned for the
Golden Jubilee of St. Augustine's Parish. (English 1 pg.)

Mc5755. K-1969
Mrs. Eileen King to J. Francis Cardinal
McIntyre
September 8, 1969. Arcata, California

There are Pellys in my family background
coming from Galway, Ireland. This family picture might show someone that you know. (English 2 pgs.) On September 25, 1969, the
Cardinal states that he has no recollection of
any member of the Pelly family. I am returning
the picture. (English 1 pg.)

Mc5756. K-1969
Arbp. Timothy Manning to Mr. Stuart Karl
September 8, 1969. Los Angeles, California

The Permanent Deacon Program is not completely organized yet. Until that time, continue
the work you are doing in the parish. (English
1 pg.)

Mc5757. K-1969
Dr. John Kiley to Arbp. Joseph McGucken
October 20, 1969. Pebble Beach, California

Seminarians would benefit from the training
and discipline of a Zen Master schooled in Tho-
mastic Philosophy. It could be post graduate
training. (English 4 pgs.)

Mc5758 C-1969
Mr. Charles Kearney to Arbp. Timothy
Manning
November 1, 1969. Pasadena, California

Are all seminaries in the United States so
crowded that the young men of other countries
could not be educated here? (English 1 pg.) On
November 17, 1969, the Archbishop states that
sometimes seminarians from other countries
find our standards too hard to follow. (English
1 pg.)

Mc5759. K-1969
Rev. Kuruville to Arbp. Timothy Manning
November 7, 1969. Chitoor, South India

A request for a donation for the two
Churches and two Chapels needed in the area
and for some money to travel to the Eucharistic
Congress in Bombay. (English 1 pg.)

Mc5760. K-1969
Mrs. Hugo Kersten to J. Francis Cardinal
McIntyre
N.D. Los Angeles, California

A note of warning that Bishops and Archbishops should not make pronouncements in
areas that are not their educational strong
points. The grape boycott is one such area. (English 1 pg.)

Mc5761. L-1969
J. Francis Cardinal McIntyre to Mrs. Clare B.
Luce
January 10, 1969. Los Angeles, California

A luncheon can be arranged for the days that
you are in Los Angeles. Please let us know your
schedule. (English 1 pg.)

Mc5762. L-1969
Mr. Howard Leederman to Msgr. Benjamin
Hawkes
January 15, 1969. Los Angeles, California

An invitation to give the invocation at the
Contractors International Meeting on March
11 is extended. (English 1 pg.) On January 20,
1969, Msgr. states that Msgr. Thomas O'Sullivan, Secretary of the Building Commission,
will be happy to give the invocation. (English
1 pg.)

Mc5763. L-1969
Bp. Giovanni Benelli to Mr. Emmet Lavery
January 21, 1969. Vatican City

Pope Paul VI appreciates the copy of your latest drama, *The Common Ground,* and imparts
to you his Apostolic Blessing. (English 1 pg.)

Mc5764. L-1969
Mr. Oscar Lawler to Msgr. Benjamin Hawkes
April 2, 1969. Los Angeles, California

The monthly report of building permits is enclosed as are the notes taken at the lecture given
by Mr. Martin to the Reserve City Bankers.
(English 1 pg.)

Mc5765. L-1969.
Mr. Gerald Lynch to J. Francis Cardinal
McIntyre
May 28, 1969. Los Angeles, California

A copy of the talk given at the Burbank
Chamber of Commerce is enclosed. References
to Don Bosco Technical Institute were well received. (English 1 pg.) On June 2, 1969, the
Cardinal states that your appraisal of the Institute is appreciated. (English 1 pg.)

Mc5766. L-1969
Rev. William Levada to Arbp. Timothy
Manning
June 14, 1969. Rome, Italy

A friendly letter of congratulations and a
progress report on the course of studies with
the address of a new residence for next year.
(English 2 pgs.) On June 20, 1969, the Archbishop states that surely the Cardinal will give
permission for the additional study time. (English 1 pg.)

Mc5767. L-1969
Mr. Peter Larsen to J. Francis Cardinal
McIntyre
June 24, 1969. Los Angeles, California

Is there a list of all the saints downgraded by
the recent Papal pronouncements? (English 1
pg.) On June 27, 1969, the Cardinal states that
all may venerate the saints as they did formerly
especially St. Christopher. (English 1 pg.)

Mc5768. L-1969
Mrs. Donald Lies to J. Francis Cardinal
McIntyre
July 24, 1969. Stanton, California

An appeal is made for a Bible study group in
every parish so more people can learn in depth
the life of Christ. (English 2 pgs.)

Mc5769. Mc-1969
Mr. Donald McCoy to J. Francis Cardinal
McIntyre
January 31, 1969. Los Angeles, California

I am a recent citizen of Los Angeles with
many years of experience in Latin America. I
am interested in working with Spanish speaking
people for the Church. (English 1 pg.) On February 6, 1969, the Cardinal ask Mr. McCoy to
make an appointment for a discussion. (English
1 pg.)

Mc5770. Mc-1969
Mr. Arthur Snyder to The City Council
February 7, 1969. Los Angeles, California

A City Resolution to give special testimony
for the work being done by Cardinal McIntyre
for the people of Los Angeles. The recent campaign to save Santa Marta Hospital and the
Community Fiesta deserve special commendation. (English 2 pgs.)

Mc5771. Mc-1969
Mrs. James McKiernan to J. Francis Cardinal
McIntyre
February 10, 1969. New York City, New York

A young man recently returned from the
Army needs work so he can support himself.
Any help will be most welcome. (English 3 pgs.)
On February 24, 1969, the Cardinal states that
the young man is working and is preparing for
civil service examinations. (English 1 pg.)

Mc5772. Mc-1969
Mrs. Bruce Schraeder to J. Francis Cardinal
McIntyre
March 3, 1969. Orange, California

A request to give some help to investigate Dr.
Gordon McCoy who is giving the sex education
lecture in the public schools and the CCD
classes. (English 3 pgs.) On March 11, 1969,
the Cardinal states that Dr. McCoy is the same
person who spoke at the Archdiocesan Council
and is approved by the Board. (English 1 pg.)

Mc5773. Mc-1969
Mr. Joseph McElligott to J. Francis Cardinal
McIntyre
July 31, 1969. San Francisco, California

Your views on education will be carried to
the Legislature in Sacramento where I will work
for the Archdiocese of Los Angeles. (English
1 pg.)

Mc5774. Mc-1969
Mrs. John McBrady to J. Francis Cardinal
McIntyre
September 17, 1969. Valencia, California

It is difficult to obtain information from the
State Department about the death of Iris Gross
who was working with the Montforte Sisters in
Africa. Any details of her death or burial will
be appreciated. (English 1 pg.)

Mc5775. Mc-1969
J. Francis Cardinal McIntyre to Mr. & Mrs.
McGuigan
September 27, 1969. Los Angeles, California

Pope Paul VI extends his Apostolic Benedica-
tion upon you for a happy and holy married
life. This blessing is given to all the members of
the wedding party. Personal blessings and congratulations accompany the Papal Blessing. (English 1 pg.)

Mc5776. Mc-1969
Mrs. Helen McGregor to Msgr. Benjamin
Hawkes
December 31, 1969. Los Angeles, California

Why is a change of address such a difficult
process at St. Basil's Church? (English 1 pg.) On
January 8, 1970, the Msgr. states that the move
was into another parish. However, you are always welcome at St. Basil's. (English 1 pg.)

Mc5777. M-1969
J. Francis Cardinal McIntyre to Mrs. George
Miller
January 6, 1969. Los Angeles, California

The death of Senator Miller leaves a vacancy
that will be impossible to fill. May Our Lady
give you consolation. (English 1 pg.)

Mc5778. M-1969
Mr. Frank Morriss to J. Francis Cardinal
McIntyre
January 30, 1969. Denver, Colorado

A few copies of Thou Art the Rock are in the
mail and many more can be sent. (English 1
pg.) On February 6, 1969, the Cardinal states
that the book will be read with pleasure. The
radio transcription of the talk was splendid.
(English 1 pg.)

Mc5779. M-1969
Mr. John MacDonald to J. Francis Cardinal
McIntyre
February 11, 1969. Houston, Texas

Some equality should be given to religion in
the White House and clergy should be invited
whose remarks will not be questioned. (English
4 pgs.)

Mc5780. M-1969
Mr. Francis Montgomery to Msgr. Benjamin
Hawkes
March 10, 1969. Los Angeles, California

Please use this check to help defray the medical expenses of Rev. Bernard Martin. (English 1
pg.) On March 11, 1969, Msgr. states that Father and the Cardinal appreciate the generous
donation. (English 1 pg.)

Mc5781. M-1969
Mrs. Helen Malchow to J. Francis Cardinal
McIntyre
April 11, 1969. Glendale, California

A letter of protest is sent about the renewal in
the Church and a plea to keep the Catholic faith
in its entirety at the Bishops' Meeting. (English
4 pgs.) On April 19, 1969, the Cardinal asks
for the people to keep praying for the church.
(English 1 pg.)

Mc5782. M-1969
Mr. William Marmion to J. Francis Cardinal
McIntyre
April 12, 1969. Garden Grove, California

Los Angeles can be revitalized by a mandate
from the Cardinal for the priests to respond to
the needs of the people. (English 2 pgs.) On
April 25, 1969, the Cardinal states that revolu-
tionary procedures are not necessary in this
Archdiocese. (English 1 pg.)

Mc5783. M-1969
Mr. Leo T. Moore to Msgr. Benjamin Hawkes
N.D. Los Angeles, California

A copy of Leo Moore's Little Scroll is enclosed for the Imprimatur. (English 1 pg.) On
June 19, 1969, Msgr. Dignan states that the
book does not need an Imprimatur. (English
1 pg.)

Mc5784. M-1969
Mr. George Montgomery to Los Angeles Times
June 30, 1969. Los Angeles, California

The demonstration at St. Basil's Church
shows the importance of the Church in the
business district of Wilshire Blvd. (English 1
pg.) On July 7, 1969, the Cardinal states that
the Church will serve many people for years.
(English 1 pg.)

Mc5785. M-1969
Arbp. Timothy Manning to Father Superior
July 1, 1969. Fresno, California

A request for hospitality at Collegio Maryknoll and for arrangements to be made for the
celebration of Mass at the tomb of St. Peter as
well as for a Papal audience. (English 1 pg.)

Mc5786. M-1969
Arbp. Timothy Manning to Mr. James
Manning
August 5, 1969. Los Angeles, California

The family lineage has no point of contact as
far as I can tell. Perhaps the Fr. Manning at San
Antonio Chancery office will identify with
some of the names. (English 5 pgs.)

Mc5787. M-1969
Msgr. Benjamin Hawkes to Msgr. Brent Eagen
August 16, 1969. Los Angeles, California

If the Chaplain at the Balboa Hospital con-
curs, could he be of assistance to the young man
who has been promised dental training in the
Navy. (English 1 pg.)

Mc5788. M-1969
Mr. Francis Montgomery to J. Francis Cardi-
nal McIntyre
August 25, 1969. Los Angeles, California

A check for the proposed Thomas Aquinas
College or San Rafael College campus is enclosed. Other donations will follow. English 1
pg.)

Mc5789. M-1969
Mr. Frank Morriss to J. Francis Cardinal
McIntyre
September 15, 1969. Denver, Colorado

A desperate appeal for funds to substitute for
a book that can no longer be sold. Anything is
welcome even moral support. (English 2 pgs.

Mc5790. M-1969
Mr. Bob Mitchell to J. Francis Cardinal
McIntyre
September 26, 1969. Los Angeles, California

An invitation is extended to the first organ
recital to be given in St. Basil's Church on October 6 at 6:30. (English 1 pg.) On October 3,
1969, the Cardinal states that he is certain that
he will be present on October 6. (English 1 pg.)

Mc5791. M-1969
Arbp. Luigi Raimondi to J. Francis Cardinal
McIntyre
October 11, 1969. Washington, D.C.

George Stuart Massey states that he is a missionary from Orai, India, and is collecting
money. There is no missionary by that name
and the mission station in Orai is closed. (English 1 pg.)

Mc5792. M-1969
Msgr. Benjamin Hawkes to Mr. John Malone
October 24, 1969. Los Angeles, California

A request to meet with Mr. John Miller during the last days of December and talk to him
about FBI work. (English 1 pg.) On October 28,
1969, Mr. Malone states it will be a pleasure to
have a meeting on December 31. (English 1 pg.)

Mc5793. M-1969
Mr. John Mulloy to J. Francis Cardinal
McIntyre
November 9, 1969. Philadelphia, Pennsylvania

The translation of the Latin Mass should be
done with reverence and care and not just to see
how quickly it can be done. (English 2 pgs.)

Mc5794. M-1969
Mr. George Montgomery to Rev. C. Kilmer
Meyers
December 1, 1969. Los Angeles, California

If the paper quotations are correct, your
statements on the Pope being led by obsolescent
theologies and that Bishops do not believe what
they teach are absolutely false. (English 2 pgs.)

Mc5795. M-1969
Arbp. Timothy Manning to Bp. Giacomo
Martin
December 23, 1969. Los Angeles, California

A stipend is enclosed for a Mass to be celebrated for Cardinal McIntyre's intentions. It is
with gratitude that we acknowledge your goodness to our visitors. (English 1 pg.)

Mc5796. N-1969
J. Francis Cardinal McIntyre to President Rich-
ard Nixon
January 7, 1969. Los Angeles, California

Senator Dirkson has requested me to give the
Benediction at the inauguration. Previous commitments make it necessary for me to forgo
this honor. My prayers are with you. (English
2 pgs.)

Mc5797. N-1969
Mr. John Peterson to J. Francis Cardinal
McIntyre
February 28, 1969. St. Louis, Missouri

If the information concerning the retirement
benefits and health insurance for both clergy
and lay employees can be sent to Nelson and
Warren, a complete analysis will be mailed for
comparison with other dioceses. (English 1 pg.)
On March 6, 1969, the Cardinal states that
there is no printed material available. (English
1 pg.)

Mc5798. N-1969
Mr. Jose Norman to J. Francis Cardinal
McIntyre
May 13, 1969. Los Angeles, California

Is taking 40 saints from the Liturgical calendar another attempt to update and renew the Church? Will they soon take Christ and Mary off the calendar? (English 1 pg.) On June 4, 1969, the Cardinal states that the article in *The Tidings* might clarify the decision. (English 1 pg.)

Mc5799. N-1969
Dr. Jose Navarro to J. Francis Cardinal
McIntyre
June 3, 1969. Los Angeles, California

A request to write another letter to the faithful explaining the changes in the Mass and the ruling on the saints. (English 1 pg.) On June 4, 1969, the Cardinal states that *The Tidings* will try to make the people more knowledgeable about the changes. (English 1 pg.)

Mc5800. N-1969
Mr. Eugene Nogar to J. Francis Cardinal
McIntyre
June 6, 1969. Marietta, Georgia

A request for a letter to an outstanding Catholic, American mother who will celebrate her 75th birthday. She is recovering from a heart attack. (English 1 pg.) On June 9, 1969, the Cardinal states that matriarchs are treasures and hopefully the spirit will develop in your family. (English 1 pg.)

Mc5801. N-1969
Mr. Bern Norpath to J. Francis Cardinal
McIntyre
July 22, 1969. Denver, Colorado

Bosworth and Sullivan Corporation forsees no reduction of interest rates into 1970 so the excesses of the current boom will be gradually squeezed out. (English 2 pgs.)

Mc5802. N-1969
J. Francis Cardinal McIntyre to Mr. William
Neff
October 13, 1969. Los Angeles, California

The artistic memorial, *Milestones in Manned Flight* will be placed in the Doheny Library at St. John's Seminary. (English 1 pg.)

Mc5803. O-1969
J. Francis Cardinal McIntyre to Mr. Walter
O'Malley
January 7, 1969. Los Angeles, California

The generous gift will be used for the inner city parishes and should accomplish much for the needy. (English 1 pg.)

Mc5804. O-1969
Dr. Howard House to J. Francis Cardinal
McIntyre
January 30. 1969. Los Angeles, California

It is generous of St. Vincent's Hospital to allow the course in Otologic surgery to be given in their hospital. (English 1 pg.)

Mc5805. O-1969
Rev. Festus Okafor to J. Francis Cardinal
McIntyre
May 1, 1969. Washington, D.C.

An appeal is made for financial assistance while studying at Catholic University from Biafra. Because the country is in need, there is no personal money for a student. (English 2 pgs.) On May 6, 1969, the Cardinal states that a small token is enclosed and Msgr. Laubacher will send regular checks. (English 1 pg.)

Mc5806. O-1969
Bp. Dermot O'Flanagan to J. Francis Cardinal
McIntyre
May 14, 1969. San Diego, California

The Confirmation tour was a most rewarding experience and pleasant interlude for a retired Bishop. The check was most generous. (English 1 pg.)

Mc5807. O-1969
J. Francis Cardinal McIntyre to Mr. & Mrs. F.
O'Connell
September 6, 1969. Los Angeles, California

Pope Paul VI extends his Apostolic Blessing to you and to all of the members of your wedding party. My personal congratulations are sent with this blessing. (English 1 pg.)

Mc5808. O-1969
Rev. Clement Connolly to Rev. Joseph
O'Riordan
September 18, 1969. Los Angeles, California

The Mission Circle assists various mission projects and their funds are sent periodically through out the year. St. Patrick's Alumni could assist Equador. (English 2 pgs.)

Mc5809. O-1969
Mrs. Henry O'Connell to Arbp. Timothy
Manning
November 8, 1969. Santa Ana, California

At Confirmation a pledge to abstain from alcohol is usually given. Please include all of the other drugs that are so widespread. (English 1 pg.) On November 17, 1969, the Archbishop states that the suggestion will be given serious thought. (English 1 pg.)

Mc5810. O-1969
Mr. John Tretton to J. Francis Cardinal
McIntyre
November 18, 1969. Northridge, California

The existentialism being taught in CCD and religion classes should be ended immediately and the return to traditional teaching begun. Cardinal Carberry has the right idea to object to this teaching. (English 1 pg.)

Mc5811. O-1969
Rev. Hugh O'Regan to Msgr. Benjamin
Hawkes
December 15, 1969. Long Beach, California

The Navy has changed my assignment from Long Beach to Rhode Island. It has been a pleasure to work in the Los Angeles Archdiocese with the priests from Holy Family Parish. (English 1 pg.)

Mc5812. O-1969
Rev. Charles Tower to Mr. Walter O'Malley
N.D. Los Angeles, California

Rev. Angel Esteve, OCD will celebrate his Golden Jubilee as a priest. He is a devoted Dodger fan and would be overjoyed with a letter from the Dodger Administration. (English 1 pg.)

Mc5813. P-1969
Mrs. Rosemary Pratt to J. Francis Cardinal
McIntyre
March 17, 1969. El Monte, California

A request is made for information concerning which religious communities would accept married women with children. (English 2 pgs.) On March 24, 1969, Bishop John Ward states the obligation to take care of children is the primary obligation of married mothers. (English 1 pg.)

Mc5814. P-1969
Mrs. Earlyne Piche to J. Francis Cardinal
McIntyre
September 21, 1969. Costa Mesa, California

The people who have received the Holy Spirit need direction and help and not indifference from the clergy and religious. (English 6 pgs.) On September 30, 1969, Archbishop Timothy Manning states that such conversations are so private that not everyone knows how to respond. (English 1 pg.)

Mc5815. P-1969
Ms. Katheryn Peters to J. Francis Cardinal
McIntyre
October 6, 1969. Los Angeles, California

An appeal to be given fair treatment when one goes into the office to ask for assistance. There are many types of discrimination in today's world. (English 4 pgs.) On October 9, 1969, the Cardinal asks Bishop Johnson for some information to answer this complaint. (English 1 pg.)

Mc5816. Q-1969
Rev. Matthew Quinn to J. Francis Cardinal
McIntyre
May 19, 1969. Los Angeles, California

An invitation is extended to join with the Chinese people who will honor Cardinal YuPin at the Golden Palace in China Town on May 28. (English 1 pg.) On May 20, 1969, the Cardinal states that he will be happy to join with the Chinese people. (English 1 pg.)

Mc5817. Q-1969
Arbp. Timothy Manning to Rev. John Quinn
August 5, 1969. Los Angeles, California

The class meeting was less humorous because of your absence. Prayers are being offered for your continued healing. (English 1 pg.)

Mc5818. P-1969
Rev. William Armstrong to J. Francis Cardinal
McIntyre
November 20, 1969. Seattle, Washington

Pornography can be given some competition by a series that introduces humor and situation comedies that are smut free. Your assistance is needed. (English 1 pg.)

Mc5819. R-1969
J. Francis Cardinal McIntyre to Mr. Ralph
Rendon
January 14, 1969. Los Angeles, California

A letter of recommendation for a White House position cannot be written since you presented no letter from your pastor and are unknown to me. (English 1 pg.)

Mc5820. R-1969
J. Francis Cardinal McIntyre to Mr. & Mrs. J.
Ricard
January 26, 1969. Los Angeles, California

Pope Paul VI extends his Apostolic Benediction on this 70th wedding anniversary. This blessing is extended to the members of the family. Personal congratulations are sent. (English 1 pg.)

Mc5821. R-1969
J. Francis Cardinal McIntyre to Mrs. John Rauen
June 6, 1969. Los Angeles, California

The birthday gathering should be a small gathering this year as it is a prelude to the opening of St. Basil's Church on June 29. (English 1 pg.)

Mc5822. R-1969
Mr. Thomas E. Rook to Arbp. Timothy Manning
June 12, 1969. Los Angeles, California

A request for a meeting at the earliest possible date for an update on the Laymen's Association work. (English 1 pg.) On June 16, 1969, the Archbishop states that when events subside, a meeting will be scheduled. (English 1 pg.)

Mc5823. R-1969
Mrs. Angela Riggs to J. Francis Cardinal McIntyre
June 17, 1969. Los Angeles, California

An organization ought to be established to counteract the radicals in the Church and allow others to persevere in the Faith. (English 3 pgs.)

Mc5824. R-1969
J. Francis Cardinal McIntyre to Mr. & Mrs. John Rauen
June 30, 1969. Los Angeles, California

The delightful evening spent with your family and friends was deeply appreciated. Your kindness to include our house guest was appreciated. (English 1 pg.)

Mc5825. R-1969
Mr. Thomas Rook to Arbp. Timothy Manning
August 20, 1969. Los Angeles, California

A list of demands for reforms from the Laymen's Association and from Concerned Catholics. (English 9 pgs.) On August 25, 1969, the Archbishop asks to please contact the Chancery Office for an appointment. (English 1 pg.)

Mc5826. R-1969
Mr. Don Rademacher to Arbp. Timothy Manning
August 24, 1969. Los Angeles, California

The Church must end the pretense that poverty and racism do not exist. Until the Church assumes leadership, the problem will continue. (English 2 pgs.)

Mc5827. R-1969
Mrs. Elizabeth Ramos to Arbp. Timothy Manning
August 26, 1969. Los Angeles, California

An invitation is extended to give the invocation at the Spanish speaking Republican Conference on September 26. (English 2 pgs.) On August 29, 1969, the Archbishop states that the Catholic Daughters Convention in Santa Rosa will make attendance impossible. (English 1 pg.)

Mc5828. R-1969
Mr. Frank Rivera to Msgr. Eugene Gilb
November 16, 1969. Los Angeles, California

The Los Angeles *Times* ought to be commended for the series of articles on the Church's position on birth control. I hope a great many people read the series. (English 1 pg.)

Mc5829. R-1969
Rev. Vincent Ryan to J. Francis Cardinal McIntyre
November 28, 1969. Joliet, Illinois

A request is made for a special blessing on the Silver Jubilee of ordination. You were the Bishop that presided at my ordination. (English 1 pg.) On December 3, 1969, the Cardinal states that he remembers the ordination well and will pray for special graces for the remaining days of ministry. (English 1 pg.)

Mc5830. R-1969
Rev. Clement Connolly to Mr. John Rauen
December 2, 1969. Los Angeles, California

The Cardinal would welcome the Papal Knights as an honor guard at the Pontifical Mass at the Cathedral at 10:45 a.m. or the Midnight Mass at St. Basil's. (English 1 pg.)

Mc5831. R-1969
Msgr. Benjamin Hawkes to Mr. & Mrs. John Rauen
December 20, 1969. Los Angeles, California

The beautiful St. Mark's tablecloth fits our table perfectly and will be used on Christmas Eve. (English 1 pg.)

Mc5832. S-1969
Miss Barbara Selna to J. Francis Cardinal McIntyre
January 9, 1969. Baldwin Park, California

There is a cabin in Mono County available for the month of January with utilities paid and food stocked. Perhaps the Seminarians could use it. (English 3 pgs.) On January 14, 1969, the Cardinal states that unfortunately no one is free in the Seminary to ski during this month. (English 1 pg.)

Mc5833. S-1969
Miss Barbara Selna to J. Francis Cardinal
McIntyre
January 15, 1969. Baldwin Park, California

A series of suggestions for the school play-ground equipment that could teach the children directions and for some equipment that could increase thigh and hip strength. (English 5 pgs.)

Mc5834. S-1969
Miss Dorothy Steets to J. Francis Cardinal
McIntyre
February 8, 1969. Hyattsville, Maryland

In searching through old family records, I found that your grandfather and my great grandfather were brothers. When you are in Washington, D.C. come to see us. (English 1 pg.) On February 21, 1969, the Cardinal states that the background of my grandfather is rather blank. (English 1 pg.)

Mc5835. S-1969
Mr. Gilbert Shea to J. Francis Cardinal
McIntyre
February 10, 1969. Los Angeles, California

The yearly donation of $1,850 for the Missions and $2,000 for an East-side school are enclosed. (English 1 pg.) On April 25, 1969, the Cardinal expresses his gratitude for the donations. The Missions will surely pray for your intentions. (English 1 pg.)

Mc5836. S-1969
Rev. William McNamara to J. Francis Cardinal
McIntyre
February 20, 1969. Sedona, Arizona

The Spiritual Life Institute has formulated a retreat based on contemplation rather than problems. It will be held from May 4–9 and geared predominantly for Bishops. (English 1 pg.)

Mc5837. S-1969
J. Francis Cardinal McIntyre to Mrs. Gene
Sherman
March 10, 1969. Los Angeles, California

Prayerful condolences are expressed on the death of Gene. The friendship of this fine gentleman was a treasure. May Our Lady guide you. (English 1 pg.)

Mc5838. S-1969
Mrs. Ruth Sollet to Msgr. Benjamin Hawkes
March 16, 1969. Los Angeles, California

It is an honor to share some of Mr. Sollet's cellar with two individuals who do so much for so many. (English 1 pg.) On March 19, 1969, Msgr. states that the St. Joseph Day gift was greatly appreciated. (English 1 pg.)

Mc5839. S-1969
J. Francis Cardinal McIntyre to Mr. William
Simon
April 14, 1969. Los Angeles, California

The copy of Mr. J. Edgar Hoover's book on communism has arrived. It will be most interesting reading material. (English 1 pg.)

Mc5840. S-1969
J. Francis Cardinal McIntyre to Mr. Joseph
Sullivan
April 25, 1969. Los Angeles, California

My present plans are to attend the Consistory in Rome. It will be impossible for me to attend the banquet. (English 1 pg.) On May 2, 1969, Mr. Sullivan states that attendance will be mandatory in Los Angeles at a later date. (English 1 pg.)

Mc5841. S-1969
Msgr. Gustav Schultheiss to J. Francis Cardinal
McIntyre
June 12, 1969. Bronx, New York

An invitation to visit the Bronx and relax in New York when Archbishop Manning is installed as coadjutor Archbishop. (English 1 pg.) On June 25, 1969, the Cardinal states that the invitation is appreciated and a reciprocal invitation is extended. (English 1 pg.)

Mc5842. S-1069
Mr. Gerald Sherry to Arbp. Timothy Manning
June 26, 1969. Fresno, California

Bishop Bernardin hinted that Archbishop Hannon would, as a member of the Communication Committee, appreciate a testimonial letter from you making him aware of your opinion. (English 1 pg.)

Mc5843. S-1969
Arbp. Timothy Manning to Rev. Giovanni
Scavuzzo
July 8, 1969. Fresno, California

The gifts from the people of Capri are most welcome. Tell the people I will place myself under the protection of St. Constanzo. Please offer a Mass for my intentions. (English 1 pg.)

Mc5844. S-1969
Miss Diane Strutz to Msgr. Patrick Roche
July 18, 1969. Newport Beach, California

The El Rodeo column in The Tidings is excellent and should be read by every Catholic. (English 1 pg.)

Mc5845. S-1969
Rev. Leonard Schwinn to Arbp. Timothy
Manning
July 21, 1969. Colorado Springs, Colorado

Is there an explanation for the use of the term
consubstantiation as used in your talk at the
dedication of the new St. Basil's Church? (English 1 pg.) On August 5, 1969, the Cardinal
states that the reporter wrote from his notes not
from the manuscript. (English 1 pg.)

Mc5846. S-1969
Ms. Annelise Carcher to Rev. Clement
Connolly
July 29, 1969. Glendale, California

An explanation of Action 365 will require its
members to be Christian every day of the year
and not just on Sunday. The organization needs
an endorsement from the Cardinal. (English 8
pgs.)

Mc5847. S-1969
Mrs. Ruth Sollet to Msgr. Benjamin Hawkes
July 31, 1969. Los Angeles, California

Please send this donation to the Missions and
request a Mass to be celebrated for your intentions for all of your goodness to others. (English
1 pg.)

Mc5848. S-1969
J. Francis Cardinal McIntyre to The Strake
Family
August 11, 1969. Los Angeles, California

George Strake was a stalwart representative
of the best in manhood and religion. His dynamic participation was a stimulus for good
works. (English 1 pg.)

Mc5849. S-1969
Br. Nivard Scheel, CFX to Arbp. Timothy
Manning
August 13, 1969. Washington, D.C.

An invitation is extended to attend the installation of the first lay president of the Catholic
University on November 9. The semi-annual
meeting of the Bishops will open on November
10. (English 1 pg.) On August 19, 1969, the
Archbishop states that the Administrative Board
will meet on November 9 so I cannot be
present. (English 1 pg.)

Mc5850. S-1969
Mr. Edward Souris to J. Francis Cardinal
McIntyre
August 17, 1969. Toronto, Ontario

Msgr. Marcel Souris will celebrate 60 years
as a priest. Please remember him in prayer. (English 1 pg.) On August 25, 1969, the Cardinal
states your work in the priesthood will continue
to give devoted service to the Master. (English 1
pg.)

Mc5851. S-1969
Bp. Fulton J. Sheen to Arbp. Timothy
Manning
August 19, 1969. Rochester, New York

Some observations and thoughts on the proposed letter to be issued by the Bishops on
priestly celibacy are enclosed. The timeliness of
the letter is important. (English 1 pg.)

Mc5852. S-1969
Mr. Thomas Sarter to J. Francis Cardinal
McIntyre
August 31, 1969. Stamford, Connecticut

A friendly letter comments on the wedding
arrangements made by the Cardinal and the necessity of cashing the checks for income tax
statements. (English 1 pg.) On September 24,
1969, the Cardinal states that the check will be
used for the Archbishop's Fund for Charity
which is the most active agency in the Diocese.
(English 1 pg.)

Mc5853. S-1969
Rev. Clement Connolly to Mrs. Alice Schimpf
September 25, 1969. Los Angeles, California

The people in Biafra are receiving funds from
the Propagation of the Faith and the Bishop's
Relief Society. Continue to pray for all persecuted people. (English 1 pg.)

Mc5854. S-1969
Mr. Ferdinand Mendenhall to Rev. Clement
Connolly
October 7, 1969. Los Angeles, California

An invitation to serve on the Honorary Committee for the testimonial dinner for Dick
Schneider. (English 1 pg.) On October 9, 1969,
Fr. states that that he must decline although I
do appreciate the great work done by Dick.
(English 1 pg.)

Mc5855. S-1969
J. Francis Cardinal McIntyre to Mr. Frank
Sheed
October 12, 1969. Los Angeles, California

An invitation is extended to return to Los
Angeles to speak to the doctors at St. John's
Hospital on the medical ethics of euthanasia.
(English 1 pg.)

Mc5856. S-1969
Mr. Francis Sauter to J. Francis Cardinal
McIntyre
October 20, 1969. Salinas, California

A request for an interview with the Cardinal
for a member of the Matrimonial Tribunal so
an explanation can be given about the advice
given for a divorce. (English 1 pg.)

Mc5857. S-1969
Mrs. Beverly Savarese to Arbp. Timothy
Manning
October 27, 1969. Burbank, California

The education of the children of St. Finbar's
Parish is exceptional from the regular classes to
the children's choir. (English 1 pg.) On October
30, 1969, the Archbishop states that this message is different from the one usually written.
(English 1 pg.)

Mc5858. T-1969
Rev. Clement Connolly to Mr. Ralph Tuchman
February 11, 1969. Los Angeles, California

The tapestry is worthy of a large, beautiful
building but at the present, the Archdiocese has
no place worthy of it. (English 1 pg.)

Mc5859. T-1969
Msgr. Benjamin Hawkes to Mr. Charles Tighe
March 3, 1969. Los Angeles, California

The beautiful rendition of the old Spanish
and Mexican ranches in Los Angeles County
will add interest to a Chancery wall. (English 1
pg.)

Mc5860. T-1969
Bp. Paul Tanner to J. Francis Cardinal
McIntyre
March 28, 1969. St. Augustine, Florida

Rev. Bruno Nicolini requests information
concerning Gypsies in any diocese. If Gypsies
reside in the diocese, please fill out the following questionnaire. (English 1 pg.) The Cardinal
states that migrant crop pickers are as close to
Gypsies that Los Angeles has. (English 1 pg.)

Mc5861. T-1969
Mrs. Edward Topper to Arbp. Timothy
Manning
August 14, 1969. Canoga Park, California

Everyone has the right to be heard in the
Chancery Office. The group who is trying to
save Father Shelbourne for the parish were
not given the chance to give their views. (English 2 pgs.)

Mc5862. T-1969
Rev. Stanislaus McGovern to J. Francis Cardi-
nal McIntyre
October 3, 1969. New York City, New York

Rev. Diosdado Talamayan would appreciate
the opportunity to solicit funds for a seminary
in Tuguegargo in the Philippines. Msgr. Laubacher has been asked to arrange it. (English
1 pg.)

Mc5863. T-1969
Mr. Roger Sullivan to J. Francis Cardinal
McIntyre
October 13, 1969. Los Angeles, California

A request to list the Archdiocese of Los Angeles as one of our clients in the legal directory.
(English 1 pg.) On October 16, 1989, the Cardinal states that he has no objection if the name
of the Archdiocese is used. (English 1 pg.)

Mc5864. U-1969
Bp. Francis Bloy to J. Francis Cardinal
McIntyre
March 12, 1969. Los Angeles, California

There will be a meeting of the Urban Coali-
tion on March 20 at 9:00 p.m. All religious
leaders should be present. (English 1 pg.) On
March 13, 1969, the Cardinal states that Msgr.
Languille will represent the Archdiocese. (English 1 pg.)

Mc5865. U-1969
Rev. Thomas Upton to Arbp. Timothy
Manning
July 14, 1969. Los Angeles, California

An urgent request is made for an appointment at your earliest convenience. (English 1
pg.) On July 30, 1969, the Archbishop states
the most convenient time for you is convenient
for me either at the Chancery Office or St.
Brendan's Church. (English 2 pgs.)

Mc5866. U-1969
Mr. Earl Neff to J. Francis Cardinal McIntyre
October 22, 1969. Cleveland, Ohio

Is the information given in the article of your
sighting a UFO at Edwards Air Force Base accurate? (English 1 pg.)

Mc5867. V-1969
Msgr. Benjamin Hawkes to Mr. Harry Volk
January 27, 1969. Los Angeles, California

Your very generous donations to Santa Marta
Hospital at the Cardinal's dinner made the
evening most enjoyable. (English 1 pg.)

Mc5868. V-1969
Egidio Cardinal Vagnozzi to J. Francis Cardi-
nal McIntyre
May 31, 1969. Vatican City

A friendly letter explains the sudden departure from the group at the North American
College and the offer to be of service whenever
it is necessary. (English 1 pg.) On June 6, 1969,
the Cardinal sends the news of the Archdiocese
and the new coadjutor Archbishop. (English
1 pg.)

Mc5869. V-1969
J. Francis Cardinal McIntyre to Egidio Cardinal Vagnozzi
December 22, 1969. Los Angeles, California

The beautiful volumes of Cardinal Ottaviani's treaties will be sent to St. John's Seminary. I am most grateful. (English 1 pg.)

Mc5870. W-1969
Mr. Richard Willis to J. Francis Cardinal McIntyre
January 23, 1969. Mountain View, California

Youngsters collecting stamps would appreciate stamps from Vatican City. I will be glad to distribute whatever you can send. (English 1 pg.)

Mc5871. W-1969
Msgr. Thomas Kirby to J. Francis Cardinal McIntyre
January 30, 1969. Sacramento, California

A request for a recommendation for Mr. Philip Wilkins for the position of Federal Judge. He was a leader in the tax exemption campaign for private schools. (English 1 pg.) On February 5, 1969, the Cardinal states that when an opportunity presents itself, Mr. Wilkins' name will be presented. (English 1 pg.)

Mc5872. W-1969
Mr. Albert Walsh to J. Francis Cardinal McIntyre
April 14, 1969 Greina, Nebraska

A request to create a positive climate for a Christian political party. The Bishops can be the ones to give the encouragement but the laymen will carry the burden of the work. (English 5 pgs.) On April 22, 1969, the Cardinal encourages the development of the idea and sends his blessing. (English 1 pg.)

Mc5873. W-1969
Mr. William Burke to J. Francis Cardinal McIntyre
July 10, 1969. Sacramento, California

An appeal for Mr. Philip Wilkins to fill the vacancy on the Federal Bench. If an inquiry should be made, he is the right man. (English 1 pg.)

Mc5874. W-1969
Mr. Nicholas Winckler to J. Francis Cardinal McIntyre
August 18, 1969. Santa Ana, California

Could two more people be invited to the dinner being given for Prince Otto of Hapsburg? The priest who was his tutor is a good friend. (English 1 pg.) On August 21, 1969, the Cardinal states the dinner will be a stag dinner for a very few people. (English 1 pg.)

Mc5875. W-1969
Mr. Robert Wagner to J. Francis Cardinal McIntyre
August 25, 1969. Los Angeles, California

The Black neighborhoods must be areas from which reforms come. Only they know what is needed and are creative enough to get the work done. (English 1 pg.)

Mc5876. W-1969
Mr. Albert Walsh to Dr. Thomas Snead
August 30, 1969. New York City, New York

The campaign to prevent population growth should be directed toward Congress. The Bishops have no more power than the laity in politics. (English 1 pg.)

Mc5877. Y-1969
Paul Cardinal YuPin to J. Francis Cardinal McIntyre
June 16, 1969. Taipei, Taiwan

Your presence at the dinner in my honor in China Town was a display of outstanding hospitality. (English 1 pg.)

Mc5878. Y-1969
Paul Cardinal YuPin to J. Francis Cardinal McIntyre
June 25, 1969. Taipei, Taiwan

To complete Fu-Jen Catholic University fifty thousand dollars is needed. Could Los Angeles give ten thousand dollars? (English 1 pg.) On July 1, 1969, the Cardinal states that money is not plentiful in Los Angeles at the present but an appeal to the Propagation of the Faith will be made. (English 1 pg.)

Mc5879. Y-1969
Paul Cardinal YuPin to Arbp. Timothy Manning
July 23, 1969. Taipei, Taiwan

A request for financial assistance for the cost of the auditorium-gymnasium being built at the present time at Catholic University in Taipei. (English 1 pg.)

Mc5880. Y-1969
Miss Mary Youngwirth to J. Francis Cardinal McIntyre
July 31, 1969. Los Angeles, California

Why don't some of the retired priests visit the rest homes and bring the Sacraments to the sick? (English 1 pg.)

Mc5881. Y-1969
Mrs. Jean Temple to J. Francis Cardinal
  McIntyre
October 22, 1969. Northridge, California

The presence of the Cardinal at a dinner honoring Evelle Younger gives acceptance to his candidacy. His policies should be investigated. (English 1 pg.)

Mc5882. Y-1969
Mr. William Ross to J. Francis Cardinal
  McIntyre
November 4, 1969. Los Angeles, California

An invitation to give the invocation at the testimonial dinner honoring Evelle Younger on November 23. (English 1 pg.) On November 6, 1969, the Cardinal states that he must decline the invitation as a previous commitment has been made. (English 1 pg.)

Mc5883. Y-1969
Mr. William Ross to Arbp. Timothy Manning
November 14, 1969. Los Angeles, California

An invitation to give the invocation at the testimonial dinner for Evelle Younger. Rabbi Magnin will give the final blessing. (English 1 pg.) On November 22, 1969, the Archbishop asks for the details of the dinner. (English 1 pg.)

Mc5884 Y-1969
Paul Cardinal YuPin to J. Francis Cardinal
  McIntyre
December 19, 1969. Taipei, Taiwan

A Christmas greeting and an invitation to the dedication of Fu-Jen University in April 1970 are enclosed. (English 1 pg.) On December 30, 1969, the Cardinal states that he is sure that he cannot be present for the dedication of the University. (English 1 pg.)

Mc5885. Z-1969
Mr. George Gore to Msgr. Benjamin Hawkes
January 28, 1969. Fort Lauderdale, Florida

The B.C. Ziegler Company states that they have worked for the Archdiocese. Are they satisfactory for a very large project. (English 1 pg.) On February 1, 1969, Msgr. states that the company has been satisfactory for Los Angeles. (English 1 pg.)

Mc5886. Z-1969
Mrs. Lillian Zeisel to J. Francis Cardinal
  McIntyre
March 18, 1969. Long Beach, California

A letter authorizing the Cardinal to obtain all medical records in order to verify a miracle of restoration to health. (English 6 pgs.)

Mc5887. Z-1969
Mrs. Stephen Zakian to Arbp. Timothy
  Manning
July 12, 1969. North Hollywood, California

An exhibit of Steve Zakian's work is being arranged and the model of St. Gregory Nazianzen would be welcomed addition. (English 1 pg.) On July 28, 1969, the Archbishop states that as soon as it is unpacked, the model can be a part of the exhibit.

Listing for the Year

1970

Mc5888. P-1969
Pope Paul VI to J. Francis Cardinal McIntyre
December 25, 1969. Vatican City

The acceptance of the letter of resignation from the Cardinal with an Apostolic Blessing for the twenty-two years of devoted service to the Archdiocese of Los Angeles. (Latin 3 pgs.)

Mc5889. C-1970
Hon. Burton W. Chase to J. Francis Cardinal McIntyre
March 11, 1970. Los Angeles, California

A tribute and plaque honoring Cardinal McIntyre and praising the work accomplished in the twenty-two years of leadership in the Archdiocese is presented. (English 1 pg.)

Mc5890. D-1970
Mr. Warren Dorn to J. Francis Cardinal McIntyre
March 11, 1970 Los Angeles, California

A letter and a plaque honoring Cardinal McIntyre and his outstanding work for the citizens of Los Angeles is presented. (English 1 pg.)

Mc5891. H-1970
Mr. Kenneth Hahn to J. Francis Cardinal McIntyre
March 11, 1970 Los Angeles, California

A tribute paid to Cardinal McIntyre for the outstanding work accomplished as the leader of the Archdiocese and for the moral strength shown to all of the citizens. (English 1 pg.)

Mc5892. H-1970
Mr. Fred B. Huesman to J. Francis Cardinal McIntyre
February 10, 1970 Los Angeles, California

An invitation is extended from the Papal Knights to a recognition dinner for the work that has been accomplished in the Archdiocese. (English 1 pg.)

Mc5893. Mc-1970
J. Francis Cardinal McIntyre to All of the Faithful
January 21, 1970 Los Angeles, California

The retirement message of Cardinal McIntyre and the announcement that Archbishop Timothy Manning will assume the responsibility of the Archdiocese at once. (English 2 pgs.)

Mc5894. M-1970
Arbp. Timothy Manning to All of the Faithful
January 21, 1970 Los Angeles, California

Archbishop Manning's letter of acceptance of the office of Archbishop asking prayers and help from Cardinal McIntyre and the people of the Archdiocese. (English 2 pgs.)

Mc5895. N-1970
Hon. Richard M. Nixon to J. Francis Cardinal McIntyre
January 23, 1970 Washington, D.C.

An expression of esteem for the work of the Cardinal and a plea for the continuation of the promised prayers is made. (English 1 pg.)

Mc5896. W-1970
Senator Lawrence Walsh to J. Francis Cardinal
  McIntyre
May 11, 1970 Sacramento, California

Senate Resolution No. 20 of the State Senate
gives recognition for the outstanding work during the twenty-two years in the Archdiocese.
(English 1 pg.)

Mc5897. R-1970
Recognition Letters

Letters from Cardinals, Archbishops and
Bishops praising the work of the Cardinal and
assuring him of their prayers for a peaceful retirement. (English 3 folders)

Mc5898. R-1970
Recognition Letters

Letters from members of the clergy, religious,
laity, and organizations of the Archdiocese and
across the United Sates assure the Cardinal of
their love and prayers. (English 5 folders)

Homilies, Addresses and Lectures

Index

A

Abbing, Msgr. John, Mc3917
Abellan, Rev. Pietro, SJ, Mc1024
Aberle, Msgr. George, Mc778
Abernathy, Mr. Robert, Mc5650
Abrahams, Msgr. Michael, Mc609
Abrahams, Mr. Norbert, Mc5652
Abramson, Rabbi Maurice, Mc3348
Accogli, Bp. Luigi, Mc5631
Acel, Rev. M., Mc4677
Aceves, Mr. Gabriel, Mc4966
Achelis, Miss Elizabeth, Mc4679
Ackerman, Bp. Richard, Mc1726, Mc1728, Mc2848
Acton, Rev. John, Mc4328
Adams, Miss Dorothy, Mc2845
Adams, Mr. Jack, Mc5190
Adams, Mr. Leonard, Mc1731
Adams, Miss Marion, Mc4680
Adams, Mr. Sherman, Mc816
Adrian, Bp. William, Mc5167
Agagianian, Gregory Cardinal, Mc811, Mc2851, Mc3357, Mc3360, Mc3717
Aggeler, Rev. Philip, Mc815
Aguilar, Msgr. Gregario, Mc1490
Aguilar, Rev. Marcelino, Mc3714
Aguilar, Mr. Michael, Mc3351
Aguirre, Bp. Lino, Mc2305
Aguirre, Bp. Salvador, Mc2857
Ahart, Miss Nellie, Mc5192
Aibinder, Mr. Arthur, Mc2312
Aiken, Mr. Thomas, Mc1724, Mc1909
Albanese, Mr. Pietro, Mc122
Albaugh, Dr. Clarence, Mc416, Mc812, Mc5189
Albers, Bp. Joseph, Mc1254, Mc2304
Alberts, Miss Carole, Mc3913
Alden, Mr. Richard, Mc2844
Alderman, Mr. Robert, Mc2313
Alemany, Senor Jose, Mc3908
Alexander, Mr. Jack, Mc1026
Algase, Miss Gertrude, Mc2308
Allen, Bp. Francis V., Mc1480, Mc1482
Allen, Mrs. Donn, Mc2300
Allen Mr. Steve, Mc4674, Mc4678
Allison, Rev. Samuel, Mc3916

Ally, Mr. Robert, Mc2299
Altenburg, Mr. John, Mc4967, Mc4971
Altman, Rev. Stanislaus, Mc4785
Alves, Rev. Manuel, Mc4307
Alter, Arbp. Karl, Mc6, Mc1020, Mc1022, Mc1023, Mc1028, Mc1244, Mc1245, Mc1483, Mc1484, Mc1486, Mc1487, Mc1489, Mc1725, Mc1918, Mc2070, Mc2302, Mc2309, Mc2840, Mc2843, Mc2853, Mc2860, Mc2862, Mc3344
Alveti, Mrs. Patrick, Mc3347
Alvin, Mr. & Mrs. J., Mc3396, Mc4327
Alza, Mr. Lucilo, Mc4962
Ambrosic, Mrs. Angela, Mc5648
Amerongea, Dr. F. K., Mc3493
Amberg, Mrs. C., Mc3352
Ames, Mrs. Elinor, Mc2852
Amendt, Mr. John T., Mc3350
Amor, Mr. Alfredo, Mc2841
Anderson, Mrs. Alice, Mc2842
Anderson, Mr. Floyd, Mc4968
Anderson, Mr. Jack, Mc1025
Anderson, Rev. James, Mc814, Mc1019
Anderon, Mrs. Katherine, Mc1248
Anderson, Mr. Robin, Mc5653
Anderson, Miss Teresa, Mc4974
Anding, Miss Mary, Mc813
Andretta, Rev. Tullio, Mc1723, Mc4326
Angelica, Lt. Roberta, Mc4671
Angelillo, Mr. Olindo, Mc3349
Angelus, Rev. Arthur S., Mc508
Annand, Mr. John, 3711
Annes, Mrs. Frederick, Mc214
Anselma, Rev. S. A., Mc215
Anspach, Mrs. Edward, Mc5414
Antczak, Mr. Al, Mc4682
Ante, Rev. Skutarich, Mc2071
Anton, Mrs. Virginia, Mc2854
Antonetti, Msgr. Lorenzo, Mc5344
Anthony, Mr. Leo, Mc2298
Antrim, Mr. R. T., Mc3354
Anwyl, Mr. J. Hugh, Mc4969
Aragon, Dr. Robert, Mc4648
Aroujo, Rev. Denis, Mc4683, Mc4972
Arceo, Bp. Sergio, Mc5191
Ardetto, Mr. James, Mc2847
Arkfeld, Bp. Leo, Mc3911, Mc3912

Armstrong, Bp. Robert, Mc1, Mc1029, Mc1256
Armstrong, Rev. William, Mc5818
Arnold, Mr. & Mrs. R., Mc4676
Arraza, Msgr. Jose, Mc608
Arrioga, Dr. Joaquin, Mc5224
Arsquowicz, Msgr. Anthony, Mc1108
Artazcog. Rev. Jenaro, Mc1255, Mc1485
Arth, Mr. Maurice, Mc5670
Arthur, Mr. Blaine, Mc2858
Artucouir, Mr. Andrija, Mc1027
Artukovica, Mr. Andrija, Mc1732
Ash, Mr. Roy L., Mc2839
Ashe, Mr. J. D., Mc1246
Aszelino, Br. Christopher, Mc3356
Atkielski, Bp. Roman, Mc1121
Atkins, Mr. J. D., Mc1919
Attipetty, Arbp. Joseph, Mc3
Atwill, Rev. William, Mc3991
Aubry, Mr. Richard, Mc5642
Audritzky, Mr. Herbert, Mc2855
Aultz, Mr. Robert, Mc4345
Ausiman, Mr. Lawrence, Mc2856
Auth, Mr. & Mrs. R., Mc4324
Avery, Mr. Donald, Mc5415
Avnon, Mr. Yaakov, Mc2311
Ayoub, Rev. Paul, Mc3914

B

Babcock, Bp. Allen, Mc836
Backs, Mr. Edward, Mc2335
Baedeker, Mr. Dan, Mc4346
Baen, Mr. Cornelis, Mc3586
Bailey, Mr. Walter, Mc5159
Bailargeon, Rev. Samuel, CSSR, Mc2879
Bailog, Mr. William, Mc4993
Baker, Mr. Arthur, Mc5497
Baker, Mr. Donald, Mc5243
Baker, Mr. James, Mc3209
Baker, Rev. Harley, Mc3925, Mc4562
Baker, Mr. M. L., Mc834
Baker, Mrs. Marie, Mc3721
Baker, Miss Marjorie, Mc5436
Balang, Rev. Gaudencio, Mc2080
Balch, Mr. Steven, Mc4333
Balduc, Mr. James, Mc5210
Balic, Rev. Charles, OFM, Mc3739
Balje, Miss Charlotte, Mc4643
Ball, Mr. William, Mc4979
Ballesteros, Miss Beatrice, Mc4372
Balyeat, Dr. Fred, Mc1737
Banahan, Rev. John, Mc826
Banks, Mrs. Duke, 2254
Banneman, Mrs. Elizabeth, Mc4628
Bannon, Mrs. Thomas, Mc5435
Bardaoui, Miss Mary, Mc1898
Bardouil, Rev. Michael, Mc3705
Barker, Mr. Robert, Mc3953
Barley, Mr. Henry, Mc4034
Barnes, Mr. John, Mc2893
Barnes, Mrs. Particia, Mc2545
Barnes, Mr. E. Richard, Mc4342, Mc5195, Mc5211
Barnwell, Mrs. Marion, Mc5000, Mc5429
Barr, Rev. William, Mc116, Mc1043, Mc1044, Mc1047

Barraza, Rev. Jose, Mc425, Mc836
Barrera, Mr. John, Mc3369
Barrett, Mr. Arthur, Mc2344
Barrett, Mr. Nicholas, Mc1052
Barrett, Mr. William, Mc3944
Barrios, Mrs. Patricia, Mc3379
Barron, Mr. Peter, Mc2877
Barry, Mr. George T., Mc2910
Barry, Rev. William, Mc2074, Mc4353, Mc4356
Barth, Mr. William, Mc4584
Barthelemy, Mrs. J., Mc4990
Bartholome, Bp. Peter, Mc828, Mc835, Mc1038
Basal, Mr. Leonard, Mc5654
Basham, Rev. James, CP, Mc4688
Bassett, Mr. William, Mc4686
Basso, Msgr. John, Mc1550
Bastian, Dr. Jur, Mc5428
Battson, Mr. Leigh, Mc4412
Bauer, Rev. Joseph, Mc18
Bauer, Dr. Leo, Mc5425
Baum, Mr. Edward, Mc2324
Bauman, Mrs. Ann, Mc1738, Mc2078, Mc2318
Baumann, Mr. P. O., Mc4760
Baumgartner, Bp. Apollinaris, Mc617
Baxter, Mr. Ernest, Mc2873
Bay, Miss Mary Lou, Mc3017
Bayer, Rev. Cyril, OSB, Mc1493
Bea, Agostini Cardinal, Mc4985
Bean, Mr. Jack, Mc5422
Beavers, Mrs. H. F., Mc3927, Mc3934
Becherer, Rev. James, Mc4994
Becker, Miss Rose, Mc840
Beckett, Mr. Garner, Mc1746
Beckman, Arbp. Francis, Mc23
Beckmeir, Mrs. Eleanor, Mc3375
Becwar, Mr. George, Mc4998
Bede, Frater, OSB, Mc619
Bedini, Mr. Silvio, Mc2314
Beebe, Mr. James, Mc2865
Begin, Bp. Floyd, Mc1106
Belanger, Rev. Roger, Mc3734
Bell, Bp. Alden, Mc625, Mc872, Mc1510, Mc1829, Mc1850, Mc1910, Mc2077, Mc2093, Mc2122, Mc2154, Mc2244, Mc2294, Mc2306, Mc2361, Mc2371, Mc2417, Mc2419, Mc2420, Mc2429, Mc2446, Mc2503, Mc2538, Mc2561, Mc2624, Mc2698, Mc2738, Mc2787, Mc2788, Mc2791, Mc2894, Mc2975, Mc2991, Mc3127, Mc3160, Mc3170, Mc3196, Mc3208, Mc3294, Mc3349, Mc3369, Mc3472, Mc3514, Mc3596, Mc3617, Mc3722, Mc3834, Mc4332, Mc4335, Mc4348, Mc4375, Mc4692, Mc4702, Mc4710, Mc4977, Mc5671
Bell, Rev. Henry, Mc4366
Bell, Mr. J. G., Mc5198, Mc5199, Mc5669
Bell, Miss Virginia, Mc2342
Bellamy, Mr. Jerry, Mc5421
Beller, Rev. Hubert, Mc217, Mc610, Mc3718
Belluii, Mr. Danotolo, Mc3938
Bender, Mr. John, Mc5196
Bender, Msgr. Wilfred, Mc1030, Mc1031
Benelli, Bp. Giovanni, Mc5227, Mc5763
Benedini, Dott Benito, Mc4693

Bennett, Mr. Joel, Mc5209
Bennett, Rev. John, CSSR, Mc2885
Bennett, Mrs. Margaret, Mc2355, Mc2878, Mc2890, Mc3364
Benziger, Miss Marieli, Mc2321
Berardi, Mr. Anthony, Mc3932
Berardi, Mr. Vito, Mc3730, Mc4369, Mc4711
Berg, Mrs. Allison, Mc2882
Bergan, Arbp. Gerald, Mc10, Mc216, Mc227, Mc623, Mc2322
Berger, Mr. Joshua, Mc4986
Berlin, Mr. Richard, Mc3942
Berling, Mr. Frank, Mc4371
Berman, Mr. David, Mc5434
Bernard, Rev. Cyril, Mc222, Mc230
Bernardin, Bp. Joseph, Mc5427, Mc5674, Mc5675
Bernarding, Bp. George, Mc4359
Berryman, Mrs. Edward, Mc4367
Beta, Rev. Angel, Mc833
Betancourt, Rev. Angel P., Mc3722
Bettazzi, Bp. Luigi, Mc4508
Bettinger, Mr. Joseph, Mc836
Betts, Rev. Dorby, Mc4337
Beu, Mr. Joseph, Mc228
Biafora, Mr. Joseph, Mc2924, Mc3727
Bialduga, Msgr. Ignatius, Mc1750
Biddle, Miss Agnes, Mc3926
Biedermann, Rev. Arnold, Mc2352
Bieschke, Mr. Benedict, Mc5417
Bigelow, Mr. C. C., Mc2075
Biggs, Mrs. Lucienne, Mc2340, Mc4338
Binns, Mr. Walter, Mc426
Binz, Arbp. Leo, Mc86, Mc621, Mc723, Mc1929, Mc2047, Mc3729
Biondi Fumasoni, Pietro Cardinal, Mc632
Birch, Mr. Jack, Mc2864
Birch, Msgr. John J., Mc820, Mc2175
Bird, Mrs. Michael, Mc5203
Birdwell, Mr. Russell, Mc2870
Birnberg, Mr. Ted, Mc4991
Biscailuz, Hon. Eugene, Mc3726
Bishop, Mr. William, Mc1261
Bittner, Mr. Egan, Mc4300
Black, Mr. D. D., Mc4697
Black, Mr. Max, Mc3380
Blackwell, Mr. Earl, Mc3448
Blaes, Mr. Emmet, Mc3951
Blair, Mr. Alan, Mc1924, Mc1927
Blalock, Mr. J. T., Mc2353, Mc2781
Bland, Mr. David, Mc4370
Blank, Rev. Benedict,OP, Mc296
Blatz, Rev. Alfred, OSB, Mc1258
Blaze, Mr. B. W., Mc2079
Blaze, Mr. Karol, Mc1506
Blinn, Mrs. Mary Ellen, Mc3931
Blitstein, Mr. Allen, Mc4336
Blomjous, Bp. Joseph, Mc3742
Bloy, Bp. Francis, Mc2362, Mc3387, Mc3737, Mc5864
Blue, Mr. Earl, Mc5672
Blum, Rev. Virgil, SJ, Mc1507, Mc3383, Mc4358, Mc4690
Boardman, Bp. John, Mc827, Mc1852
Boaz, Mrs. Walter, Mc2336
Boccanera, Mrs. Aida, Mc3929
Bock, Mrs. Josephine, Mc1041
Bodkin, Mr. Henry, Mc3371

Bodkin, Mrs. Ruth, Mc2264
Boeddeker, Rev. Alfred,OFM, Mc2871, Mc4368
Bohachevsky, Bp. Constantine, Mc304, Mc824
Boland, Arbp. Thomas, Mc1264, Mc1268, Mc3740
Boland, Mr. Walter, Mc3937
Bolger, Mr. Michael, Mc4745, Mc5032
Bolint, Mrs. Arthur, Mc4685
Bollier, Mrs. M., Mc5663
Bolman, Mrs. Lee, Mc5431
Bona, Bp. Stanislaus, Mc1921
Bonano, Rev. Salvatore,CMF, Mc939
Bonelli, Hon. Frank, Mc2111, Mc2881
Bonner, Miss Valerie, Mc3377
Bonpane, Mr. Blase, Mc3386
Bonta, Mr. Robert, Mc3378
De Bonzo, Mrs. Consuelo, Mc3725
Booth, Rev. George, Mc17
Booth, Msgr. James, Mc1932, Mc3919, Mc4085, Mc4701, Mc5201
Borgatello, Mrs. Marge, Mc2891
Boric, Bp. Vladimiro, Mc3933
Borsa, Mr. Anthony, Mc3954
Bortignon, Bp. Girolamo, Mc2666
Boryszewski, Mr. Ralph, Mc3939
Boser, Mr. John, Mc5418
Bossi, Rev. Louis,CMF, Mc1925, Mc5205
Boudreaux, Bp. Warren, Mc4379
Bouillon, Mrs. Kathleen, Mc1931
Boultwood, Rev. Alban,OSB, Mc5594
Bourland, Mr. Curtis, Mc3920
Boute, Rev. Paschal, Mc2887
Bower, Capt. C. R., Mc3731, Mc3735
Bower, Mr. Joseph, Mc4981
Bowman, Mr. W. G., Mc3389
Bowron, Mayor Fletcher, Mc229
Boyle, Bp. Hugh, Mc52, Mc4996
Boyle, Mrs. Thomas, Mc4983
Bracci, Msgr. Francisco, Mc420, Mc423
Bradfort, Miss Louise, Mc1710
Bradley, Msgr. Christopher, Mc3243, Mc3384, Mc3383
Bradley, Miss Margaret, Mc3923
Bradley, Mrs. Emmet, Mc4703
Brady, Mr. James T., Mc2337
Brady, Mr. John, Mc2804
Brady, Bp. Joseph T., Mc223
Brady, Mr. Mark, Mc3641
Brady, Bp. Matthew, Mc1425, Mc1504, Mc1734, Mc1736, Mc1741, Mc1742, Mc1745, Mc1748, Mc1756, Mc1858
Brady, Bp. William, Mc888, Mc1849
Brambilla, Msgr. Franco, Mc4330, Mc5223
Brandlin, Mr. J. J., Mc2334, Mc3947, Mc4973, Mc4982, Mc5204, Mc5208, Mc5322, Mc5420, Mc5424
Brandman, Mr. D. C., Mc2329
Brangham, Mr. William, Mc3981
Brannick, Mrs. C. M., Mc4708
Brannigan, Rev. Fionan,SJ, Mc1265
Branowetz, Mr. Leonard, Mc4365
Brant, Mr. Bruce, Mc2869, Mc3364, Mc5200
Brant, Mr. David, Mc2863, Mc2899, Mc5432
Brasseur, Bp. William, Mc236
Brauer, Mr. Gerald, Mc4351
Bray, Mr. Bill, Mc4715
Bray, Mr. Robert, Mc5659, Mc5668

Bremm, Miss Hazel, Mc5426
Brennan, Miss Eileen, Mc1259
Brennan, Msgr. Robert, Mc1920, Mc2349,
  Mc2351, Mc2357, Mc3428, Mc3431,
  Mc3433, Mc5411
Breslin, Mr. George, Mc2892
Breyer, Mr. Irving, Mc3940
Bricken, Mr. W. W., Mc2348
Brickman, Dr. Harry, Mc3405
Bridges, Mr. R. Douglas, Mc2876
Bridwell, Mr. Charles, Mc4709
Brindel, Mr. Paul, Mc4704, Mc4713, Mc4714
Brindel, Rev. Paul, OSB, Mc2874, Mc2896
Brings, Mr. L. M., Mc5022
Brink, Mr. Benno, Mc1036
Brizgys, Bp. Vincent, Mc2349, Mc3812,
  Mc4094, Mc4988
Brockman, Mrs. Frances, Mc4997
Broderick, Msgr. Edwin, Mc1922, Mc2872
Broidy, Mr. Steve, Mc3740
Brokhage, Rev. James, Mc2331
Brooks, Mr. Walter, Mc3935
Brophy, Mr. Frank, Mc3723, Mc3928,
  Mc4684, Mc4694, Mc4975
Brosman, Mrs. Ellen, Mc1497
Brother Gilbert, MM, Mc4777
Brother Robert, CSC, Mc3002
Brookins, Rev. Hartford, Mc3373
Broun, Mrs. Catherine, Mc3946
Bouwers, Msgr. Anthony, Mc33, Mc81,
  Mc842, Mc1454, Mc2316
Brown, Mr. Cecil, Mc5262
Brown, Hon. Edmund G., Mc2315
Brown, Dr. Francis, Mc4350
Brown, Dr. Harry, Mc3367
Brown, Rev. John, CSV, Mc1032, Mc1821
Brown, Mrs. Margaret, Mc5661
Brown, Mr. Robert, Mc4980
Brown, Mr. Walter, Mc1501
Brown, Dr. William, Mc2356
Browne, Dr. & Mrs. Francis, Mc2330,
  Mc4707, Mc4992
Browne, Mrs. Margaret, Mc819, Mc1928,
  Mc3390, Mc3949
Browne, Bp. Michael, Mc4343
Bruce, Mr. Frank, Mc446
Bruch, Mr. M B., Mc2076
Bruein, Mr. John, Mc4699
Brugger, Mr. Otto, Mc1923
Bruner, Mrs. Edward, Mc5423
Bruno, Giuseppi Cardinal, Mc1051
Bryant, Miss Suzanne, Mc418
Brynda, Rev. Gerald, Mc4344
Buchenau, Mrs. Jacoba, Mc1049
Bucher, Rev. Mark, Mc220
Buckley, Mr. Fred, Mc2879
Buckley, Mr. William, Mc3372, Mc5662
Bucknum, Mr. John, Mc2333, Mc2335
Buddy, Bp. Charles, Mc15, Mc68, Mc159,
  Mc419, Mc422, Mc626, Mc628, Mc630,
  Mc631, Mc633, Mc830, Mc831, Mc832,
  Mc839, Mc1039, Mc1042, Mc1046,
  Mc1257, Mc1263, Mc1270, Mc1271,
  Mc1495, Mc1503, Mc1508, Mc1509,
  Mc1727, Mc1735, Mc1926, Mc2085,
  Mc2086, Mc22087, Mc2088, Mc2364,
  Mc2443, Mc2959, Mc2965, Mc3724,

Mc3732, Mc3733, Mc3736, Mc3943,
  Mc3945, Mc3950, Mc4354, Mc4976
Budreau, Rev. Paul, Mc2010
Bugnini, Rev. A. CM, Mc5433
Buhr, Rev. Eugene, Mc2299
Bunn, Rev. Edward, SJ, Mc4908
Burbage, Rev. Joseph, Mc2172
Burch, Mr. & Mrs. John, Mc2358, Mc5655
Burden, Mr. Shirley, Mc2327, Mc2339,
  Mc2341, Mc3374
Burg, Mr. M. J., Mc5657
Burgess, Mrs. Annette, Mc2889
Burke, Mr. Andrew, Mc2082, Mc2880,
  Mc2883, Mc3733, Mc3738, Mc3941
Burke, Mr. & Mrs. E., Mc4694
Burke, Msgr. Edward, Mc1753, Mc2093
Burke, Rev. Eugene, CSP, Mc3599
Burke, Rev. James, Mc3700
Burke, Mr. John, 1492
Burke, Bp. Joseph, Mc821, Mc1930
Burke, Hon. Louis, Mc2884, Mc4363
Burke, Mr. Paul, Mc627
Burke, Mr. Robert, Mc2901
Burke, Mr. William, Mc1262, Mc2082,
  Mc2328, Mc3087, Mc4695, Mc5873
Burkley, Mr. Francis, Mc301
Burness, Mr. Carl, Mc5207
Burns, Rev. Charles, OMI, Mc4331
Burns, Mr. Fritz B., Mc1048
Burns, Miss Hilda, Mc4254
Burns, Mr. L. C., Mc2866
Burns, Mr. Patrick, Mc4291
Burns, Mr. Philip, Mc1293
Burns, Mr. & Mrs. Robert, Mc2320, Mc3924
Burroughs, Mrs. Mary Mc4352
Burson, Mrs. Ruth Mc5419
Burt, Rev. Ronald, CSP, Mc3574
Burton, Mr. John, Mc2081, Mc2083, Mc2168,
  Mc2169, Mc2418, Mc2899
Burton, Mrs. Mary, Mc4357
Bushu, Mr. Frank, Mc2360
Bush, Col. Newton, Mc2886
Bushman, Mr. W. A., Mc4355, Mc4496
Buswell, Bp. Charles, Mc5601
Butchko, Miss Susan, Mc5212
Butkowsky, Rev. Alexander, Mc1751
Butler, Mr. David, Mc2350
Butler, Mr. Eddie, Mc5660
Butler, Mr. Eugene, Mc855
Butler, Mr. Paul, Mc3922
Butler, Rev. William, Mc3930
Buttini, Rev. Mario, Mc622
Byrd, Mrs. Thelma, Mc5430
Byrne, Bp. Christopher, Mc21
Byrne, Rev. Daniel, Mc234
Byrne, Arbp. Edwin, Mc218, Mc624, Mc1739,
  Mc1740
Byrne, Rev. Harry,, Mc20
Byrne, Bp. James, Mc1749
Byrne, Msgr. John W., Mc428
Byrne, Bp. Joseph,CSSP, Mc11, Mc13, Mc14,
  Mc19, Mc22, Mc219, Mc231, Mc234,
  Mc240, Mc614, Mc615, Mc616, Mc620,
  Mc822, Mc825, Mc829, Mc838, Mc1033,
  Mc1034, Mc1035, Mc1050, Mc1266,
  Mc1267, Mc1498, Mc1499, Mc2325,
  Mc2875

Chavez, Rev. Angelico, OFM, Mc1292
Cheatham, Mrs. Jeanne, Mc2368
Cheou-Kang-Sie, Mc3881
Cherne, Mr. Leo, Mc5280, Mc5453
Cherry, Dr. Clifford, Mc3405, Mc3748, Mc5446
Chidester, Mrs. Odelia, Mc4447
Chisholm, Mrs. Flora, Mc3744
Chizea, Mr. Francis, Mc2929
Chladek, Mr. Joseph, Mc4732
Chmekir, Mr. Irvin, Mc3413
Choi, Bp. John A., Mc5222
Christensen, Mrs. Ann, Mc3402
Christensen, Mrs. Norma, Mc4718
Christensen, Dr. Robert, Mc3415
Christian, Hon. Winslow, Mc4375
Christopher, Mr. R. F., Mc4377
Christy, Mr. John, Mc2919
Chromoga, Rev. Eugene, Mc1936
Chval, Mr. Richard, Mc4741
Cia, Arbp. Evelio, Mc2397
Ciaffa, Mr. Philip, Mc4735
Cicognani, Arbp. Amleto, Mc31, Mc41, Mc71,
    Mc439, Mc451, Mc740, Mc742, Mc1371,
    Mc1477, Mc1514, Mc1516, Mc1533,
    Mc1694, Mc1752, Mc11831, Mc2108,
    Mc3975, Mc3976, Mc3980, Mc3984,
    Mc4534, Mc5001, Mc5015, Mc5183,
    Mc5221, Mc5568
Ciernick, Mr. David, Mc5216
Ciriaci, Pietro Cardinal, Mc1938
Cisler, Mr. Walker, Mc3962
Clair, Rev. Francis, Mc447
Clairborne, Rev. Martha, Mc5052
Clancy, Mr. Edward, Mc3724
Clancy, Rev. Patrick, OP, Mc2098
Clancy, Rev. Raymond, Mc34
Clar, Mr. Harold, Mc849
Clarizio, Bp. Emanuele, Mc637, Mc1273,
    Mc1275, Mc2101, Mc4534, Mc4728
Clark, Rev. Edward, SJ, Mc2909
Clark, Mrs. Frank, Mc3964
Clark, Mr. Harry, Mc996
Clark, Rev. Laurence, Mc4730
Clark, Mrs. Mary, Mc3401
Clark, Miss Miriam, Mc3986
Clark, Mr. William, Mc3746, Mc3747
Clarke, Rev. James, Mc2097
Clarke, Msgr. John, Mc2371, Mc2907,
    Mc2938, Mc2949, Mc4737
Clarke, Mr. William, Mc1944
Clarke, Mr. K. J., Mc1771
Clary, Mr. Milner, Mc4426
Clavet, Mr. & Mrs. B., Mc5003
Clay, Mr. Russell, Mc3310
Clifton, Mr. Charles, Mc450
Clinch, Bp. Harry, Mc924, Mc1772, Mc3334
Clinnin, Mrs. Winifred, Mc5444
Clinton, Mr. Clifford, Mc2398
Clinton, Mr. William, Mc4373
Clish, Mr. Herbert, Mc5020
Clougherty, Mr. & Mrs. B., Mc4717
Clyne, Msgr. James, Mc2457, Mc3745,
    Mc3749
Coburn, Rev. Vincent, Mc250
Cochrane, Mr. Charles, Mc5452
Cody, John Cardinal, Mc186, Mc438,
    Mc1277, Mc1759, Mc2100, Mc2384,
    Mc2587, Mc3184, Mc3394, Mc3959

Coerver, Rev. Robert, CM, Mc846
Coffey, Rev. John J., Mc841
Coffey, Mr. John M., Mc3410
Coffey, Rev. Patrick, Mc636, Mc4393
Cogley, Mr. John, Mc3963
Cogliandro, Rev. Alfred, SDB, Mc2367
Cohalan, Bp. Daniel, Mc452, Mc646
Cohn, Rabbi Franklin, Mc2421
Cohn, Mr. John, Mc5009
Coleman, Br. Bertram, Mc5698
Coleman, Mr. John, Mc2912, Mc5449
Collin, Mrs. Ann, Mc4720
Collins, Mrs. C. A., Mc2422
Collins, Mr. Charles, Mc5226
Collins, Dr. Donald, Mc2383
Collins, Mr. Edward, Mc2377
Collins, Msgr. Harold, Mc25, Mc28, Mc442,
    Mc847
Collins, Mr. James, Mc2374, Mc5443
Collins, Mr. & Mrs. Joseph, Mc2924
Collins, Miss Mary, Mc5441
Collins, Mr. Nick, Mc2948
Collins, Rev. Patrick, Mc1967
Comber, Bp. John, MM, Mc2913
Commins, Hon. Thomas, Mc3985
Concannan, Rev. John, Mc2393
Condon, Bp. William, Mc5004
Confalonieri, Carlo Cardinal, Mc1119,
    Mc5008
Congdon, Mr. John, Mc3967
Conley, Miss Eileen, Mc2340
Conlin, Mr. & Mrs. J., Mc3416
Conneally, Rev. Philip, SJ, Mc3974
Connell, Msgr. Francis, CSSR, Mc2388,
    Mc2407, Mc3978
Connell, Mr. Michael, Mc3414
Connelly, Rev. F. X., SJ, Mc4975
Connelly, Miss Helen, Mc2366
Connelly, Mr. Joseph, Mc5215
Connolly, Msgr. Clement, Mc5584, Mc5633,
    Mc5657, Mc5663, Mc5808, Mc5853,
    Mc5858
Connolly, Rev. John, Mc1059, Mc1066
Connolly, Rev. Nicholas, Mc1250, Mc1251
Connolly, Arbp. Thomas, Mc29, Mc30, Mc43,
    Mc253, Mc430, Mc437, Mc640, Mc641,
    Mc1057, Mc1063, Mc1285, Mc1290,
    Mc1939, Mc2390, Mc2399, Mc2914,
    Mc4319, Mc5122
Connor, Msgr. Robert, Mc2934
Connors, Mrs. C. E., Mc5438
Connors, Msgr. Edward 4019
Connors, Mrs. Grace, Mc4738
Connors, Mrs. Helen, Mc2382
Connors, Mrs. M., Mc2922
Conrad, Mr. Arthur, Mc2905, Mc4627,
    Mc5439
Conroy, Mr. Charles, Mc320
Conroy, Rev. Peter, Mc642
Consedine, Mr. John, Mc247
Consedine, Rev. William, Mc5689
Conte, Mr. Angelo, Mc5690
Conte, Mr. Louis, Mc5451
Conway, Mr. T. W., Mc4261
Coogan, Mrs. Agnes, Mc3159
Cook, Rev. Richard, Mc648
Cook, Mr. S. F., Mc2939
Cooke, Msgr. Terence, Mc2935
Cooley, Miss Cynthia, Mc4384

Delaney, Mr. James, Mc5025, Mc5099
De la Torre, Carlos Cardinal, Mc3759
Delaunay, Rev. John, CSC, Mc258, Mc860, Mc1072
Del Campo, Rev. Raphael, SJ, Mc2920
De Leon, Rev. Gustov, Mc459, Mc503, Mc668
Deliman, Rev. George, Mc299
Del Junco, Dr. Tirso, Mc3420
Dell, Rev. William, Mc52, Mc652
Dell'Acqua, Bp. Angelo, Mc3995
De Longue, Mr. Lawrence, Mc3994
De Luna, Mr. Julian, Mc5454
De Martinis, Mr. R., Mc661
Demeny, Rev. Robert, Mc5565
Demers, Mrs. Robert, Mc4012
Demetrois, Bp., Mc1555
De Meulle, Mr. James, Mc2439
De Mille, Mr. Cecil B., Mc1775, Mc2426
Deming, Mrs. H. C., Mc2427
Dempsy, Rev. Martin, Mc48
Denny, Mr. George, Mc2278
De Pal, Mrs. M., Mc2453
De Pauw, Rev. Gommar, Mc4424
Denton, Mr. Richard, Mc3076
DePatie, Mrs. Edward, Mc4087
Dermot, Rev. C. P., Mc57
De Sales, Rev. Francis, CD, Mc1543
De Silva, Mrs. Maria, Mc2962
Des Marteau, Mrs. Jean, Mc4401
Des Marteau, Mr. Philip, Mc4399
Desmond, Mr. Fred, Mc2976
Dessert, Rev. James, Mc1077
De Valera, Hon Eamon, Mc1309
Devaney, Rev. Louis, SJ, Mc2953
Devlin, Msgr. John, Mc655
Dhanis, Rev. Eduardo, SJ, Mc4008
Dias de Dufs, Mrs. Elba, Mc3434
Diaz, Mr. Edward, Mc4423
Dighton, Mr. Ralph, Mc5027
Dignan, Msgr. Patrick, Mc1676, Mc2660, Mc3590, Mc3692, Mc3997, Mc4653, Mc5448
Dignam, Dr. William, Mc5456
Dillhoefer, Mr. E. M., Mc3427, Mc3607
Dillon, Msgr. Francis, Mc650
Dineen, Msgr. Aloysius, Mc262, Mc653, Mc1298, Mc1538, Mc4397
Dingle, Mrs. Mary, Mc4415
Dingler, Mrs. Thelma, Mc2424
Dingman, Msgr. M. J., Mc2961
Di Martich, Rev. Felix, Mc1078
Diomedi, Rev. Giulio, Mc1773
Distel, Mr. Larry, Mc4004
Diviney, Msgr. Charles, Mc5234
Dixon, Mrs. Nemesic, Mc3479
Dockweiler, Mr. Frederick, Mc4409
Dockweiler, Mr. Thomas, Mc1779, Mc1947, Mc2489, Mc2979
Doderlein, Mr. George, Mc4013, Mc5031, Mc5033
Doheny, Countess Estelle, Mc53, Mc54, Mc56, Mc268, Mc545, Mc1547, Mc1776, Mc1781
Doheny, Mr. William, Mc4406
Doheny, Msgr. William,CSC, Mc651, Mc1553, Mc2479, Mc3593, Mc4010, Mc4113
Doherty, Msgr. Denis, Mc5469

Doherty, Mr. Frank, Mc2117, Mc2373, Mc2445, Mc2447, Mc2975, Mc3921; Mc4407, Mc4411, Mc4422
Doherty, Rev. Vincent, SJ, Mc861
Doi, Arbp. Peter Tatuso, Mc1540
Dolan, Msgr. Bernard, Mc865, Mc1318
Dolan, Msgr. James, Mc919
Dolly, Miss Consuelo, Mc5457
Domanski, Rev. Francis, SJ, Mc1278
Domiano, Arbp. Celestine, Mc1954
Dominic, Rev., Mc864, Mc1304
Donahue, Mr. & Mrs. David, Mc1552, Mc2118
Donahue, Mrs. Francis, Mc4003
Donahue, Bp. Joseph, Mc454, Mc456, Mc1550
Donahue, Bp. Stephen, Mc56, Mc257, Mc1539
Donant, Mr. Frank, Mc3440
Dondero, Mrs. E. A., Mc3992
Doneran, Bp. John A., Mc1303
Donnellon, Rev. James, Mc4805
Donnelly, Bp. Henry E., Mc1303
Donnelly, Rev. Lawrence, Mc1258, Mc1307, Mc1371, Mc1437, Mc1546
Donnelly, Mr. Michael, Mc2442
Donoghue, Rev. Robert, Mc5704
Donohoe, Bp. Hugh, Mc2561, Mc3437, Mc3595
Donohoe, Msgr. Robert, Mc55, Mc1100
Donohue, Mrs. Catherine, Mc2981
Donohue, Sir Daniel, Mc3758, Mc3760, Mc5036, Mc5370
Donovan, Mr. James, Mc866, Mc1301
Donovan, Bp. John, Mc221, Mc3876, Mc5026
Doolan, Mr. Jerome, Mc2115, Mc4420
Doolittle, Mr. Alfred, Mc2966
Dopfner, Julius Cardinal, Mc4262
Doran, Rev. John, Mc266
Doran, Mr. Joseph, Mc5231
Doran, Hon. Warren, Mc1952
Dere, Hon. Edward, Mc1080
Dorias, Miss Irene, Mc3439
Dorn, Mr. Warren, Mc3120, Mc4419
Dorr, Mrs. Norma, Mc3432
Doty, Mr. & Mrs. Roy, Mc4429
Dougherty, Rev. Cornelius, Mc4214
Dougherty, Denis Cardinal, Mc264
Dougherty, Rev. John, Mc665, Mc1777
Dougherty, Bp. Joseph, Mc663, Mc2433, Mc2950, Mc2974, Mc319, Mc3421, Mc3424
Dougherty, Mr. William, Mc2448
Dowd, Rev. Francis, CSSR, Mc2967, Mc4405, Mc4417
Dowd, Mr. Patrick, Mc5463
Downey, Mr. Alvin, Mc5702
Downey, Mr. J., Mc4009
Downey, Mrs. Kathryn, Mc4011
Downey, Rev. Richard, Mc1554
Downs, Br. Finbar, Mc50
Downs, Mrs. Mary, Mc5068
Doxie, Msgr. Donald, Mc4007, Mc5238
Doyle, Mrs. James, Mc4403
Doyle, Dr. John, Mc5235, Mc5237
Doyle, Mr. John P., Mc1782
Doyle, Mr. Michael, Mc1955
Drake, Mr. Emery, Mc4398, Mc4428

Drake, Mr. George, Mc2116
Draper, Mrs. Abbey, Mc2444
Dreis, Mrs. Richard, Mc2972
Drew, Mr. Louis, Mc5037
Drinkwater, Mr. Terrell, Mc2956
Driscoll, Mrs. H. G., Mc2968
Droesch, Mrs. Frank, Mc5464
DuBay, Rev. William, Mc5465
Dubois, Rev. Elmeric, Mc338
Dudick, Rev. Michael, Mc1296
Duesner, Rev. Joseph, Mc256
Duff, Mr. John, Mc5133
Duffy, Mrs. Elizabeth, Mc2435
Duffy, Mrs. J. W., Mc1780
Duffy, Dr. Raymond, Mc2957
Duggan, Rev. Albert, Mc2429
Duggan, Mr. Lawrence, Mc4647
Duggan, Rev. William, Mc3109
Duhig, Arbp. James, Mc1778
Duke, Arbp. William, Mc260, Mc1079,
  Mc1948
Dulles, Mrs. J. Foster, Mc2438
Dumas, Mr. Jacque, Mc4817
Dumont, Rev. Albert, OP, Mc3752
Duncan, Rev. Edward, Mc669
Dunham, Mr. Franklin, Mc2952
Dunlap, Mr. George, Mc5468
Dunleavy, Rev. Joseph, Mc259
Dunn, Mr. Charles, Mc47
Dunn, Rev. John, Mc2419
Dunn, Msgr. Patrick, Mc659
Duperray, Bp. Jean, Mc261
Duque, Mr. & Mrs. Ernest, Mc2121, Mc2455,
  Mc2963
Durand, Mr. Bernard, Mc4235
Durand, Mr. Gilbert, Mc2430
Duren, Mrs. Mary, Mc3672
Durick, Bp. Joseph, Mc1537
Durst, Mr. Willis, Mc662
Du Zan, Mr. Duane, Mc2648
Dwight, Mr. M. E., Mc2964, Mc4014
Dworschak, Abbot Baldwin, Mc660
Dworschak, Bp. Leo, Mc455, Mc458, Mc509,
  Mc511, Mc862
Dwyer, Rev. Frank, Mc1300
Dwyer, Bp. George, Mc2772
Dwyer, Rev. Richard, Mc460, Mc3754
Dwyer, Arbp. Robert, Mc667, Mc863,
  Mc1069, Mc1075, Mc1076, Mc1308,
  Mc1549, Mc1774
Dyer, Rev. Raymond, Mc2960

E

Eagen, Msgr. Brent, Mc5787
Earley, Msgr. Thomas, Mc1562
Eaton, Dr. Hubert, Mc2125
Eberhardt, Rev. Newman, Mc4020
Eberhart, Mrs. Zoe, Mc4016
Eberle, Mr. John, Mc4433
Echeverria, Bp. Bernardino, Mc3450
Eckenrode, Mr. William, Mc1083
Eckstrom, Miss Marie, Mc3443
Edmonds, Mr. Charles, Mc3764
Edrich, Rev. Paul, Mc2404
Edwards, Mr. John, Mc4431
Edwards, Mr. Walter, Mc4649

Egan, Mr. & Mrs. Edward, Mc2122, Mc2463,
  Mc3446
Eggers, Mr. John, Mc2985
Ehardt, Msgr. George, Mc58, Mc670, Mc671,
  Mc673, Mc677, Mc868, Mc1081, Mc1564,
  Mc1785, Mc2124, Mc2466
Eidenschink, Rev. John,OSB, Mc2989
Eisenhower, Hon. Dwight D., Mc2564,
  Mc4318
Elbert, Rev. John A., Mc541
Elder, Mrs. Mary, Mc2457
Elespe, Mr. Santos, Mc5213
Elhatton, Rev. Thomas,OP, Mc3181, Mc3346,
  Mc3684
Elko, Bp. Nicholas, Mc1557, Mc5043
Ellena, Mrs. Louise, Mc2465
Ellensohn, Mr. Ronald, Mc4712
Ellgner, Mr. Ernest, Mc3447
Elliot, Rev. Robert, CSSR, Mc1787, Mc2123
Ellis, Mrs. Amy, Mc5707
Ellis, Rev. Ezra, Mc3761
Ellis, Rev. John T., Mc2988
Elliott, Mr. Norman, Mc4434
Ellison, Miss Mary, Mc2990
Elner, Mr. Donald, Mc3452
Emerson, Mr. Thomas, Mc5706
Emge, Mrs. Joan, Mc2456, Mc2982, Mc3449
Empey, Rev. James, Mc269
Emzweiler, Mr. Joseph, Mc5471
Endecott, Mr. Thomas, Mc2461
Engle, Mr. Clair, Mc3765
Englend, Mrs. Mary, Mc2986
English, Msgr. Michael, Mc270, Mc465
English, Mr. Richard, Mc3133
Enloe, Miss Mary, Mc5240
Enright, Miss Dorothy, Mc2462, Mc2983,
  Mc2984, Mc4015, Mc4017, Mc4430,
  Mc4749
Erbach, Mrs. Mark, Mc3445
Erickson, Mr. Leif, Mc4435
Ernest, Rev. Albert, Mc1789
Esbenshade, Mrs. Richard, Mc4315
Escalante, Bp. Alonso, Mc3451
Espelage, Bp. Bernard, Mc674, Mc867,
  Mc1082, Mc1312, Mc1556, Mc1558,
  Mc1559, Mc1560, Mc1563, Mc1783,
  Mc2459, Mc2987
Eubanks, Rev. M. Guerris, Mc1310
Eunice, Mrs. Mary, Mc4748
Eustace, Bp. Bartholomew, Mc59, Mc271,
  Mc464, Mc1311, Mc1313, Mc1784,
  Mc1788, Mc1790
Evanko, Mr. Paul, Mc1084
Evers, Mr. Larry, Mc5470
Evich, Mr. Walter, Mc5679
Eyre, Mr. Ainsworth, Mc5472
Eyzaguirre, Bp. Ramon, Mc165

F

Fairbanks, Mr. Jerry, Mc2480, Mc4030
Falkenburg, Miss Ginevra, Mc876
Falkenstein, Miss Claire, Mc5480, Mc5712
Falkenstein, Miss Roberta, Mc4033
Falvey, Mr. Hugh, Mc44756
Faires, Mr., McIntyre, Mc898

Farley, Mrs. Rebecca, Mc5048
Farrell, Msgr. Joseph, Mc467
Farricher, Msgr. William, Mc3008, Mc5482
Farrow, Mr. John V., Mc2476, Mc2478, Mc2842
Fasolino, Arbp. Nicholas, Mc4743
Fassnacht, Mr. Richard, Mc272
Fattinnanzi, Msgr. Armando, Mc3004
Faust, Mr. Robert, Mc2469
Fawcett, Mr. Hugh, Mc1326
Fay, Mr. Robert, Mc3457
Fearns, Bp. John, Mc279, Mc873, Mc877, Mc1085, Mc1569, Mc4451, Mc5045
Fearons, Mr. George, Mc2475
Fecht, Mr. Leo, Mc5249
Federal, Bp. Joseph L., Mc678, Mc1087, Mc1724, Mc3048, Mc4025, Mc5050, Mc5055
Feeley, Miss Winifred, Mc2994
Feeney, Rev. Thomas, SJ, Mc874
Felici, Bp. Pericle, Mc3007, Mc3454, Mc3463, Mc3768, Mc4024, Mc4031, Mc4453, Mc4637
Feliu, Dr. Eddie, Mc5477
Feliz, Mrs. Elmira, Mc4436
Fellows, Mrs. Maren, Mc2365
Felten, Mr. Gene, Mc2477
Fergus, Bp. James, Mc2126
Fernandez, Bp. Jerome, Mc1567
Ferrari, Rev. Guy,OSB, Mc3775
Ferraris, Miss Anne, Mc5049
Ferrell, Mr. Patrick, Mc3012
Ferretti, Rev. Augustine, Mc65
Ferretto, Bp. Giuseppe, Mc1320, Mc1325, Mc1570, Mc2130, Mc2468, Mc4758
Ferrini, Rev. Pilippus, Mc871
Ferro, Mr. Louis, Mc3461
Feuerstein, Miss Ida, Mc5473
Fiedler, Rev. Ernest, Mc2405
Fiedler, Hon. George, Mc5058
Fifield, Dr. James, Mc2470, Mc3003, Mc3688, Mc3766, Mc4022, Mc5053, Mc5714
Filipponi, Mr. Lawrence, Mc1328
Findley, Rev. Charles, OSB, Mc5426
Fink, Mr. Francis, Mc142, Mc235, Mc562
Finn, Bp. Richard, Mc2483
Finneran, Mr. Thomas, Mc5713
Firestone, Mr. & Mrs. J., Mc2473
Fischer, Mrs. Olga, Mc5715
Fishburn, Mr. Luke, Mc1383
Fisher, Mr. Frank, Mc5710
Fisk, Mr. George, Mc2487
Fitzgerald, Msgr. Charles, Mc273
Fitzgerald, Mc2993, Mc3769
Fitzgerald, Miss Kathryn, Mc4437
Fitzgerald, Rev. Maurice,CSP, Mc3465
Fitzgerald, Rev. William, Mc1322, Mc1792
Fitzpatrick, Mr. Brian, Mc4446
Fitzpatrick, Mr. Edward, Mc1323
Fitz-Patrick, Mr. F. G., Mc64
Fitzpatrick, Mr. H. B., Mc5245
Fitzpatrick, Msgr. John, Mc4761
Fitzpatrick, Mr. William, Mc5387
Fitzsimons, Mr. Frank, Mc4452
Fitzsimons, Rev. Frank, Mc681
Flaherty, Mr. Vincent, Mc5244
Flaherty, Dr. Walter, Mc5474
Flanagan, Mr. Al, Mc2973

Flanigan, Mr. John, Mc3359
Flavin, Bp. Glennon, Mc1960
Fleming, Msgr. John M., Mc1548, Mc1639, Mc2474
Fletcher, Bp. Albert, Mc4757, Mc4762
Fletcher, Mr. Brad, Mc5483
Fletcher, Mr. Clifford, Mc278
Flick, Mr. Frank, Mc2490
Flint, Mr. Ellis, Mc4032
Flood, Mr. Patrick, Mc3001
Flood, Rev. Patrick, Mc679, Mc927, Mc1086, Mc1321, Mc1959
Flynn, Mr. Bernard, Mc4445
Flynn, Rev. Daniel, Mc2484
Flynn, Rev. John, Mc24485
Fochtman, Mr. Daniel, Mc466
Fogarty, Mr. John, Mc870
Foley, Rev. Albert, SJ, Mc1565
Foley, Mr. Edward, Mc3809
Foley, Mr. John, Mc4450
Foley, Arbp, Victor, Mc5039
Folsom, Mr. Frank, Mc4758
Foltz, Rev. Henri, Mc3772
Fontaine, Rev. Barry, Mc1884
Fontinelli, Mr. Eugene, Mc5279
Footz, Mr. George, Mc3458
Foran, Mr. Paul, Mc5476
Ford, Mr. Henry II, Mc1350, Mc2999
Ford, Dr. James, Mc5481
Ford, Mr. John Anson, Mc2491
Ford, Mr. John J., Mc4440
Ford, Mrs. Mary Jane, Mc5709
Forde, Rev. John F., Mc1315, Mc1319, Mc1324, Mc1327
Forest, Rev. Joseph, OFM, Mc63
Forester, Msgr. William, Mc4027
Forn, Mr. Albert, Mc1316
Forrest, Rev. M. D., MSC, Mc2971
Forrester, Rev. Donal, Mc276
Forrester, Rev. William, Mc1317, Mc3771
Fortenberry, Rev. Jerome, CM, Mc1958
Fortezzo, Mrs. Ralph, Mc5711
Fortin, Mr. Jaques, Mc3459
Fortner, Mr. Lee, Mc4378
Fossati, Maurilio Cardinal, Mc62
Foster, Mr. & Mrs. F., Mc2488, Mc2996, Mc3011
Foster, Mr. Thomas, Mc2131
Fournier, Mr. Louis, Mc4449
Fousek, Mr. Stanley, Mc2467
Fox, Mr. Francis, Mc3770
Fox, Abbot James, Mc280
Fox, Dr. Myron, Mc4554, Mc4844
Fragiacomo, Mrs. Marino, Mc4023
Fraine, Mr. Kenneth, Mc4029
Frame, Mr. & Mrs. W., Mc4439
Franco, Rev. Jose A., Mc274
Frank, Mr. Thomas, Mc2992
Franz, Bp. John, Mc680
Frazier, Mr. Raymond, Mc4441, Mc4753
Fredrickson, Mr. C. M., Mc5247
Free, Mrs. Maude, Mc3006
Freeman, Mr. Frank, Mc2472, Mc2997
Freeman, Mr. Roger, Mc4754
Freeman, Mr. Robert, Mc2127
Freking, Bp. Frederick, Mc3773
Frey, Msgr. Joseph, Mc869
Friedrich, Mr. John, Mc5251, Mc5479

Kiely, Rev. Edward, Mc491
Kilasara, Bp. Joseph, Mc3089
Kiley, Dr. John, Mc5757
Kiley, Rev. Stephan, Mc1363, Mc3319
Killian, Msgr. Lawrence, Mc2166
Killion, Rev. Edward, Mc90
Kim, Rev. Joseph, Mc4807
Kimball, Rev. Arthur, Mc893, Mc1116
Kimball, Mr. Daniel, Mc2168
Kimball, Mrs. Marian, Mc2165, Mc3526
Kindelberger, Mr. J. H., Mc487
King, Mrs. Eileen, Mc5755
King, Miss Eva, Mc1124
King Mr. Frank, Mc2174
King, Miss Mary, Mc5529
Kingman, Rev. Stephan, Mc900
Kinney, Mr. Edward, Mc84
Kirby, Msgr. Edmund A., Mc1976
Kirby, Mr. Frederick, Mc1377
Kirby, Mr. Patrick, Mc3798
Kirby, Msgr. Thomas, Mc1128, Mc1247,
    Mc1249, Mc1252, Mc1603, Mc1606,
    Mc1608, Mc5871
Kircher, Mr. William, Mc5687
Kirchof, Mr. Edward, Mc715
Kirk, Rev. O. W., OSA, Mc1613
Kirt, Mrs. Irene, Mc1117
Kish, Mr. George, Mc4493
Klasner, Rev. W. F., Mc311
Klein, Mr. A. D., Mc4803
Klein, Mr. Daniel, Mc4497
Klein, Rev. Edward, Mc87, Mc709
Kleinman, Rabbi Solomon, Mc2560
Klekotka, Rev. John, OSA, Mc3083
Klinglesmith, Rev. Joseph, Mc1786, Mc1825
Klock, Mr. Frank, Mc4806
Klonowski, Bp. Henry, Mc1351
Knauf, Mr. Robert, Mc4490
Knight, Hon. & Mrs. Goodwin, Mc894,
    Mc902, Mc2171
Knight, Mr. Louis, Mc2582
Knight, Mr. Vick, Mc3655
Knowland, Hon. William, Mc1241
Knox, Bp. James R., Mc3366
Knox, Mrs. John, Mc2167
Kocisko, Bp. Stephen, Mc1820
Koenig, Msgr. Bernard, Mc5083
Koeper, Rev. Francis, CM, Mc312, Mc706,
    Mc707, Mc708, Mc896, Mc1120, Mc3093,
    Mc3627
Kokat, Rev. Ivan, Mc1607
Kolar, Mrs. George, Mc897
Kolitsch, Mr. L. J., Mc5292
Koller, Mrs. Helen, Mc3530
Koltusky, Rev. Michael, Mc4808
Komora, Msgr. Emil, Mc3094
Konoske, Rev. Paul, Mc5752
Konzen, Mrs. Margot, Mc2569
Kooi, Mr. Ray C., Mc3081
Kopfman, Rev. William, OP, Mc1819
Korkowski, Mr. C. A., Mc4492
Kornljak, Rev. Plato, Mc1375
Koval, Mr. Henry, Mc5749
Koval, Mr. M. J., Mc2578
Krae, Miss Dorothy, Mc5526
Kramer, Rev. Edward, Mc85
Kramer, Rev. George, Mc1981
Krauch, Mr. Bob, Mc3355

Kreppein, Miss Catherine, Mc4804
Kribbs, Mr. Herman, Mc1129
Kirbs, Mr. Lewis, Mc5293
Krippendorf, Mr. & Mrs. L. H., Mc2559,
    Mc2570
Kristy, Mrs. Marge, Mc5748
Kroe, Mrs. Katherine, Mc1365
Kroger, Dr. William, Mc4110
Krok, Mrs. Frank, Mc3522
Krol, John Cardinal, Mc1127, Mc3376,
    Mc3524, Mc3817, Mc4501, Mc4809
Krouskoff, Mr. Robert, Mc3095
Kucharick, Mr. Stephen, Mc2519
Kucingis, Rev. John, Mc1115, Mc2326,
    Mc3803
Kukoljsa, Dr. Stephen, Mc188
Kuleto, Mrs. Rosemary, Mc4651
Kuruville, Rev. F., Mc2563, Mc5759
Kussman, Mr. Edward, Mc5059
Kutchera, Rev. Alvin, Mc2584

L

Laband, Mr. W. H., Mc2181
LaBarre, Mrs. P., Mc1279
Labonge, Mr. Bob, Mc3518, Mc5677
Lacy, Mrs. John, Mc4810, Mc5530
LaFeir, Rev. Alvin, Mc4111
Laghi, Arbp. Pio, Mc3180
Lahita, Mr. Robert, Mc3099
Lahn, Mr. Ilse, Mc1036
Laidlaw, Rev. John, Mc334
Lakrantz, Mrs. Susan, Mc3554
Lalar, Rev. Michael, Mc500
LaMar, Mr. Lawrence, Mc4811
Lamb, Mr. Andre, Mc2702
Lamb, Mrs. Bess, Mc1988
Lamb, Bp. Hugh L., Mc1132
Lamb, Mr. Joseph, Mc3112, Mc3550, Mc3552
Lamb, Miss Rose, Mc2178
Lambe, Rev. Peter, Mc1138
Lambertz, Mr. John, Mc909
Lampasski, Mr. Richard, Mc3104
Landay, Mr. Andrew, Mc4132
Landsowne, Mr. Paul, Mc4137
Lane, Mrs. Kitty, Mc4125
Lane, Bp. Raymond, MM, Mc96, Mc316,
    Mc729, Mc3999
Lane, Rev. William, Mc98
Lang, Rev. Derek, OSM, Mc5206
Languille, Msgr. John, Mc1895, Mc2598,
    Mc2603, Mc2744, Mc3630, Mc4112
    Mc4149, Mc4166, Mc4210, Mc4362,
    Mc4512, Mc5545, Mc5625
Lani, Rev. Mathias, Mc319, Mc540
Lank, Mrs. Agnes, Mc3547
Lans, Rev. Maurice, Mc796
Lansan, Mr. Henry, Mc2592
Lansburg, Mr. Mark, Mc3810
Lanza, Mrs. Evelyn, Mc5535
Laraneta, Mr. Joseph, Mc5097
Lardone, Bp. Francisco, Mc318
LaRira, Rev. Giorgio, Mc4127
Larkin, Rev. Francis, Mc138, Mc719, Mc5632
Larkin, Rev. James, CSV, Mc1136
Larkin, Rev. J. W., OSA, Mc906, Mc915,
    Mc1616

Larraona, Arcadio Cardinal, Mc913, Mc4514
Larsen, Mr. Paul, Mc5090
Larsen, Mr. Roy, Mc3701
Laubacher, Msgr. Harold, Mc4813, Mc5699
Laubacher, Rev. James, SS, Mc497, Mc722,
  Mc725, Mc2179
Lavery, Rev. Paulinus, OFM, Mc1546
Lawler, Mr. Oscar, Mc3549, Mc4116,
  Mc4515, Mc5764
Lawrence, Rev. Anthony, Mc97
Lawson, Mr. Jack, Mc3983
Lawson, Mr. R. S., Mc4502
Lawton, Bp. Edward, Mc4516
Leary, Rev. Daniel B., Mc716
Leavey, Mr. & Mrs. T. E., Mc728, Mc22604,
  Mc3546, Mc3807, Mc4140
Leckie, Mr. Robert, Mc5299
LeCocq, Mrs. Ann, Mc4138
Lecrivain, Mr. John, Mc5089
Ledvina, Bp. Emmanuel, Mc27
Lee, Mr. David C., Mc1134, Mc2606
Leederman, Mr. Howard, Mc5762
Lefebvre, Miss Sophie, Mc5305
Leipzig, Bp. Francis, Mc501, Mc727, Mc910,
  Mc916, Mc1130, Mc1131, Mc1135
  Mc1389, Mc1390, Mc1617, Mc1828,
  Mc1986, Mc1989, Mc1990, Mc1991,
  Mc2176, Mc3105, Mc3111, Mc3114,
  Mc3553, Mc33808, Mc4117, Mc4119,
  Mc4133
Lemieux, Rev. A. A., Mc4691
Lenahan, Rev. Henry J., Mc94
Lenarth, Mr. Herman, Mc3098
Lennon, Miss Diane, Mc3113
Lenz, Mrs. Elizabeth, Mc4818
Lercaro, James Cardinal, Mc5092, Mc5304,
  Mc5308
LeRoy, Mr. & Mrs. M., Mc5537
Lescoe, Mr. Richard, Mc4510
Leslie, Mrs. Shane, Mc44815
Lespron, Mr. Joseph, Mc5298
Lester, Msgr. Nicholas, Mc5306
Levada, Rev. William, Mc5766
Leven, Bp. Stephen, Mc2182
Levenkron Mr. David, Mc5531
Levine, Mr. Irving, Mc3811
Levitt, Mr. David, Mc3555
Levoy, Mr. Gordon, Mc2548
Lewis, Mr. Frank, Mc2605
Lewis, Mr. Fulton Jr., Mc2183
Lewis, Mrs. Gwendolin, Mc3542
Lewis, Mrs. Loretta, Mc5093
Lewis, Mrs. Warren F., Mc1018
Lewis, Mr. William, Mc4506
Liberty, Mr. Robert, Mc4129
Lichten, Mr. Joseph, Mc5294
Lieber, Dr. David, Mc4134
Lies, Mrs. Donald, Mc4768
Liggeri, Mr. Dan P., Mc3469
Liguori, Mr. Joseph, Mc5685
Ligutti, Msgr. Luigi, Mc718, Mc3102
Lillie, Mrs. Mildred, Mc1614
Lilly, Rev. Joseph, Mc35
Lindemann, Dr. Eva, Mc3583
Linn, Mrs. Margaret, Mc4135
Lippold, Mr. Carol, Mc4812
Lira, Mr. F. Lopez, Mc3106
Lisandrini, Rev. P. Antonio, Mc907

Liston, Bp. James, Mc1566, Mc3107
Liston, Rev. John, Mc101
Litchfield, Mr. & Mrs. J., Mc5300
Liven, Bp. Stephen, Mc2593
Livington, Mr. G., Mc2589
Llobert, Rev. Joseph, Mc100, Mc238
Llovera, Rev. J. Garcia, Mc3116
Loebbecker, Mr. Ernest, Mc3100
Lockwood, Mr. James, Mc5532
Lockwood, Mr. Paul, Mc4128
Locraft, Mr. Thomas, Mc4120
Loehr, Rev. Edward, Mc502
Logar, Mrs. James, Mc5302
Lokrantz, Mrs. Sven, Mc1387, Mc4507
Lombardi, Mr. John, Mc5094
Lombardi, Rev. Richard, SJ, Mc3545, Mc4513
Lombardi, Mrs. Stephanie, Mc4816
Lombardo, Mr. Josef, Mc4511
Looker, Mr. Robert, Mc4999
Loomis, Mr. Arthur, Mc2608
Lord, Mr. Bill, Mc2590
Lord, Rev. Daniel, SJ, Mc93, Mc908
Lorenzo, Mr. A. G., Mc4040
Lorraine, Miss Eva, Mc1980
Love, Rev. John, Mc314
Lowery, Mr. W. R., Mc1615
Licas, Dr. Daisy, Mc2597
Luce, Mrs. Clare Booth, Mc102, Mc5297,
  Mc5761
Lucero, Mrs. Enriqueta, Mc2596
Lucey, Bp. Cornelius, Mc505, Mc911,
  Mc1379, Mc1380, Mc1381
Lucey, Arbp. Robert E., Mc99, Mc317,
  Mc320, Mc495, Mc496, Mc498, Mc724,
  Mc914, Mc1133, Mc2599, Mc3118,
  Mc3806, Mc5091
Luckman, Mr. Charles, Mc4141, Mc4517,
  Mc4819, Mc5095
Lujan, Mrs. Jerry, Mc4118
Lundberg, Mrs. Jack, Mc3541
Lupi, Msgr. Achille, Mc2394, Mc2607
Luque, Bp. Crisanto, Mc905
Lutz, Mr. Charles, Mc3110
Lux, Msgr. Joseph, Mc1378
Lugio, Msgr. Salvatore, Mc95, Mc1137,
  Mc1829
Lynch, Rev. Edward, SJ, Mc4136
Lynch, Mr. Gerald, Mc3544, Mc5765
Lynch, Bp. Joseph, Mc499, Mc883
Lynch, Rev. Kevin, CSP, Mc3101
Lynch, Mrs. Kitty, Mc4131
Lynch, Rev. Oliver, OFM, Mc1386
Lynn, Mr. Norman, Mc3696
Lyon, Mr. Charles, Mc3108
Lyons, Rev. Daniel, SJ, Mc5247
Lyons, Miss Florence, Mc4139
Lyons, Rev. James, Mc1384

MC

MacConastair, Rev. Alfred,CP, Mc1067
MacDonald, Mr. Frank, Mc4528
MacDonald, Dr. Ian, Mc1142
MacDonald, Arbp. John, Mc2621, Mc2633
MacDonald, Mr. John, Mc5779
MacEachin, Rev. Jerome, Mc1391
MacEoin, Mr. Gary, Mc4156

Mc2618, Mc2619, Mc2625, Mc2630,
Mc3123, Mc3453, Mc3560, Mc3563,
Mc3656, Mc3818, Mc3821, Mc3822,
Mc4150, Mc4151, Mc4383, Mc4523,
Mc4526, Mc4527, Mc5125, Mc5127,
Mc5130, Mc5133
Mc Guigan, James Cardinal, Mc926, Mc1623
Mc Guigan, Mr. & Mrs., Mc5775
Mc Guire, Mr. Constantine, Mc4518
Mc Guire, Mrs. James, Mc2610
Mc Hale, Mr. John J., Mc1147
Mc Hale, Mrs. Mary, Mc4148
Mc Hale, Rev. William, Mc435
Mc Hugh, Rev. Francis, OMI, Mc3143
Mc Intyre, Miss Alice, Mc2191
Mc Intyre, Rev. Harry, Mc4944
Mc Intyre, Rev. James, Mc3135
Mc Intyre, J. Francis Cardinal, Mc31, Mc54,
   Mc70, Mc111, Mc125, Mc129, Mc132,
   Mc140, Mc141, Mc179, Mc198, Mc213,
   Mc214, Mc217, Mc227, Mc257, Mc262,
   Mc268, Mc279, Mc284, Mc293, Mc294,
   Mc309, Mc318, Mc325, Mc330, Mc337,
   Mc340, Mc348, Mc356, Mc365, Mc370,
   Mc378, Mc390, Mc404, Mc413, Mc420,
   Mc428, Mc431, Mc439, Mc448, Mc451,
   Mc459, Mc467, Mc476, Mc485, Mc495,
   Mc502, Mc513, Mc519, Mc526, Mc532,
   Mc544, Mc556, Mc561, Mc567, Mc573,
   Mc576, Mc580, Mc592, Mc596, Mc606,
   Mc614, Mc623, Mc627, Mc630, Mc634,
   Mc638, Mc640, Mc648, Mc653, Mc656,
   Mc668, Mc692, Mc713, Mc735, Mc742,
   Mc746, Mc749, Mc760, Mc767, Mc772,
   Mc777, Mc780, Mc783, Mc786, Mc799,
   Mc812, Mc819, Mc825, Mc835, Mc839,
   Mc846, Mc853, Mc868, Mc874, Mc879,
   Mc885, Mc889, Mc892, Mc895, Mc905,
   Mc917, Mc925, Mc937, Mc945, Mc955,
   Mc979, Mc989, Mc997, Mc1014, Mc1017,
   Mc1021, Mc1026, Mc1041, Mc1045,
   Mc1049, Mc1063, Mc1082, Mc1104,
   Mc1111, Mc1115, Mc1138, Mc1145,
   Mc1149, Mc1152, Mc1162, Mc1178,
   Mc1192, Mc1197, Mc1202, Mc1215,
   Mc1219, Mc1224, Mc1238, Mc1245,
   Mc1251, Mc1256, Mc1270, Mc1274,
   Mc1292, Mc1298, Mc1301, Mc1309,
   Mc1323, Mc1349, Mc1353, Mc1358,
   Mc1367, Mc1372, Mc1381, Mc1399,
   Mc1410, Mc1421, Mc1434, Mc1441,
   Mc1448, Mc1461, Mc1471, Mc1584,
   Mc1487, Mc1495, Mc1508, Mc1513,
   Mc1523, Mc1528, Mc1532, Mc1539,
   Mc1545, Mc1550, Mc1568, Mc1578,
   Mc1590, Mc1594, Mc1623, Mc1636,
   Mc1647, Mc1651, Mc1656, Mc1663,
   Mc1666, Mc1672, Mc1680, Mc1689,
   Mc1697, Mc1711, Mc1719, Mc1729,
   Mc1734, Mc1739, Mc1745, Mc1748,
   Mc1756, Mc1770, Mc1775, Mc1781,
   Mc1788, Mc1802, Mc1817, Mc1835,
   Mc1842, Mc1854, Mc1859, Mc1863,
   Mc1867, Mc1873, Mc1880, Mc1887,
   Mc890, Mc1894, Mc1900, Mc1905,
   Mc1911, Mc1914, Mc1926, Mc1947,
   Mc1950, Mc1954, Mc1963, Mc1970,
   Mc1979, Mc1994, Mc1998, Mc2006,

Mc2020, Mc2039, Mc2045, Mc2050,
Mc2069, Mc2074, Mc2079, Mc2084,
Mc2096, Mc2101, Mc2106, Mc2118,
Mc2124, Mc2079, Mc2084, Mc2096,
Mc2101, Mc2106, Mc2118, Mc2124,
Mc2157, Mc2164, Mc2178, Mc2188,
Mc2193, Mc2203, Mc2209, Mc2216,
Mc2230, Mc2234, Mc2257, Mc2277,
Mc2287, Mc2291, Mc2295, Mc2307,
Mc2315, Mc2330, Mc2341, Mc2345,
Mc2354, Mc2362, Mc2370, Mc2375,
Mc2387, Mc2394, Mc2402, Mc2408,
Mc2413, Mc2426, Mc2445, Mc2455,
Mc2471, Mc2478, Mc2488, Mc2491,
Mc2494, Mc2500, Mc2521, Mc2528,
Mc2576, Mc2587, Mc2666, Mc2669,
Mc2670, Mc2690, Mc22695, Mc2704,
Mc2717, Mc2723, Mc2732, Mc2743,
Mc2764, Mc2778, Mc2782, Mc2795,
Mc2802, Mc2822, Mc2825, Mc2836,
Mc2847, Mc2853, Mc2858, Mc2860,
Mc2867, Mc2880, Mc2899, Mc2903,
Mc2935, Mc2946, Mc2980, Mc2995,
Mc2997, Mc3007, Mc3011, Mc3024,
Mc3038, Mc3048, Mc3069, Mc3075,
Mc3082, Mc3094, Mc3108, Mc3111,
Mc3124, Mc3128, Mc3147, Mc3154,
Mc3161, Mc3177, Mc3182, Mc3185,
Mc3191, Mc3197, Mc3201, Mc3215,
Mc3238, Mc3257, Mc3268, Mc3285,
Mc3290, Mc3299, Mc3302, Mc3307,
Mc3317, Mc3323, Mc3338, Mc3342,
Mc3374, Mc3387, Mc3398, Mc3418,
Mc3440, Mc3458, Mc3463, Mc3477,
Mc3485, Mc3502, Mc3520, Mc3564,
Mc3572, Mc3595, Mc3601, Mc3609,
Mc3611, Mc3637, Mc3650, Mc3654,
Mc3660, Mc3677, Mc3685, Mc3691,
Mc3702, Mc3712, Mc3728, Mc3759,
Mc3767, Mc3774, Mc3781, Mc3795,
Mc3805, Mc3814, Mc3829, Mc3829,
Mc2837, Mc3845, Mc3848, Mc3863,
Mc3871, Mc3875, Mc3880, Mc3891,
Mc3908, Mc3919, Mc3943, Mc3969,
Mc3980, Mc3997, Mc4018, Mc4024,
Mc4039, Mc4045, Mc4052, Mc4081,
Mc4092, Mc4097, Mc4126, Mc4133,
Mc4145, Mc4154, Mc4159, Mc4169,
Mc4173, Mc4187, Mc4196, Mc4199,
Mc4223, Mc4247, Mc4266, Mc4270,
Mc43278, Mc4287, Mc4295, Mc4319,
Mc4324, Mc4335, Mc4363, Mc4400,
Mc4421, Mc4438, Mc4451, Mc4457,
Mc4483, Mc4488, Mc4492, Mc4503,
Mc4524, Mc4529, Mc4531, Mc4536,
Mc4543, Mc4563, Mc4570, Mc4577,
Mc4591, Mc4595, Mc4596, Mc4602,
Mc4610, Mc4616, Mc4627, Mc4630,
Mc4650, Mc4656, Mc4667, Mc4710,
Mc4734, Mc4744, Mc4760, Mc4813,
Mc4821, Mc4830, Mc4857, Mc4871,
Mc4878, Mc4882, Mc4897, Mc4911,
Mc4920, Mc4924, Mc4929, Mc4935,
Mc4961, Mc4976, Mc4983, Mc4992,
Mc5010, Mc5014, Mc5029, Mc5036,
Mc5044, Mc5078, Mc5089, Mc5117,
Mc5121, Mc5127, Mc5137, Mc5141,
Mc5145, M5156, Mc5161, Mc5189,

Mohan, Mr. Francis X., Mc2670
Moldenhauer, Mr. L. T., Mc5075
Molloy, Rev. P. J., Mc3067
Molloy, Bp. Thomas, Mc275, Mc340, Mc546, Mc741
Molony, Dr. William, Mc336
Monaghan, Msgr. John, Mc2007
Monsky, Mr. Leo, Mc2634
Monsour III, Mr. Nicholas, Mc3172
Montanari, Mrs. Elena, Mc2406, Mc2414, Mc3573, Mc3591
Montgomery, Miss Carol, Mc4721
Montgomery, Mr. Francis, Mc337, Mc4549, Mc5780, Mc5788
Montgomery, Mr. George, Mc5550, Mc5784, Mc5794
Montgomery, Mr. Ross, Mc1984, Mc4542
Montini, Giovanni Cardinal, Mc1164, Mc1414, Mc3168
Montiz, Bp. Vincent, Mc5188
Montrose, Bp. Donald, Mc4500, Mc4834, Mc5320, Mc5323, Mc5536
Moody, Rev. Joseph N., Mc139
Mooney, Edward Cardinal, Mc745, Mc2198
Mooney, Mrs. John, Mc4902
Moore, Mrs. Laura, Mc4544
Moore, Mr. Leo T., Mc5783
Moore, Countess Mary Young, Mc3528
Moore, Rev. Pius, Mc554
Moore, Mr. Richard, Mc5104, Mc5366
Moore, Mr. Robert E., Mc4167
Moore Mrs. Roland, Mc2661
Moore, Rev. Thomas V., Mc738
Moore, Mr. William, Mc120
Moore, Rev. William, Mc1161
Mooring, Mr William, Mc3174, Mc3179, Mc5108
Moran, Mr. J. Bell, Mc941, Mc2637
Moran, Mr. James, Mc2055, Mc4418
Moran, Mr. John, Mc2431
Morandini, Mr. D., Mc2639
Moreton, Mr. William, Mc4801
Morgan, Mrs. Robert, Mc2208
Morgan, Rev. William, Mc5105
Moriarty, Rev. Francis, Mc557
Moriarty, Rev. Oisin, Mc3362
Morin, Rev. J. Sylvio, Mc135, Mc333
Morkovsky, Bp. John, Mc1843, Mc5110
Moroney, Hon. J. Francis, Mc1408
Morris, Mrs. Charles, Mc3188
Morris, Mrs. Helen, Mc1003
Morris, Mr. Thomas, Mc4550
Morrison, Mr. E., Mc4184
Morrison, Mrs. Mary, Mc5325
Morriss, Mr. Frank, Mc5778, Mc5789
Morriss, Mr. J. G. Mc2638
Morrissey, Mr. Patrick, Mc2003
Morrow, Bp. Louis, Mc115, Mc119, Mc339, Mc736, Mc940, Mc1167, Mc2195, Mc3175, Mc3588, Mc3589
Mortensen, Mr. Antonio, Mc3828
Mortz, Mr. Joseph, Mc4836
Mosbergen, Mr. W. H., Mc4832
Mosk, Mr. Stanley, Mc2673
Moss, Mrs. Jo Nelle, Mc3170
Moss, Mrs. James E., Mc3647
Mother M. Anne, Mc4670

Mother M. Anslem, Mc3341, Mc3342, Mc3716
Mother M. Augusta, OSB, Mc2301
Mother M. Benigna, Mc4716, Mc4995
Mother M. Carmel, DMJ, Mc2096
Mother M. Eucharia, Mc5239
Mother M. Gerard, Mc72
Mother Mary of Jesus, Mc4839
Mother M. Macaria, OSF, Mc1641
Mother M. Margarita, SSHJP, Mc2196, Mc2446
Mother M. Teresina, FSCC, Mc3303
Moynahan, Rev. Joseph A., Mc134, Mc341, Mc534, Mc738, Mc95, Mc938, Mc948, Mc2215
Moynihan, Bp. Denis, Mc1636
Moyihan, Rev. James, Mc5546
Moyihan, Mr. Patrick, Mc1634
Mozeries, Rev. Damasus, Mc8
Mozier, Rev. Augustine, Mc675, Mc676, Mc1791
Muench, Arbp. Aloisius, Mc1999, Mc2002
Muench Arbp. L. J., Mc1632
Muessiggang, Rev Emmanuel, Mc4301
Mullahy, Rev. Bernard, CSC, Mc1630
Mullen, Mrs. Cis, Mc3587
Mullen, Mr. Hugh, Mc3162
Mullen, Rev. Peter, Mc5318
Mullendore, Mr. W. C., Mc2207
Muller, Mr. Frank, Mc2199
Muller, Mrs. Walter, Mc5315
Mullin, Rev. Lawrence,CP, Mc931
Mulloy, Mr. John, Mc5793
Mulvihill, Rev. Louis, Mc154
Mundt, Mr. Karl, Mc4840
Munger, Mr. Charles, Mc2652
Mungovan, Msgr. E. J., Mc559
Munnell, Mr. William, Mc5197
Murnane, Mr. Edward, Mc3192
Muro, Miss Yara, Mc4552
Murphy, Rev. Dan, CC, Mc3176
Murphy, Mr. Herbert, Mc3178
Murphy, Mr. & Mrs. L., Mc4834
Murphy, Mr. C. Morgan, Mc2005
Murphy, Mr. D. J., Mc2635
Murphy, Mr. Edward, Mc1148
Murphy, Rev. James A., Mc1154
Murphy, Msgr. Leo, Mc2162
Murphy, Rev. Max, Mc539, Mc743, Mc1409, Mc2194
Murphy, Mr. Richard, Mc1635
Murphy, Mr. Robert, Mc2227, Mc2389, Mc2660
Murphy, Msgr. Thomas, Mc2306
Murray, Rev. Augustine, Mc2665
Murray, Rev. Bernard, Mc3196
Murray, Rev. Daniel, Mc1410
Murray, Mrs. Dorothy, Mc155
Murray, Mr. J. Edward, Mc784
Murray, Rev. James, Mc1957
Murray, Rev. Oliver, OFM, Mc2214
Murray, Mr. Thomas, Mc1951
Murrieta, Dr. A. J., Mc4188
Murtagh, Rev. Stephen, Mc542
Murtha, Mr. Vincent, Mc4556
Mussio, Bp. John, Mc1648
Myers, Mr. John, Mc3161
Myska, Mrs. Ethel, Mc3173

Righi, Msgr. Vittore, Mc779, Mc982, Mc983
Rigney, Msgr. James, Mc5372
Rimpau, Mr. Edward, Mc1166
Ring, Rev. Harold, SJ, Mc386, Mc3863
Riolout, Rev. Antonio, Mc3870
Ritchey, Mrs. Katherine, Mc5355
Ritter, Joseph Cardinal, Mc164, Mc4607
Rivera, Mr. Frank, Mc5150, Mc5282, Mc5828
Rivera, Jose Cardinal, Mc1687, Mc3862,
 Mc4592, Mc4595, Mc5042
Rizzi, Rev. Julius, Mc984
Rizzo, Mr. Muriel, Mc4252
Ro, Bp. Raul M., Mc1215
Roach, Mr. J. Maloy, Mc5595
Roach, Mr. Leonard, Mc379
Roach, Msgr. Patrick, Mc4142
Robbins, Mrs. Alameda, Mc3119
Robets, Mrs. B. G., Mc3252
Roberts, Mr. Edward, Mc5385
Roberts, Arbp. Thomas, Mc4596
Robinson, Mr. Jackie, Mc2741
Robinson, Mrs. Marge, Mc5136
Robinson, Mr. Mark, Mc3819
Robinson, Mrs. Robert, Mc4879
Robinson, Mr. R. G., Mc3626
Robinson, Mr. Williams, Mc3264
Rocca, Msgr. Mario, Mc3266
Rocco, Arbp. Antonio, Mc4600
Roche, Msgr. Patrick, Mc943, Mc2073,
 Mc2543, Mc2733, Mc3868, Mc4603
Roche, Rev. Redmond, SJ, Mc4880, Mc4885,
 Mc5140, Mc5347
Rock, Rev. Francisco, SJ, Mc1210
Rock, Mr. Russell, Mc3864
Rockefeller, Mr. Nelson, Mc179
Rodin, Rev. Victor, CM, Mc5153
Rodgers, Mrs. E. R., Mc5139
Rodgers, Bp. Joseph, Mc1801
Rodrigues, Msgr. Rosendo, Mc2048
Rodriguez, Rev. Aloyssius, Mc1212
Rodtke, Rev. T. J., Mc589
Roeller, Mrs. Mary J., Mc4250
Rogers, Mr. Thomas, Mc5154, Mc5352
Rohracher, Arbp. Andrew, Mc302, Mc383,
Rolf, Rev. Richard, SJ, Mc4884
Rolls, Miss Lucille, Mc584
Romadka, Mr. F. J., Mc4889
Rondeau, Miss Carol, Mc4241
Rook, Mr. Thomas, Mc5822, Mc5825
Root, Mrs. Gladys, Mc4838
Rosales, Arbp. Julio, Mc1213
Rosecrans, Mr. W. S., Mc695, Mc4591
Rosecrants, Rev Gerald, Mc5348
Rosenberg, Mr. Harold, Mc4828
Rose, Mr. Kenneth, Mc2740
Ross, Mr. Leonard, Mc5353
Ross, Mr. Williams, Mc1685, Mc2724,
 Mc2736, Mc4242, Mc4243, Mc5882,
 Mc5883
Rossetti, Mr. Victor, Mc3257
Rossi, Mrs. Grace, Mc992
Rossi, Rev. Giovanni, Mc775
Roth, Mrs. Maria, Mc2046
Rounds, Mrs. Marie, Mc173
Rountree, Dr. Brendan, Mc3634
Rowe, Mr. David, Mc5149
Rowan, Mrs. Dorothy, Mc4237
Rozsaly, Rev. Francis, Mc1207

Rozzini, Mr. Louis, Mc2410
Rubner, Miss Marianne, Mc3637
Ruffini, Ernesto Cardinal, Mc4240
Rugambwa, Laurena Cardinal, Mc3636
Ruivenkamp, Mr. John, Mc2739
Rummell, Arbp. Joeph, Mc376, Mc588,
 Mc1204
Rupp, Arbp. Jean, Mc5337
Rush, Mrs. Celeste, Mc5345
Rush, Hon. Kevin, Mc3255
Rusk, Hon. Dean, Mc3867, Mc4236
Russell, Mr. Anthony, Mc2248
Russell, Mr. Bruce, Mc3393, Mc4245
Russell, Mr. E. A., Mc5485
Russell, Bp. John J., Mc1881, Mc2246,
 Mc3639
Russell, Msgr. Lloyd V., Mc2539
Ryan, Rev. Christopher, Mc1526, Mc1686
Ryan, Mr. Clendenin, Mc176
Ryan, Msgr. Daniel, Mc5143
Ryan, Mr. Donald E., Mc3625
Ryan, Rev. Edward, CFM, Mc4885
Ryan, Mrs. Elisa, Mc3631
Ryan, Rev. Gerald, OFM, Mc4957
Ryan, Rev. James T., Mc172
Ryan, Rev. Lawrence, Mc178
Ryan, Mr. Martin, Mc2730, Mc4248
Ryan, Msgr. Patrick, Mc4247
Ryan, Rev. Raymond, OSA, Mc2729
Ryan, Msgr. Theodore, Mc2725
Ryan, Rev. Thomas, Mc3624
Ryan, Bp. Vincent, Mc177, Mc777
Ryan, Rev. Vincent, Mc5829
Ryan, Mr. William, Mc171
Rychmans, Abbe A., Mc987, Mc991, Mc1208,
 Mc1216, Mc1436, Mc1439
Ryder, Rev. John, SJ, Mc818, Mc985
Ryder, Mr. Kenneth, Mc3260

S

St.John, Mr. Eugene, Mc5161
St.John, Msgr. Richard, Mc1227
St.Julien, Miss Deborah, Mc2759
Sabo, Msgr. John, Mc2758
Saffo, Dr. Paul, Mc1892
Saidy, Mr. Gilbert, Mc1891
Sala, Rev. Evaristus, Mc4915
Salazar, Rev. Armando, Mc2763
Saling, Mrs. Richard J., Mc2769, Mc2789
Salles, Bp. Eugenio, Mc2274
Salman, Bp. Paul, Mc185
Salazar, Rev. Armando, Mc1222
Salvatore, Rev. William, Mc3274
Samaniego, Mr. Eduardo, Mc2773
Samore, Arbp, Antonio, Mc3667, Mc3882
Sampson, Mr. J. Joseph, Mc3276
Samson, Mrs. Catherine, Mc1542
Sanchez, Rev. Luis, Mc3879
Sanchez, Bp. Manuel, Mc3269
Sancho, Arbp. Santiago, Mc1224
Sanniola, Rev. Anselme, Mc3647
Saric, Arbp. Joanne, Mc1452
Sarte, Rev. Concordio, Mc5164
Sartor, Mr. Thomas, Mc5852
Sartos, Mrs. Thomas, Mc5377
Sastre, Rev. Gerardo, Mc195

CALIFORNIA HISTORICAL · SOCIETY ·

THE CALIFORNIA HISTORICAL SOCIETY

IS PROUD TO PRESENT

The Award of Merit for Scholarship

to

Sister Mary Rose Cunningham, C.S.C.

for her invaluable work in archival research and cataloguing at the Archival Center of the Archdiocese of Los Angeles, providing invaluable research materials for the history of the Catholic Church.

WE HAVE HEREUNTO SET OUR HANDS & THE SOCIETY SEAL

THIS DAY OF *October 1, 1993*

_____
PRESIDENT

_____
EXECUTIVE DIRECTOR

Sketch of Compiler

Sister Mary Rose Cunningham was born on May 20, 1920, the youngest of four children brought into the world by Matthew and Ann (O'Gorman) Cunningham, at the family home, Saint Agnes Parish, Los Angeles.

She attended Nativity Parochial School, Saint Agnes High School and Mount Saint Mary's College prior to entering the Congregation of the Holy Cross in 1942.

Professed in 1947, Sister Mary Rose held several teaching assignments in the Western Region of her community including San Joaquin (Fresno), Holy Rosary Academy (Woodland), Saint Catherine's (San Buenaventura), Saint Agnes (Los Angeles), Holy Cross (Mountain View), Bishop Gorman (Las Vegas), Saint Mary of the Wasatch (Salt Lake City), Bishop Kelly (Boise), Mater Dei (Santa Ana) Saint Francis (Mountain View), and Judge Memorial (Salt Lake City). For nineteen years Sister Mary Rose served as either Dean of Women of Dean of Studies at various secondary schools.

Since 1987, Sister Mary Rose has been Associate Archivist for the Archdiocese of Los Angeles. She is a charter member of the Academy of Certified Archivists.